9.5 Volume formula (3D)

power

$\pi r^2 h$

$\pi(5)^2(6)$

$\pi(25)(6)$

~~$\pi(150)$~~ $150\pi(ft^3)$ exact amount!!

2) 4, 4, 8 cm

SA = 2(l·h) + 2(wh) 2(lw)

2(8×4) + 2(4)(4) + 2(8)(4)

VOLUME

2(32) 2(16) 2(32) cm

(64) (32) (64)

128 = 160 cm²

128
32
160

(Combine Like terms!)

$(110\pi)\ ft^2$ (Area²)

approximate

$= 110 \times (3.14)$

$(345.4)\ ft^2$

$2\pi 30 + 2\pi(25)$ ~~2π~~ $(60\pi) + (50\pi)$

TAX MAIL - try!

3pm - guys!

mom homework mon

$V =$ rectangular

$(l \times w \times h)$

(30) questions

Final mult choice test

$l = 8 \quad w = 4 \quad h = 4$

$(8)(4)(4)$

$$\begin{array}{r} 32 \\ \times \ 4 \\ \hline 128 \end{array} \text{ cm}^3$$

$5 \times 5 = 25$

$\times 3$

75

7. Sphere

10 in

$r = 5$

$V = \frac{4}{3} \pi r^3$

Surface $SA = 4 \pi r^2$

$\frac{4}{3}(3.14) 5^3$

$4 (3.14) 5^2$

$\frac{4}{3}(3.14) \frac{125}{1}$

$4 (3.14)(25)$

$(100 \pi) \text{ in}^2$

$\frac{4}{3} \cdot \frac{125}{1} (\pi)$

$166\frac{2}{3} (\pi) \text{ in})^3$

$\frac{500}{3} (\pi)$

(785)

Volume etc

4/14 Ch. 9.4 – 9.5

(Wed DUE 6.5 Homework 9.3 – 9.5)
Review in CLASS – WED

MON 21st – TEST #4 (6.1 – 6.5 9.3 – 9.5)

W. Ch 8 MATH 100 or 092
Solving Equations !!

Algebra I

A Reference Guide and Problem Sets

Monday!! MAY 5th – Math Final!!!...

$\frac{22}{7} \cdot \frac{544}{1} \quad \frac{11,968}{7}$

$\left(\frac{22}{7} = \pi\right)$

$(5^3 = 125)$

25.00×3.14

4.00×3.14

10000
2500
750
785,000

Book Staff and Contributors

Paul Thomas *Senior Content Specialist*
Suzanne Montazer *Senior Art Director*
Stephanie Shaw *Designer*
Christopher Yates *Cover Designer*
Bruce Avera Hunter *Illustrations Editor*
Lee Horton *Illustrations Editor*
Donna Ledbetter *Text Editor*
Mary Beck Desmond *Text Editor*
Joseph Rincione *Project Manager*
Christopher Frescholtz *Senior Project Manager*

Bror Saxberg *Chief Learning Officer*
John Holdren *Senior Vice President for Content and Curriculum*
Maria Szalay *Senior Vice President for Product Development*
Tom DiGiovanni *Senior Director, Product Development*
Kim Barcas *Creative Director*
Charles Kogod *Director of Media and IP Management*
Jeff Burridge *Managing Editor*
Corey Maender *Program Manager, High School*

Lisa Dimaio Iekel *Production Manager*
John G. Agnone *Director of Publications*

About K12 Inc.

Founded in 1999, K12 Inc. is an elementary and secondary school service combining rich academic content with powerful technology. K^{12} serves students in a variety of education settings, both public and private, including school classrooms, virtual charter schools, home schools, and tutoring centers. K^{12} currently provides comprehensive curricular offerings in the following subjects: Language Arts/English, History, Math, Science, Visual Arts, and Music. The K^{12} curriculum blends high-quality offline materials with innovative online resources, including interactive lessons, teacher guides, and tools for planning and assessment. For more information, call 1-888-YOUR K12 or visit www.K12.com.

Printed in China.

ISBN 1-60153-028-5

Algebra I

A Reference Guide and Problem Sets

Contents

How to Use This Book

Welcome to *Algebra I: A Reference Guide and Problem Sets*

This reference guide was developed to accompany the online portion of K12 Inc.'s High School Algebra I program and also serves as a reference for any student of algebra. Each section of the book presents an overview of a topic area. You can use this book to familiarize yourself with aspects of algebra, or to review materials you are studying in other books or online sources.

How This Book Is Organized

Units of Study

The following units of study are included in this reference guide.

- Algebra Basics
- Properties of Real Numbers
- Operations with Real Numbers
- Solving Equations and Inequalities
- Applying Fractions
- Linear Equations and Inequalities
- Systems of Equations
- Relations and Functions
- Rationals, Irrationals, and Radicals
- Working with Polynomials
- Factoring Polynomials
- Quadratic Equations
- Rational Expressions
- Logic and Reasoning

Pronunciation Guide

See page 530 for a key to the pronunciations in the Glossary.

Glossary

See page 531 for a Glossary with brief definitions of some key terms.

Symbols

See page 536 for a list of mathematical symbols.

Properties

See page 537 for a list of number properties.

Formulary

See page 542 for a list of formulas with illustrations.

Sample Graphs

See page 545 for some sample graphs.

Selected Answers

See pages 546–578 for answers to selected problem-set questions.

Navigating a Topic

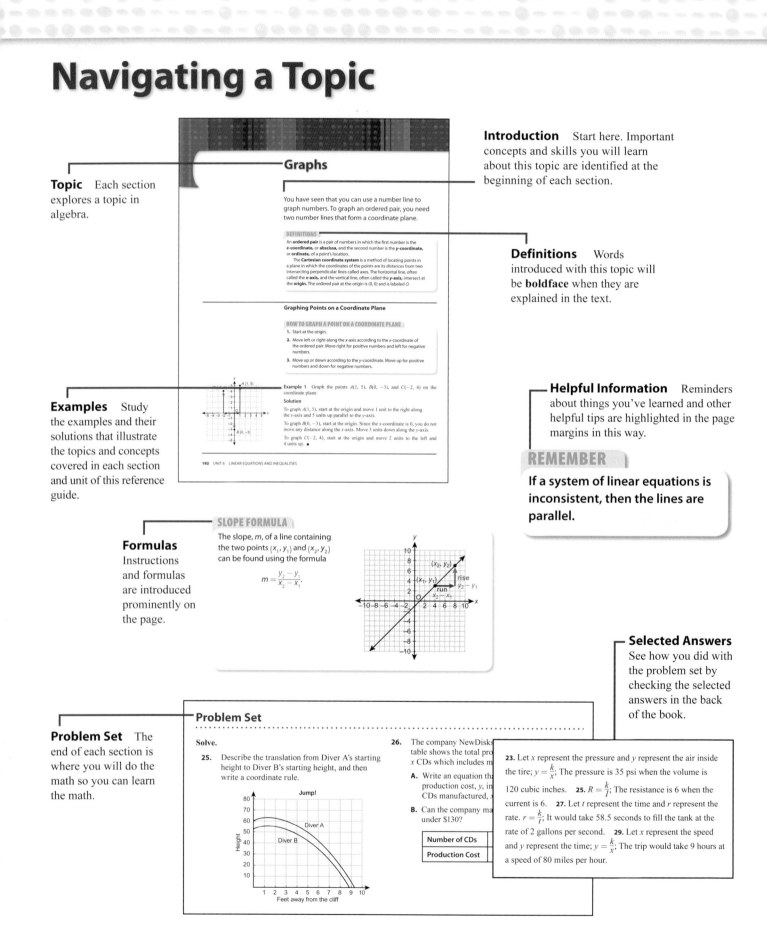

Topic Each section explores a topic in algebra.

Introduction Start here. Important concepts and skills you will learn about this topic are identified at the beginning of each section.

Graphs

You have seen that you can use a number line to graph numbers. To graph an ordered pair, you need two number lines that form a coordinate plane.

DEFINITIONS

An **ordered pair** is a pair of numbers in which the first number is the ***x*-coordinate,** or **abscissa,** and the second number is the ***y*-coordinate,** or **ordinate,** of a point's location.

The **Cartesian coordinate system** is a method of locating points in a plane in which the coordinates of the points are its distances from two intersecting perpendicular lines called axes. The horizontal line, often called the ***x*-axis,** and the vertical line, often called the ***y*-axis,** intersect at the **origin.** The ordered pair at the origin is (0, 0) and is labeled *O*.

Definitions Words introduced with this topic will be **boldface** when they are explained in the text.

Graphing Points on a Coordinate Plane

HOW TO GRAPH A POINT ON A COORDINATE PLANE

1. Start at the origin.
2. Move left or right along the *x*-axis according to the *x*-coordinate of the ordered pair. Move right for positive numbers and left for negative numbers.
3. Move up or down according to the *y*-coordinate. Move up for positive numbers and down for negative numbers.

Example 1 Graph the points $A(1, 5)$, $B(0, -3)$, and $C(-2, 4)$ on the coordinate plane.

Solution

To graph $A(1, 5)$, start at the origin and move 1 unit to the right along the *x*-axis and 5 units up parallel to the *y*-axis.

To graph $B(0, -3)$, start at the origin. Since the *x*-coordinate is 0, you do not move any distance along the *x*-axis. Move 3 units down along the *y*-axis.

To graph $C(-2, 4)$, start at the origin and move 2 units to the left and 4 units up. ■

192 UNIT 6 LINEAR EQUATIONS AND INEQUALITIES

Examples Study the examples and their solutions that illustrate the topics and concepts covered in each section and unit of this reference guide.

Helpful Information Reminders about things you've learned and other helpful tips are highlighted in the page margins in this way.

REMEMBER

If a system of linear equations is inconsistent, then the lines are parallel.

Formulas Instructions and formulas are introduced prominently on the page.

SLOPE FORMULA

The slope, m, of a line containing the two points (x_1, y_1) and (x_2, y_2) can be found using the formula

$$m = \frac{y_2 - y_1}{x_2 - x_1}.$$

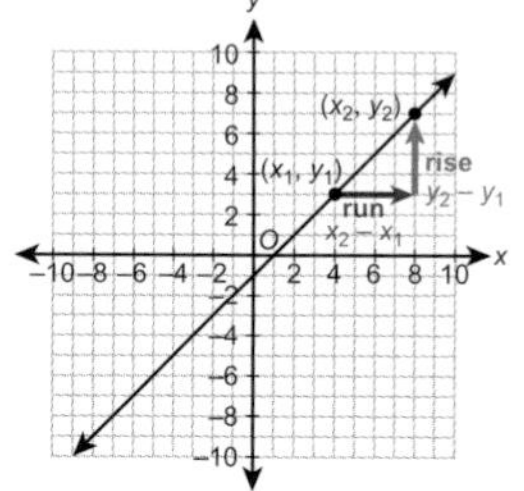

Selected Answers See how you did with the problem set by checking the selected answers in the back of the book.

Problem Set The end of each section is where you will do the math so you can learn the math.

Problem Set

Solve.

25. Describe the translation from Diver A's starting height to Diver B's starting height, and then write a coordinate rule.

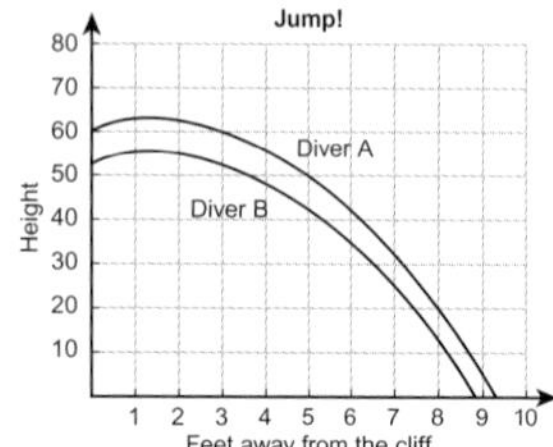

26. The company NewDisks table shows the total pro *x* CDs which includes m

A. Write an equation th production cost, *y*, in CDs manufactured, *x*

B. Can the company ma under $130?

Number of CDs
Production Cost

23. Let x represent the pressure and y represent the air inside the tire; $y = \frac{k}{x}$; The pressure is 35 psi when the volume is 120 cubic inches. **25.** $R = \frac{k}{I}$; The resistance is 6 when the current is 6. **27.** Let t represent the time and r represent the rate. $r = \frac{k}{t}$; It would take 58.5 seconds to fill the tank at the rate of 2 gallons per second. **29.** Let x represent the speed and y represent the time; $y = \frac{k}{x}$; The trip would take 9 hours at a speed of 80 miles per hour.

Introduction

Algebra is the key to unlocking the power of math. With arithmetic, you learned how to add, subtract, multiply, and divide numbers. With algebra, you learn how to generalize the skills and ideas of arithmetic to solve more and more problems. Once you learn algebra, you will be prepared for further studies in math and science. You will also be prepared for a great variety of occupations that rely on mathematical and reasoning skills.

Math is learned at the tip of a pencil. As you work through the topics in this book, you will see several worked examples that show you how to solve some problems, but the most important part of each topic is the problem set at the end. Reading problem solutions can help you find good strategies and best practices for solving problems, but you really learn math only when you solve problems yourself. Do the math to learn the math.

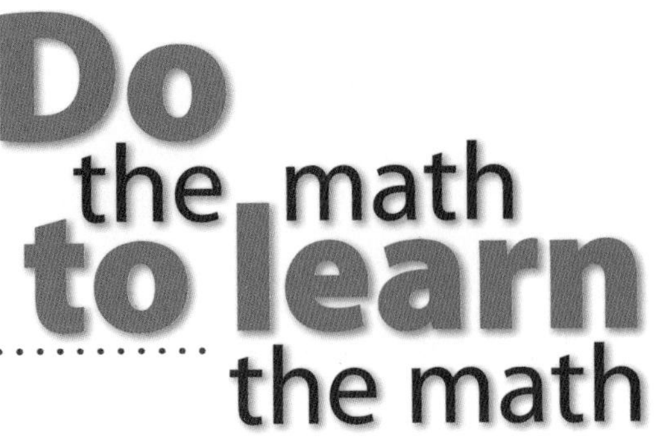

UNIT 1 Algebra Basics

In medieval times, a barber called himself an algebrista.

The English word *algebra* and the Spanish word *algebrista* both come from the Arabic word *al-jabr,* which means "restoration." A barber in medieval times often called himself an algebrista. The algebrista also was a bonesetter who restored or fixed bones. Mathematicians today use algebra to solve problems. Algebra can help you find solutions and "fix" certain problems that you encounter.

Big Ideas

- Expressions, equations, and inequalities express relationships between different entities.
- If you can create a mathematical model for a situation, you can use the model to solve other problems that you might not be able to solve otherwise. Algebraic equations can capture key relationships among quantities in the world.

Unit Topics

- Expressions
- Variables
- Translating Words into Variable Expressions
- Equations
- Translating Words into Equations
- Replacement Sets
- Problem Solving

Expressions

A **numerical expression** consists of numbers and one or more operations.

Some examples of numerical expressions are shown below.

$18 - 2 \qquad 7 + 2 \cdot 3 \qquad 4 + 2[3 - 4 \div (12 - 8)] \qquad \dfrac{(5 + 3)^2}{10 - 3(4 - 2)}$

To find the value of a numerical expression, you need to *simplify the expression* or *evaluate the expression.* To simplify a numerical expression, perform the indicated operation(s).

Consider the expression $7 + 2 \cdot 3$. If you add and then multiply, you get the value 27. But if you multiply and then add, you get the value 13. Because an expression can have only one value, mathematicians have agreed on a process to follow so that everyone simplifies expressions the same way. This process is the **order of operations**.

NOTATION

8^2 **An exponent indicates repeated multiplication, so $8^2 = 8 \cdot 8$.**

ORDER OF OPERATIONS

Step 1 Perform operations within grouping symbols. For nested grouping symbols, simplify in the innermost group first.
Step 2 Evaluate powers (as indicated by exponents).
Step 3 Multiply and divide from left to right.
Step 4 Add and subtract from left to right.

TIP

You can use "**P**lease **E**xcuse **M**y **D**ear **A**unt **S**ally" to remember the order of operations.

P: Parentheses
E: Exponents
M/D: Multiply and Divide
A/S: Add and Subtract

So, the correct way to simplify $7 + 2 \cdot 3$ is to multiply and then add: $7 + 2 \cdot 3 = 7 + 6 = 13$.

The most common grouping symbols are parentheses ( ). Grouping symbols can affect the value of an expression. Nested grouping symbols (grouping symbols within grouping symbols) contain brackets [ ] and sometimes braces { }.

Simplifying Expressions with and without Grouping Symbols

Example 1 Simplify.

A. $5 \cdot 2 + 7$

Solution

$5 \cdot 2 + 7 = 10 + 7$ Multiply.
$= 17$ Add. ■

B. $5 \cdot (2 + 7)$

Solution

$5 \cdot (2 + 7) = 5 \cdot (9)$ Add first because addition appears inside parentheses.
$= 45$ Multiply. ■

TIP

The expression $5 \cdot (2 + 7)$ is also written as $5(2 + 7)$.

Simplifying Expressions with Several Operations

Example 2 Simplify.

A. $3 \cdot 7 - 10 \div 2 \cdot 3$

Solution

$$\begin{aligned} 3 \cdot 7 - 10 \div 2 \cdot 3 &= 21 - 10 \div 2 \cdot 3 && \text{Multiply and divide in order from left to right.} \\ &= 21 - 5 \cdot 3 \\ &= 21 - 15 \\ &= 6 && \text{Subtract. } \blacksquare \end{aligned}$$

B. $4 + 2[3 - 4 \div (12 - 8)]$

Solution

$$\begin{aligned} 4 + 2[3 - 4 \div (12 - 8)] &= 4 + 2[3 - 4 \div 4] && \text{Parentheses are nested within brackets. Subtract.} \\ &= 4 + 2[3 - 1] && \text{Divide inside the brackets.} \\ &= 4 + 2[2] && \text{Subtract inside the brackets.} \\ &= 4 + 4 && \text{Multiply.} \\ &= 8 && \text{Add. } \blacksquare \end{aligned}$$

Simplifying an Expression with a Fraction Bar

A fraction bar indicates division. It is also a grouping symbol, separating the numerator from the denominator.

THINK ABOUT IT

In Example 3, the expression can be written as $(5 + 3)^2 \div (1 + 2^5 - 23)$.

Example 3 Simplify. $\dfrac{(5 + 3)^2}{1 + 2^5 - 23}$

Solution Treat the fraction bar as a grouping symbol. Simplify the numerator and denominator, and then divide.

$$\begin{aligned} \frac{(5 + 3)^2}{1 + 2^5 - 23} &= \frac{(8)^2}{1 + 2^5 - 23} && \text{Perform the operation inside the parentheses.} \\ &= \frac{64}{1 + 32 - 23} && \text{Evaluate powers: } 8^2 = 8 \cdot 8 = 64 \text{ and } 2^5 = 2 \cdot 2 \cdot 2 \cdot 2 \cdot 2 = 32. \\ &= \frac{64}{10} && \text{Add and subtract from left to right to simplify the denominator.} \\ &= \frac{32}{5} \\ &= 6.4 && \text{Reduce the fraction or divide to simplify. } \blacksquare \end{aligned}$$

Placing Grouping Symbols to Get a Specified Value

You can get different values for an expression by changing the placement of grouping symbols.

Example 4 Place grouping symbols in the expression $2 \cdot 8 + 2^3 \cdot 10$ to get expressions that have these values: 20,000 and 80,000.

Solution The method is trial-and-error. Some possible placements of grouping symbols are $2 \cdot (8 + 2)^3 \cdot 10$, $[2 \cdot (8 + 2)]^3 \cdot 10$, and $(2 \cdot 8 + 2)^3 \cdot 10$. Evaluate these expressions, and try other placements if necessary. The two correct expressions are shown below.

$2 \cdot (8 + 2)^3 \cdot 10 = 2 \cdot (10)^3 \cdot 10$	Perform the operation inside the parentheses.
$= 2 \cdot 1000 \cdot 10$	Evaluate the power: $10^3 = 10 \cdot 10 \cdot 10 = 1000$.
$= 2000 \cdot 10$	Multiply from left to right.
$= 20{,}000$	Multiply.
$[2 \cdot (8 + 2)]^3 \cdot 10 = [2 \cdot (10)]^3 \cdot 10$	Perform the operation inside the parentheses.
$= [20]^3 \cdot 10$	Perform the operation inside the brackets.
$= 8000 \cdot 10$	Evaluate the power: $20^3 = 20 \cdot 20 \cdot 20 = 8000$.
$= 80{,}000$	Multiply. ■

Problem Set

Simplify the expression.

1. $6 \cdot 3 + 10$
2. $2 \cdot 10 - 7$
3. $4^2 + 5$
4. $3 \cdot (8 - 3)$
5. $(4 + 8) \cdot 4$
6. $4 + 9 \cdot 2 \div 3 - 1$
7. $5 \cdot 3 - 8 \div 2 \cdot 3$
8. $5 + 4[3 + 4 \div (11 - 7)]$
9. $7 \cdot [5 + 2 \cdot (16 \div 2)] - 1$
10. $\dfrac{(7 - 2)^2}{4 + 3^4 - 10}$
11. $\dfrac{2 \cdot 7^2 - 10}{(9 + 1)^3}$
12. $10 \div 2 - 3$
13. $\dfrac{7 - 6}{2 + 4}$
14. $16 - 4[3 + 2 \div (9 - 7)]$
15. $10 \div 1^5 - 3$
16. $100 \div (3 + 22)$
17. $2 \cdot 9 - 14 \div 7 \cdot 4$
18. $5 + [2 \cdot (14 - 2) \div 8] \cdot 3$
19. $(3^2 + 1) \cdot 2$
20. $12 - (27 \div 3)$
21. $\dfrac{8 \cdot 2}{19 - 3}$
22. $\dfrac{10 \div 2 + 5 - 8}{6(2 + 5) - 3}$
23. $12 - 5 \cdot 2 + 6 \div 6$
24. $30 \div (9 + 6)$
25. $\dfrac{2 + 8 \cdot 3 \div 4}{30 - 3 \cdot (2 + 4) + 2}$

Place grouping symbols in each expression to get expressions that have the given value.

26. $3 \cdot 4 + 3^2 \cdot 8$

A. 312

B. 168

27. $8 + 9^2 - 7 \cdot 10$

A. 820

B. 748

28. $6^2 \cdot 2 + 5 \cdot 20$

A. 1540

B. 5040

29. $720 \div 2 + 7 \cdot 2^3$

A. 10

B. 2936

30. $159 - 81 \div 3^3 + 12$

A. 168

B. 2

Solve.

***31.** **Challenge** 2 ▢ 3 ▢ 7^3 ▢ 18 ▢ 9 Place one of each of the four basic math operations ($+ - \cdot \div$) in the blanks to get an expression with a value of 347.

***32.** **Challenge** Simplify. $\dfrac{312 - (4 + 8) \div 3 \cdot 5}{[(1 + 4^2) \cdot 9] - 7}$

Variables

A **variable** is a symbol that represents a value.

Variables are usually represented by lowercase letters in italics. Most books use x, y, a, and n more than other letters. A **variable expression** is a combination of variables, numbers, and operations. Examples of variable expressions are shown below.

$$x - 2 \qquad 5n + 7 \qquad \frac{c+1}{d-2} \qquad 2y - 21z + 6$$

Unlike numerical expressions, to evaluate variable expressions, **substitute**, or replace, numbers for the variables. So, the value of a variable expression depends on the numbers chosen for the variable(s).

THINK ABOUT IT

A variable expression can also be called an algebraic expression.

Evaluating Variable Expressions

To **evaluate** a variable expression, replace all the variables in the expression with numbers and simplify the resulting numerical expression.

Example 1 Evaluate.

A. $5n + 7$ when $n = 8$

Solution

$5n + 7 = 5 \cdot 8 + 7$ Substitute 8 for n.

$= 40 + 7$ Multiply.

$= 47$ Add. ■

B. $\frac{c+1}{d-2}$ when $c = 3$ and $d = 4$

Solution

$\frac{c+1}{d-2} = \frac{3+1}{4-2}$ Substitute 3 for c and 4 for d.

$= \frac{4}{2}$ Simplify the numerator, then the denominator.

$= 2$ Divide. ■

NOTATION

$5n$ When a number and variable are written together, the operation is multiplication, so $5n = 5 \cdot n$.

Identifying Terms

Variable expressions consist of terms. **Terms** are the parts of an expression that are added or subtracted. A term that has no variables is a **constant**.

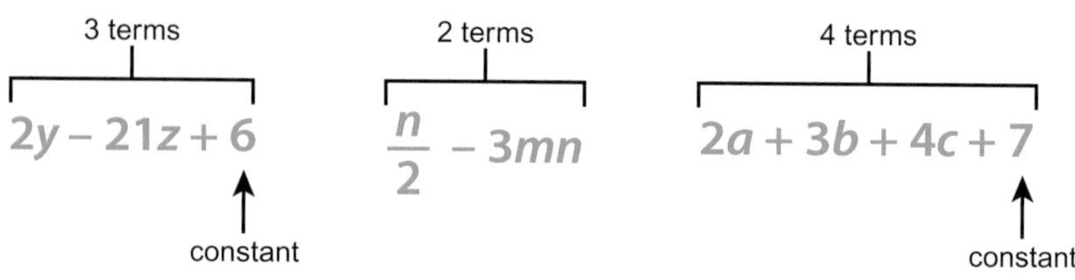

REMEMBER

A constant is a term.

Example 2 Identify the terms of the expression $3x + y + 23$.

Solution Each term is separated by a "+" sign. The terms are $3x$, y, and 23. The number 23 is a constant since there is no variable. ■

Identifying Coefficients and Factors

Terms can consist of two or more **factors**. The numerical part of a term is the **coefficient**. When the coefficient of a term is 1, it is usually not written.

REMEMBER

In $2 \cdot 3 = 6$, 2 and 3 are called *factors* and 6 is called the product.

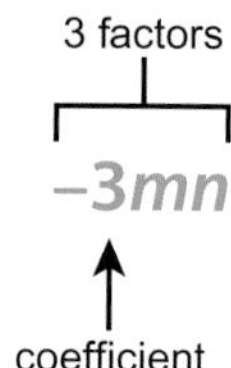

Example 3 Identify the coefficient and factors of each term.

A. $-mn$

Solution You can write the term $-mn$ as $-1 \cdot m \cdot n$. So, the coefficient is -1. The factors are -1, m, and n. ■

B. $\frac{n}{2}$

Solution You can write the term $\frac{n}{2}$ as $\frac{1}{2} \cdot n$. So, the coefficient is $\frac{1}{2}$. The factors are $\frac{1}{2}$ and n. ■

Applications: Measurement and Distance Traveled

You can use expressions to solve many types of problems, including those involving measurement.

Example 4

A. Natalie jogged once around the perimeter of a football field, which has a length of 100 yards and a width of 60 yards. Find the total number of yards she jogged.

Solution Use the expression $2l + 2w$, where l is the length of the rectangle and w is the width of the rectangle, to find the perimeter. Evaluate $2l + 2w$ when $l = 100$ and $w = 60$.

$2l + 2w = 2 \cdot 100 + 2 \cdot 60$	Substitute 100 for l and 60 for w.
$= 200 + 120$	Multiply.
$= 320$	Add.

Natalie jogged 320 yards. ■

B. Find the area of the triangle shown below.

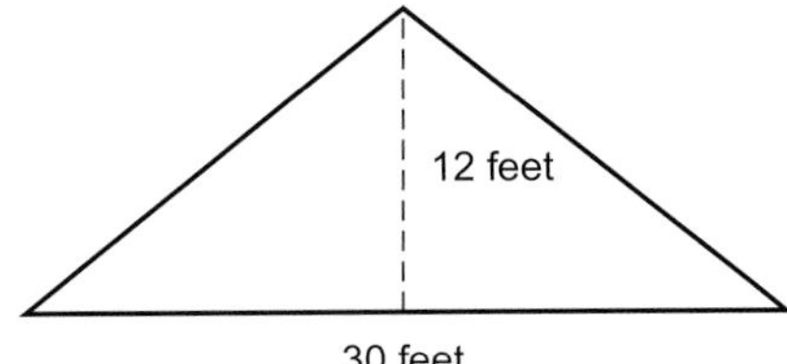

Solution Use the expression $\frac{1}{2}bh$, where b is the length of the base and h is the height of the triangle, to find the area. Evaluate $\frac{1}{2}bh$ when $b = 30$ and $h = 12$.

$\frac{1}{2}bh = \frac{1}{2} \cdot 30 \cdot 12$ Substitute 30 for b and 12 for h.

$= 15 \cdot 12$ Multiply from left to right.

$= 180$ Multiply.

The area of the triangle is 180 square feet. ■

REMEMBER

Area is measured in square units.

C. Find the number of miles the Perez family traveled if they drove nonstop for 2.5 hours at a rate of 60 miles per hour.

Solution Use the expression rt, where r is the rate of travel in miles per hour and t is the number of hours traveled, to find the number of miles the vehicle traveled. Evaluate rt when $r = 60$ and $t = 2.5$.

$rt = 60 \cdot 2.5$ Substitute 60 for r and 2.5 for t.

$= 150$ Multiply.

The Perez family traveled 150 miles. ■

Problem Set

Evaluate the expression.

1. $3x - 9$ when $x = 5$
2. $5 + 4z$ when $z = 7$
3. $\frac{m + 3}{n + 4}$ when $m = 2$ and $n = 6$
4. $\frac{5 - a}{b + 2}$ when $a = 1$ and $b = 10$
5. $5a + 3b - 6c$ when $a = 2$, $b = 8$, and $c = 3$
6. $\frac{2a - 7}{6b + 3}$ when $a = 5$ and $b = 9$
7. $\frac{2x - 2y + 2}{36 - 3x}$ when $x = 7$ and $y = 2$
8. $14 + 5x$ when $x = 13$
9. $75m + 11n$ when $m = 3$ and $n = 8$
10. $20 + 3c + 17d$ when $c = 8$ and $d = 2$
11. $\frac{9a}{c}$ when $a = 3$ and $c = 14$

Identify the terms of the expression.

12. $a + 3b - 18$
13. $5x^2 - 3y$

Identify the coefficient and factors of the term.

14. $3bc$

15. $\frac{2x}{3}$

16. bcd

17. $\frac{3xy}{7}$

18. $-xyz$

Identify the terms and constant of the expression.

19. $z^3 - 6x + 4$

20. $\frac{2m}{4} - n^2 + \frac{3p}{2}$

21. $\frac{3m}{2n} - 12$

22. $3x - y + 5z$

23. $\frac{47}{3x} + 2y - \frac{19}{51}$

Solve.

For problems 24 and 25: The expression for the perimeter of a rectangle is $2l + 2w$. The expression for the area of a rectangle is lw.

24. 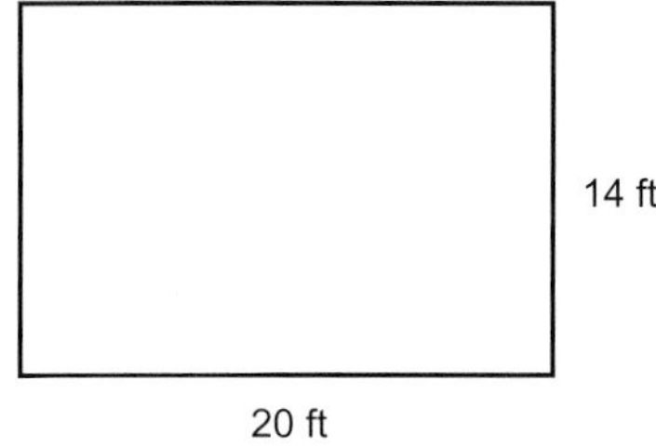

A. Find the perimeter of the rectangle shown.

B. Find the area of the rectangle.

25. 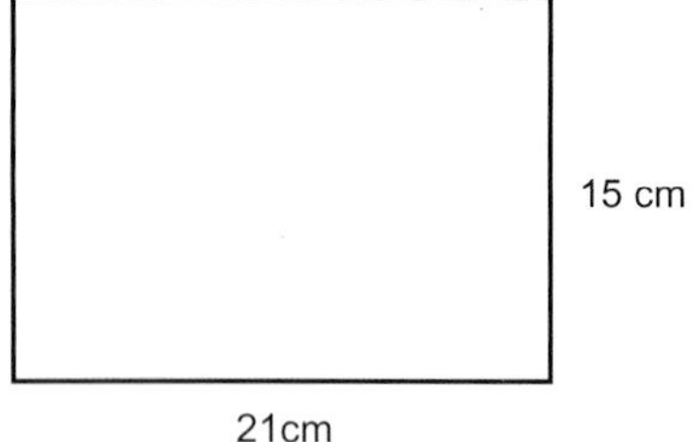

A. Find the perimeter of the rectangle shown.

B. Find the area of the rectangle.

For problems 26 and 27: The expression for the area of a triangle is $\frac{1}{2}bh$.

26. Find the area of the triangle shown.

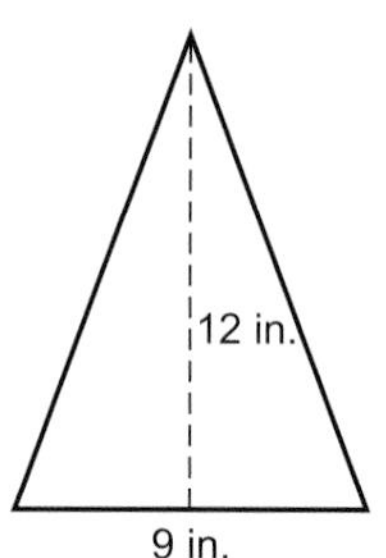

27. Jaya's garden is in the shape of this triangle. In order to buy the correct amount of fertilizer, she needs to know how many square feet the garden measures. Find the area of the garden.

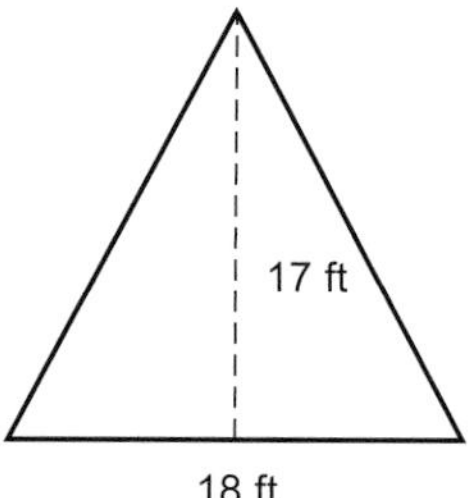

For problems 28 through 30: The expression for distance traveled is *rt*, where *r* represents rate and *t* represents time.

28. Find the distance Amita bicycled if she rode for 2 hours at a rate of 19 miles per hour.

29. Find the distance traveled if a plane flew for 3.5 hours at 550 miles per hour.

*30. **Challenge** Julio walked his dog around his neighborhood 3 times. He walked for 0.75 hour at a rate of 4 miles per hour. How many miles would Julio have walked if he walked his dog around his neighborhood once?

Translating Words into Variable Expressions

It is sometimes necessary to write a variable expression from words or phrases.

The table below shows common words and phrases for each of the four basic operations.

Operation	Words and Phrases
Addition	plus, more than, increased by, sum
Subtraction	minus, less than, decreased by, difference
Multiplication	times, product
Division	divided by, quotient

TIP

The phrases "y less than x" and "x is decreased by y" are represented by the same expression: $x - y$.

The phrase "the quantity" indicates that grouping symbols should appear in the expression. For example, the expression $4x + 8$ represents the phrase "four times x plus eight," but the expression $4(x + 8)$ represents the phrase "four times the quantity x plus eight."

Translating Word Phrases into Variable Expressions

Example 1 Translate each word phrase into a variable expression. Use n to represent "a number" in each expression.

A. twenty-five times a number

Solution $25n$ ■

B. six less than twice a number

Solution $2n - 6$ ■

C. twice the sum of nine and a number

Solution $2(9 + n)$ ■

D. the quotient of three and a number

Solution $\frac{3}{n}$ ■

REMEMBER

Unless stated otherwise, you can choose any letter for the variable(s).

Using Only One Variable to Write a Variable Expression

Sometimes it is useful to write different quantities in terms of the same variable. For example, suppose you know the length of a rectangle is three times its width. Instead of using two variables, l and w, to represent the length and width, you can use w for width and $3w$ for length.

Example 2 There are twelve more girls than boys in a classroom. Write expressions for the number of boys and the number of girls using the same variable b.

Solution If b represents the number of boys, you can also represent the number of girls in terms of b.

Number of boys: b

Number of girls: $b + 12$

You can check your work by substituting a number for b. So, if there are 8 boys, then the number of girls is $8 + 12$, or 20. ■

Application: Measurement

You can write a variable expression to help you convert from one unit of measure to another.

Example 3 Find the number of feet in 2 yards, 5 yards, and y yards.

Solution There are 3 feet in 1 yard, so the number of feet is equal to the number of yards times 3.

Number of Yards	Number of Feet
2	$3 \cdot 2 = 6$
5	$3 \cdot 5 = 15$
y	$3 \cdot y = 3y$

There are 6 feet in 2 yards, 15 feet in 5 yards, and $3y$ feet in y yards. ■

Application: Geometry

Geometric formulas are basically expressions that describe how to figure out values such as perimeter or area.

Example 4

A. Write and simplify an expression for the perimeter of the quadrilateral.

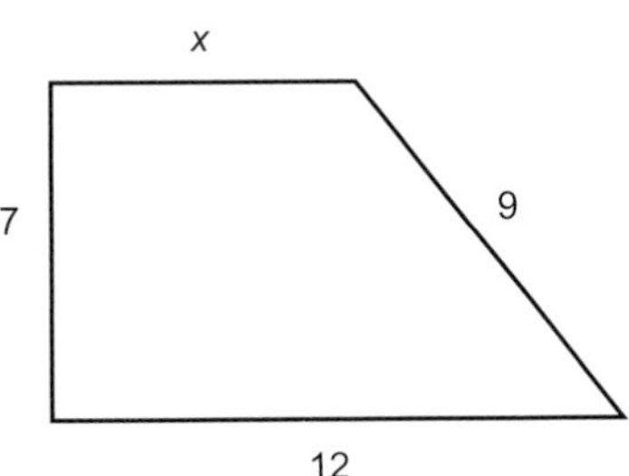

B. Use the simplified expression to find the perimeter when $x = 5$.

Solution

A. $x + 7 + 9 + 12$ Sum of all four sides

$= x + 28$ Add.

The simplified expression for the perimeter is $x + 28$. ■

B. Evaluate $x + 28$ when $x = 5$.

$x + 28 = 5 + 28$ Substitute 5 for x.

$= 33$ Add.

When $x = 5$, the perimeter is 33 units. ■

Problem Set

Translate each word phrase into a variable expression.

1. twelve times a number

2. five more than three times a number

3. four times the sum of five and a number

4. three less than the product of a number and six

5. a number decreased by seven

6. one-half the sum of a number and three

7. the quotient of a number and ten

***8.** **Challenge** two more than the sum of a number and four divided by nine

For each situation, write variable expressions using only one variable.

9. Armen owns twelve fewer DVDs than CDs. Express the number of DVDs and the number of CDs Armen owns in terms of the number of CDs c.

10. Fatima is three times the age of her younger sister Melody. Express both ages in terms of Melody's age m.

11. There are a total of one hundred nine cars and trucks in a parking lot. Express the number of each automobile in terms of the number of trucks t.

12. Ciara's algebra book cost half as much as her biology book. Express the price of each book in terms of the price of the biology book b.

13. A band traveled all day to reach a state competition. In the morning, they traveled twenty-five miles less than twice the distance they traveled in the afternoon. Express each distance traveled in terms of the distance traveled in the afternoon a.

14. A deluxe salad costs seven times more than one-fourth of the price of a garden salad. Express the price of each salad in terms of the price of the garden salad g.

15. There are four more women than men at a golf club. Express the number of men and the number of women in terms of the number of men m.

*16. **Challenge** A clothing store has twice as many blue shirts as red shirts, and one-tenth as many yellow shirts as blue shirts.

A. Express the number of each shirt in terms of the number of red shirts r.

B. If the store has twenty red shirts, how many red, blue, and yellow shirts does the store have total?

Solve. Write a variable expression when needed.

17. Find the number of inches in each.

A. 2 feet

B. 6 feet

C. x feet

18. Find the number of quarts in each.

A. 3 gallons

B. 5 gallons

C. n gallons

19. Find the number of minutes in each.

A. 5 hours

B. 7 hours

C. $2y$ hours

20. How many hours are in $3x$ days?

21. How many meters are in $\frac{5}{n}$ kilometers?

Solve.

22.

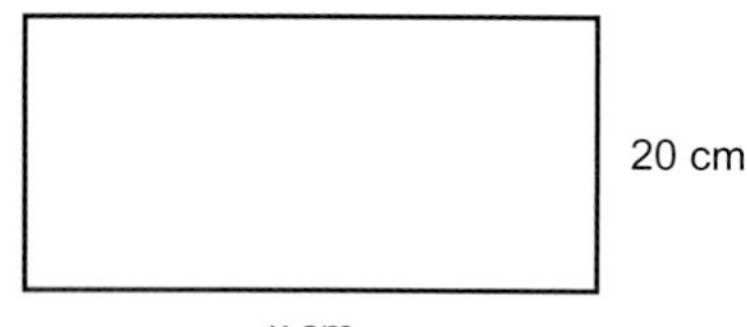

A. Write an expression for the perimeter of the rectangle.

B. Find the perimeter when $x = 42$.

C. Write an expression for the area of the rectangle.

D. Find the area when $x = 42$.

23.

n

$4n$

A. Write an expression for the perimeter of the rectangle.

B. Find the perimeter when $n = 3$.

C. Write an expression for the area of the rectangle.

D. Find the area when $n = 3$.

24.

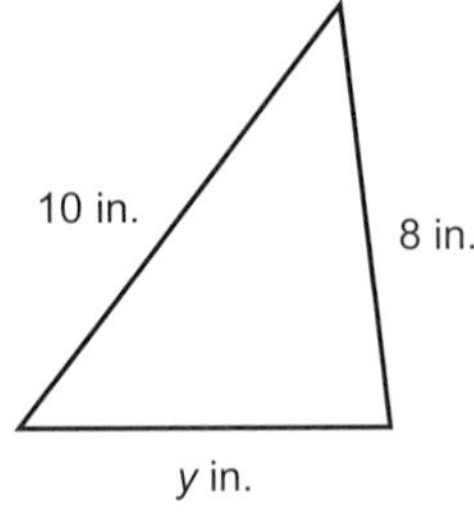

A. Write an expression for the perimeter of the triangle.

B. Find the perimeter when $y = 7$.

25.

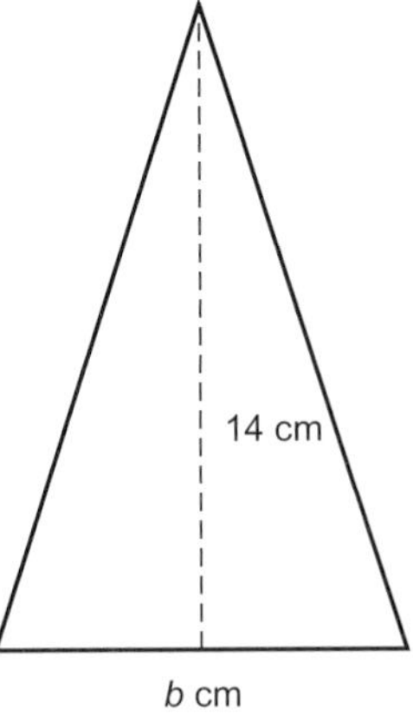

A. Write an expression for the area of the triangle.

B. Find the area when $b = 9$.

26.

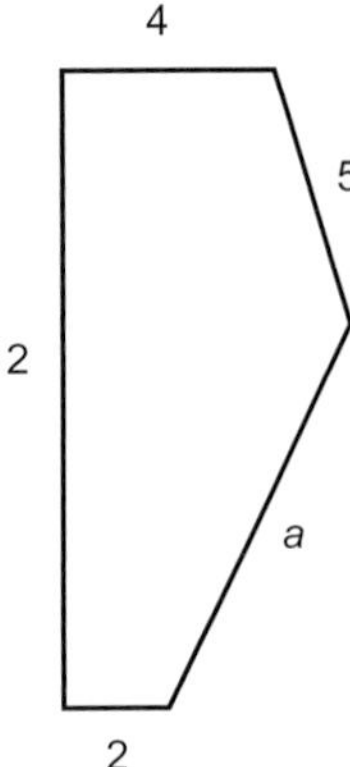

A. Write and simplify an expression for the perimeter of the figure.

B. Find the perimeter when $a = 8$.

27.

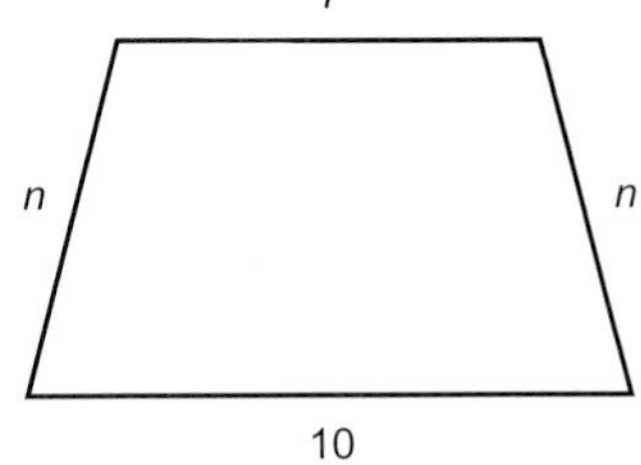

A. Write and simplify an expression for the perimeter of the quadrilateral.

B. Find the perimeter when $n = 6$.

Use the expression *rt* to answer the following questions.

28. **A.** Write an expression for the distance traveled for t hours at 50 miles per hour.

B. Find the distance when $t = 2.5$.

29. **A.** Write an expression for the distance traveled for t hours at 35 miles per hour.

B. Find the distance when $t = 8$.

30. **A.** Write an expression for the distance traveled for 3.6 hours at r miles per hour.

B. Find the distance when $r = 48$.

Equations

When you join two expressions with an equals sign, you create an equation.

The expressions $2 + 5$ and $1 + 6$ each simplify to the same value, 7. Because they have the same value, you can join them together with an equals sign to form an equation: $2 + 5 = 1 + 6$.

DEFINITION

An **equation** is a number sentence that indicates that two expressions have the same value.

One way to distinguish between an equation and an expression is to look for an equals sign. Equations have an equals sign and expressions do not. Also, equations correspond to sentences, and expressions correspond to phrases.

Expression	Equation
$7 + 3$	$7 + 3 = 10$
Phrase: the sum of seven and three	Sentence: The sum of seven and three is ten.

Determining if Two Expressions Form an Equation

When two expressions are not equal, they do not form an equation. Instead of joining them with an equals sign, join them with the "not equals" sign ($\neq$).

Example 1 Write $=$ or $\neq$.

A. $5 \cdot 2 + 7$ ▢ $5 \cdot (2 + 7)$

Solution Use the order of operations to simplify the expressions.

$$5 \cdot 2 + 7 = 10 + 7 \qquad 5 \cdot (2 + 7) = 5 \cdot (9)$$
$$= 17 \qquad\qquad = 45$$

The expression on the left has a different value than the expression on the right. So, the expressions do not form an equation: $5 \cdot 2 + 7 \neq 5 \cdot (2 + 7)$. ■

B. $3[5(2 + 1)]$ ▢ $100 - 5 \cdot 11$

Solution $3[5(2 + 1)] = 3[5(3)]$ $\qquad 100 - 5 \cdot 11 = 100 - 55$

$$= 3[15] \qquad\qquad = 45$$
$$= 45$$

Both expressions have the same value. So, the expressions form an equation: $3[5(2 + 1)] = 100 - 5 \cdot 11$. ■

Determining if a Given Value Makes an Open Sentence True

An equation that contains a variable is an **open sentence**. This means that you do not know if the sentence is true or false until a value is substituted for the variable.

THINK ABOUT IT

Not all open sentences are equations. For instance, $3 + y \neq 5$ is an open sentence.

Example 2 Determine if the given value makes the open sentence true or false.

A. $5a - 4 = 2; a = 2$

Solution Substitute the given value into each occurrence of the variable to see if the left and right sides of the equation are the same value.

$$5a - 4 = 2$$
$$5 \cdot 2 - 4 \stackrel{?}{=} 2$$
$$10 - 4 \stackrel{?}{=} 2$$
$$6 \neq 2$$

The sentence is false when $a = 2$. ■

B. $10 = 0.5x; x = 40$

Solution $10 = 0.5x$

$$10 \stackrel{?}{=} 0.5 \cdot 40$$
$$10 \neq 20$$

The sentence is false when $x = 40$. ■

C. $5n = 7n - 6; n = 3$

Solution $5n = 7n - 6$

$$5 \cdot 3 \stackrel{?}{=} 7 \cdot 3 - 6$$
$$15 \stackrel{?}{=} 21 - 6$$
$$15 = 15 \checkmark$$

The sentence is true when $n = 3$. ■

Application: Phone Plan

Example 3 A phone company offers two monthly plans. The first plan costs \$25 per month plus \$0.10 per minute. The second plan costs \$10 per month plus \$0.25 per minute. Determine if the monthly cost is the same when 100 minutes are used.

Solution To determine if the cost is the same when 100 minutes are used, evaluate $25 + 0.10x = 10 + 0.25x$ when $x = 100$.

$$25 + 0.10x = 10 + 0.25x$$
$$25 + 0.10 \cdot 100 \stackrel{?}{=} 10 + 0.25 \cdot 100$$
$$25 + 10 \stackrel{?}{=} 10 + 25$$
$$35 = 35 \checkmark$$

Yes, the monthly costs are the same when 100 minutes are used. ■

Problem Set

Write = or ≠ to make a true statement.

1. $3 \cdot 6 - 4$ ▒ $3 \cdot (6 - 4)$
2. $10 \cdot 7 - 3$ ▒ $10 \cdot (7 - 3)$
3. $4[6(2 + 3)]$ ▒ $125 - 5 \cdot 1$
4. $4[3(5 + 2)]$ ▒ $95 - 4 \cdot 3$
5. $2 \cdot 10 - 4$ ▒ $2 \cdot (10 - 4)$
6. $4 \cdot 7 - 2 \cdot 10$ ▒ $4(7 - 2) \cdot 10$
7. $5 \cdot 11 + 12 \cdot 3$ ▒ $19 + 3(8 \cdot 3)$
8. $2[5(7 - 1)]$ ▒ $15 + 3(5)$
9. $12[1 + (2 \cdot 2)]$ ▒ $36 - 4(2 + 4)$
10. $\frac{4 + 3 \cdot 6}{3 \cdot 2 + 5}$ ▒ $\frac{12 - 2 \cdot 3}{2 \cdot 1 + 1}$
11. $16 \div [10 + (7 - 1)]$ ▒ $16 \div (10 + 7 - 1)$

Determine if the given value makes the open sentence true or false.

12. $6a + 3 = 15; a = 1$
13. $16 = 0.4x; x = 40$
14. $3z = 2z + 5; z = 5$
15. $4b - 2 = 10; b = 3$
16. $8 - 4x = 4x; x = 1$
17. $0.1x = 12; x = 120$
18. $3 + 0.25x = x; x = 16$
19. $8b = 48; b = 7$
20. $15 = 3d - 3; d = 6$
21. $9 = 0.5y; y = 45$
22. $6g = 2g + 28; g = 7$

Solve.

23. FitGym offers two monthly membership plans. Suri chose the plan that is $35 per month so she can attend all offered classes for free. Arni chose the plan that is $10 per month and he must pay $5 to attend each offered class. Determine if Suri and Arni were charged the same in the month of July if they each attended five classes.

24. Khali has $300 and is saving $50 every month. Tara has $650 and is spending $75 every month. Will the girls have an equal amount of money after three months?

25. Speed-ee car rental charges $22 per day to rent a car, and $0.15 per mile driven over the limit. Zip-ee car rental charges $18 per day to rent a car, and $0.20 per mile driven over the limit. Determine if a car will cost the same at both agencies if it is driven 30 miles over the limit.

26. A local salad bar charges $3 per pound or $7.50 per container. Bianca chose to pay per pound and her salad weighed 2.5 pounds. Simon filled one container and chose to pay per container. Determine if Bianca and Simon spent the same amount.

27. At an amusement park, you can choose to pay $60 for a wrist band and ride unlimited rides or pay $10 to enter and $3 per ride. Determine if the two ways of paying result in the same cost if you ride 20 rides.

*28. **Challenge** Window Fixers charges a fee of $55 and $20 per window for installation. We Fix Panes charges an $85 fee and $10 per window for installation.

   A. Is the cost of having four windows installed the same at both companies?

   B. Which company will charge less to install eight windows?

*29. **Challenge** Arturo and Andi took a test that had 30 multiple choice questions worth 2 points each and 8 open-ended questions worth 5 points each. Arturo answered all of the multiple choice questions correctly and 6 of open-ended questions correctly. Andi answered 25 of the multiple choice questions correctly and all of the open-ended questions correctly. Determine if Arturo and Andi received the same score.

Translating Words into Equations

Use the same words and phrases that allow you to translate word phrases into variable expressions to translate word sentences into equations.

Verbal sentences often use the word "is" and the phrase "is equal to." Represent each by an equals sign in an equation.

Translating Sentences into Equations

Example 1 Translate each sentence into an equation.

A. Two less than five times a number is equal to seven.

Solution $\underbrace{\text{Two less than five times a number}}_{5n-2}\ \underbrace{\text{is equal to}}_{=}\ \underbrace{\text{seven}}_{7}.$

The equation is $5n - 2 = 7$. ■

B. The quotient of a number and four is the sum of six and the number.

Solution $\underbrace{\text{The quotient of a number and four}}_{\frac{n}{4}}\ \underbrace{\text{is}}_{=}\ \underbrace{\text{the sum of six and the number.}}_{6+n}$

The equation is $\frac{n}{4} = 6 + n$. ■

Finding True Statements

You may be asked to find the value of a variable that would make a verbal sentence true. If so, start by translating the sentence into an equation.

Example 2 Find a value of the variable that makes each statement true.

A. The product of six and a number is forty-two.

Solution $\underbrace{\text{The product of six and a number}}_{6n}\ \underbrace{\text{is}}_{=}\ \underbrace{\text{forty-two}}_{42}.$

The equation is $6n = 42$. Find the value of n by answering the question: What number times 6 equals 42? The answer is 7. ■

(continued)

B. Twelve less than a number is equal to nine.

Solution $\underbrace{\text{Twelve less than a number}}_{n\,-\,12}\ \underbrace{\text{is equal to}}_{=}\ \underbrace{\text{nine.}}_{9}$

The equation is $n - 12 = 9$. Find the value of n by answering the question: What number reduced by 12 equals 9? The answer is 21. ∎

Applications: Distance and Geometry

Equations can represent many real-world situations. These applications include problems involving distance traveled, as well as dimensions of common geometric shapes.

Example 3

Carly rode her bicycle at a constant speed of 4 miles per hour to her friend's house. Write an equation to represent the distance Carly rode.

Solution The formula for the distance traveled is $d = rt$, where d is the distance, r is the rate (or speed), and t is the time traveled. Since Carly's speed is 4 miles per hour, $r = 4$. Substitute 4 for r to obtain the equation $d = 4t$. ∎

Example 4

A. A rectangle is 2 meters long, but the width is unknown. Write equations for the perimeter and area of the rectangle.

Solution The formula for the perimeter of a rectangle is $P = 2l + 2w$, and the formula for the area of a rectangle is $A = lw$. Substitute the known information into each formula and simplify as needed.

$P = 2l + 2w \qquad A = lw$

$P = 2 \cdot 2 + 2w \qquad A = 2w$

$P = 4 + 2w$

The equations are $P = 4 + 2w$ and $A = 2w$. ∎

B. Write an equation for the perimeter of the triangle.

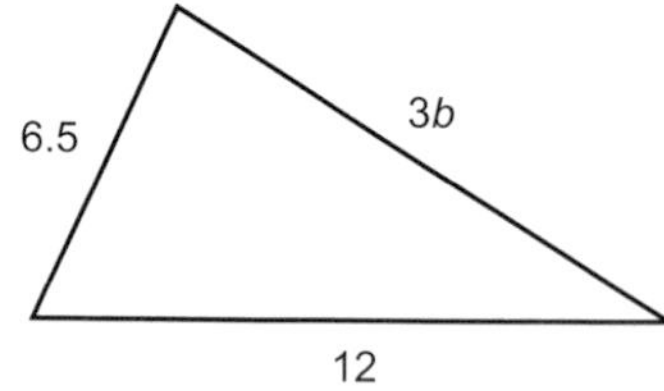

Solution The perimeter of a figure is the sum of the side lengths of the figure.

$P = 12 + 6.5 + 3b$

$P = 18.5 + 3b$

The equation is $P = 18.5 + 3b$. ∎

Problem Set

Translate each sentence into an equation.

1. Three more than four times a number is equal to twelve.
2. The sum of a number and two is twice the number.
3. The quotient of a number and twelve is the sum of eight and the number.
4. Five more than three times a number is equal to eight.
5. The sum of a number and six is seven times the number.
6. The quotient of a number and six is equal to nine.
7. Seven less than a number is two.
8. Twenty-seven is the product of three and a number.
9. Twelve less than six times a number is equal to three times the number.
10. The product of two and the quotient of a number and four is equal to three less than ten times the number.

Find a value of the variable that makes each statement true.

11. The product of five and a number is equal to forty-five.
12. Fifteen is equal to ten less than a number.
13. The quotient of nine and a number is one.
14. Seventeen is equal to eleven less than a number.
15. The quotient of a number and five is eight.
16. The sum of a number and six is equal to the sum of two times the number and one.
17. The product of twelve and a number is equal to seventy-two.
18. The quotient of twenty and a number is four.
19. The product of eight and the quotient of a number and three is equal to three.
20. Forty less than a number is equal to five.

Solve.

21. Tran drove his car at a constant speed of 55 miles per hour. Write an equation for the distance Tran drove.

22.

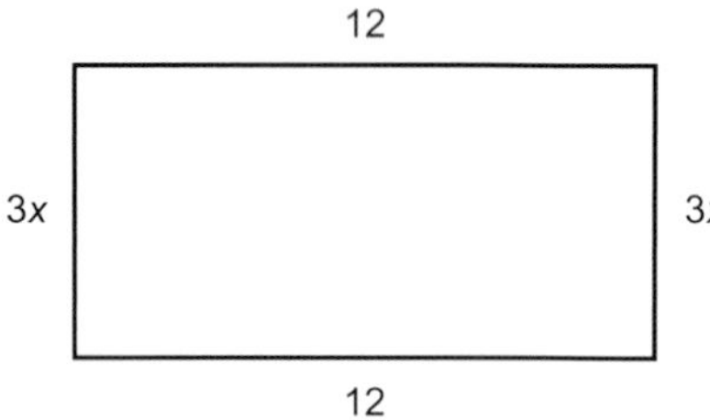

A. Write an equation for the perimeter of the rectangle shown.

B. Write an equation for the area of the rectangle.

23. The formula for the area of a triangle is $A = \frac{1}{2}bh$, where b is the length of the base of the triangle and h is the height of the triangle. Write an equation to find the area of a triangle with a base length of 6 cm and an unknown height.

24. Hooke's law states that $F = -kx$, where F is the force by the spring, k is the spring constant, and x is the displacement (distance). Write an equation for the force by a spring with a spring constant of 30 N/m and an unknown displacement.

25. The weight of an object is found by the formula $W = mg$, where m is the mass of the object and g is the acceleration due to gravity. Write an equation for the weight of an object with an unknown mass, with an acceleration due to gravity of 9.8 m/s^2.

26. Lorrae swims laps at a constant speed. If Lorrae swims for 2 hours, write a formula for the distance she swims.

27. Write an equation for the area of the square.

***28.** **Challenge** Projectile motion can be modeled using the equation $y = v_0t - \frac{1}{2}gt^2$, where y is the height the object reaches, g is the acceleration due to gravity, t is the time, and v_0 is the initial velocity.

A. Write an equation for the height of a baseball thrown into the air with an initial velocity of 16 m/s, and an acceleration due to gravity of 9.8 m/s^2.

B. What is the height of the baseball after 3 seconds?

***29.** **Challenge** The formula for the area of a trapezoid is $A = \frac{1}{2}(b_1 + b_2)h$.

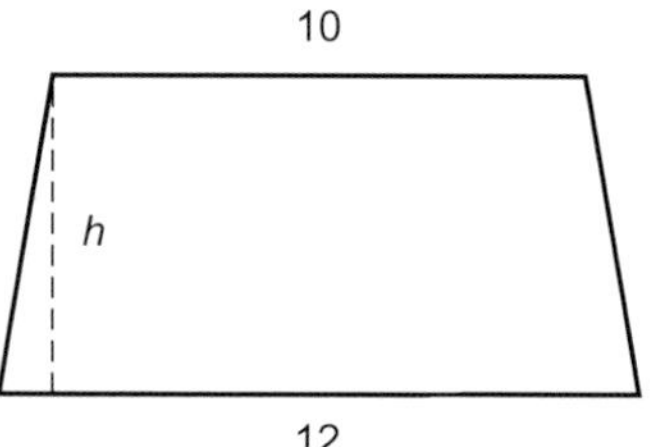

A. Write an equation for the area of the trapezoid shown.

B. Find the area if $h = 5$.

Replacement Sets

One method you can use to solve an open sentence involves replacement sets.

Because $10 - 3x = 4$ is a true statement when $x = 2$, the number 2 is a **solution** of the equation. The process of finding a value that makes an open sentence true is called **solving** the equation or inequality.

A **set** is a collection of objects, and each member of the set is an **element** of the set. The elements of a set are enclosed in braces, so the set containing the elements 10, 15, and 20 is written as $\{10, 15, 20\}$. To show that a value is an element of a set, you can use the symbol $\in$.

NOTATION

$\in$ is an element of

For instance, $2 \in \{2, 4, 6, 8\}$.

DEFINITIONS

A set of values that are allowable as a solution to an open sentence is called the **replacement set,** or **domain.** The elements of the replacement set that make an open sentence true become the **solution set.**

Finding a Solution Set

Example 1 Find the solution set for $5x + 3 = 18$ given the replacement set $\{0, 1, 2, 3, 4, 5\}$.

Solution Substitute each element of the replacement set for x to see which, if any, make the open sentence true.

$5x + 3 = 18$	$5x + 3 = 18$	$5x + 3 = 18$
$5 \cdot 0 + 3 \stackrel{?}{=} 18$	$5 \cdot 1 + 3 \stackrel{?}{=} 18$	$5 \cdot 2 + 3 \stackrel{?}{=} 18$
$0 + 3 \stackrel{?}{=} 18$	$5 + 3 \stackrel{?}{=} 18$	$10 + 3 \stackrel{?}{=} 18$
$3 \neq 18$	$8 \neq 18$	$13 \neq 18$

$5x + 3 = 18$	$5x + 3 = 18$	$5x + 3 = 18$
$5 \cdot 3 + 3 \stackrel{?}{=} 18$	$5 \cdot 4 + 3 \stackrel{?}{=} 18$	$5 \cdot 5 + 3 \stackrel{?}{=} 18$
$15 + 3 \stackrel{?}{=} 18$	$20 + 3 \stackrel{?}{=} 18$	$25 + 3 \stackrel{?}{=} 18$
$18 = 18$ ✓	$23 \neq 18$	$28 \neq 18$

The open sentence is true when $x = 3$. The solution set is $\{3\}$. ■

THINK ABOUT IT

The *open sentence* $5x + 3 = 18$ is an *equation* with solution $x = 3$.

Special Cases: Empty and Null Sets

NOTATION

{ } or ∅ null or empty set

In Example 1, only one element from the replacement set became part of the solution set. It is possible for there to be two or more solutions of an open sentence. It is also possible that none of the elements in the replacement set make the open sentence true. When no elements in the replacement set make the open sentence true, the solution is the **empty set,** written as ∅ or { }.

Example 2 Find the solution set for each open sentence given the replacement set {1, 2, 3, 4}.

A. $5x + 3 = 2(x + 3) - 3 + 3x$

Solution

$$\begin{aligned} 5x + 3 &= 2(x + 3) - 3 + 3x \\ 5 \cdot 1 + 3 &\stackrel{?}{=} 2(1 + 3) - 3 + 3 \cdot 1 \\ 5 + 3 &\stackrel{?}{=} 2 \cdot 4 - 3 + 3 \\ 8 &\stackrel{?}{=} 8 - 3 + 3 \\ 8 &\stackrel{?}{=} 5 + 3 \\ 8 &= 8 \checkmark \end{aligned}$$

$$\begin{aligned} 5x + 3 &= 2(x + 3) - 3 + 3x \\ 5 \cdot 2 + 3 &\stackrel{?}{=} 2(2 + 3) - 3 + 3 \cdot 2 \\ 10 + 3 &\stackrel{?}{=} 2 \cdot 5 - 3 + 6 \\ 13 &\stackrel{?}{=} 10 - 3 + 6 \\ 13 &\stackrel{?}{=} 7 + 6 \\ 13 &= 13 \checkmark \end{aligned}$$

$$\begin{aligned} 5x + 3 &= 2(x + 3) - 3 + 3x \\ 5 \cdot 3 + 3 &\stackrel{?}{=} 2(3 + 3) - 3 + 3 \cdot 3 \\ 15 + 3 &\stackrel{?}{=} 2 \cdot 6 - 3 + 9 \\ 18 &\stackrel{?}{=} 12 - 3 + 9 \\ 18 &\stackrel{?}{=} 9 + 9 \\ 18 &= 18 \checkmark \end{aligned}$$

$$\begin{aligned} 5x + 3 &= 2(x + 3) - 3 + 3x \\ 5 \cdot 4 + 3 &\stackrel{?}{=} 2(4 + 3) - 3 + 3 \cdot 4 \\ 20 + 3 &\stackrel{?}{=} 2 \cdot 7 - 3 + 12 \\ 23 &\stackrel{?}{=} 14 - 3 + 12 \\ 23 &\stackrel{?}{=} 11 + 12 \\ 23 &= 23 \checkmark \end{aligned}$$

The solution set is every member of the replacement set {1, 2, 3, 4}. ■

B. $5x + 3 = 2(x + 3) - 6 + 3x$

Solution

$$\begin{aligned} 5x + 3 &= 2(x + 3) - 6 + 3x \\ 5 \cdot 1 + 3 &\stackrel{?}{=} 2(1 + 3) - 6 + 3 \cdot 1 \\ 5 + 3 &\stackrel{?}{=} 2 \cdot 4 - 6 + 3 \\ 8 &\stackrel{?}{=} 8 - 6 + 3 \\ 8 &\stackrel{?}{=} 2 + 3 \\ 8 &\neq 5 \end{aligned}$$

$$\begin{aligned} 5x + 3 &= 2(x + 3) - 6 + 3x \\ 5 \cdot 2 + 3 &\stackrel{?}{=} 2(2 + 3) - 6 + 3 \cdot 2 \\ 10 + 3 &\stackrel{?}{=} 2 \cdot 5 - 6 + 6 \\ 13 &\stackrel{?}{=} 10 - 6 + 6 \\ 13 &\stackrel{?}{=} 4 + 6 \\ 13 &\neq 10 \end{aligned}$$

$$\begin{aligned} 5x + 3 &= 2(x + 3) - 6 + 3x \\ 5 \cdot 3 + 3 &\stackrel{?}{=} 2(3 + 3) - 6 + 3 \cdot 3 \\ 15 + 3 &\stackrel{?}{=} 2 \cdot 6 - 6 + 9 \\ 18 &\stackrel{?}{=} 12 - 6 + 9 \\ 18 &\stackrel{?}{=} 6 + 9 \\ 18 &\neq 15 \end{aligned}$$

$$\begin{aligned} 5x + 3 &= 2(x + 3) - 6 + 3x \\ 5 \cdot 4 + 3 &\stackrel{?}{=} 2(4 + 3) - 6 + 3 \cdot 4 \\ 20 + 3 &\stackrel{?}{=} 2 \cdot 7 - 6 + 12 \\ 23 &\stackrel{?}{=} 14 - 6 + 12 \\ 23 &\stackrel{?}{=} 8 + 12 \\ 23 &\neq 20 \end{aligned}$$

No member of the replacement set makes the open sentence true. The solution set is the empty set, ∅. ■

Application: Perimeter

Replacement sets can help you solve real-world problems that have a set list of possible answers.

Example 3 Darrell is building a tree house with a rectangular floor. Two opposite sides are already set in place, each 10 feet long. He wants the perimeter of the floor to be 50 feet. Find the solution set for $50 = 2l + 20$ given the replacement set $\{8, 10, 12, 15\}$ to determine which size boards Darrell should buy to build the remaining sides of the floor.

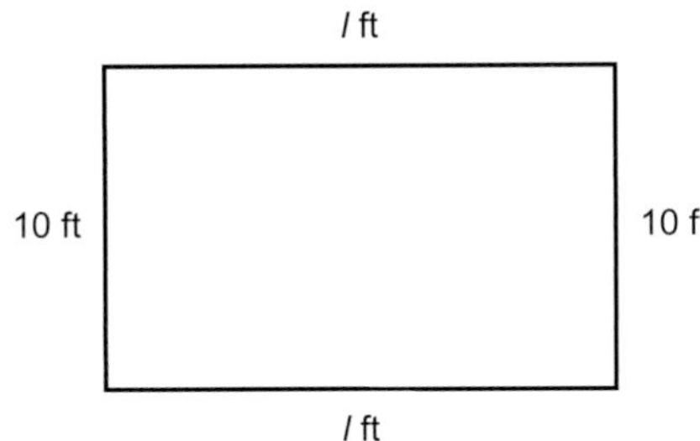

Solution Substitute each element of the replacement set for l.

$50 = 2l + 20$	$50 = 2l + 20$	$50 = 2l + 20$	$50 = 2l + 20$
$50 \stackrel{?}{=} 2 \cdot 8 + 20$	$50 \stackrel{?}{=} 2 \cdot 10 + 20$	$50 \stackrel{?}{=} 2 \cdot 12 + 20$	$50 \stackrel{?}{=} 2 \cdot 15 + 20$
$50 \stackrel{?}{=} 16 + 20$	$50 \stackrel{?}{=} 20 + 20$	$50 \stackrel{?}{=} 24 + 20$	$50 \stackrel{?}{=} 30 + 20$
$50 \neq 36$	$50 \neq 40$	$50 \neq 44$	$50 = 50$ ✓

The solution set is $\{15\}$. So, Darrell should buy 15-foot boards for the remaining sides. ■

Problem Set

Find the solution set for each open sentence with the given replacement set.

1. $2x - 3 = 5$, $\{0, 1, 2, 3, 4, 5\}$
2. $y + 5 = -1$, $\{-2, -4, -6, -8\}$
3. $4x + 2 = 7(x - 1) + 2x$, $\{1, 3, 5, 7, 9\}$
4. $2x - 1 = 3(x + 2) - 4x - 7$, $\{0, 1, 2, 3, 4\}$
5. $m^2 + 4 = 5$, $\{-2, -1, 0, 1, 2\}$
6. $b - (-3b - 3) = 4b + 3$, $\{1, 2, 3, 4\}$
7. $t - 1 = 7 - t$, $\{0, 4, 8, 12\}$
8. $1.5n + (-2 + 0.5) = 3 - 2(4.5 + 0.5)$, $\{-5, -4, -3, -2, -1\}$
9. $-10v + 10 = -10$, $\{0, 1, 2, 3, 4, 5\}$
10. $|z + 1| = |2z + 1 - z|$, $\{-5, 0, 5, 10\}$
11. $y - 1 = 0$, $\{1, 2, 3, 4, 5, 6\}$
12. $2f + 23 = 3(f - 7)$, $\{14, 15, 16, 17, 18\}$
13. $12n - 40 = -20 - (-160)$, $\{0, 5, 10, 15\}$
14. $\left|\frac{a}{2} + 10\right| = 20 + (-10 - 5)$, $\{-30, -10, 10, 30\}$
15. $4n + 2 = 2(1 + 2n)$, $\{11, 12, 13, 14\}$
16. $x^2 + 2 = x(4 - x) + x$, $\{0, 1, 2, 3, 4)$
17. $t + 17 = 13$, $\{-12, -8, -4, 0, 4\}$
18. $2\left(\left|\frac{100}{c}\right|\right) = (20 - |c|) + \left|\frac{c}{2}\right|$, $\{-20, -10, 10, 20\}$
19. $4 - t = 1$, $\{1, 2, 3, 4\}$
20. $3v - (7 - 1) = 5 + (2 + 1)$, $\{-1, 0, 1, 2\}$

Solve.

21. Merrie wants to paint an accent wall in her living room. She knows that the wall is 18 feet long, but she cannot remember the exact height. She knows that it is somewhere around 10 feet high, and she previously calculated that she would need paint to cover 162 square feet. Find the solution set for $18h = 162$ given the replacement set $\{8, 9, 10, 11\}$ to determine the height of her ceiling.

22. Charo is buying food for her friends and is ordering from the \$1 and \$2 value menus. She knows that she needs three \$1 sandwiches, two \$2 parfaits and two \$2 salads. Drinks are \$1, and she has \$13 in her wallet. Find the solution set for $3 \cdot 1 + 2 \cdot 2 + 2 \cdot 2 + d \cdot 1 = 13$ given the replacement set $\{0, 1, 2, 3\}$ to determine how many drinks she can purchase.

23. Jacob is making two replicas of his favorite team's triangular pennant. He only has 17 feet of the special trim that he wants to use to border both pennants. He wants the base of each pennant to be 1.5 feet. He also wants the sides of each pennant to be longer than the base. Find the solution set for $2(1.5 + 2s) = 17$ given the replacement set $\{2, 2.5, 3, 3.5, 4\}$ to determine what length each side of the two pennants should be.

24. A movie theater customer bought two \$3.50 popcorns, four \$2.50 drinks, and four cups of mixed fruit for a total cost of \$29. Find the solution set for $2 \cdot 3.5 + 4 \cdot 2.5 + 4c = 29$ given the replacement set $\{1.5, 2, 2.5, 3\}$ to determine the cost of each cup of mixed fruit.

25. Joaquim and three of his friends are planting flowers in a circular garden. Each of them guessed the radius of the garden. They know the circumference of the garden is 157 feet. Find the solution set for $3.14 \cdot 2r = 157$ given the replacement set $\{20, 25, 30, 35\}$ to determine the radius of the garden.

26. Travis decides to participate in a local charity event and fill a shoebox with presents for local children who are less fortunate. He goes to the store and buys two \$5 toys, one \$3 toy, three \$4 toys, and three games that cost the same amount. The cashier rings up the total, then realizes that the games are supposed to be on sale, so she subtracts the original cost of one game to cover the price difference. The total cost is \$35. Find the solution set for $2 \cdot 5 + 1 \cdot 3 + 3(4 + g) - g = 35$ given the replacement set $\{2, 3, 4, 5\}$ to determine the original cost of each game.

27. A park maintenance crew is laying recycled rubber mulch in a rectangular ground area to provide padding for a play area. They want the length of the area that is covered to be twice as long as the width that is covered. They have enough mulch to cover 750 square feet. Find the solution set for $2w \cdot w = 800$ given the replacement set $\{10, 15, 20, 25, 30\}$ to determine how wide they can make the area covered by the rubber mulch.

28. Three thirsty friends drink an entire 64-ounce bottle of juice. Benito drank twice as much as Tala, and Amy drank 11 ounces less than Benito. Find the solution set for $t + 2t + (2t - 11) = 64$ given the replacement set $\{10, 15, 20, 25\}$ to find out how many ounces of juice Tala drank.

29. Chelsea is starting to train for a triathlon and must run 1 mile every day. The rectangular path that she runs on is 1 mile long and its width is 0.125 mile. Find the solution set for $2 \cdot 0.125 + 2l = 1$ given the replacement set $\{0.125, 0.25, 0.375, 0.5\}$ to determine the length of the path.

30. A swimmer swims 30 laps along the length of a rectangular pool. The distance that he swims is the same as if he swam 10 times around the perimeter of a pool with the same length and a width of 25 m. Find the solution set for $30l = 10(2l + 2 \cdot 25)$ given the replacement set $\{40, 50, 60, 70\}$ to determine the length of each lap.

Problem Solving

When using math to solve real-world problems, it can help to have a plan. The following suggested problem-solving strategy has five steps.

PROBLEM-SOLVING PLAN

Step 1 *Identify*
Read the problem and identify the unknowns. What are you being asked to find? Write it down in words. If you can, estimate the answer.

Step 2 *Strategize*
Select and define variables and variable expressions for all the unknowns.

Step 3 *Set Up*
Write an equation, inequality, system of equations, or whatever other tools you need that model the problem that is being solved.

Step 4 *Solve*
Solve the model (equation, inequality, system, etc.).

Step 5 *Check*
Check your answer for reasonableness and accuracy with the original problem statement.

Application: Groups of People

Example 1 There are 5 times as many students as teachers. There are 12 teachers. How many students are there?

Solution Work through the five steps of the problem-solving plan.

Step 1 *Identify* The unknown is the number of students. You are asked to find the number of students. Estimate: There are more students than teachers, so the answer will be greater than 12. Twelve is close to 10, so a possible estimate is 50 students because $10 \cdot 5 = 50$.

Step 2 *Strategize* Define variables.
Number of teachers: t
Number of students: s

Step 3 *Set Up* Write an equation to represent the fact that the number of students is five times the number of teachers: $s = 5t$.

(continued)

RECONNECT TO THE BIG IDEA

Algebraic equations can capture key relationships among quantities in the world.

Step 4 *Solve* Substitute the number of teachers into the equation.

$s = 5t$

$s = 5 \cdot 12$

$s = 60$

There are 60 students.

Step 5 *Check* The answer of 60 is close to the estimate of 50 and is reasonable. Because $60 \div 5 = 12$, the answer is correct. ■

Application: Perimeter and Area

You can also use the problem-solving plan to solve geometry problems.

Example 2 The area of a rectangle is 70 square units and the width of the rectangle is 5 units. Find the perimeter of the rectangle.

Solution You can use the problem-solving plan to solve problems involving distance, rate, and time.

Step 1 *Identify* You are asked to find the perimeter. To find the perimeter, you must know both the length and width of the rectangle. The width is known, but the length is not known.

Step 2 *Strategize* Write and solve an equation for the area of a rectangle to find the value of the length. Then find the perimeter of the rectangle. Define variables. Use w for width, l for length, A for area, and P for perimeter.

Step 3 *Set Up* Write an equation to represent the area.

$A = lw$

$70 = l \cdot 5$

TIP

One way to check for accuracy is to use a different method than the one used to solve the problem. In this check, we add all four side lengths instead of finding the sum of twice the length and twice the width.

Step 4 *Solve* Think: "What number times 5 equals 70?" You can guess and check, or divide: $70 \div 5 = 14$. The length is 14 units. To find the perimeter, substitute 5 and 14 into $P = 2l + 2w$.

$P = 2 \cdot 14 + 2 \cdot 5$

$= 29 + 10$

$= 39$

Step 5 *Check* $5 \cdot 14 = 70$. The given area is 70, so the length is correct. The perimeter is the sum of the sides: $5 + 14 + 5 + 14 = 38$. The answer is correct. ■

Application: Distance, Rate, and Time

Example 3 LeAnn drove 125 miles at a rate of 50 miles per hour. How long did it take her to drive this distance?

Solution

Step 1 *Identify* You are given the distance and rate and are asked to find the time. Because $50 \cdot 2 = 100$, the answer should be greater than 2 hours.

Step 2 *Strategize* Use d for distance, r for rate, and t for time.

Step 3 *Set Up* Distance is the product of the rate and the time, or $d = rt$. Substitute the known information into the general equation: $125 = 50t$.

Step 4 *Solve* To determine how many times 50 divides into 125, divide 125 by 50: $125 \div 50 = 2.5$.

Step 5 *Check* Two and one-half hours is a reasonable time to drive 125 miles at a rate of 50 mph. Multiply to check for accuracy: $50 \cdot 2.5 = 125$. ■

Problem Set

Solve. For each problem:

A. Define variables for the unknowns.
B. Write an equation to model the problem.
C. Solve the equation.
D. Give your answer in a complete sentence.

1. There are 10 more boys than girls in class. There are 14 girls. How many boys are there?

2. There are 3 fewer than twice the number of tiles in the box than on the floor. There are 100 tiles on the floor. How many tiles are in the box?

3. The area of a rectangle is 80 square units and the width of the rectangle is 4 units. Find the perimeter of the rectangle.

4. Sean deposited \$200 into an account and earned \$36 in interest after 3 years. Use the formula $I = prt$, where I represents simple interest, p represents principal, r represents interest rate, and t represents time in years to compute the interest rate.

5. Roxy drove 200 miles at a rate of 50 miles per hour. How long did it take her to drive this distance?

6. Alban drove 1200 miles in 30 hours. What was his rate of travel in miles per hour?

7. Amida earned $60 in interest on her deposit after 5 years with a 0.04 interest rate. Use the formula $I = prt$, where I represents simple interest, p represents principal, r represents interest rate, and t represents time in years to compute the principal amount deposited.

8. The number of boys at a movie theatre is 6 times greater than the number of girls at a movie theatre. The number of girls at the movie theatre is 25. How many boys are at the movie theatre?

9. All sides of an equilateral triangle have equal length. If the perimeter of an equilateral triangle is 39 centimeters, what is the length of each side?

10. The area of a square field is 529 square feet. Find the length of each side of the square.

11. Zahira drove at a rate of 50 miles per hour for 3.5 hours. How many miles did she travel?

12. The number of girls who work at Super Shopper is 2 more than 3 times the number of boys. If 30 boys work at Super Shopper, how many girls work there?

13. Ms. Zambia has three more students in her class than Mr. Powan. If Mr. Powan has 22 students in his class, how many students are in Ms. Zambia's class?

14. Laura deposits $150 at a 5% interest rate. Use the formula $I = prt$, where I represents simple interest, p represents principal, r represents interest rate, and t represents time in years to compute her simple interest after 2 years.

15. Benoit plays baseball 3 times as much as he plays soccer. If Benoit plays soccer 6 hours per week, how many hours does he play baseball?

16. The number of backpacks sold at Out Door Adventure equals 10 fewer than 3 times the number of backpacks in the store. There are 30 backpacks in the store. How many backpacks were sold?

17. The sum of two equal angles is 110°. What is the measure of each of these angles?

18. The number of concert tickets sold today is 800 more than 6 times the number of tickets sold last year. One thousand tickets were sold last year. How many tickets were sold today?

19. Sarabi drove 20 miles at 40 miles per hour. How long did she drive?

20. The area of a triangle is 60 square units and the base of the triangle is 5 units. Find the height of the triangle.

21. Gita is 3 times as old as her son, Ajeet. If Gita is 36 years old, how old is Ajeet?

22. Katya works 8 more hours per week than Suzi. If Suzi works 16 hours per week, how many hours does Katya work?

23. Janel needs to convert the temperature 80°F to Celsius. If $C = \frac{5}{9}(F - 32)$, where C represents degrees Celsius and F represents degrees Fahrenheit, what is the temperature in degrees Celsius?

24. Jeb can paint a room in 3 hours and Matthew can paint the same size room in 2.5 hours. If Jeb paints 5 rooms and Matthew paints 6 rooms, what is the total amount of time spent painting?

25. Jamal worked 20 hours per week and earned \$5.25 per hour. How much money did he earn?

26. Antonio has \$1.65 in change. Three of those coins are dimes, 5 are quarters, and the remaining coins are nickels. How many nickels does Anthony have?

27. The width of a rectangular garden is 5 feet. The length of the garden is 3 times the width. How many feet of fencing is needed to enclose the garden?

28. Two computers are for sale. Computer A costs \$700 less than 2 times the price of Computer B. If Computer B costs \$900, how much does Computer A cost?

*29. **Challenge** Cerise has \$5.67. She has 5 one-dollar bills, 2 quarters, and 3 nickels. What other coins does Cerise have?

*30. **Challenge** The length of a rectangle is 3 more than 2 times its width. The perimeter of the rectangle is 24 units. Find the width and length of the rectangle.

UNIT 2 Properties of Real Numbers

The colors in a rainbow form a set.

There are many different kinds of numbers. Negative numbers, positive numbers, integers, fractions, and decimals are just a few of the many groups of numbers. What do these varieties of numbers have in common? They all obey the rules of arithmetic. They can be added, subtracted, multiplied, and divided.

Big Ideas

- The laws of arithmetic can be used to simplify algebraic expressions and equations.
- A set is a well-defined collection of numbers or objects. Sets and operations defined on sets provide a clear way to communicate about collections of numbers or objects.
- A number is an entity that obeys the laws of arithmetic; all numbers obey the laws of arithmetic. The laws of arithmetic can be used to simplify algebraic expressions.

Unit Topics

- Number Lines
- Sets
- Comparing Expressions
- Number Properties
- The Distributive Property
- Algebraic Proof
- Opposites and Absolute Value

Number Lines

A number line can represent all real numbers. You can use a number line to graphically display values, compare and order numbers, and solve real-world problems.

DEFINITIONS

A **number line** is a line that has equally spaced intervals labeled with coordinates.
A **coordinate** is a number that indicates the location of a number on a number line.
The **origin** is the point with coordinate zero.

Numbers to the left of the origin are negative. Numbers to the right of the origin are positive.

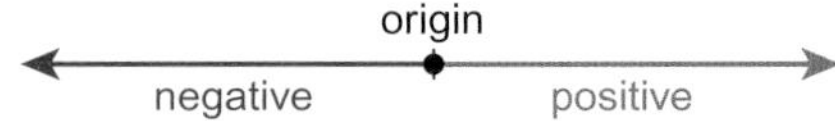

Finding the Coordinate of a Point on a Number Line

Example 1 What is the coordinate of each point?

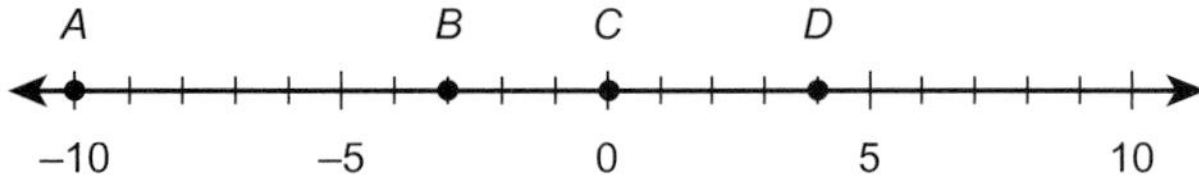

Solution Find the corresponding coordinate of each point on the number line. Locate the origin and use it as a starting point.

Point A is located 10 units to the left of the origin. The coordinate of point A is -10.

Point B is located 3 units to the left of the origin. The coordinate of point B is -3.

Point C is at the origin. The coordinate of point C is 0.

Point D is located 4 units to the right of the origin. The coordinate of point D is 4. ■

Number Lines Divided by Fractional Amounts

The tick marks on the number line in Example 1 divide the line at locations that are integers. Sometimes tick marks divide number lines by fractional amounts.

Example 2 What is the coordinate of each point?

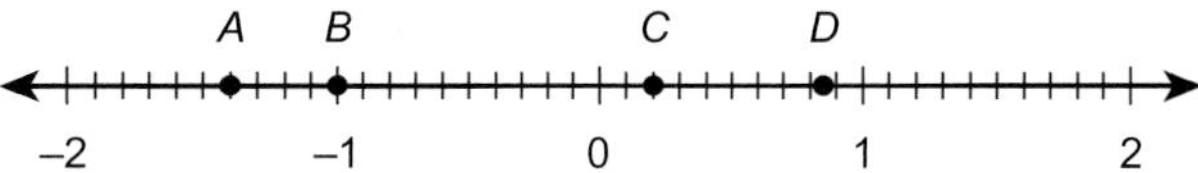

Solution Count the number of equal spaces between each integer. There are 10, so the number line is divided into tenths. Each tick mark between the integers represents one-tenth.

Point A is located one whole and four-tenths units to the left of the origin. The coordinate of point A is $-1\frac{4}{10}$ or $-1\frac{2}{5}$ or -1.4.

Point B is located one whole unit to the left of the origin. The coordinate of point B is -1.

REMEMBER

The fraction $\frac{8}{10}$ could be written an infinite number of ways. In general, pick one that is convenient or in simplest form.

Point C is located two-tenths units to the right of the origin. The coordinate of point C is $\frac{2}{10}$ or $\frac{1}{5}$ or 0.2.

Point D is located about halfway between eight-tenths units and nine-tenths units to the right of the origin. One way to find the point halfway between $\frac{8}{10}$ and $\frac{9}{10}$ is to write the fractions as decimals, add the values, and divide the result by 2.

$$\frac{8}{10} = 0.8 \text{ and } \frac{9}{10} = 0.9$$

$$\frac{0.8 + 0.9}{2} = \frac{1.7}{2} = 0.85$$

The coordinate of point D is about 0.85. ■

Plotting Points on a Number Line

Example 3 Draw a number line from -3 to 3. Divide the intervals between the numbers into thirds. Plot and label the points $-2\frac{2}{3}$ and $1\frac{1}{3}$ on the number line.

Solution Draw a number line and label -3, -2, -1, 0, 1, 2, and 3. To divide the intervals into thirds, make two equally spaced shorter marks between each integer.

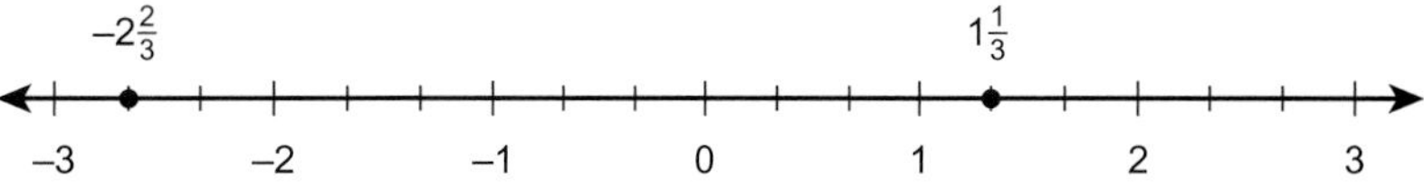

The point $-2\frac{2}{3}$ is two and two-thirds units to the left of 0. The point $1\frac{1}{3}$ is one and one-third units to the right of 0. ■

Using a Number Line to Compare and Order Numbers

You can use a number line to compare and order numbers.

Example 4

A. Fill in the operator using <, >, or =.

$$-1\frac{3}{10} \ \blacksquare \ -1.5$$

Solution Plot each number on a number line and use the number line to compare the numbers.

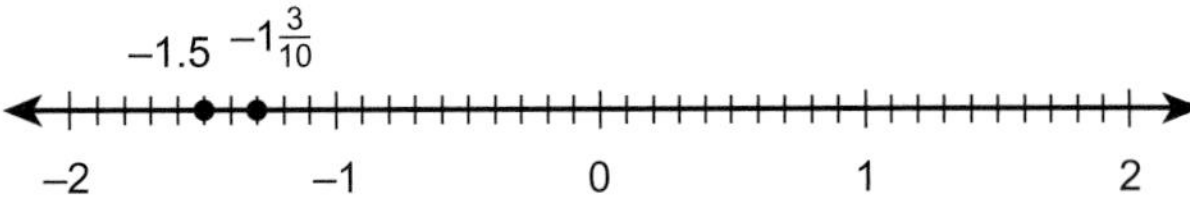

Since $-1\frac{3}{10}$ is to the right of -1.5 on the number line, $-1\frac{3}{10} > -1.5$. ■

REMEMBER

On a number line, values increase as you move right and decrease as you move left.

B. List the following set of numbers in increasing order.

$$\frac{4}{5}, -1.8, 1\frac{9}{10}, 0, -0.5, -1.2$$

Solution Plot each number on a number line and use the number line to order the numbers.

−1.8 −1.2 −0.5 0 $\frac{4}{5}$ $1\frac{9}{10}$

−2 −1 0 1 2

List the numbers from left to right. The numbers in increasing order are:

$$-1.8, -1.2, -0.5, 0, \frac{4}{5}, 1\frac{9}{10}.$$ ■

Application: Golf Scores

You can use number lines to solve application problems.

Example 5 Scores in golf are calculated relative to the par of the golf course. Given the following information, list the golfers in order from best (lowest) to worst (highest) score.

Golfer	Padraig	Juan	Inga	Nick
Standing	7-over par	2-over par	5-over par	3-under par

Solution Use a number line. Let par be at the origin of the number line.

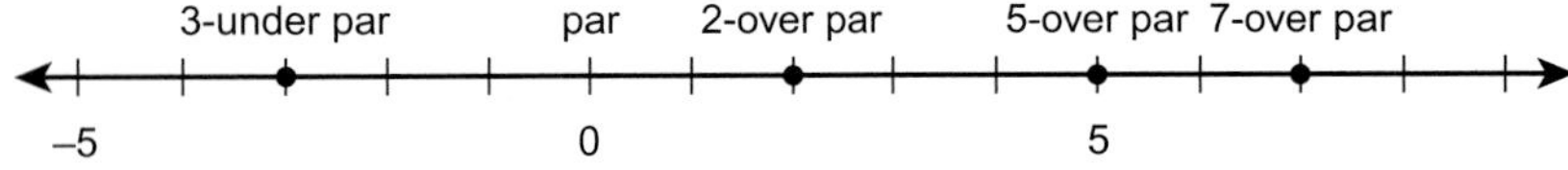

From left to right, read the names of the golfers whose scores are on the number line:

Nick, Juan, Inga, Padraig. ■

Problem Set

Determine the approximate coordinate of each point.

1. 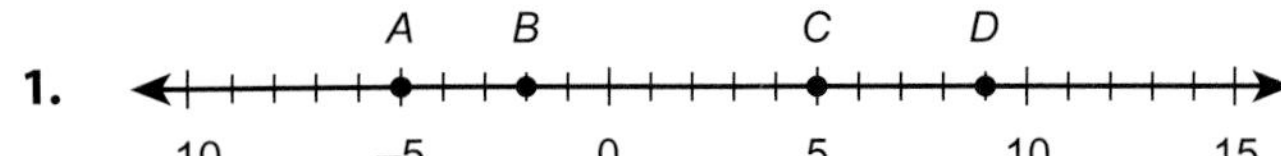

2. A B C D
−10 −5 0 5 10 15

3. A B C D
−2 −1 0 1 2

4. A B C D
−2 −1 0 1 2

5. A B C D
−10 −5 0 5 10 15

6. A B C D
−2 −1 0 1 2

7. A B C D
−10 −5 0 5 10 15

8. A B C D
−2 −1 0 1 2

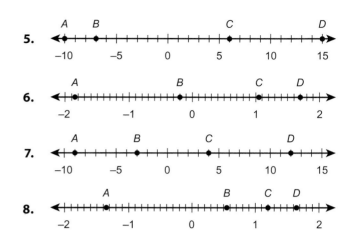

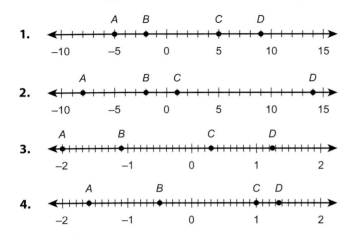

9. Draw a number line from −2 to 3. Use tick marks to mark half units on the number line. Plot and label the points $-1\frac{1}{2}$ and $2\frac{1}{2}$.

10. Draw a number line from 0 to 2. Use tick marks to mark quarter units on the number line. Plot and label the points $\frac{1}{4}$ and $1\frac{3}{4}$.

11. Draw a number line from −2 to 2. Use tick marks to mark every fifth unit. Plot and label the points $-\frac{4}{5}$ and $1\frac{2}{5}$.

12. Draw a number line from −1 to 1. Use tick marks to mark every sixth unit. Plot and label the points $-\frac{5}{6}$ and $\frac{1}{2}$.

Use a number line to compare the numbers. Fill in the operator using $<$, $>$, or $=$.

13. $1\frac{3}{4}$ ▢ 1.25

14. 1.2 ▢ $1\frac{1}{5}$

15. −1.6 ▢ −1.2

16. 1.75 ▢ 1.5

17. 1.4 ▢ $1\frac{2}{5}$

18. $\frac{1}{3}$ ▢ $\frac{1}{2}$

Use a number line to compare the numbers. List the set of numbers in increasing order.

19. $0.75, \frac{1}{2}, 0, 1, 0.25$

20. $-1\frac{7}{10}, 1, -1.2, 0.6, -0.1, \frac{3}{10}$

21. $\frac{6}{5}, -\frac{4}{5}, \frac{3}{5}, -0.2, \frac{1}{5}$

22. $-1\frac{2}{5}, \frac{10}{5}, 1.2, -0.8, \frac{3}{5}$

23. $-0.6, -1, -\frac{8}{5}, 0, \frac{2}{5}, 1.6$

24. $1\frac{1}{2}, -0.2, -2, 0.8, 1.7, 0.5$

Solve.

25. The approximate altitudes for four locations are given in the table. Use a number line to compare the values. List the locations in order from the least to greatest altitude.

Location	Mount Everest	Death Valley	Mont Blanc	Mount Snow
Altitude (m)	8847	−61	5000	567

26. Sam likes to play a game where he gets 10 points every hand he wins and −10 points every hand he loses. Listed are his winnings (+) and losses (−). Use a number line to compare the values. List the days in order from fewest wins to most wins.

Day	Monday	Tuesday	Wednesday	Thursday
Points Scored	+20	−30	+60	−80

27. The low temperatures of five cities for August 26, 2007 are shown below. Use a number line to compare the values. List the cities in order from the greatest to least temperature.

City	Honolulu	Base Esperanza	Nome	Washington, D.C.
Low Temp. (°F)	73	−5	47	72

28. The final results of the 2007 Masters Golf Tournament are given. Use a number line to compare the values. List the golfers in order from best (lowest) to worst (highest) score.

Player	J. Kelly	R. Sabbatini	Z. Johnson	T. Woods
Standing	4-over par	3-over par	1-over par	3-over par

***29. Challenge** The final results of the 1997 Masters Golf Tournament are given.

Player	T. Kite	T. Tolles	T. Watson	T. Woods
Standing	6-under par	5-under par	4-under par	18-under par

A. Use a number line to compare the values. Place the golfers in order from best (lowest) to worst (highest) score.

B. Compare the 1997 results to the 2007 results (#28). Based on the final scores, which tournament was more competitive? Explain.

Sets

Use sets to group objects.

REMEMBER

A set is a collection of objects. Each member in a set is called an element of the set.

There are different ways to name sets. Here are two ways to indicate the same set.

- the set of odd numbers between 4 and 10
- $\{5, 7, 9\}$

Roster Notation for Sets

One common way to name a set of numbers is to use roster notation. Roster notation lists each element of the set separated by a comma and enclosed in braces ($\{\}$). If each element cannot be listed, you can use an ellipsis (. . .) to indicate that the elements continue in the same pattern.

Example 1 List the elements of each set in roster notation.

A. even numbers between 1 and 11

Solution The even numbers between 1 and 11 are 2, 4, 6, 8, and 10. The set is expressed in roster notation as $\{2, 4, 6, 8, 10\}$. ■

B. multiples of 4 greater than 10

Solution The multiples of 4 greater than 10 are 12, 16, 20, 24, 28, and so on. The set is expressed in roster notation as $\{12, 16, 20, 24, 28, \ldots\}$. ■

Some Special Sets

TIP

To distinguish the natural numbers from the whole numbers, remember that the whole numbers include zero, which looks like a hole.

DEFINITIONS

The **counting** or **natural numbers** are the set of numbers $\mathbb{N} = \{1, 2, 3, \ldots\}$.

The **whole numbers** are the set of numbers $\mathbb{W} = \{0, 1, 2, 3, \ldots\}$.

The **integers** are all the counting numbers, their opposites, and zero. The integers are denoted as $\mathbb{Z} = \{\ldots, -2, -1, 0, 1, 2, \ldots\}$.

The **real numbers** are the set of numbers that can be written as decimals. The letter $\mathbb{R}$ is used to denote the set of real numbers.

The following diagram represents the relationship of these sets of numbers.

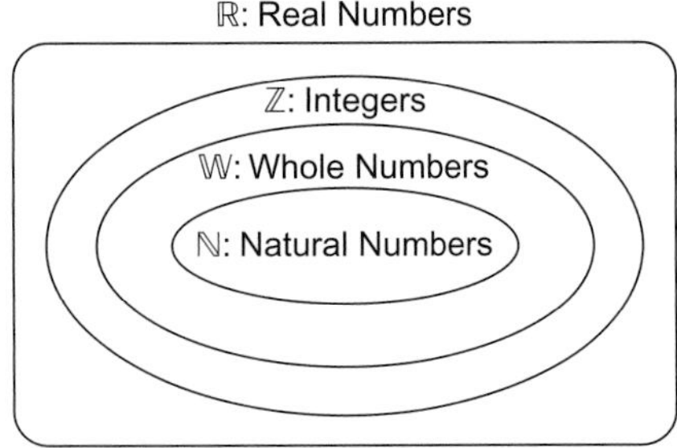

THINK ABOUT IT

A natural number is also a whole number, an integer, and a real number.

Example 2 For each number in the table, name the set or sets of which it is an element.

Solution

Number	Sets to Which the Number Belongs
0	whole numbers, integers, real numbers
12	natural numbers, whole numbers, integers, real numbers
-6	integers, real numbers
$\frac{10}{5}$	natural numbers, whole numbers, integers, real numbers $\frac{10}{5}$ simplifies to 2.
$-\frac{12}{3}$	integers, real numbers $-\frac{12}{3}$ simplifies to -4. ■

Set Operations

Operations can be performed on sets. Two operations often performed on sets are the union and intersection of sets. Sometimes an intersection of two sets can produce a set that has no elements. For example, there are no even prime numbers greater than 2. So, the intersection of the set of even numbers greater than 2 and the set of prime numbers has no elements.

REMEMBER

A set with no elements is the empty, or null, set.

DEFINITIONS

The **union** of two sets *A* and *B*, written $A \cup B$ is the set of elements in either *A* or *B* or both.
The **intersection** of two sets *A* and *B*, written $A \cap B$ is the set of elements in both *A* and *B*.

NOTATION

$\cup$ **union**
$\cap$ **intersection**
$\{\}$ **or** $\varnothing$ **null set**

Example 3 Find the indicated union and intersections.

Let $A = \{4, 8, 12, 16, 20, 24\}$, $B = \{5, 10, 15, 20, 25\}$, and $C = \{8, 16, 24\}$.

Find $A \cup B$, $A \cap B$, and $B \cap C$.

(continued)

Solution

$A \cup B$ is the union of sets A and B. List the elements that are in either A or B. If an element is in both sets it is listed only once.	$A \cap B$ is the intersection of sets A and B. List the elements that are in both A and B.	$B \cap C$ is the intersection of sets B and C. There are no elements that are in both B and C, so the intersection is the null set.
$A \cup B = \{4, 5, 8, 10, 12, 15, 16, 20, 24, 25\}$	$A \cap B = \{20\}$	$B \cap C = \varnothing$ ■

Application: Team Roster

Not all sets are sets of numbers.

Example 4 The table shows the positions (infield, outfield, or pitcher) played by the members of a baseball team.

Mudville Mudhens Baseball Team Positions		
Infield	**Outfield**	**Pitcher**
Bates	Bell	Carson
Bell	Nelson	Duncan
Johnson	Perez	Garcia
Jones	Robinson	Lee
Kim	Rodriquez	Lowenstein
May	Snyder	
Nelson	Thomas	
Perez	Washington	
Skaggs		
Tau		

A. What is the intersection of the infielders and the outfielders? What does the intersection represent?

B. What is the intersection of the infielders and the pitchers? What does the intersection tell you?

C. What does the union of all three positions represent? How many players are in the union of the three positions? How many players are on the team?

Solution

A. The intersection of the infielders and outfielders is the set {Bell, Nelson, Perez}. The intersection represents those players who play both an infield and an outfield position.

B. The intersection of the infielders and the pitchers is the null set. The intersection tells you that no pitchers are also members of the infield.

C. The union of all three positions represents the entire team. There are 20 members in the union of all three positions, so there are 20 players on the team. ■

Problem Set

List the elements of each set in roster notation.

1. odd numbers between 2 and 14
2. multiples of 3 greater than 7
3. even numbers greater than 5
4. multiples of 2 greater than 7
5. odd numbers between 2 and 20
6. odd numbers greater than 2
7. even numbers between 29 and 33
8. multiples of 4 less than 21
9. multiples of 5 between 9 and 52

For each number, name the set(s) of which it is an element. Choose from the following sets: natural numbers, whole numbers, integers, and real numbers.

10. $9, -7, 100, \frac{20}{2}, -\frac{5}{1}$
11. $27, 2.6, -\frac{24}{12}, \frac{7}{10}, \frac{1}{5}$
12. $0.4, -2.5, 1000, \frac{0}{10}, \frac{1}{7}$
13. $\frac{5}{15}, -13, 0.001, -1.4, \frac{30}{3}$
14. $-1, 2.77, \frac{9}{12}, -\frac{100}{10}, \frac{5}{0}$

Find the indicated union(s) and intersection(s) for the given sets.

$D = \{5, 6, 7, 8, 9, 10\}, E = \{1, 3, 5, 7, 9, 11\}, F = \{3, 6, 9, 12\}$

15. **A.** $D \cup E$ **B.** $E \cap F$ **C.** $D \cup F$
16. **A.** $D \cap E$ **B.** $E \cup F$ **C.** $D \cap F$

$D = \{3, 6, 9, 12, 15\}, E = \{-5, -3, -1, 1, 3, 5\}, F = \{3, 4, 8, 9, 12, 15, 16\},$

$G = \{2, 4, 6, 8, 10\}, H = \{-1, 0, 1, 2, 3, 4\}, I = \{-4, -3, -2, -1, 0\}$

17. **A.** $G \cap H$ **B.** $G \cap I$ **C.** $G \cup I$
18. **A.** $G \cup E$ **B.** $D \cap E$ **C.** $H \cup F$
19. **A.** $G \cup H$ **B.** $H \cap I$ **C.** $G \cap D$
20. **A.** $D \cup E$ **B.** $E \cap F$ **C.** $H \cap I \cap E$
21. **A.** $G \cap F$ **B.** $D \cap I$ **C.** $E \cup F$
22. **A.** $H \cap F$ **B.** $D \cap F$ **C.** $H \cup I$
23. **A.** $D \cap E \cap F$ **B.** $G \cup D \cup E$ **C.** $G \cap H \cap D$

Solve.

24. The table shows the music styles preferred by students in Mr. Smith's class.

Rock	Rap	Country
Hagar Carlita Carmen Evan Hera Kenya	Carlita Evan Hera Louis Manny	Carmen Kenya Manny Neil Otis

A. What is the union of rock and rap? What does this union represent?

B. How many people are in Mr. Smith's class?

25. Three students have listed their favorite presidents in the table below.

Bo	Jericho	Cindy
J. Adams Clinton T. Roosevelt Washington	J. Adams G.W. Bush Jefferson Lincoln Reagan	Clinton Fillmore Harding Lincoln Washington

A. What is the intersection of Bo's choices and Jericho's choices? What does the intersection represent?

B. Is any president liked by all three students?

C. Is this a union or intersection?

26. Kadri has made a chart of the names of her friends' pets.

Cats	Dogs
Speck Storm Oliver Jamine	Scruff Toby Mavi Dillon

A. What is the intersection of the pets' names? Why?

B. What is the union of the pets' names?

C. How many pets do Kadri's friends have?

27. The local high school has published a list of its top lacrosse and soccer players.

Lacrosse	Soccer
Billings Clove Eddger Humphrey Ibsen Klopfer Riser Vaughn	Clove Humphrey Ibsen Klopfer Vaughn Williams

A. What is the union of lacrosse and soccer players?

B. What does this union represent?

C. Who plays both sports?

D. What symbol would you use to represent this?

28. A class has created a table that shows the sports they play.

Baseball	Basketball	Football
Andrew	Andrew	Anna
Bilal	Bilal	Bilal
Charminque	Jeb	Charminque
Eve	Parisa	Eve
	Tyler	Heather
		Parisa
		Tyler

A. What is the intersection of baseball, basketball, and football?

B. What does this intersection represent?

C. If you wished to determine the total number of students who play at least one sport, would you use union or intersection?

*29. **Challenge** Students who were recognized for their excellent grades and community service are listed below.

Honor Role	Service
Dole	Adare
Fuller	Ziegler
Jones	.
Lowe	.
Smith	.
Woods	
.	
.	
.	

The list above is incomplete. If honor role ∩ service = {Fuller, Lowe, Morgan, Smith}, then fill in the missing names in the chart.

*30. **Challenge** A class took a survey to determine what fruits they liked best. The results are below.

Apple	Strawberry	Banana
Bahar	Bahar	Brittany
Brittany	Bob	Jael
John	Jamal	Randy
Suharto	Randy	Suharto
Travis	Suharto	

A. Who chose both apple and strawberry as the fruits they liked best?

B. What would have to change to make the intersection of apple and strawberry equal the intersection of strawberry and banana?

C. Who likes all of the fruit?

D. Write this in a statement using set notation.

Comparing Expressions

An expression is a grouping of numerical and algebraic symbols.

NOTATION

$<$ less than
$>$ greater than
$\leq$ less than or equal to
$\geq$ greater than or equal to

THINK ABOUT IT

The equality symbol ($=$) is more commonly known as the equals sign.

Sometimes you need to determine the relationship between two expressions, and you can use math symbols to represent these relationships.

You have learned that an equation containing variables is an *open sentence.* Another type of open sentence is an inequality.

DEFINITIONS

An **inequality** is an open sentence that includes one of the symbols $<$, $>$, $\leq$, or $\geq$.

The symbols $<$, $>$, $\leq$, and $\geq$ are inequality symbols. Since the symbol $=$ shows that two expressions have the same value, it is called an equality symbol.

REMEMBER

Use **PEMDAS** to remember the order of operations:

P: Parentheses
E: Exponents
M/D: Multiply and Divide
A/S: Add and Subtract

Comparing Expressions

To compare two expressions, use the order of operations to evaluate each expression. Then use mathematical symbols to compare the two values.

Example 1

A. Use $=$, $<$, or $>$ to compare the two expressions.

$8 \cdot (3 + 4) \; \square \; 8 \cdot 3 + 4$

Solution Use the order of operations to evaluate each expression.

$$8 \cdot (3 + 4) \; \square \; 8 \cdot 3 + 4$$
$$8 \cdot 7 \; \square \; 24 + 4$$
$$56 \; \square \; 28$$
$$56 > 28 \; ■$$

B. Use =, <, or > to compare the two expressions when $x = -3$.

$-2x^2 + 1 \; \square \; (-2x)^2 + 1$

Solution Substitute -3 into each expression for x. Then use the order of operations to evaluate each expression.

$$-2x^2 + 1 \; \square \; (-2x)^2 + 1$$
$$-2 \cdot (-3)^2 + 1 \; \square \; [-2(-3)]^2 + 1$$
$$-2 \cdot 9 + 1 \; \square \; 6^2 + 1$$
$$-18 + 1 \; \square \; 36 + 1$$
$$-17 \; \square \; 37$$
$$-17 < 37 \; \blacksquare$$

Testing Open Sentences

Not all values will make an open sentence true.

THINK ABOUT IT

The open sentence in Example 2A is true when $x = 7$.

$$2(7) - 5 = 9$$
$$14 - 5 = 9$$
$$9 = 9$$

Example 2 Determine whether the given value makes a true sentence.

A. $2x - 5 = 9$ when $x = -7$

Solution Substitute -7 into the expression for x.

$2x - 5 = 9 \longrightarrow 2 \cdot (-7) - 5 = 9$

Evaluate the expression on the left side of the equation.

$2 \cdot (-7) - 5 \stackrel{?}{=} 9$

$-14 - 5 \stackrel{?}{=} 9$ Multiply.

$-19 \neq 9$ Subtract.

The sentence is false when $x = -7$. ■

B. $6y + 9 \geq 8y - 1$ when $y = 4$

Solution Substitute 4 into the expression for y.

$6y + 9 \geq 8y - 1 \longrightarrow 6 \cdot 4 + 9 \geq 8 \cdot 4 - 1$

Evaluate the expressions on each side of the inequality.

$6 \cdot 4 + 9 \stackrel{?}{\geq} 8 \cdot 4 - 1$

$24 + 9 \stackrel{?}{\geq} 32 - 1$ Multiply.

$33 \geq 31$ ✓ Add and subtract.

The sentence is true when $y = 4$. ■

Application: Prices

Open sentences can be helpful in solving many real-world problems.

Example 3 A movie ticket costs \$9. A small box of popcorn costs \$3. A group of four people are going to watch a movie. They have a total of \$45. If the group purchases four movies tickets, how many boxes of popcorn can they purchase?

(continued)

REMEMBER

Use the Problem-Solving Plan.

1 *Identify*
2 *Strategize*
3 *Set Up*
4 *Solve*
5 *Check*

Solution Use the Problem-Solving Plan.

Step 1 *Identify* Find the number of boxes of popcorn the group can purchase.

Step 2 *Strategize* Let p represent the number of boxes of popcorn.

Step 3 *Set Up* Write an inequality.

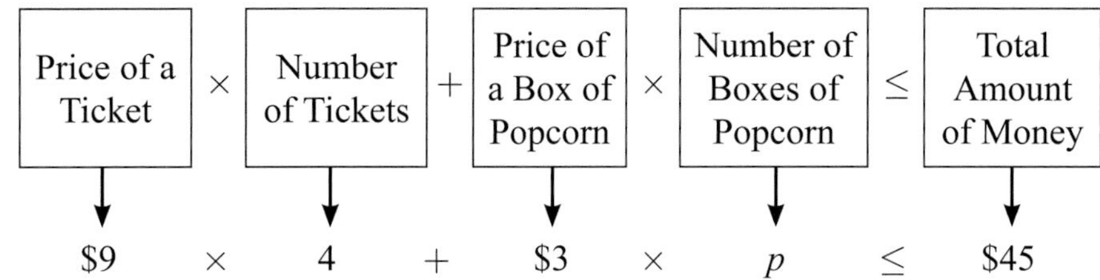

Step 4 *Solve* Test the open sentence for values of p to find the greatest value that makes a true sentence.

$$9 \cdot 4 + 3 \cdot p \leq 45 \qquad 9 \cdot 4 + 3 \cdot p \leq 45 \qquad 9 \cdot 4 + 3 \cdot p \leq 45 \qquad 9 \cdot 4 + 3 \cdot p \leq 45$$

$$9 \cdot 4 + 3 \cdot 1 \overset{?}{\leq} 45 \qquad 9 \cdot 4 + 3 \cdot 2 \overset{?}{\leq} 45 \qquad 9 \cdot 4 + 3 \cdot 3 \overset{?}{\leq} 45 \qquad 9 \cdot 4 + 3 \cdot 4 \overset{?}{\leq} 45$$

$$36 + 3 \overset{?}{\leq} 45 \qquad 36 + 6 \overset{?}{\leq} 45 \qquad 36 + 9 \overset{?}{\leq} 45 \qquad 36 + 12 \overset{?}{\leq} 45$$

$$39 \leq 45 \checkmark \qquad 42 \leq 45 \checkmark \qquad 45 \leq 45 \checkmark \qquad 48 \not\leq 45$$

The group has enough money to attend the movie and purchase 3 boxes of popcorn.

Step 5 *Check* It costs \$36 for a group of four people to attend the movie. $45 - 36 = 9$. The group has \$9 to spend. Three boxes of popcorn cost \$9. The answer is correct. ■

Problem Set

Use the order of operations to evaluate each expression. Then, use =, <, or > to compare the two expressions.

1. $6 \cdot 5 + 7$ □ $6 \cdot (5 + 7)$
2. $(14 - 8) \div 2$ □ $14 - 8 \div 2$
3. $(2x)^2 - 1$ □ $2 \cdot (x^2 - 1)$ when $x = 6$
4. $5 \cdot (7 - n)^2$ □ $5 \cdot 7 - n^2$ when $n = -2$
5. $10 - 4 \cdot 3$ □ $(10 - 4) \cdot 3$
6. $12 \div x + 2x$ □ $12 \div (x + 2x)$ when $x = 6$
7. $4 \cdot (6 - a)^2 + 8$ □ $4 \cdot 6 - a^2 + 8$ when $a = 3$
8. $8 - 12 \div 2 + 3$ □ $(12 - 8) \div 2 + 3$
9. $4 - (-5) \cdot 3 + 8$ □ $-4 \cdot 5 + 3 \cdot 8$
10. $8 \cdot 9 - n^2$ □ $(9 - n)^2 + 6n + 1$ when $n = 5$
11. $2 \cdot 2 + 2$ □ $2 \cdot (2 + 2)$
12. $\frac{y}{4} + 18 \div 2$ □ $\left(\frac{y}{4} + 18\right) \div 2$ when $y = 2$

Determine whether the given value makes a true sentence.

13. $3b - 5 < 2b + 7$ when $b = 6$
14. $5y^2 - 16 = 29$ when $y = -3$

15. $3 - 4r + r^2 \leq r^2 - 5$ when $r = -2$

16. $\left(3 - \frac{x^2}{8}\right) \cdot 12 = 3x$ when $x = 4$

17. $5p - 1 \geq 3p + 7$ when $p = 4$

18. $-2t > 5 - 3 \cdot (t - 5)$ when $t = 13$

19. $5x - \frac{x}{2} = 0$ when $x = 0.25$

20. $3y - 5 \geq 5y - 3$ when $y = -2$

21. $14 - 3m \leq 8 + 3m$ when $m = -4$

22. $4 \cdot (z + 6) < 6 \cdot (z + 4)$ when $z = 3$

Solve. For each problem:

A. Define a variable.
B. Write an inequality.
C. Test the open sentence to solve.
D. Give your answer in a complete sentence.

23. Mr. Le is buying books and star charts for his astronomy group. His budget allows him to spend no more than $135. He plans to buy 7 books at $13 each. How many star charts could he also buy, at $9 each?

24. At the back-to-school sale, a box of pencils costs $1, a set of pens costs $3, and notebooks cost $2 each. Caitlyn has $13 and wants to buy 2 boxes of pencils and 2 sets of pens. How many notebooks could she afford?

25. The Latin Club raised $265 for admission for their museum field trip. Forty students plan to attend, at $6 admission per student. The teacher will attend at no charge. Other adults may attend at $8 admission each. How many adults could attend, not including the teacher?

26. Five people are attending a baseball game. Tickets cost $12.50 each and souvenir programs cost $6 each. If the group has a total of $77, how many souvenir programs can they buy?

27. Bruce bought 4 concert tickets that cost $72 per ticket. T-shirts were sold at the concert for $9 per t-shirt. Bruce had $320 to spend. How many t-shirts could he pay for?

28. Dori starts off with $110 to spend on shirts and jeans. She buys 3 shirts for $13.50 each. Jeans cost $31.75 per pair. How many pairs of jeans can she buy?

29. Ms. Brooks bought frozen fruit pops for each of her 4 children. The frozen fruit pops cost $3.25 each. She also wants to buy bottled water, at $1.05 per bottle. If she started with $18, how many bottles of water can she buy?

*30. **Challenge** Harlan has $21 to spend on ingredients for grilled cheese sandwiches for his party. He has chosen 3 loaves of bread at $2 per loaf. He needs 4 pounds of cheese. He can buy American cheese at $2 per pound, cheddar at $3 per pound, or Swiss cheese at $4 per pound. What is the most expensive cheese he can afford?

Number Properties

When you perform operations with numbers, certain properties apply to those operations.

It is important to know the properties of real numbers and the properties of equality since they can be used to justify your steps when solving equations.

Properties of Real Numbers and Equality

PROPERTIES OF REAL NUMBERS

The following properties apply for all real numbers a, b, and c.

Property	Addition	Multiplication
Commutative Property	$a + b = b + a$	$a \cdot b = b \cdot a$
Associative Property	$(a + b) + c = a + (b + c)$	$(a \cdot b) \cdot c = a \cdot (b \cdot c)$

PROPERTIES OF EQUALITY

Let a, b, and c be real numbers.

Reflexive Property	$a = a$
Symmetric Property	If $a = b$, then $b = a$.
Transitive Property	If $a = b$ and $b = c$, then $a = c$.

Example 1 Identify the property shown by each statement in the table.

Solution

Statement	Property
$(4 \cdot 1) \cdot 9 = 4 \cdot (1 \cdot 9)$	Associative Property of Multiplication
$-10 \cdot (x \cdot 4) = (-10 \cdot x) \cdot 4$	
$0 = 0$	Reflexive Property
$-2.3 = -2.3$	
If $3 = x$, then $x = 3$.	Symmetric Property
$14 + (-10) = -10 + 14$	Commutative Property of Addition
$7.4 + a = a + 7.4$	
$(4 + 3) + a = 4 + (3 + a)$	Associative Property of Addition
$(-2 + 1.4) + 9 = -2 + (1.4 + 9)$	
If $y = 2$ and $2 = q$, then $y = q$.	Transitive Property
$-3 \cdot 8 = 8 \cdot (-3)$	Commutative Property of Multiplication ■
$r \cdot 7.21 = 7.21 \cdot r$	

Closure

A set is closed under an operation if the result of the operation on any two elements of the set is also an element of the set.

CLOSURE PROPERTY

Let *a* and *b* be elements of set *S* and # be some operation, then *S* is closed under the operation # if *a* # *b* is an element of the set S.

Example 2 Determine whether each set is closed under the given operation. If it is not closed under that operation, use an example to show why not.

A. the set $\{-1, 0, 1\}$ under multiplication and subtraction

Solution Find the product using every possible combination of elements in the set as factors. Since multiplication is commutative, the order of the factors does not matter. In other words, $-1 \times 0 = 0 \times (-1)$.

REMEMBER

A factor is a number being multiplied.

$-1 \times 0 = 0$ $\quad 0 \times 1 = 0$ $\quad -1 \times 1 = -1$

$-1 \times (-1) = 1$ $\quad 1 \times 1 = 1$ $\quad 0 \times 0 = 0$

Because each product is an element of the set $\{-1, 0, 1\}$, the set is closed under multiplication.

(continued)

Now find differences using some possible permutations of the elements in the set. Subtraction is not commutative so $-1 - 0 \neq 0 - (-1)$.

$-1 - 0 = -1 \qquad 0 - 1 = -1 \qquad -1 - 1 = -2$

$0 - (-1) = 1 \qquad 1 - 0 = 1 \qquad 1 - (-1) = 2$

Since -2 and 2 are not elements of the set $\{-1, 0, 1\}$, the set is not closed under subtraction. You don't need to test every possible combination since you have already found that the set is not closed. ■

B. the set of whole numbers under addition, subtraction, multiplication, and division

Solution The sum of any two whole numbers is always a whole number, so the set of whole numbers is closed under addition.

The difference between two whole numbers is not always a whole number. For example, $6 - 8 = -2$ which is not a whole number. So, the set of whole numbers is not closed under subtraction.

THINK ABOUT IT

Division by 0 is not defined, so it does not affect whether the set is closed.

The product of any two whole numbers is always a whole number, so the set of whole numbers is closed under multiplication.

The quotient of two whole numbers is not always a whole number. For example, $4 \div 8 = 0.5$ which is not a whole number. So, the set of whole numbers is not closed under division. ■

Problem Set

Identify the property shown by each statement.

1. $-5 = -5$
2. $(5 + x) + 7 = 5 + (x + 7)$
3. $4 \cdot 2n = 2n \cdot 4$
4. If $43 = y$, then $y = 43$.
5. $21 + 3w = 3w + 21$
6. $b + (12.7 + 4.5) = (b + 12.7) + 4.5$
7. If $p = -8$ and $-8 = z$, then $p = z$.
8. $6 \cdot (-18) = (-18) \cdot 6$
9. If $j = 5.75$, then $5.75 = j$.
10. $(4y \cdot 9) \cdot 7 = 4y \cdot (9 \cdot 7)$
11. $92x + 31z = 31z + 92x$
12. $\frac{3}{4}n = \frac{3}{4}n$
13. If $r = b$ and $b = t$, then $r = t$.
14. $(2m \cdot 3) \cdot (-4) = -4 \cdot (2m \cdot 3)$

*15. **Challenge** $(4 \cdot 5a) \cdot (6 \cdot 1) = 4 \cdot (5a \cdot 6) \cdot 1$

Determine whether each set is closed under the given operation. If it is not closed under that operation, use an example to show why not.

16. the set of natural numbers under

A. addition

B. subtraction

17. the set $\{-1, -2, 1, 2\}$ under

A. multiplication

B. division

18. the set of integers under

A. multiplication

B. division

19. the set of negative numbers under addition

20. the set of whole numbers under subtraction

21. the set $\{0, 1\}$ under multiplication

22. the set of decimals greater than 1 under addition

23. the set of negative numbers under multiplication

24. the set $\{0, 1, 2, 3\}$ under subtraction

25. the set of natural numbers under addition

26. the set $\{-2, -1, 0, 1, 2\}$ under addition

27. the set of tenths between 0 and 2 under subtraction

28. the set of whole numbers under multiplication

29. the set of positive real numbers under division

***30.** **Challenge** the set of fractions under multiplication

The Distributive Property

You can use the distributive property to find the product of a number and a sum or the product of a number and a difference.

DISTRIBUTIVE PROPERTY

Let a, b, and c be real numbers.

$$a(b + c) = a \cdot b + a \cdot c \text{ and } a(b - c) = a \cdot b - a \cdot c$$

Using the Distributive Property to Evaluate Expressions

Sometimes expressions are easier to evaluate when you apply the distributive property. The distributive property can also help you evaluate expressions using mental math.

Example 1 Use the distributive property to evaluate each expression.

A. $11 \cdot 62$

Solution

$11 \cdot 62 = (10 + 1) \cdot 62$	Write 11 as the sum of 10 and 1.
$= 10 \cdot 62 + 1 \cdot 62$	Distributive Property
$= 620 + 62$	Multiply.
$= 682$	Add. ■

B. $8 \cdot 14 + 8 \cdot 6$

Solution

$8 \cdot 14 + 8 \cdot 6 = 8(14 + 6)$	Distributive Property
$= 8 \cdot 20$	Add.
$= 160$	Multiply. ■

Like Terms

The distributive property is also the property that allows you to combine like terms. Terms that contain the same variables raised to the same powers are **like terms.** In other words, like terms have identical variable parts.

REMEMBER

Terms are the parts of an expression that are added or subtracted.

Example 2 Name the like terms in each expression.

A. $10a + 3a^2 + 5a + 2x^2$

Solution The terms $10a$ and $5a$ have the same variable parts so they are like terms. ■

B. $4 + 8 + 3x^2 + 9x^2y + 5x^2$

Solution The terms $3x^2$ and $5x^2$ have the same variable parts so they are like terms. The constant terms 4 and 8 are also like terms. ■

Example 3 Combine the like terms in each expression.

A. $10a + 3a^2 + 5a + 2x^2$

Solution From Example 2, you know the terms $10a$ and $5a$ are like terms. Simplify the expression.

$$\begin{aligned}10a + 3a^2 + 5a + 2x^2 &\\ &= 10a + 5a + 3a^2 + 2x^2\\ &= 15a + 3a^2 + 2x^2\end{aligned}$$ ■

B. $4 + 8 + 3x^2 + 9x^2y + 5x^2$

Solution From Example 2, you know $3x^2$ and $5x^2$ and 4 and 8 are like terms. Simplify the expression.

$$\begin{aligned}4 + 8 + 3x^2 + 9x^2y + 5x^2 &\\ &= 4 + 8 + 3x^2 + 5x^2 + 9x^2y\\ &= 12 + 8x^2 + 9x^2y\end{aligned}$$ ■

Terms may also have common factors. A **common factor** occurs when terms have at least one identical factor.

THINK ABOUT IT

Like terms will always have a common factor.

Example 4 Name the common factors of the terms $9x^3$, $3x^2$, and $6x$.

Solution Write the factors of each term.

$9x^3 = 3 \cdot 3 \cdot x \cdot x \cdot x$

$3x^2 = 3 \cdot x \cdot x$

$6x = 2 \cdot 3 \cdot x$

Each term has one 3 and one x. So, the common factors are 1, 3, x, and $3x$. ■

Using the Distributive Property to Simplify Expressions

You can also use the distributive property to remove parentheses when simplifying expressions. To completely simplify an expression, remove any grouping symbols and combine all like terms.

Example 5 Simplify.

A. $3(y + 4) + 2y$

Solution

$3(y + 4) + 2y = 3 \cdot y + 3 \cdot 4 + 2y$	Distributive Property
$= 3y + 12 + 2y$	Multiply.
$= 3y + 2y + 12$	Commutative Property of Addition
$= 5y + 12$	Combine like terms. ■

(continued)

B. $-8 + 2(x - 15) - x$

Solution

$-8 + 2(x - 15) - x = -8 + 2 \cdot x - 2 \cdot 15 - x$	Distributive Property
$= -8 + 2x - 30 - x$	Multiply.
$= -8 - 30 + 2x - x$	Commutative Property of Addition
$= -38 + x$	Combine like terms.
$= x - 38$	Commutative Property of Addition ■

Application: Cost

Example 6 A plumber charges \$75 for the first hour of service and \$60 per hour for each additional hour. Write an equation to find the total cost C in terms of time in hours h.

Solution

Step 1 Write a verbal model. Then write an equation.

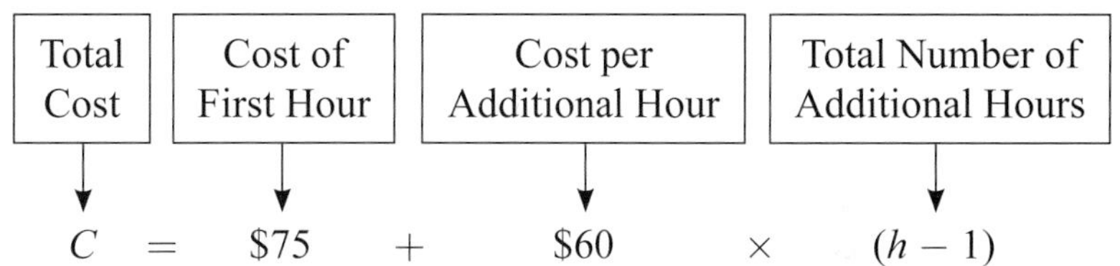

Step 2 Simplify the expression on the right side of the equation.

$$\begin{aligned} C &= 75 + 60(h - 1) \\ &= 75 + 60h - 60 \\ &= 15 + 60h \\ &= 60h + 15 \end{aligned}$$

The equation $C = 60h + 15$ can be used to find the total cost of the plumber's service. ■

Problem Set

Solve. For each expression:

A. Use the distributive property to rewrite the expression to make it easier to calculate or simplify.
B. Evaluate the expression.

1. $12 \cdot 53$
2. $6 \cdot 13 + 6 \cdot 7$
3. $17 \cdot 43$
4. $9 \cdot 12 + 9 \cdot 8$
5. $16 \cdot 34$
6. $12 \cdot 11 + 12 \cdot 9$
7. $3(y + 7) + 8y$
8. $9(x + 3) + 15x$
9. $11(x + 8) + 17x$
10. $6(y + 13) + 21y$
11. $4(y + 6) + 5y$
12. $-9 + 5(y + 3) - 2y$

Name the like terms in each expression.

13. $16x + 12y^2 + 4a + 12x$

14. $9 + 5 + 7x^2 + 3x^2y + 2x^2$

15. $10x + 11y^2 + 3b + 8x$

16. $7x^2 + 10y + 9y^2 + 6x^2$

Combine the like terms to simplify each expression.

17. $16x + 12y^2 + 4a + 12x$

18. $8 + 3 + 8x^2 + 2xy^2 + 11x^2$

19. $8x + 2y^3 + 9a + 12x$

20. $9 + 21 + 5x + 3xy^2 + 11x$

21. $8 + 4 + 15x + 3xy^2 + 7x + 6 + 3x$

Name the common factors of the terms.

22. $12x^3$, $18x^2$, and $9x$

23. $20x^3$, $8x^2$, and $4x$

24. $14x^4$, $28x^3$, and $42x^2$

25. $35x^3$, $20x^2$, and $15x$

Solve.

26. An electrician charges \$65 for the first hour of service and \$50 per hour for each additional hour. Write an equation to find the total cost C in terms of time in hours h.

27. Happy Maids cleaning service charges \$82 for the first hour of service and \$30 per hour for each additional hour. Write an equation to find the total cost C in terms of time in hours h.

28. Wall-to-Wall Painters charges \$100 for the first hour of service and \$80 per hour for each additional hour. Write an equation to find the total cost C in terms of time in hours h.

*29. **Challenge** Renting a car at Speedy-Go Car Agency costs \$25 for the first day of rentals and \$10 for each additional day.

A. Write an equation to find the total cost C in terms of time in days d.

B. Use the equation to find the cost of renting a car for 7 days.

*30. **Challenge** Renting a skating rink at SkateTown costs \$15 for the first hour of rentals and \$8 for each additional hour.

A. Write an equation to find the total cost C in terms of time in hours h.

B. Use the equation to find the cost of renting a rink for 4 hours.

Algebraic Proof

In algebra, you are often asked to justify the steps you take when evaluating an expression or solving an equation. In doing so, you are creating an algebraic proof.

DEFINITIONS

A **proof** is a clear, logical structure of reasoning that begins from accepted ideas and proceeds through logic to reach a conclusion.

Many accepted ideas used in proofs are postulates, definitions, or proven theorems. A **postulate** is a mathematical statement assumed to be true. A **theorem** is a mathematical statement that has been or is to be proven on the basis of established definitions and properties. Postulates do not need to be proven, but theorems do.

Deductive Reasoning and Proof

Deductive reasoning is a type of reasoning that uses previously proven or accepted properties to reach conclusions. Deductive reasoning uses logic to proceed from one statement to the next. Proofs use deductive reasoning.

Example 1 Prove each statement.

A. $11x + 4(1 - 2x) - 15 = 3x - 11$

Solution To prove the statement algebraically, justify each step with a definition, property, or previously proven statement.

Statement	Reason
$11x + 4(1 - 2x) - 15 = 11x + (4 \cdot 1) + [4 \cdot (-2x)] - 15$	Distributive Property
$= 11x + 4 + (-8x) - 15$	Multiplication
$= 11x + (-8x) + 4 - 15$	Commutative Property of Addition
$= (11 - 8)x + 4 - 15$	Distributive Property
$= [11 + (-8)]x + 4 + (-15)$	Definition of subtraction
$= 3x + (-11)$	Addition
$= 3x - 11$	Definition of subtraction ■

B. $(10z) \cdot (-0.20) = -2z$

Solution Justify each step.

Statement	Reason
$(10z) \cdot (-0.20) = -0.20 \cdot (10z)$	Commutative Property of Multiplication
$= (-0.20 \cdot 10)z$	Associative Property of Multiplication
$= -2 \cdot z$	Multiplication
$= -2z$	Multiplication ■

C. $(b + c)a = ba + ca$

Solution Justify each step.

Statement	Reason
$(b + c)a = a(b + c)$	Commutative Property of Multiplication
$= ab + ac$	Distributive Property
$= ba + bc$	Commutative Property of Multiplication ■

A Theorem About the Sum of Any Two Even Numbers

Any even number can be expressed in the form $2n$, where n is an integer, and for any integer n, $2n$ is an even number. For example, if $n = 5$, then $2 \cdot 5 = 10$ is an even number. What happens when you add two even numbers? Let's look at some examples.

$$2 + 2 = 4 \qquad 2 + 6 = 8 \qquad 2 + 10 = 12$$

$$6 + 14 = 20 \qquad 30 + 20 = 50 \qquad 100 + 102 = 202$$

Each sum is also an even number, so it might be true that the sum of any two even numbers is an even number. The next Example proves this theorem.

THINK ABOUT IT

Examples do not prove anything. You need to use deductive reasoning to prove any result.

Example 2 Prove that the sum of any two even numbers is an even number.

Solution Let $2a$ and $2b$ be any two even numbers, where a and b are integers. Then their sum is $2a + 2b$.

$2a + 2b = 2(a + b)$ Distributive Property

By the closure property of integers, $a + b$ is an integer. Represent $a + b$ as the integer k. Then $2(a + b) = 2k$, which is an even number. Therefore, $2a + 2b$ is an even number. So, the sum of any two even numbers is an even number. ■

Problem Set

Fill in the missing reason(s) for the step(s) of each proof.

1. Prove that $5(3 + x) - 2 = 5x + 13$.

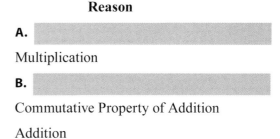

Statement	Reason
$5(3 + x) - 2 = (5 \cdot 3) + (5 \cdot x) - 2$	**A.**
$= 15 + 5x - 2$	Multiplication
$= 15 + 5x + (-2)$	**B.**
$= 5x + 15 + (-2)$	Commutative Property of Addition
$= 5x + 13$	Addition

2. Prove that $3a + 5(a - 1) + 7 = 2c$ if $2 + 8a = 2c$.

Statement	Reason
$3a + 5(a - 1) + 7 = 3a + 5[a + (-1)] + 7$	Definition of subtraction
$= 3a + (5 \cdot a) + [5 \cdot (-1)] + 7$	Distributive Property
$= 3a + 5a + (-5) + 7$	Multiplication
$= 8a + 2$	Addition
$= 2 + 8a$	Commutative Property of Addition
If $3a + 5(a - 1) + 7 = 2 + 8a$ and $2 + 8a = 2c$, then $3a + 5(a - 1) + 7 = 2c$.	

3. Prove that $6 \cdot 4s \cdot (-2) = -48s$.

Statement	Reason
$6 \cdot 4s \cdot (-2) = 6 \cdot 4 \cdot (-2) \cdot s$	**A.**
$= 24 \cdot (-2) \cdot s$	Multiplication
$= -48 \cdot s$	Multiplication
$= -48s$	**B.**

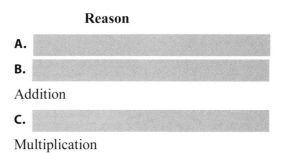

4. Prove that $(4 \cdot 3)l + (2 \cdot 4)l = 20l$.

Statement	Reason
$(4 \cdot 3)l + (2 \cdot 4)l = (4 \cdot 3)l + (4 \cdot 2)l$	**A.**
$= 4(3l + 2l)$	**B.**
$= 4(5l)$	Addition
$= (4 \cdot 5)l$	**C.**
$= 20l$	Multiplication

5. Prove that $(v \cdot 2u) \cdot 2u = 4u^2v$.

Statement	Reason
$(v \cdot 2u) \cdot 2u = (v \cdot 2u) \cdot 2 \cdot u$	Multiplication
$= v \cdot (2u \cdot 2) \cdot u$	**A.**
$= v \cdot (2 \cdot u \cdot 2) \cdot u$	Multiplication
$= v \cdot (2 \cdot 2 \cdot u) \cdot u$	Commutative Property of Multiplication
$= v \cdot (4 \cdot u) \cdot u$	Multiplication
$= v \cdot 4 \cdot (u \cdot u)$	**B.**
$= v \cdot 4 \cdot u^2$	Multiplication
$= 4 \cdot v \cdot u^2$	**C.**
$= 4 \cdot u^2 \cdot v$	Commutative Property of Multiplication
$= 4u^2v$	Multiplication

6. Prove that $9 \cdot w(w + 2) = 9w^2 + 18w$.

Statement	Reason
$9 \cdot w(w + 2) = 9 \cdot (w \cdot w + w \cdot 2)$	**A.**
$= 9 \cdot (w \cdot w + 2 \cdot w)$	Commutative Property of Multiplication
$= 9 \cdot w \cdot w + 9 \cdot 2\,w$	**B.**
$= 9w^2 + 18w$	Multiplication

7. Prove that $11 \cdot k \cdot 7 = 77k$.

Statement	Reason
$11 \cdot k \cdot 7 = 11 \cdot 7 \cdot k$	
$= 77k$	Multiplication

8. Prove that $12 \cdot [j \cdot (2 \cdot k) \cdot 3] = 72jk$.

Statement	Reason
$12 \cdot [j \cdot (2 \cdot k) \cdot 3] = 12 \cdot [j \cdot 2 \cdot (k \cdot 3)]$	Associative Property of Multiplication
$= 12 \cdot [j \cdot 2 \cdot (3 \cdot k)]$	Commutative Property of Multiplication
$= 12 \cdot [j \cdot (2 \cdot 3) \cdot k]$	**A.**
$= 12 \cdot (j \cdot 6 \cdot k)$	Multiplication
$= 12 \cdot (6 \cdot j \cdot k)$	Commutative Property of Multiplication
$= 12 \cdot (6 \cdot jk)$	Multiplication
$= (12 \cdot 6) \cdot jk$	**B.**
$= 72 \cdot jk$	Multiplication
$= 72jk$	Multiplication

Fill in the missing step for the reason of the proof.

9. Prove that $18t + (20 + 72t) = 90t + 20$.

Statement	Reason
$18t + (20 + 72t) = 18t + (72t + 20)$	Commutative Property of Addition
$=$ ▇▇▇▇▇▇	Associative Property of Addition
$= 90t + 20$	Addition

10. Prove that $5 \cdot n \cdot 4 \cdot n = 20n^2$.

Statement	Reason
$5 \cdot n \cdot (4 \cdot n) = 5 \cdot n \cdot (n \cdot 4)$	Commutative Property of Multiplication
$=$ ▇▇▇▇▇▇	Associative Property of Multiplication
$= 5 \cdot n^2 \cdot 4$	Multiplication
$= 5 \cdot 4 \cdot n^2$	Commutative Property of Multiplication
$= 20 \cdot n^2$	Multiplication
$= 20n^2$	Multiplication

11. Prove that $(13 + a) + 2 = 15 + a$.

Statement	Reason
$(13 + a) + 2 = 13 + (a + 2)$	Associative Property of Addition
$=$ ▇▇▇▇▇▇	Commutative Property of Addition
$= (13 + 2) + a$	Associative Property of Addition
$= 15 + a$	Addition

12. Prove that $6(2 \cdot x - y) = 12x - 6y$.

Statement	Reason
$6(2 \cdot x - y) =$ ▇▇▇▇▇▇	Definition of subtraction
$= 6 \cdot 2 \cdot x + 6 \cdot (-y)$	Distributive Property
$= 12x + (-6y)$	Multiplication
$= 12x - 6y$	Definition of subtraction

Fill in the missing step and reason for the proof.

13. Prove that $45y + 12 + 2(6 + y) = 47y + 24$.

Statement	Reason
$45y + 12 + 2(6 + y) =$ **A.** ______	Distributive Property
$= 45y + 12 + 12 + 2y$	Multiplication
$= 45y + 24 + 2y$	Addition
$= 45y + 2y + 24$	**B.** ______
$= 47y + 24$	Addition

14. Prove that $7 \cdot (x \cdot 9) \cdot 2 = 126x$.

Statement	Reason
$7 \cdot (x \cdot 9) \cdot 2 = 7 \cdot x \cdot (9 \cdot 2)$	**B.** ______
$= 7 \cdot x \cdot 18$	Multiplication
$=$ **A.** ______	Commutative Property of Multiplication
$= 126x$	Multiplication

15. Prove that $2 \cdot (v + 7) + (4v + 29) = 6v + 43$.

Statement	Reason
$2 \cdot (v + 7) + (4v + 29) = 2 \cdot v + 2 \cdot 7 + (4v + 29)$	**B.** ______
$= 2v + 14 + (4v + 29)$	Multiplication
$= 2v + 14 + (29 + 4v)$	Commutative Property of Addition
$=$ **A.** ______	Associative Property of Addition
$= 2v + 43 + 4v$	Addition
$= 2v + 4v + 43$	Commutative Property of Addition
$= 6v + 43$	Addition

16. Prove that $90 + (m + 75) + 3m = 4m + 165$.

Statement	Reason
$90 + (m + 75) + 3m = (90 + m) + 75 + 3m$	Associative Property of Addition
$= (m + 90) + 75 + 3m$	Commutative Property of Addition
$= m + (90 + 75) + 3m$	**B.** ______
$= m + 165 + 3m$	Addition
$=$ **A.** ______	Commutative Property of Addition
$= 4m + 165$	Addition

17. Prove that $7 \cdot (1 - l) \cdot 2 = 14 - 14l$.

Statement	Reason
$7 \cdot (1 - l) \cdot 2 =$ **A.**	Definition of subtraction
$= [7 \cdot 1 + 7 \cdot (-l)] \cdot 2$	Distributive Property
$= [7 + (-7l)] \cdot 2$	Multiplication
$= 2 \cdot [7 + (-7l)]$	**B.**
$= 2 \cdot 7 + 2 \cdot (-7l)$	Distributive Property
$= 14 + 2 \cdot (-7 \cdot l)$	Associative Property of Multiplication
$= 14 + (-14 \cdot l)$	Multiplication
$= 14 + (-14l)$	Multiplication
$= 14 - 14l$	Definition of subtraction

Opposites and Absolute Value

You can find the opposite of a number and the absolute value of a number using a number line. You can also find opposites and absolute values by using their definitions.

Opposites

DEFINITION

A number that has the opposite sign of a given number is called the **opposite** of the number. If a is the given number, its opposite is $-a$. The opposite of 0 is 0. The opposite of $-a$ is $-(-a) = a$.

Let a be a real number.

If $a > 0$, then $-a < 0$.
If $a = 0$, then $-a = 0$.
If $a < 0$, then $-a > 0$.

NOTATION

$-a$ **the opposite of** a

Opposites are an equal distance from 0 on the number line. For example, 3 and –3 are opposites because they are both three units from zero.

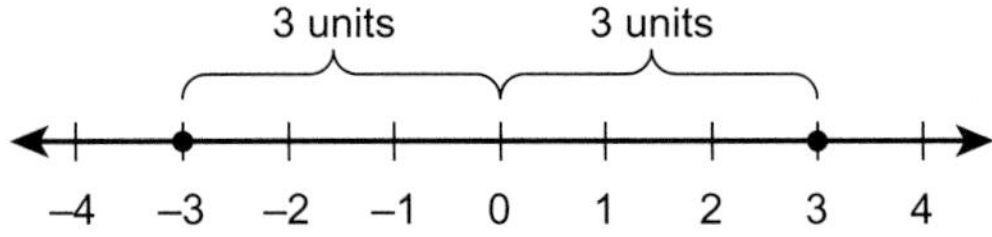

Example 1 Find the opposite of each number.

A. $\frac{4}{5}$

Solution The opposite of $\frac{4}{5}$ is $-\frac{4}{5}$. ■

B. -2.35

Solution The opposite of -2.35 is $-(-2.35) = 2.35$. ■

C. 0

Solution The opposite of 0 is 0. ■

D. 3

Solution The opposite of 3 is -3. ■

Absolute Value

NOTATION

$|a|$ **the absolute value of** a

DEFINITION

The positive number of any pair of opposite nonzero real numbers is the **absolute value** of each number. The absolute value of 0 is 0. The symbol $|a|$ is read "the absolute value of a."

Let a be a real number.

If $a > 0$, then $|a| = a$.
If $a = 0$, then $|a| = 0$.
If $a < 0$, then $|a| = -a$.

The absolute value of a number is its distance from 0 on the number line. For example, the distance between -3 and 0 is 3, so $|-3| = 3$.

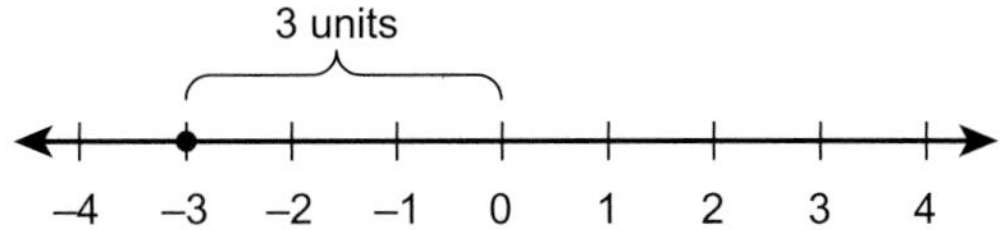

Example 2 Find the absolute value of each number.

A. $|5|$

Solution Since $5 > 0$, $|5| = 5$. ■

B. $|-16|$

Solution Since $-16 < 0$, $|-16| = -(-16) = 16$. ■

Comparing and Simplifying Expressions

You can use the definitions of opposite and absolute value to simplify and compare expressions.

Example 3 Use <, >, or = to compare each pair of expressions.

A. $|9|$ ▒ $|-9|$

Solution $|9| = 9$ and $|-9| = 9$, so $|9| = |-9|$. ■

B. $|-8|$ ▒ 7.2

Solution $|-8| = |8|$ and $8 > 7.2$, so $|-8| > 7.2$. ■

C. $-(-14)$ ▒ $-|-14|$

Solution $-(-14) = 14$ and $-|-14| = -14$, so $-(-14) > -|-14|$. ■

D. -7 ▒ $-(-7)$

Solution $-(-7) = 7$ and $7 > -7$, so $-7 < -(-7)$ ■

Example 4 Simplify.

A. $-(-7)$

Solution

$-(-7)$ means the opposite of -7. The opposite of -7 is 7, so $-(-7) = 7$. ■

B. $-|-2|$

Solution

$-|-2| = -[-(-2)]$	Definition of absolute value
$= -(2)$	The opposite of -2 is 2.
$= -2$	The opposite of 2 is -2. ■

C. $12.5 - |6|$

Solution

$12.5 - |6| = 12.5 - 6$	Definition of absolute value
$= 6.5$	Simplify. ■

D. $8 + |y| - |x|$ when $x = -10$ and $y = -5$

Solution Substitute the values of x and y into the expression, then simplify.

$8 + |-5| - |-10| = 8 + -(-5) - [-(-10)]$	
$= 8 + 5 - 10$	Definition of absolute value
$= 13 - 10$	Simplify.
$= 3$	■

Simple Absolute Value Equations

PROPERTY OF ABSOLUTE VALUE

If $|x| = a$ for some positive number a, then $x = a$ or $x = -a$.

The equation $|x| = 4$ has two solutions because the statement is true when $x = 4$ or when $x = -4$. Both 4 and -4 are the same distance from 0 on the number line.

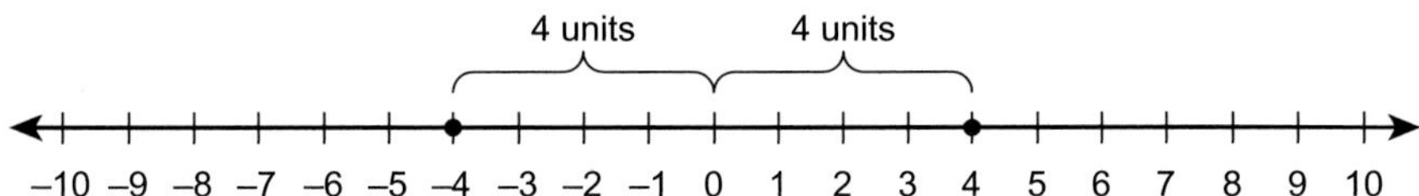

Example 5 Solve.

A. $|x| = 12$

Solution The equation is true when $x = 12$ or $x = -12$. The solution set is $\{-12, 12\}$. ■

B. $|-x| = 8.2$

Solution The equation is true when $-x = 8.2$ or $-x = -8.2$. Solve each equation by finding the opposite of both sides.

$-x = 8.2$	$-x = -8.2$
$-(-x) = -8.2$	$-(-x) = -(-8.2)$
$x = -8.2$	$x = 8.2$

The solution set is $\{-8.2, 8.2\}$. ■

Application: Elevation

Finding the absolute value of a number can be useful in real world applications, such as when comparing distances.

Example 6 The table shows the elevations of different geographical locations on land and under water. Which location is the greatest distance from sea level?

Location	Elevation (m)
Mauna Loa, United States	4169
South Sandwich Trench, Atlantic Ocean	−7235
Diamantina Deep, Indian Ocean	−8047
Manaslu Mountain, Nepal	8156
Mount St. Helens, United States	2549

Solution Think of sea level as 0 on the number line. You are being asked to find which elevation is the greatest distance from 0. In other words, which elevation has the greatest absolute value?

Location	Elevation (m)	Absolute Value of the Elevation (m)
Mauna Loa, United States	4169	4169
South Sandwich Trench, Atlantic Ocean	−7235	7235
Diamantina Deep, Indian Ocean	−8047	8047
Manaslu Mountain, Nepal	8156	8156
Mount St. Helens, United States	2549	2549

Manaslu Mountain in Nepal is the greatest distance from sea level. ■

Problem Set

Find the opposite of each number.

1. $-\frac{40}{7}$
2. $\sqrt{3}$

Use <, >, or = to compare each pair of expressions.

3. $2 \;\square\; |-3|$
4. $|-8| \;\square\; |-7|$
5. $|-3.9| \;\square\; -[-(-9.3)]$
6. $-\left(\frac{47}{4}\right) \;\square\; \left|-\frac{4}{47}\right|$
7. $-(13) \;\square\; -|-13|$

Simplify.

8. $|27|$
9. $|-(-43{,}249)|$
10. $|-34.43|$
11. $\left|-\frac{100}{9}\right|$
12. $-(4.326)$
13. $-(-6275)$
14. $-\left|\frac{12}{19}\right| + \left|-\frac{4}{19}\right|$
15. $-(-98) - |-72|$
16. $-|-(-1.75)| - (-(3.25))$

17. $-x + |-y|$ when $x = 2$ and $y = -1$

18. $40 - 3(-|y| + |-x|)$ when $x = -10$ and $y = -30$

19. $-\left(-\frac{4}{5}\right) - \left[-y\left(-x + \frac{1}{5}\right)\right]$ when $x = \frac{2}{5}$ and $y = -7$

20. $-|x| - 17 + (-2)(|y - 4|)$ when $x = 12$ and $y = 8$

Solve.

21. $-|-x| = -76$

22. $|-x - 33| = -21$

23. $|1 - x| = 4.3$

24. $\left|x + \frac{2}{3}\right| = \frac{1}{3}$

25. $|-4 + x| = 240$

26. The table shows transactions from Damon's bank account. On which date did he have the biggest transaction?

Date	Transaction ($)
2/9/07	+87.50
2/11/07	−60
2/14/07	−100
2/16/07	+95.75

27. On Kimee's drive to the grocery store, she changed her speed at several locations. The table below shows some of her speed changes and what caused them. Which situation caused the greatest change in her speed?

Cause	Speed Change (mph)
Stop sign	−35
Entering highway	+20
Exiting highway	−10
Stop light	−45

28. Shania is driving on a one-way road past a bookstore. The table below shows her distance from the bookstore at several points on the road. At which point is she the greatest distance from the bookstore?

Point	Distance (mi)
1	−2.5
2	−1.0
3	−0.5
4	1.5
5	3.0

*29. **Challenge** Tandra played cards and kept track of her total score after each round. Which round had the greatest affect (increase or decrease) on her score?

Round	Total Score
1	25
2	30
3	0
4	15
5	0

*30. **Challenge** The table below shows the number of forward (positive) and backward (negative) steps that Shilpa took. Each step represents the distance from her previous position. At what position was she farthest from her starting point?

Position	Steps
1	0
2	+2
3	−3
4	+5
5	−6

UNIT 3 Operations with Real Numbers

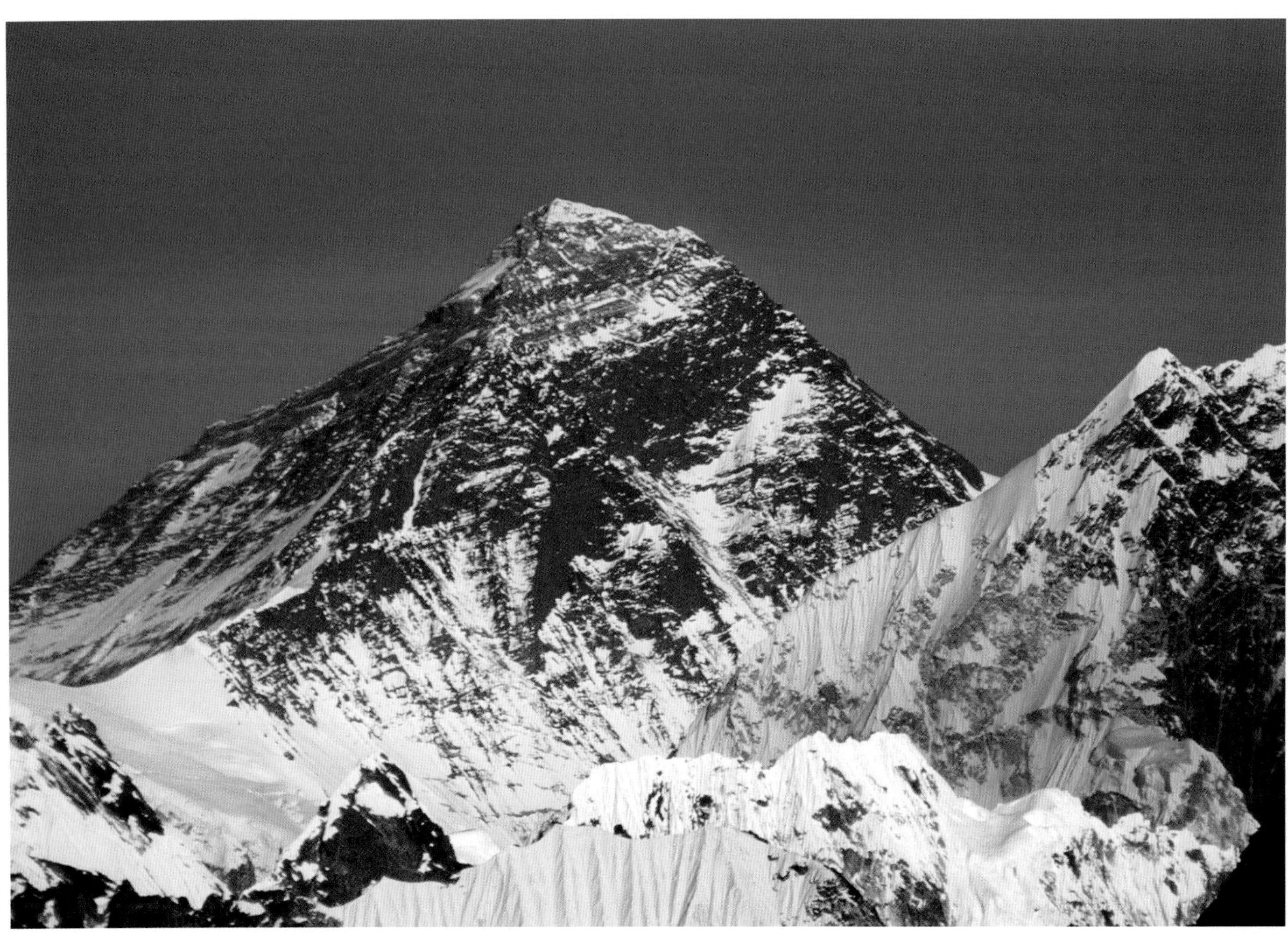

Mount Everest is 9.256 kilometers higher than the Dead Sea.

There are many different kinds of numbers. Negative numbers, positive numbers, integers, fractions, and decimals are just a few of the many groups of numbers. What do these varieties of numbers have in common? They all obey the rules of arithmetic. They can be added, subtracted, multiplied, and divided.

Big Idea

- A number is anything that obeys the laws of arithmetic; all numbers obey the laws of arithmetic. You can use the laws of arithmetic to simplify algebraic expressions.

Unit Topics

- Addition
- Subtraction
- Multiplication
- Reciprocals and Division
- Applications: Number Problems

Addition

To understand the rules for adding any two real numbers, it helps to look at a number line.

When using a number line to model addition, start at zero and move left or right according to the sign of the first addend. Then move left or right again according to the sign of the second addend. The resulting location is the sum.

REMEMBER

In the expression $a + b$, a and b are both called addends.

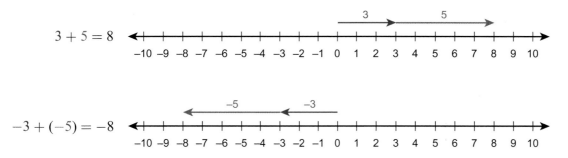

$3 + 5 = 8$

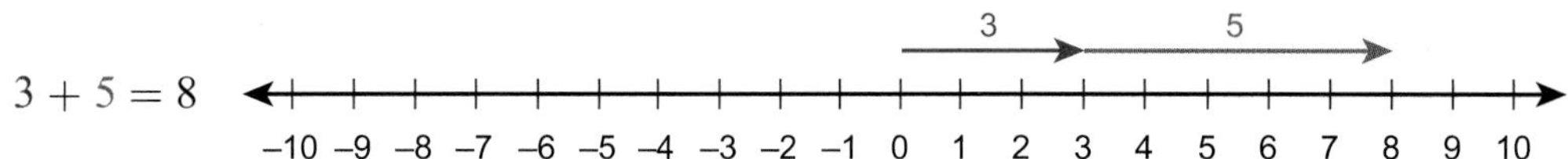

$-3 + (-5) = -8$

−5 −3

−10 −9 −8 −7 −6 −5 −4 −3 −2 −1 0 1 2 3 4 5 6 7 8 9 10

Adding Real Numbers with Like Signs

In the examples above, the addends have like signs (both positive or both negative). The sums are the same number of units from zero, but on opposite sides of zero. Use the following rules for adding numbers with like signs.

ADDITION PROPERTIES: ADDENDS WITH LIKE SIGNS

For all $a > 0$ and $b > 0$, $a + b = |a| + |b|$.
For all $a < 0$ and $b < 0$, $a + b = -(|a| + |b|)$.

REMEMBER

$a > 0$ means a is a positive number. $a < 0$ means a is a negative number.

In words, add the absolute values of the addends. Then give the resulting sum the same sign as each addend.

(continued)

Example 1

A. Simplify $2.3 + 4.5$.

Solution

$2.3 + 4.5 = \|2.3\| + \|4.5\|$	Add the absolute values of the addends.
$= 2.3 + 4.5$	Evaluate the absolute values.
$= 6.8$	Simplify. ■

B. Evaluate $a + b$ when $a = -16.2$ and $b = -0.8$.

Solution

$a + b = -16.2 + (-0.8)$	Substitute -16.2 for a and -0.8 for b.
$= -(\|-16.2\| + \|-0.8\|)$	Add the absolute values of the addends.
$= -(16.2 + 0.8)$	Evaluate the absolute values.
$= -(17)$	Simplify.
$= -17$	Distributive Property ■

Adding Real Numbers with Unlike Signs

The number line is also a good way to show how numbers with unlike signs are added.

$3 + (-5) = -2$

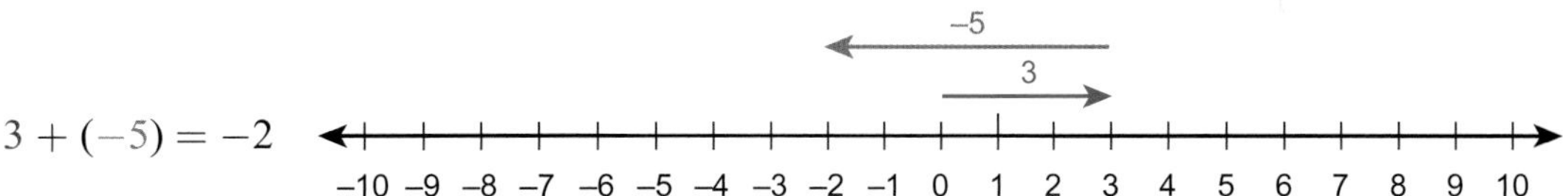

$-3 + 5 = 2$

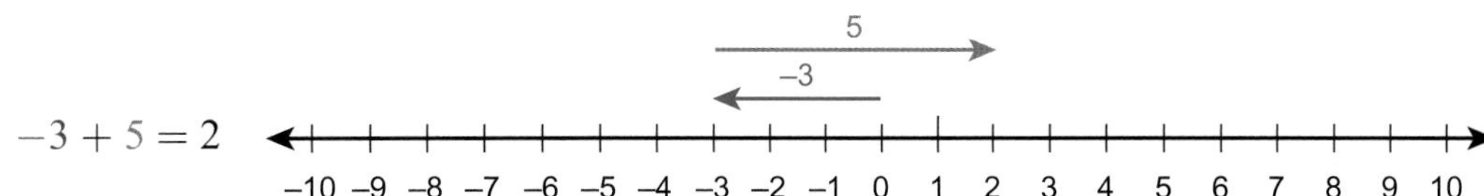

Notice that both sums are two units from zero, but on opposite sides of the number line. So, the sign of the sum is the same as the sign of the addend with the greater absolute value.

ADDITION PROPERTIES: ADDENDS WITH UNLIKE SIGNS

For all $a > 0$ and $b < 0$,

If $|a| > |b|$, then $a + b = |a| - |b|$.

If $|a| < |b|$, then $a + b = -(|b| - |a|)$.

In words, subtract the lesser absolute value from the greater absolute value. Then apply the sign of the addend with the greater absolute value.

Example 2

A. Simplify $2.3 + (-4.5)$.

Solution

$2.3 + (-4.5) = -(\lvert -4.5\rvert - \lvert 2.3\rvert)$	Subtract the absolute values (lesser from greater).
$= -(4.5 - 2.3)$	Evaluate the absolute values.
$= -(2.2)$	Simplify.
$= -2.2$	Distributive Property ■

B. Evaluate $x + y$ when $x = -32.5$ and $y = 48$.

Solution

$x + y = -32.5 + 48$	Substitute -32.5 for x and 48 for y.
$= \lvert 48\rvert - \lvert -32.5\rvert$	Subtract the absolute values (lesser from greater).
$= 48 - 32.5$	Evaluate the absolute values.
$= 15.5$	Simplify. ■

Application: Climbing

Example 3 A climber on Mount Everest started the day at an elevation of 8000 meters. During the day she climbed 1200 meters down the mountain to reach the next campsite. Write and simplify an addition expression to find the climber's elevation at the end of the day.

Solution Because the climber was climbing *down,* add -1200 to her starting elevation.

$8000 + (-1200) = \lvert 8000\rvert - \lvert -1200\rvert$	Subtract the absolute values (lesser from greater).
$= 8000 - 1200$	Evaluate the absolute values.
$= 6800$	Simplify.

The climber's elevation at the end of the day was 6800 meters. ■

Addition Properties and Proof

When two addends are opposite numbers, their sum is zero.

$5 + (-5) = 0$

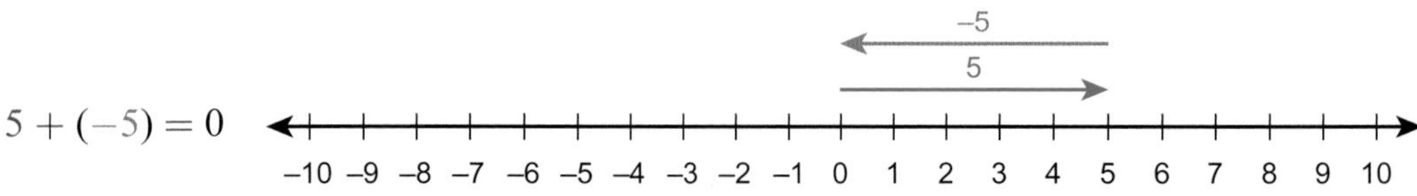

$-5 + 5 = 0$

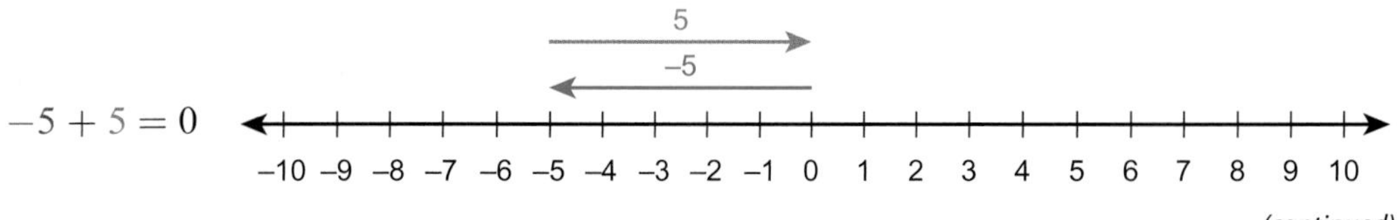

(continued)

TIP

The sum of a number and its additive inverse is always the additive identity.

ADDITION PROPERTIES

Additive Inverse Property: For any real number a, there is a unique opposite, $-a$, called the **additive inverse,** such that $a + (-a) = 0$.

Identity Property for Addition: For any real number a, $a + 0 = a$, and 0 is called the **additive identity.**

For all real numbers a and b, the opposite of the sum of two numbers is equal to the sum of the opposites of the numbers: $-(a + b) = -a + (-b)$.

These addition properties can be used along with the properties you have already learned to justify steps in a proof.

Example 4 Prove that $-(x + y) + x = -y$.

Solution

$-(x + y) + x = -x + (-y) + x$	The opposite of a sum is the sum of the opposites.
$= -y + (-x) + x$	Commutative Property of Addition
$= -y + 0$	Additive Inverse Property
$= -y$	Identity Property for Addition ■

Problem Set

Simplify.

1. $3.4 + 6.1$
2. $2.8 + 7.4$
3. $-12.5 + (-8.1)$
4. $-2.8 + (-9.9)$
5. $4.5 + (-7.9)$
6. $-5.1 + 3.9$
7. $7.8 + 3.9$
8. $16.7 + 2.9$
9. $-41.1 + 26.7$
10. $10.9 + (-14.8)$
11. $-13.6 + (2.7)$

Evaluate.

12. $a + b$, when $a = 16.4$ and $b = 7.3$
13. $x + y$, when $x = 21.8$ and $y = 12.4$
14. $x + y$, when $x = -17.6$ and $y = 13.2$
15. $x + y$, when $x = 48.6$ and $y = -52.7$
16. $a + b$, when $a = -23.6$ and $b = -12.5$
17. $a + b$, when $a = -7.3$ and $b = -26.9$
18. $x + y$, when $x = 19.3$ and $y = -38.2$
19. $a + b$, when $a = -42.7$ and $b = -18.3$
20. $x + y$, when $x = -19.2$ and $y = 12.1$
21. $a + b$, when $a = -8.6$ and $b = -18.4$

Prove each statement.

22. Prove $-(a - b) + a = b$.

Statement	Reason
$-(a - b) + a = -a - (-b) + a$	Distributive Property
$= -a + b + a$	Definition of Subtraction
$= -a + a + b$	Commutative Property of Addition
$= 0 + b$	**A.**
$= b$	**B.**

23. Prove $c + d - c = d$.

Statement	Reason
$c + d - c = c + d + (-c)$	Definition of Subtraction
$= c + (-c) + d$	Commutative Property of Addition
$= 0 + d$	**A.**
$= d$	**B.**

Solve. For each problem:

A. Write an expression to model the situation.
B. Simplify the expression.
C. Answer the question.

24. The Empire State building in New York City is 1454 feet tall. The observatory on the 86th floor is 404 feet from the top of the building. How high is the observatory above the ground?

25. The tallest living woman is 8.6 inches shorter than the tallest living man, who is 99.6 inches tall. How tall is the tallest living woman?

26. Jinah and Janna are making party favors. Jinah has made 108 favors and Janna has made 442 favors. How many favors have Jinah and Janna made together?

***27.** **Challenge** Frank and Fiona are running in a marathon. Frank ran 21.6 miles, and has 4.6 miles left to run. Fiona ran 24 miles. How many miles does Fiona have left to run?

***28.** **Challenge** Veda spent $12.50 on a shirt and $32 on a pair of pants. If she had $50 before her purchase, how much money does she have left? Assume no tax was charged for the clothes.

Subtraction

You can use a number line to model subtraction.

REMEMBER

In the expression $x - y$, x is the minuend and y is the subtrahend.

When using a number line to model subtraction, start at zero and move left or right according to the sign of the minuend. Then move left or right again according to the sign of the subtrahend. The resulting location is the difference.

$5 - 3 = 2$

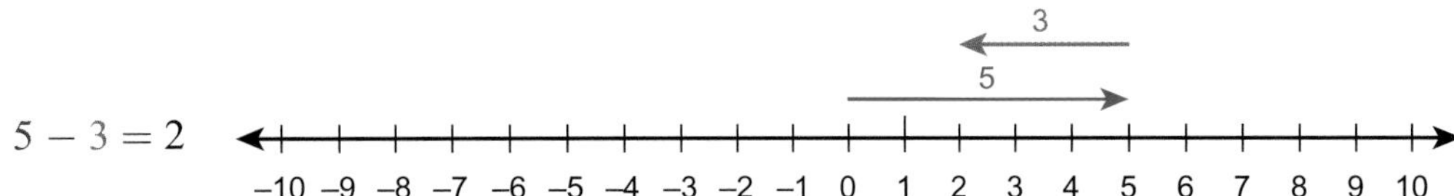

$3 - 5 = -2$

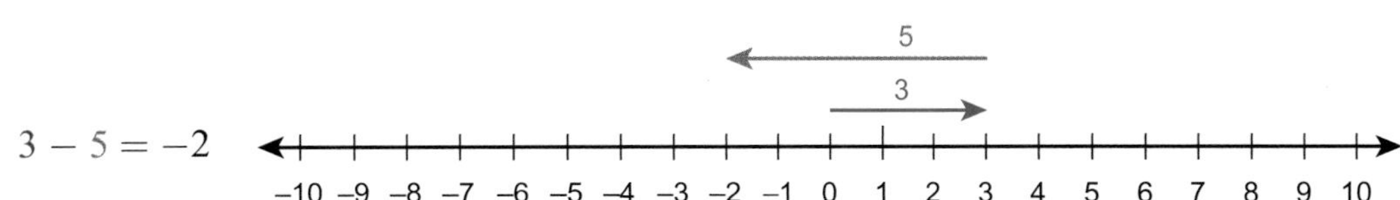

$-3 - 5 = -8$

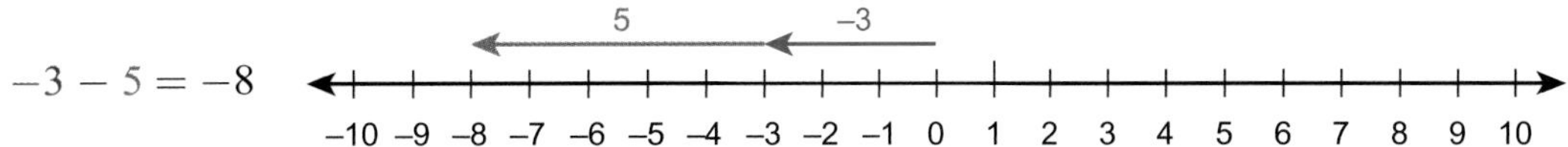

$-3 - (-5) = 2$

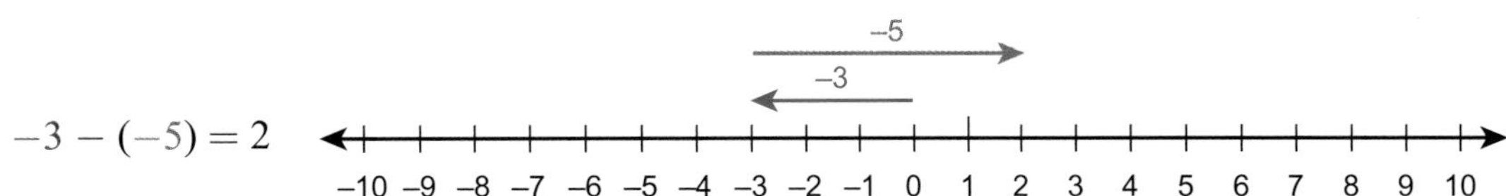

Each of these expressions can be rewritten using addition.

$5 - 3 = 2$ is the same as $5 + (-3) = 2$.

$3 - 5 = -2$ is the same as $3 + (-5) = -2$.

$-3 - 5 = -8$ is the same as $-3 + (-5) = -8$.

$-3 - (-5) = 2$ is the same as $-3 + 5 = 2$.

Subtracting Real Numbers

SUBTRACTION

For all real numbers a and b, $a - b = a + (-b)$.

TIP

Subtraction is "addition of the opposite."

In words, to subtract one number from another, change the minus sign to a plus sign and change the subtrahend to its opposite.

Example 1

A. Simplify $2.3 - 4.5$.

Solution Add the opposite of 4.5 to 2.3.

$2.3 - 4.5 = 2.3 + (-4.5)$ Definition of subtraction

$= -2.2$ Add. ■

B. Simplify $5 + 10x - 7x$.

Solution

$5 + 10x - 7x = 5 + 10x + (-7x)$ Definition of subtraction

$= 5 + 3x$ Combine like terms. ■

C. Evaluate $a - b$ when $a = 3.1$ and $b = -4.6$.

Solution

$a - b = 3.1 - (-4.6)$ Substitute 3.1 for a and -4.6 for b.

$= 3.1 + 4.6$ Definition of subtraction

$= 7.7$ Add. ■

D. Evaluate $x - |-y| - 2x$ when $x = -6$ and $y = 4$.

Solution

$x - |-y| - 2x = -6 - |-4| - 2(-6)$ Substitute -6 for x and 4 for y.

$= -6 - 4 - 2(-6)$ Evaluate $|-4|$.

$= -6 - 4 - (-12)$ Multiply.

$= -6 + (-4) + 12$ Definition of subtraction

$= -10 + 12$ Add from left to right.

$= 2$ Add. ■

Determining If Subtraction Is Commutative or Associative

Example 2 Use specific examples to determine whether subtraction is commutative or associative.

A. Determine if $5 - 3 = 3 - 5$.

Solution Simplify each side.

Left expression:	Right expression:
$5 - 3 = 5 + (-3)$	$3 - 5 = 3 + (-5)$
$= 2$	$= -2$

Since $2 \neq -2$, subtraction is not commutative. ■

B. Determine if $5 - (3 - 2) = (5 - 3) - 2$.

Solution Simplify each side.

Left expression:	Right expression:
$5 - (3 - 2) = 5 + \{-[3 + (-2)]\}$	$(5 - 3) - 2 = [5 + (-3)] + (-2)$
$= 5 + (-1)$	$= 2 + (-2)$
$= 4$	$= 0$

Since $4 \neq 0$, subtraction is not associative. ■

Addition and multiplication of real numbers are both commutative and associative. Subtraction, however, is neither commutative nor associative.

Application: Temperature

Example 3 The low temperature on Monday was −6.5°C and the low temperature on Tuesday was −17°C. Write and simplify a subtraction expression to find how much lower the low temperature was on Tuesday than on Monday.

Solution To find how much lower the low temperature was on Tuesday than on Monday, subtract −17 from −6.5.

$-6.5 - (-17) = -6.5 + 17$	Definition of subtraction
$= 10.5$	Add.

It was 10.5° warmer on Monday, so the temperature was 10.5° lower on Tuesday than Monday.

Suppose you subtracted −6.5 from −17:

$-17 - (-6.5) = -17 + 6.5$	Definition of subtraction
$= -10.5$	Add.

Here you are subtracting Monday's temperature from Tuesday's temperature. So, instead of arriving at the answer 10.5, you obtain the answer −10.5. As long as you interpret the answer correctly, you should still arrive at the conclusion that the temperature was 10.5° lower on Tuesday than Monday. ■

Problem Set

Simplify.

1. $12 - 7.1$
2. $0.3x - 2.1x - 4$
3. $-2 - 8$
4. $-\frac{1}{4} - \left(-\frac{3}{4}\right)$
5. $12.5t - 2.5 - 3t + 4 - 3.5t$
6. $2 + \frac{12}{17}y - 7 - \frac{3}{17}y$
7. $72.51 - (-53.72)$
8. $3h - 12 - (-7h) - 2h$
9. $431 - 89n - 11n$
10. $\frac{9}{14} - \frac{7}{2}$

Evaluate.

11. $y - (-x)$, when $y = 7.6$ and $x = 6.7$
12. $g + 2h - 3g - 4h$, when $g = -\frac{4}{3}$ and $h = \frac{1}{3}$
13. $-|-p| - |q| - 3q$, when $p = -16$ and $q = -8$
14. $|j| - k$, when $j = -8.4$ and $k = 2.9$
15. $-a - 2b$, when $a = -53$ and $b = -19$
16. $34 - |(m - |n|)|$, when $m = 52$ and $n = 73$
17. $-|r| + |-s| - t$, when $r = -1$, $s = -1$ and $t = -1$
18. $b - 2c - 4a$, when $a = 62$, $b = -51$ and $c = -33$
19. $|c + d| - d$, when $c = 3$ and $d = -6$
20. $5.3u - 7.1v$, when $u = -10$ and $v = -100$
21. $n - (-4m) - 3$, when $m = -3.5$ and $n = 9.5$
22. $-x - |y| - 2x$, when $y = -10$ and $x = -5$

Use these examples to determine if subtraction is commutative or associative.

23. Determine if $(12.4 - 16.3) - 8.4 = 12.4 - (16.3 - 8.4)$.
24. Determine if $\frac{2}{7} - \left(-\frac{3}{7}\right) = -\frac{3}{7} - \frac{2}{7}$.

Solve. For each problem:

A. Write an expression to model the situation.
B. Simplify the expression.
C. Answer the question.

25. Buffalo, New York, received 78.2 inches of snow during the 2005–2006 season and 88.9 inches during the 2006–2007 season. How much more snow did Buffalo receive during the 2006–2007 season than during the 2005–2006 season?
26. Mauna Kea in Hawaii has a peak height of about 4240 meters relative to sea level. Its base is actually on the sea floor at about –5960 meters relative to sea level. What is the height from the base (which is under water) to the peak?
27. A company's net worth during its first year of operation was –$56,000. During its second year of operation, its net worth was –$5000. How much more was the company worth after the second year of operation than after the first year?
28. One day, the temperature in Philadelphia was 21°F and the temperature in Detroit was –7°F. How much lower was the temperature in Detroit than in Philadelphia?

*29. **Challenge** Lucinda's speeds at several points during a road trip are shown below. How much greater was her change in speed between points 3 and 4 than her change in speed between points 1 and 2?

Point	1	2	3	4
Speed (mph)	60	45	55	30

*30. **Challenge** The balances of Akmed's checking account at the end of the week are shown below for a period of 5 weeks. How much greater was the change in his balance from week 2 to week 3 than from week 1 to week 5?

Week	1	2	3	4	5
Balance ($)	148	77	61	101	180

Multiplication

You can use patterns to discover rules about multiplying real numbers.

$4 \times 3 = 12$ $4 \times 2 = 8$ $4 \times 1 = 4$	Multiply 4 by decreasing positive integers. Each product decreases by four.
$4 \times 0 = 0$	Multiply 4 by zero.
$4 \times (-1) = -4$ $4 \times (-2) = -8$ $4 \times (-3) = -12$	Now, multiply 4 by decreasing negative integers. Each product continues to decrease by four.

THINK ABOUT IT

Just as 4 groups of 2 equals 8, 4 groups of −2 equals −8.

The pattern suggests that the product of two positive factors is positive, the product of a positive factor and zero is zero, and the product of a positive factor and a negative factor is negative. Use this last statement to create another pattern.

$-4 \times 3 = -12$ $-4 \times 2 = -8$ $-4 \times 1 = -4$	Multiply −4 by decreasing positive integers. Each product increases by four.
$-4 \times 0 = 0$	Multiply −4 by zero.
$-4 \times (-1) = 4$ $-4 \times (-2) = 8$ $-4 \times (-3) = 12$	Now, multiply −4 by decreasing negative integers. Each product continues to increase by four.

This pattern suggests that the product of a negative factor and a positive factor is negative, the product of a negative factor and zero is zero, and the product of two negative factors is positive.

MULTIPLICATION

For all $a > 0$ and $b > 0$, $a \cdot b > 0$.

For all $a < 0$ and $b < 0$, $a \cdot b > 0$.

For all $a < 0$ and $b > 0$, $a \cdot b < 0$.

In words, the product of two numbers with like signs is positive. The product of two numbers with unlike signs is negative. This implies that any product with an even number of negative factors is positive, and any product with an odd number of negative factors is negative.

The patterns also show the following properties.

MULTIPLICATION PROPERTIES

Identity Property for Multiplication: For any real number a, $a \cdot 1 = a$.

For any real number a, $a \cdot 0 = 0$.

For any real number a, $a \cdot (-1) = -a$.

THINK ABOUT IT

The phrase "for any real number a" can be represented by: "for all $a \in \mathbb{R}$."

The **multiplicative identity** is the number that, when multiplied by any real number, results in that number. Therefore, the multiplicative identity is 1.

REMEMBER

The additive identity is 0.

Multiplying Real Numbers

Example 1

A. Evaluate $5 \cdot x \cdot 4$ when $x = -1, 0$, and 1.

Solution Substitute each value for x and simplify.

$$\begin{aligned} 5 \cdot x \cdot 4 &= 5 \cdot (-1) \cdot 4 \\ &= -5 \cdot 4 \\ &= -20 \end{aligned} \qquad \begin{aligned} 5 \cdot x \cdot 4 &= 5 \cdot 0 \cdot 4 \\ &= 0 \cdot 4 \\ &= 0 \end{aligned} \qquad \begin{aligned} 5 \cdot x \cdot 4 &= 5 \cdot 1 \cdot 4 \\ &= 5 \cdot 4 \\ &= 20 \end{aligned}$$ ■

B. Evaluate $7(a - 2b)$ when $a = 5$ and $b = -4$.

Solution

$7(a - 2b) = 7[5 - 2 \cdot (-4)]$	Substitute 5 for a and -4 for b.
$= 7[5 - (-8)]$	Perform the multiplication inside the brackets.
$= 7(5 + 8)$	Definition of subtraction
$= 7 \cdot 13$	Perform the addition inside the parentheses.
$= 91$	Multiply. ■

C. Simplify $5 \cdot (-7) + 11 \cdot 4 - 7 \cdot (-3)$.

Solution

$5 \cdot (-7) + 11 \cdot 4 - 7 \cdot (-3) = -35 + 44 - (-21)$	Multiply from left to right.
$= -35 + 44 + 21$	Definition of subtraction
$= 9 + 21$	Add from left to right.
$= 30$	Add. ■

(continued)

D. Simplify $-2(x - 2) - 7(3 + 5a)$.

Solution

$-2(x - 2) - 7(3 + 5a) = -2x + 4 - 21 - 35a$	Distribute -2 and -7.
$= -2x - 17 - 35a$	Combine like terms. ■

Application: Recreation

You can now solve real-life applications that involve repeated addition more easily using multiplication.

Example 2 Jimmy is playing a hopping game. Every time he hops forward he must travel a distance of 3 feet, and every time he hops backward he must travel a distance of 2 feet. The expression $3f + |(-2)b|$ is used to calculate the total number of feet Jimmy will travel after f hops forward and b hops backward. Use the expression to find the distance Jimmy will cover if he takes 6 hops backward and 4 hops forward.

Solution

$3f + |(-2)b| = 3 \cdot 4 + |(-2) \cdot 6|$	Substitute 4 for f and 6 for b.
$= 12 + |(-2) \cdot 6|$	Multiply.
$= 12 + |-12|$	Multiply.
$= 12 + 12$	Evaluate the absolute value.
$= 24$	Add.

Jimmy will travel a distance of 24 feet. ■

Problem Set

Evaluate.

1. $x \cdot 5 \cdot 2$, when $x = -2$, 0, and 3
2. $-10 \cdot x \cdot 5$, when $x = -1$, 4, and 5
3. $2(a - b)$, when $a = 10$ and $b = -3$
4. $4(2a - b)$, when $a = -1$ and $b = 5$
5. $3(a - 2b)$, when $a = 6$ and $b = -7$
6. $-1 \cdot x \cdot 8$, when $x = -3$, 0, and 1
7. $-2(x - 4y)$, when $x = -1$ and $y = -3$
8. $-(-2x + 8y)$, when $x = 9$ and $y = -5$
9. $6 \cdot -2 \cdot x$, when $x = -5$, -2, and 1
10. $-3 \cdot -5 \cdot x$, when $x = -1$, 2, and 7
11. $8(a + 6b)$, when $a = -2$ and $b = -10$

Simplify the expression.

12. $4 \cdot 3 + 7 \cdot 1$
13. $(-3) \cdot (-5)$
14. $2(a + 1)$
15. $2 \cdot (-4) + 8 \cdot 3 - 6 \cdot (-1)$
16. $2 + 5 \cdot (-9) - 4 \cdot 3 + 6 \cdot 7$
17. $3(x + 5) + 4(2 + 7a)$
18. $-6(x - 4) + 8(-1 + 3a)$
19. $10 \cdot 3 - 11 \cdot (-2) + 20 \cdot (-9)$
20. $-(y + 3) - 2(10 - a)$
21. $-5\,(y - 4) + 2(a - 10) - (17 - b)$
22. $(-7) \cdot 0 + 12 \cdot 5 + 15 \cdot (-2) - 6$
23. $-7(x + 5) - (-3)(a + 4)$
24. $(-7) \cdot (-6) - 2 \cdot (-13) - 4 \cdot 11 + 2$
25. $-9(x - 1) - 3(a + 16) + (-2)(20 - 2b)$

Solve. For each problem:

A. Substitute values into the given expression and simplify.
B. Answer the question.

26. Jamal is calculating his cell phone bill. He pays \$15.99 per month plus \$0.50 per long distance call. As a sign-up bonus, his phone provider is deducting \$5.99 from his bill this month. The expression $m + 0.50n - b$ (where m represents monthly rate, n represents number of long distance calls, and b represents bonus) is used to calculate Jamal's monthly bill. If Jamal made 23 long distance calls this month, how much is his total phone bill?

27. Sang joins a CD club advertised on TV. Every time he orders he must pay \$8.99 per CD and \$6.99 for shipping. As a sales incentive, the CD company will give Sang a discount of 0.60 times the number of orders he makes. If this is Sang's 6th order and he wishes to buy 5 CDs, how much money will he spend? Use the expression $8.99c + 6.99 - 0.60n$ (where c represents number of CDs ordered and n represents number of orders).

28. Six months ago, Tamika opened a bank account. Each month she makes a \$30 deposit, two \$24 deposits, and withdraws \$17. How much money does she have in her account after six months? Use the expression $6(d - w + 2t)$, where d represents the \$30 deposit, w represents the withdrawal amount, and t represents each \$24 deposit.

29. A tower at an amusement park lifts riders vertically for 100 feet. The ride then drops 20 feet, rises 10 feet, drops 20 feet, and so on, until the riders reach the ground. Use the expression $100 + |-20d| + 10r$ (where d represents number of 20 feet drops and r represents number of 10 feet rises) to determine the distance total distance traveled per one ride. Assume each ride drops 20 feet 9 times and rises 10 feet 8 times.

30. Jackson earns \$5.50 per hour mowing lawns. He spends \$6 for gas per week and \$10 per week for tool repair. If he mows 20 hours per week and works four and a half weeks during August, how much money will he have at the end of the month? Use the expression $w(5.50h - 6 - 10)$, where w represents the number of weeks worked and h represents the number of hours worked.

*31. **Challenge** At a restaurant, Uri and Will drank 4 glasses of juice and ate 2 appetizers. If each juice cost \$1.50, each appetizer cost \$7, and they left a \$4 tip, how much money did they spend? Write and simplify an expression to determine the answer. Let j represent the number of glasses of juice and a represent the number of appetizers.

*32. **Challenge** Ray took his 4 dogs and 3 cats to the vet for shots. Each dog shot cost \$50 and each cat shot cost \$35. Ray paid an additional \$20 per cat for exams but received a \$5 discount per dog because of a previous bill overpayment. Write and simplify an expression to determine Ray's total vet bill. Let d represent the cost of a dog shot and c represent the cost of a cat shot.

Reciprocals and Division

For any nonzero real number a, the **reciprocal,** or **multiplicative inverse,** of a is $\frac{1}{a}$. The product of a nonzero number and its multiplicative inverse is the multiplicative identity, 1.

RECIPROCAL PROPERTIES

Reciprocal Property of Multiplication: For any nonzero real number a: $a \cdot \frac{1}{a} = 1$.

For all nonzero real numbers a and b: the reciprocal of $\frac{a}{b}$ is $\frac{b}{a}$.

For any nonzero real number a: $\frac{1}{-a} = \frac{-1}{a} = -\frac{1}{a}$.

For all nonzero real numbers a and b: $\frac{1}{ab} = \frac{1}{a} \cdot \frac{1}{b}$.

TIP

For all nonzero real numbers a and b: $\frac{-a}{b} = \frac{a}{-b} = -\frac{a}{b}$.

Finding Reciprocals

Example 1 Use the reciprocal properties to find the reciprocal of each number.

A. -5

Solution The reciprocal of -5 is $\frac{1}{-5} = -\frac{1}{5}$.

Check $-5 \cdot \left(-\frac{1}{5}\right) = 1$. ■

B. 1.5

Solution First change 1.5 to an improper fraction: $1.5 = 1\frac{1}{2} = \frac{3}{2}$.

The reciprocal of $\frac{3}{2}$ is $\frac{2}{3}$.

Check $1.5 \cdot \frac{2}{3} = \frac{3}{2} \cdot \frac{2}{3} = 1$. ■

C. $-\frac{7}{2}$

Solution The reciprocal of $-\frac{7}{2}$ is $-\frac{2}{7}$.

Check $-\frac{7}{2} \cdot \left(-\frac{2}{7}\right) = 1.$ ■

Dividing Real Numbers

Division is the inverse operation of multiplication. To divide two numbers, multiply the dividend by the reciprocal of the divisor. The result is the **quotient.**

REMEMBER

In $6 \div 3$, 6 is the dividend and 3 is the divisor.

DIVISION PROPERTIES

For any real number a and nonzero real number b: $a \div b = a \cdot \frac{1}{b}$.

For all real numbers a and b and nonzero real number c: $\frac{a+b}{c} = \frac{a}{c} + \frac{b}{c}$.

The sign rules for division are the same as those for multiplication.

DIVISION RULES

For all $a > 0$ and $b > 0$, $a \div b > 0$.

For all $a < 0$ and $b < 0$, $a \div b > 0$.

For all $a < 0$ and $b > 0$, $a \div b < 0$.

In words, the quotient of two numbers with like signs is positive. The quotient of two numbers with unlike signs is negative.

Example 2 Simplify $35 \div (-5)$.

Solution

$35 \div (-5) = 35 \cdot \left(-\frac{1}{5}\right)$ Multiply the dividend by the reciprocal of the divisor.

$= -7$ The signs are different so the quotient is negative.

Check $-7 \cdot (-5) = 35.$ ■

Multiplication and division are related. For example, $35 \div (-5) = -7$ and $-5 \cdot (-7) = 35$ are related equations, so you can use the multiplication equation to check your work when you divide.

Simplifying Fractional Expressions

The division properties are also useful for simplifying fractional expressions involving division.

Example 3

A. Simplify. $-\frac{1}{2} \div \left(-\frac{3}{5}\right)$

Solution Change the division sign to a multiplication sign and change the divisor to its reciprocal.

$-\frac{1}{2} \div \left(-\frac{3}{5}\right) = -\frac{1}{2} \cdot \left(-\frac{5}{3}\right) = \frac{5}{6}$ ■

B. Simplify. $5x \div \frac{1}{2}$

Solution

$5x \div \frac{1}{2} = \frac{5x}{1} \cdot \frac{2}{1} = \frac{10x}{1} = 10x$ ■

C. Simplify. $\frac{3}{y} + \frac{4}{y}$

Solution

$\frac{3}{y} + \frac{4}{y} = \frac{3+4}{y} = \frac{7}{y}$ ■

D. Evaluate $\frac{x-z}{2y}$ when $x = 3$, $y = -2$, and $z = -4$.

REMEMBER

The answer to Example 3D can also be written as $-1\frac{3}{4}$.

Solution

$\frac{x-z}{2y} = \frac{3-(-4)}{2 \cdot (-2)}$	Substitute 3 for x, -2 for y, and -4 for z.
$= \frac{7}{-4}$	Simplify the numerator and the denominator.
$= -1.75$	Simplify. The signs are different so the quotient is negative. ■

Application: Distance, Rate, and Time

The formula $d = rt$, where d represents distance, r represents rate, and t represents time, can also be written as: $r = \frac{d}{t}$ or $t = \frac{d}{r}$. Choose the form that fits what you are trying to find.

Example 4

A. Roger ran a distance of 2800 feet at a rate of 700 feet per minute. What was Roger's time?

Solution Because we are looking for time, use $t = \frac{d}{r}$: $t = \frac{2800}{700} = 4$.

Roger's time was 4 minutes. ■

B. A scuba diver descends 12 meters below the water's surface in 60 seconds. What is the diver's rate of descent?

Solution Because we are looking for rate, use $r = \frac{d}{t}$: $r = \frac{-12}{60} = -0.2$.

The diver's rate of descent is -0.2 meters/second. ■

Problem Set

Find the reciprocal of each number.

1. 3
2. $-\frac{3}{8}$
3. 2.25
4. -7
5. $2b$
6. $\frac{a}{-8}$

*7. **Challenge** -6.125

Simplify.

8. $48 \div (-8)$
9. $-17 \div \frac{1}{4}$
10. $-\frac{1}{3} \div \left(-\frac{1}{2}\right)$
11. $-6y \div \frac{2}{3}$
12. $\frac{-5}{a} + \frac{7}{a}$
13. $-36 \div 3$
14. $6a \div \left(-\frac{2}{5}\right)$
15. $-\frac{3}{7} \div \frac{3}{5}$
16. $24 \div \left(-\frac{3}{2}\right)$
17. $\frac{1}{8} \div \left(-\frac{2}{9}\right)$
18. $\frac{5}{b} - \frac{18}{b}$
19. $-2 \div \frac{4x}{5}$
20. $-18 \div (-6)$

*21. **Challenge** $\frac{2p}{3} - \frac{5p}{3} + \frac{2s}{3}$

Evaluate.

22. $\frac{a + 2b}{3c}$, when $a = 5$, $b = -3$, and $c = -2$
23. $\frac{3a + 2b}{2c - 4}$, when $a = 4$, $b = -2$, and $c = -3$
24. $\frac{-3p - 2r}{6 + 4s}$, when $p = 1$, $r = -7$, and $s = -2$
25. $\frac{x(y - 2)}{2z}$, when $x = 4$, $y = -7$, and $z = -3$

Use a form of $d = rt$ to solve.

26. Rosa's kite rose into the air at the rate of 5 feet per second. How many feet did it rise in $\frac{2}{3}$ minute?
27. Meaghan grew 9.75 inches in 3 years. What was her average yearly rate of growth?
28. Hamish drove 162 miles at an average speed of 45 miles per hour. How long was he driving?
29. Charles earns $61.50 for 6 hours of work. What is his rate of pay? (Use his total pay for *d*.)

*30. **Challenge** Kim and Edward stood back-to-back, and then walked directly away from each other in a straight line. Kim walked at a rate of 3 feet per second, and Edward walked at 3.5 feet per second. After 20 seconds, how far apart were they?

Applications: Number Problems

Many number problems in mathematics involve consecutive integers.

Consecutive integers are a sequence of integers that increase by one. For example, 77 and 78 are consecutive integers, as are -6, -5, and -4.

Guess and Check

Number problems with consecutive integers can sometimes be solved by using a guess and check method.

Example 1 The product of two consecutive integers is 156. Find the integers.

Solution Guess a pair of two consecutive numbers whose product is greater than 100.

$10 \cdot 11 = 110$

The product is too low. Try larger pairs until the product is 156.

$11 \cdot 12 = 132$

$12 \cdot 13 = 156$

The two consecutive integers with a product of 156 are 12 and 13. ■

THINK ABOUT IT

Since $-12 \cdot (-13) = 156$, -12 and -13 are also two consecutive integers with a product of 156.

Guess and Check Using an Equation

The guess and check method can also be used by first writing an equation and then guessing the value of the variable.

Example 2 The sum of two consecutive integers is -57. Find the integers.

Solution If the first number in the pair is n, then the second number in the pair is one more than n, or $n + 1$.

$n + n + 1 = -57$ The sum of n and $n + 1$ is -57.

$2n + 1 = -57$ Combine like terms.

A negative number is a good guess because the sum is negative.

Guess: $n = -30$ Try a greater number. ⟶ **Guess:** $n = -29$

$2 \cdot (-30) + 1 \stackrel{?}{=} -57$ $2 \cdot (-29) + 1 \stackrel{?}{=} -57$

$-60 + 1 \stackrel{?}{=} -57$ $-58 + 1 \stackrel{?}{=} -57$

$-59 \neq -57$ $-57 = -57$ ✓

too low

REMEMBER

Check your answer.
$-29 + (-28) = -57$

So, $n = -29$ and $n + 1 = -28$. The two consecutive integers are -29 and -28. ■

Consecutive Even Integers

Consecutive even and odd integers are a sequence of integers that increase by two. For example, 88 and 90 are consecutive even integers while -13 and -11, and 7, 9, and 11 are consecutive odd integers.

Example 3 The sum of two consecutive even integers is –26. Find the integers.

Solution The first even integer can be represented by n. The next even integer is $n + 2$ (consecutive even and odd integers increase by two).

$n + n + 2 = -26$ Write the equation.

$2n + 2 = -26$ Combine like terms.

Start with a reasonable guess for n. Then adjust the guess as needed.

Guess: $n = -15$ Try a greater number. ⟶ **Guess:** $n = -14$

$2 \cdot (-15) + 2 \stackrel{?}{=} -26$ $2 \cdot (-14) + 2 \stackrel{?}{=} -26$

$-30 + 2 \stackrel{?}{=} -26$ $-28 + 2 \stackrel{?}{=} -26$

$-28 \neq -26$ $-26 = -26$ ✓

too low

So, $n = -14$ and $n + 2 = -12$. The integers are -14 and -12. ■

Application: Age

Example 4 Use a number problem to solve.

A. When Mrs. Harrison was asked how old her three sons were, she replied, "Their ages are consecutive odd numbers, and the sum of their ages is 87." How old are Mrs. Harrison's sons?

Solution The first odd integer can be represented by n. The second odd integer is $n + 2$, and the third odd integer is $n + 4$ (consecutive odd integers increase by two).

$n + n + 2 + n + 4 = 87$ Write the equation.

$3n + 6 = 87$ Combine like terms.

(continued)

Guess: $n = 25$	**Guess:** $n = 31$	**Guess:** $n = 27$
$3 \cdot 25 + 6 \stackrel{?}{=} 87$	$3 \cdot 31 + 6 \stackrel{?}{=} 87$	$3 \cdot 27 + 6 \stackrel{?}{=} 87$
$75 + 6 \stackrel{?}{=} 87$	$93 + 6 \stackrel{?}{=} 87$	$81 + 6 \stackrel{?}{=} 87$
$81 \neq 87$	$99 \neq 87$	$87 = 87$ ✓
too low	**too high**	

So, $n = 27$, $n + 2 = 29$, and $n + 4 = 31$. The sons' ages are 27, 29, and 31. ■

B. The ages of Sarabi's three horses are consecutive even integers, and the sum of their ages is 41. How old are Sarabi's horses?

Solution The first even integer can be represented by n. The second even integer is $n + 2$, and the third even integer is $n + 4$ (consecutive even integers increase by two).

$n + n + 2 + n + 4 = 41$ Write the equation.

$3n + 6 = 41$ Combine like terms.

Guess: $n = 10$	**Guess:** $n = 12$
$3 \cdot 10 + 6 \stackrel{?}{=} 41$	$3 \cdot 12 + 6 \stackrel{?}{=} 41$
$30 + 6 \stackrel{?}{=} 41$	$36 + 6 \stackrel{?}{=} 41$
$36 \neq 41$	$42 \neq 41$
too low	**too high**

NO SOLUTION

The numbers 10 and 12 are consecutive even integers. 10 is too low, but 12 is too high. There is no solution. Three consecutive even integers cannot equal an odd number. ■

Problem Set

Find the integers.

1. The product of two consecutive integers is 72.
2. The sum of two consecutive integers is 29.
3. The sum of two consecutive odd integers is 48.
4. The product of two consecutive even integers is 48.
5. The sum of two consecutive even integers is –22.
6. The sum of three consecutive integers is 63.
7. The sum of three consecutive odd integers is 99.
8. The sum of three consecutive even integers is 306.
9. The sum of three consecutive even integers is –54.
10. The sum of two consecutive integers is 80.
11. The sum of two consecutive integers is –37.
12. The sum of three consecutive odd integers is –9.
13. The sum of two consecutive integers is 61.
14. The sum of three consecutive odd integers is 51.

Solve.

15. Nancy's three sons have heights that are consecutive integers. Find their heights if the sum of the three heights is 147 inches.
16. George's age is an even number. Nick is 2 years older than George, and Fred is 2 years older than Nick. Together, the sum of their ages is 54. What are their ages?

17. Brenda's three daughters have heights that are consecutive even integers. Find their heights if the sum of the three heights is 120 inches.

18. Haley's age is an odd number. Heather is 2 years older than Haley, and Hope is 2 years older than Heather. Together the sum of their ages is 87. What are their ages?

19. Brady has a piece of wood that is 69 inches long. She wants to cut three shelves that are odd, consecutive integer lengths and use up the entire piece of wood. What lengths should the shelves be?

20. Dan, Don, and Derek earn allowances that are consecutive integers. Together they make \$24 per week. How much does each boy earn?

21. Tony's math class has a piece of string that is 144 inches long. The students need to cut the string so that they have three pieces that have even, consecutive integer lengths and use up the entire piece of string. What lengths should the strings be?

22. The width and length of a rectangle are consecutive integers. What is the width and length of the rectangle if the perimeter is 26 cm?

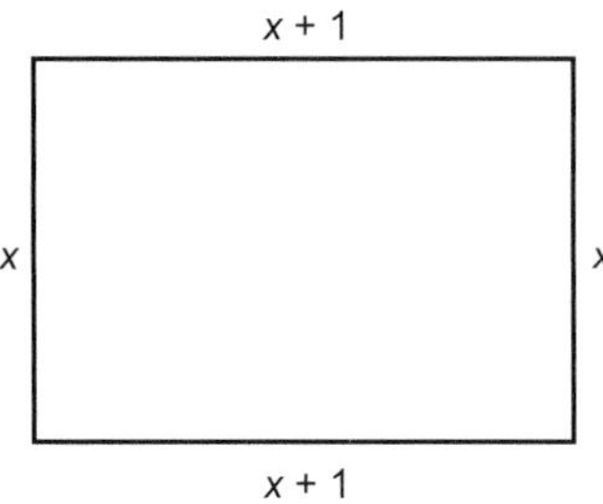

23. Tim scored a total of 24 points in three basketball games last week. The number of points he scored in each game are consecutive even integers. Find the integers.

24. The lengths of the sides of a triangle are consecutive even integers. What are the lengths of the sides if the perimeter is 72 inches?

25. Dana, Denise, and Debbie earn allowances that are consecutive integers. Together they make \$27 per week. How much does each girl earn?

***26.** **Challenge** The width and length of a rectangle are consecutive even integers. What is the width and length of the rectangle if the perimeter is 20 cm?

27. The lengths of the sides of a triangle are consecutive odd integers. What are the lengths of the sides if the perimeter is 45 inches?

28. Adam scored 15 goals in three soccer games last weekend. The number of goals he scored each game are consecutive odd integers. Find the integers.

29. Baki placed money into a savings account for three weeks. The amounts of money he deposited each week are consecutive even integers. How much did Baki deposit each week if the total amount deposited is \$101?

***30.** **Challenge** Hannah has two brothers. Charlie is 2 years older than she is and Colby is 2 years younger than she is. All of their ages are even numbers and together they add up to 42. Find their ages.

UNIT 4 Solving Equations and Inequalities

The Parthenon is in Athens, Greece.

The Greek mathematician Diophantus is often called "the father of algebra." His book *Arithmetica* described the solutions to 130 problems. He did not discover all of these solutions himself, but he did collect many solutions that had been found by Greeks, Egyptians, and Babylonians before him. Some people of long ago obviously enjoyed doing algebra. It also helped them—and can help you—solve many real-world problems.

Big Ideas

- ► You can use the laws of arithmetic to solve algebraic equations and inequalities.
- ► Solving an equation or inequality means finding values for the variable or variables that make the equation or inequality a true statement.

Unit Topics

- ► Addition and Subtraction Equations
- ► Multiplication and Division Equations
- ► Multiple Transformations
- ► Variables on Both Sides
- ► Transforming Formulas
- ► Estimating Solutions
- ► Applications: Cost Problems
- ► Inequalities
- ► Solving Inequalities
- ► Combined Inequalities
- ► Absolute Value Equations and Inequalities
- ► Applications: Inequalities

Addition and Subtraction Equations

Use *properties of equality* and what you know about *inverse operations* to solve addition and subtraction equations.

An equation is a number sentence indicating that two expressions have the same value. A **solution** of an equation is a value for the variable that makes the equation a true statement. To **solve** an equation, you need to find all the solutions of the equation. Some one-variable equations have more than one solution.

One way to solve an equation is to find a series of equivalent equations, each one simpler than the one before. **Equivalent equations** are equations with the same solution or solutions.

PROPERTIES OF EQUALITY

Addition Property of Equality	If $a = b$, then $a + c = b + c$ and $c + a = c + b$.
Subtraction Property of Equality	If $a = b$, then $a - c = b - c$.
Substitution Property of Equality	If $a = b$, then a may be replaced with b in any expression or equation.

TIP

Use the addition and subtraction properties to solve an equation. Use the substitution property to check your solution.

The addition property of equality tells you that you can add the same value to each side of an equation to create an equivalent equation. The subtraction property of equality tells you that you can subtract the same value from each side of an equation to create an equivalent equation.

Solving a Subtraction Equation

Remember that addition and subtraction are inverse operations, so use the addition property of equality to solve subtraction equations.

Example 1 Solve $x - 12 = 8$.

Solution You need to isolate x. The expression $x - 12$ indicates that 12 is subtracted from x. To "undo" the subtraction, use the inverse operation, addition.

$x - 12 = 8$

$x - 12 + 12 = 8 + 12$ Add 12 to each side. (Addition Property of Equality)

$x = 20$ Simplify.

(continued)

REMEMBER

The solution in Example 1 is 20, not 8.

Check

$x - 12 = 8$	Write the original equation.
$20 - 12 \stackrel{?}{=} 8$	Substitute 20 for x. (Substitution Property of Equality)
$8 = 8$ ✓	The solution is correct because $8 = 8$ is a true statement. ■

Look back at Example 1. The equations $x - 12 = 8$ and $x = 20$ are equivalent equations. The equation $x = 20$ has the variable isolated on one side of the equals sign, so it names the solution, 20.

Solving an Addition Equation

Use the Subtraction Property of Equality to solve addition equations.

Example 2 Solve $21 = b + 9$.

Solution

$21 = b + 9$	
$21 - 9 = b + 9 - 9$	Subtract 9 from each side. (Subtraction Property of Equality)
$12 = b$	Simplify.

Check

$21 = b + 9$	Write the original equation.
$21 \stackrel{?}{=} 12 + 9$	Substitute 12 for b. (Substitution Property of Equality)
$21 = 21$ ✓	The solution is correct because $21 = 21$ is a true statement. ■

Simplify First

THINK ABOUT IT

In Example 3A, these are all equivalent equations:

$5 + x - 14 = -15$

$x + 5 - 14 = -15$

$x - 9 = -15$

$x - 9 + 9 = -15 + 9$

$x = -6$

The last one, $x = -6$, names the solution.

Sometimes, it helps if you simplify each side of an equation before trying to solve it.

Example 3 Solve.

A. $5 + x - 14 = -15$

Solution

$5 + x - 14 = -15$	
$x + 5 - 14 = -15$	Use the commutative property of addition to rewrite $5 + x$ as $x + 5$. Then simplify: $5 - 14 = -9$.
$x - 9 = -15$	$x - 9 = -15$ is a subtraction equation. The inverse of subtraction is addition, so add 9 to each side.
$x - 9 + 9 = -15 + 9$	
$x = -6$	

Check

$5 + x - 14 = -15$ Write the original equation.

$5 + (-6) - 14 \stackrel{?}{=} -15$ Substitute -6 for x.

$-15 = -15$ ✓ The solution is correct. ■

B. $17 - (8 - q) = 10$

Solution

$17 - (8 - q) = 10$

$17 - 8 + q = 10$ Distributive Property

$9 + q = 10$ Simplify.

$9 - 9 + q = 10 - 9$ Subtract 9 from each side.

$q = 1$

Check

$17 - (8 - q) = 10$ Write the original equation.

$17 - (8 - 1) \stackrel{?}{=} 10$ Substitute 1 for q.

$17 - 7 \stackrel{?}{=} 10$ Use the order of operations. Simplify $8 - 1$ first because it is inside grouping symbols.

$10 = 10$ ✓ ■

> **TIP**
>
> **In Example 3B, the distributive property is used as follows.**
>
> $17 - (8 - q)$
>
> $= 17 + (-1)(8 - q)$
>
> $= 17 + (-1) \cdot 8 + (-1) \cdot (-q)$
>
> $= 17 - 8 + q$

Application: Change in Elevation

You can use an addition or subtraction equation to solve many real-world problems including problems with changing altitude.

Example 4 A hot air balloon descended (went down) 150 feet to a height of 3500 feet. How high was the hot air balloon before its descent?

Solution

Step 1 Write an equation.

Let x represent the height of the balloon before its descent.

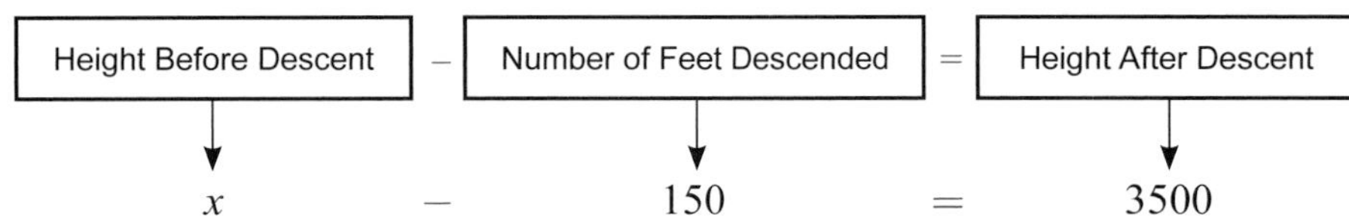

Step 2 Solve the equation.

$x - 150 = 3500$

$x - 150 + 150 = 3500 + 150$ Add 150 to each side.

$x = 3650$ Simplify.

Step 3 Check the solution.

$x - 150 = 3500$ Write the original equation.

$3650 - 150 \stackrel{?}{=} 3500$ Substitute 3650 for x.

$3500 = 3500$ ✓ Simplify.

The height of the hot air balloon before its descent was 3650 feet. ■

Solving Absolute Value Equations

To solve equations involving absolute value, use the following property:

If $|x| = a$ for some positive number a, then $x = a$ or $x = -a$.

Example 5 Solve.

A. $|c| + 2 = 10$

Solution

$\lvert c\rvert + 2 = 10$	
$\lvert c\rvert + 2 - 2 = 10 - 2$	Subtract 2 from each side to isolate the absolute value.
$\lvert c\rvert = 8$	Simplify.
$c = 8$ or $c = -8$	If $\lvert x\rvert = a$ for some positive number a, then $x = a$ or $x = -a$.

THINK ABOUT IT

If either 8 makes the equation true *or* −8 makes the equation true, then both numbers are solutions. That is, 8 *and* −8 are solutions. Of course, *only one number at a time* makes the equation true.

Check

$\lvert c\rvert + 2 = 10$	$\lvert c\rvert + 2 = 10$
$\lvert 8\rvert + 2 \stackrel{?}{=} 10$	$\lvert -8\rvert + 2 \stackrel{?}{=} 10$
$8 + 2 \stackrel{?}{=} 10$	$8 + 2 \stackrel{?}{=} 10$
$10 = 10$ ✓	$10 = 10$ ✓

The solutions are 8 and −8. That is, the solution set is $\{-8, 8\}$. ■

B. $-3 - |k| = -5$

Solution

$-3 - \lvert k\rvert = -5$	
$-3 + 3 - \lvert k\rvert = -5 + 3$	Add 3 to each side to isolate the absolute value.
$-\lvert k\rvert = -2$	Simplify.
$\lvert k\rvert = 2$	$-\lvert k\rvert$ is the opposite of $\lvert k\rvert$, so if $-\lvert k\rvert = -2$, then $\lvert k\rvert = 2$.
$k = 2$ or $k = -2$	

Check

$-3 - \lvert k\rvert = -5$	$-3 - \lvert k\rvert = -5$
$-3 - \lvert 2\rvert \stackrel{?}{=} -5$	$-3 - \lvert -2\rvert \stackrel{?}{=} -5$
$-3 - 2 \stackrel{?}{=} -5$	$-3 - 2 \stackrel{?}{=} -5$
$-5 = -5$ ✓	$-5 = -5$ ✓

The solutions are 2 and −2. That is, the solution set is $\{-2, 2\}$. ■

Problem Set

Solve the equation.

1. $y - 9 = 41$
2. $x - 1.2 = 3$
3. $x + 3 = 12$
4. $b + 0.9 = 5.1$
5. $14 + z = 12$
6. $2 + r + 10 = 13$
7. $-15 + p + 3 = 17$
8. $|y| - 8 = 32$
9. $-19 - |s| = -22$
10. $-46 + x = 25$
11. $8 = 33 + y$
12. $21 = 4 + t$
13. $3 = x - 19$
14. $17 = r - 2$
15. $-4 = -(-k - 86) + 10$
16. $-(-y + 18) + 11 = 1$
17. $x - \frac{2}{7} = \frac{6}{7}$
18. $x - \frac{1}{3} = \frac{2}{3}$
19. $(s + 22) - 18 = 30$
20. $(m + 7) - 19 = -13$
21. $d - (-12) = 100$
22. $4 - (-c) = 84$
23. $|f| - (-3) = 11$
24. $|z| + 13 = 11$

Solve. For each problem:

A. Define a variable for the unknown.
B. Write an equation to model the situation.
C. Answer the question.

25. You purchased a shirt on sale for \$17.55. The discount on the shirt was \$5.85. What was the original price of the shirt?
26. There are a total of 24 students in a class. If there are 12 boys in the class, how many girls are in the class?
27. There were f fans at Saturday's baseball game. There were 129 fewer fans at Sunday's baseball game. If 2373 fans attended Sunday's baseball game, how many fans attended Saturday's baseball game?
28. Today's temperature is 7° cooler than yesterday's temperature. Today's temperature is 79°F. What was yesterday's temperature?
29. It takes Tanya 3 minutes longer than Lourdes to walk a mile. Tanya can walk a mile in 20 minutes. How long does it take Lourdes to walk a mile?
30. Sean begins hiking a trail at an elevation of 830 feet. He reaches the peak of the mountain at an elevation of 2350 feet. What is the change in elevation from where Sean began hiking to the peak of the mountain?
31. Kelly has been saving her allowance to buy a music player that costs \$119 and headphones that cost \$12. She has saved \$48. How much more money does she need to save?
32. Lorenzo is donating \$300 to three charities. He donates \$105 to the first charity and \$125 to the second charity. How much does Lorenzo donate to the third charity?
33. Cindy spends 2 hours doing English, geometry, and history homework. It takes her 35 minutes to do English homework and 55 minutes to do geometry homework. How much time does Cindy spend on history homework?

*34. **Challenge** Tavi spent \$12.95 on a gift and a card. He spent \$4.15 on the card. How much more money did Tavi spend on the gift than on the card?

*35. **Challenge** It took John two days to drive 1029 miles. On the first day, he drove 473 miles. How many more miles did he drive on the second day than on the first day?

Multiplication and Division Equations

You can use properties of equality to solve equations involving multiplication and division.

(MORE) PROPERTIES OF EQUALITY

Multiplication Property of Equality	If $a = b$, then $ca = cb$ and $ac = bc$.
Division Property of Equality	If $a = b$ and $c \neq 0$, then $\frac{a}{c} = \frac{b}{c}$.

The multiplication property of equality tells you that you can multiply each side of an equation by the same value to create an equivalent equation. The division property of equality tells you that you can divide each side of an equation by the same *nonzero* value to create an equivalent equation.

Solving a Division Equation

Recall that you use inverse operations to solve equations. So, use the multiplication property of equality to solve division equations.

Example 1 Solve $\frac{x}{4} = 8$.

Solution You need to isolate x. The expression $\frac{x}{4}$ indicates that x is divided by 4. To "undo" the division, use the inverse operation, multiplication.

$\frac{x}{4} = 8$

$4 \cdot \frac{x}{4} = 4 \cdot 8$ Multiply each side by 4. (Multiplication Property of Equality)

$x = 32$ Simplify.

Check

$\frac{x}{4} = 8$ Write the original equation.

$\frac{32}{4} \stackrel{?}{=} 8$ Substitute 32 for x. (Substitution Property of Equality)

$8 = 8$ ✓ Simplify. The solution is correct because $8 = 8$ is a true statement.

The solution is 32. You can also say the solution set is $\{32\}$. ■

Solving a Multiplication Equation

Use the division property of equality to solve multiplication equations.

Example 2 Solve $15 = -3n$.

Solution The expression $-3n$ indicates multiplication. Use division to "undo" the operation.

$15 = -3n$

$\frac{15}{-3} = \frac{-3n}{-3}$ Divide each side by -3. (Division Property of Equality)

$-5 = n$ Simplify. ■

THINK ABOUT IT

The equation in Example 1 could be written as $\frac{1}{4}x = 8$; then multiplying by 4 is multiplying by the reciprocal of $\frac{1}{4}$. In Example 2, dividing by -3 is equivalent to multiplying by $-\frac{1}{3}$, which is the reciprocal of -3.

Using a Reciprocal Property for Multiplication to Solve Equations

You don't really need the division property of equality. Instead of dividing, you could always multiply by the reciprocal. Still, the division property of equality can be convenient.

When an equation shows a variable multiplied by a fraction, use a reciprocal property for multiplication.

Example 3 Solve.

A. $\frac{1}{6}b = 12$

Solution

$\frac{1}{6}b = 12$

$6 \cdot \frac{1}{6}b = 6 \cdot 12$ Multiply each side by 6, which is the reciprocal of $\frac{1}{6}$.

$1 \cdot b = 72$ Simplify. $6 \cdot \frac{1}{6} = 1$ by a reciprocal property for multiplication.

$b = 72$ Simplify. $1 \cdot b = b$ by the multiplicative identity property. ■

REMEMBER

One of the reciprocal properties for multiplication says that for all $a \in \mathbb{R}, a \cdot \frac{1}{a} = 1$ if $a \neq 0$.

B. $\frac{2t}{5} = 14$

Solution

$\frac{2t}{5} = 14$

$\frac{2}{5}t = 14$ Rewrite the equation as a multiplication equation.

$\frac{5}{2} \cdot \frac{2}{5}t = \frac{5}{2} \cdot 14$ Multiply each side by $\frac{5}{2}$, which is the reciprocal of $\frac{2}{5}$.

$t = 35$ Simplify. ■

Solving Absolute Value Equations

To solve equations that have an absolute value, keep in mind that if $|x| = a$ for some positive number a, then $x = a$ or $x = -a$.

Example 4 Solve.

A. $5|y| = 30$

Solution

$5|y| = 30$

$\frac{5|y|}{5} = \frac{30}{5}$ Divide each side by 5.

$|y| = 6$ Simplify.

$y = 6$ or $y = -6$ If $|x| = a$ for some positive number a, then $x = a$ or $x = -a$. ■

B. $\frac{|x|}{15} = -3$

Solution

$\frac{|x|}{15} = -3$

$15 \cdot \frac{|x|}{15} = 15 \cdot (-3)$ Multiply each side by 15.

$|x| = -45$ Simplify.

NO SOLUTION An absolute value is never negative.

The solution set is the empty set, represented by either { } or ∅. ■

Application: Find a Unit Price

Multiplication and division equations are useful for solving certain types of real-world problems such as unit price, which is a type of unit rate.

Example 5 Mr. Boswell buys a package of 150 file folders for $6.00. What is the unit price per file folder?

Solution

Step 1 Write an equation.

Let f represent the unit price per file folder in dollars.

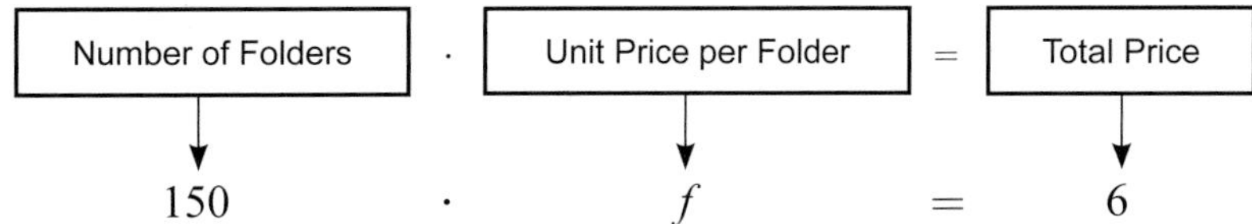

Step 2 Solve the equation.

$150f = 6$

$\frac{150f}{150} = \frac{6}{150}$ Divide each side by 150.

$f = 0.04$ Simplify.

Step 3 Check the solution.

$150f = 6$ Write the original equation.

$150 \cdot 0.04 \stackrel{?}{=} 6$ Substitute 0.04 for f.

$6 = 6$ ✓ Simplify. The solution is correct.

The unit price is \$0.04 per folder. ■

Problem Set

Solve.

1. $\frac{x}{3} = 12$

2. $\frac{m}{5} = 4$

3. $-27 = 9z$

4. $6w = 144$

5. $\frac{1}{3}n = 6$

6. $\frac{2y}{3} = 16$

7. $4|x| = 36$

8. $\frac{|m|}{14} = 5$

9. $-5y = 60$

10. $-3 = \frac{a}{6}$

11. $17 = 5|m|$

12. $-14 = \frac{1}{4}x$

13. $-8 = \frac{|n|}{5}$

14. $-\frac{3}{5}x = 18$

15. $\frac{y}{2} = 8.7$

16. $-\frac{1}{5}b = -3.5$

17. $14 = \frac{2a}{9}$

18. $-20.8 = -4n$

19. $23x = 92$

20. $\frac{|a|}{-3} = -9$

21. $-\frac{1}{8}t = 4$

22. $-15 = \frac{-5m}{7}$

23. $\frac{x}{18} = -3$

***24.** **Challenge** $-6|y| = 42$

Solve. For each problem:

A. Define variables for the unknowns.
B. Write and simplify an equation to model the problem.
C. Solve the equation.
D. Give your answer in a complete sentence.

25. Cameron paid \$15 for a package of 250 sheets of drawing paper. What was the unit price per sheet?

26. At the movie store sale, Muhammad paid \$33.75 for 9 used DVDs. What was the unit price per DVD?

27. Six friends are driving in one minivan to a state park. The park charges \$5 per vehicle, and the friends plan to split the cost evenly. How much will each pay?

28. Paige pays \$3 for a box of 25 pretzels. What is the unit price per pretzel?

29. Alejandra stayed 3 nights in a hotel for a total of \$254.91. If each night was the same price, what did Alejandra pay per night?

***30.** **Challenge** Ms. Kiefer paid \$20.72 for 2 pounds of apples, 2.5 pounds of oranges, 1.5 pounds of pears, and 1 pound of grapes. What was the average price per pound of the fruit Ms. Kiefer bought?

Multiple Transformations

Solving an equation involves using the properties of equality and inverse operations to transform the original equation into a series of equivalent equations.

For example, $x - 12 = 8$ is transformed into $x = 20$ by the addition property of equality, and $\frac{x}{4} = 8$ is transformed into $x = 32$ by the multiplication property of equality.

Solving a Division/Subtraction Equation

To solve an equation such as $\frac{x}{4} - 12 = 8$, you need to make multiple transformations, using various properties and inverse operations.

Example 1 Solve $\frac{x}{4} - 12 = 8$.

Solution Using the correct order of operations, take note of the order in which operations are applied to x.

$\frac{x}{4} - 12 = 8$	First, x is divided by 4. Second, 12 is subtracted from the quotient $\frac{x}{4}$.

Now use the properties of equality and inverse operations to "undo" these operations in reverse order.

$\frac{x}{4} - 12 = 8$	
$\frac{x}{4} - 12 + 12 = 8 + 12$	First, add 12 to each side to "undo" the subtraction. (Addition Property of Equality)
$\frac{x}{4} = 20$	Simplify.
$4 \cdot \frac{x}{4} = 4 \cdot 20$	Second, multiply each side by 4 to "undo" the division. (Multiplication Property of Equality)
$x = 80$	Simplify.

Check

$\frac{x}{4} - 12 = 8$ Write the original equation.

$\frac{80}{4} - 12 \stackrel{?}{=} 8$ Substitute 80 for x. (Substitution Property of Equality)

$20 - 12 \stackrel{?}{=} 8$ Use the order of operations to simplify.

$8 = 8$ ✓ The solution is correct.

The solution is 80, and the solution set is {80}. ■

Using Multiple Transformations to Solve an Equation

Multiple-transformation equations are not limited to subtraction and division, nor are they limited to two operations.

Example 2 Solve.

A. $3x + 18 = -39$

Solution Here x is multiplied by 3 and then 18 is added.

$3x + 18 = -39$

$3x + 18 - 18 = -39 - 18$ Subtract 18 from each side to "undo" the addition. (Subtraction Property of Equality)

$3x = -57$ Simplify.

$\frac{3x}{3} = \frac{-57}{3}$ Divide each side by 3 to "undo" the multiplication. (Division Property of Equality)

$x = -19$ Simplify. ■

TIP

To solve for a variable in an equation, use the reverse order of operations.

B. $3 = \frac{1 - 7n}{5}$

Solution Here n is multiplied by -7, 1 is added to the product, and then the sum is divided by 5.

$3 = \frac{1 - 7n}{5}$

$5 \cdot 3 = 5 \cdot \frac{1 - 7n}{5}$ Multiply each side by 5.

$15 = 1 - 7n$ Simplify.

$15 - 1 = 1 - 7n - 1$ Subtract 1 from each side.

$15 - 1 = (1 - 1) - 7n$ Combine like terms. (Commutative and Associative Properties of Addition)

$14 = -7n$ Simplify.

$\frac{14}{-7} = \frac{-7n}{-7}$ Divide each side by -7.

$-2 = n$ Simplify. ■

TIP

If you prefer, use the commutative property of addition to rewrite the difference $1 - 7n$ as the sum $-7n + 1$.

Simplifying First

It is helpful to simplify each side of an equation before trying to solve it.

Example 3 Solve $3(g - 7) + g = 3$.

Solution You can solve this equation in two ways.

Strategy 1

$3(g - 7) + g = 3$	
$3g - 21 + g = 3$	Distribute.
$(3g + g) - 21 = 3$	Combine like terms.
$4g - 21 = 3$	Simplify.
$4g - 21 + 21 = 3 + 21$	Add 21 to each side.
$\frac{4g}{4} = \frac{24}{4}$	Divide each side by 4.
$g = 6$	Simplify.

Strategy 2

$3(g - 7) + g = 3$	
$\frac{3(g - 7) + g}{3} = \frac{3}{3}$	Divide each side by 3.
$\frac{3(g - 7)}{3} + \frac{g}{3} = \frac{3}{3}$	Simplify.
$g - 7 + \frac{1}{3}g = 1$	Simplify.
$\left(g + \frac{1}{3}g\right) - 7 = 1$	Combine like terms.
$\frac{4}{3}g - 7 = 1$	Simplify.
$\frac{4}{3}g - 7 + 7 = 1 + 7$	Add 7 to each side.
$\frac{4}{3}g = 8$	Simplify.
$\frac{3}{4} \cdot \frac{4}{3}g = \frac{3}{4} \cdot 8$	Multiply each side by $\frac{3}{4}$, which is the reciprocal of $\frac{4}{3}$.
$g = 6$	Simplify. ■

Simplifying first can make solving a complicated equation easier.

Application: Perimeter

TIP

Use the Problem-Solving Plan.

Step 1 *Identify*
Step 2 *Strategize*
Step 3 *Set Up*
Step 4 *Solve*
Step 5 *Check*

REMEMBER

Perimeter is the distance around a figure.

Example 4 The width of a rectangle is 2 inches less than its length. The perimeter of the rectangle is 40 inches. What are the length and width of the rectangle?

Solution

Step 1 *Identify* Find the length and width of the rectangle, given the perimeter.

Step 2 *Strategize* Let l represent the length in inches. The width is 2 inches less than the length, or $l - 2$.

Step 3 *Set Up* Write an equation.

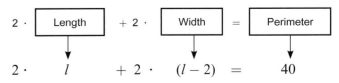

2 ·	Length	+ 2 ·	Width	=	Perimeter
2 ·	l	+ 2 ·	$(l - 2)$	=	40

Step 4 *Solve*

$$2l + 2(l - 2) = 40$$

$2l + 2l - 4 = 40$	Distribute.
$4l - 4 = 40$	Combine like terms.
$4l - 4 + 4 = 40 + 4$	Add 4 to each side.
$\frac{4l}{4} = \frac{44}{4}$	Divide each side by 4.
$l = 11$	Simplify.

If $l = 11$, then the expression $l - 2 = 11 - 2 = 9$. The length of the rectangle is 11 inches and the width is 9 inches.

Step 5 *Check* An informal way to check your work is to sketch the rectangle and find its perimeter.

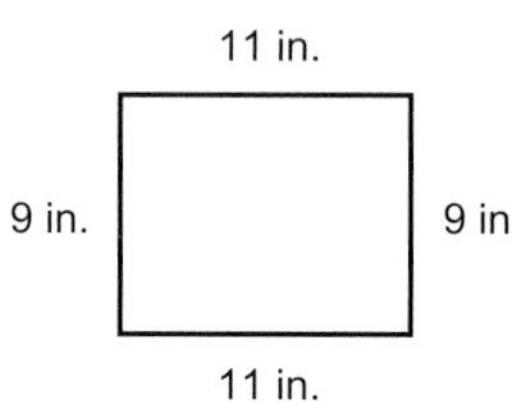

Perimeter = 9 in. + 11 in. + 9 in. + 11 in. = 40 in. ✓ ■

Problem Set

Solve.

1. $\frac{x}{6} - 7 = 2$
2. $\frac{n}{3} - 5 = 12$
3. $4y + 13 = 37$
4. $2 = \frac{5p - 7}{4}$
5. $8(y - 5) + 2y = -10$
6. $3(p + 2) - 7p = 18$
7. $9s + 20 = -16$
8. $\frac{t}{5} + 3 = 9$
9. $\frac{y}{6} + 12 = 10$
10. $13 + \frac{m}{4} = 6$
11. $4 = \frac{5z + 2}{3}$
12. $\frac{3w + 8}{2} = 25$
13. $-5(2x - 6) + 8x = 22$
14. $-2n + 3 = 8$
15. $7 = \frac{3}{5}t - 2$
16. $21 = 5n - 2(n - 3)$
17. $15 - \frac{x}{8} = 4$
18. $16 - 3q = 10$
19. $2(5m + 3) - 8m = 4$
20. $12x - 4 = 32$
21. $5 - \frac{3}{4}s = -1$

*22 **Challenge** $\frac{3\left(t - \frac{1}{3}\right)}{2} - 4 = 6$

*23. **Challenge** $\frac{3x}{5} + 2 = 5.6$

Solve. For each problem:

A. Write and simplify an equation to model the problem.

B. Solve the equation.

C. Give your answer in a complete sentence.

24. The length of a rectangle is 5 more than its width. The perimeter is 50 feet. What are the length and width of the rectangle? (Hint: The perimeter of a rectangle is given by the formula $P = 2l + 2w$.)

25. The length of a rectangle is equal to 3 more than 3 times the width. The perimeter is 54 feet. What are the length and width of the rectangle?

26. George is drawing a rectangular plan for a playhouse he is building for his little sister. First, he chose a measurement for the length. For the measurement of the width, he doubled the length and then subtracted 12 inches. The perimeter of George's rectangular plan is 36 inches. What are the length and width?

27. The length of the rectangular parking lot at Bonita's office is 7 feet less than the width. The perimeter of the parking lot is 150 feet. What are the length and width?

28. In this trapezoid, side v is twice as long as side w. Each side labeled t is 2 units longer than the side labeled w. The perimeter is 24. Find the lengths of t, v, and w.

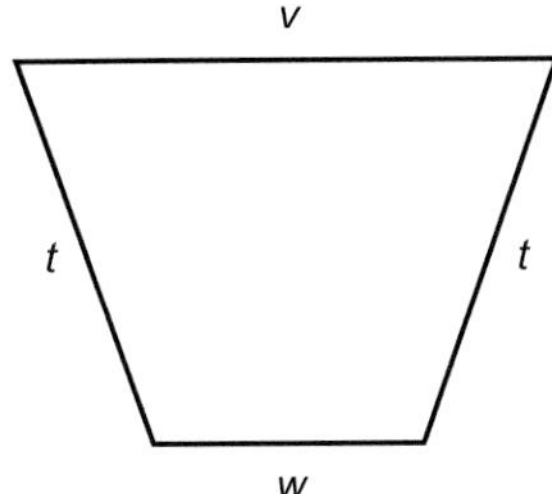

***29.** **Challenge** In this triangle, side x is twice the length of side y. Side y is 4 units shorter than side z. The perimeter of the triangle is 16. Give the length of each side.

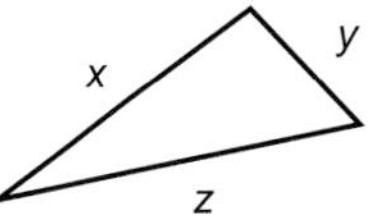

***30.** **Challenge** In this hexagon, each side labeled b is twice the length of side a. Each side labeled c is 7 units shorter than b. The perimeter of the hexagon is 67 centimeters. Give the lengths for a, b, and c.

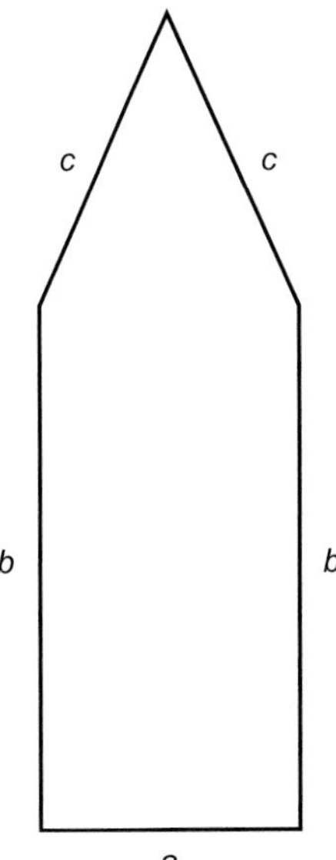

Variables on Both Sides

Some equations have variable terms on both sides of the equals sign.

When an equation has variables on both sides of the equals sign, use the properties of equality and inverse operations to isolate the variable terms on one side of the equation and isolate the constant terms on the other side.

Collecting Variables on One Side

In general, it does not matter on which side you isolate the variable terms. However, these two guidelines can help make your solutions easier:

- If one side of the equation contains only a variable term, isolate the variable terms on that side.
- If both sides of the equation contain both variable and constant terms, isolate the variable terms on the side with the greater variable coefficient.

Example 1 Solve.

A. $5x = 3x - 18$

Solution Because $5x$ is already isolated on the left side, it is best to isolate all of the variable terms on the left and isolate the constants on the right. Use the subtraction property of equality to "undo" the $3x$ that is currently added to -18 on the right side.

$5x = 3x - 18$	
$5x - 3x = 3x - 18 - 3x$	Subtract $3x$ from each side.
$5x - 3x = (3x - 3x) - 18$	Combine like terms.
$2x = -18$	Simplify.
$\frac{2x}{2} = -\frac{18}{2}$	Divide each side by 2.
$x = -9$	Simplify.

Check

$5x = 3x - 18$	
$5 \cdot (-9) \stackrel{?}{=} 3 \cdot (-9) - 18$	Substitute -9 for each x in the original equation and simplify.
$-45 \stackrel{?}{=} -27 - 18$	
$-45 = -45$ ✓	

The solution set is $\{-9\}$. ■

(continued)

B. $n - 4 = \frac{5n + 1}{2}$

Solution

$n - 4 = \frac{5n + 1}{2}$	
$2 \cdot (n - 4) = 2 \cdot \frac{5n + 1}{2}$	Multiply each side by 2.
$2n - 8 = 5n + 1$	Simplify.
$2n - 8 - 2n = 5n + 1 - 2n$	Subtract $2n$ from each side to isolate the variable terms on the right.
$(2n - 2n) - 8 = (5n - 2n) + 1$	Combine like terms.
$-8 = 3n + 1$	Simplify.
$-8 - 1 = 3n + 1 - 1$	Subtract 1 from each side to isolate the constant terms on the left.
$-9 = 3n$	Simplify.
$\frac{-9}{3} = \frac{3n}{3}$	Divide each side by 3.
$-3 = n$	Simplify.

The solution set is $\{-3\}$. ■

Simplifying First

As with any equation, it helps if you simplify each side first.

TIP

To shorten your solutions, you can combine consecutive steps of addition and subtraction or consecutive steps of multiplication and division.

Example 2 Solve $8(d + 2) - 36 = 2 + 6(1 - d)$.

Solution

$8(d + 2) - 36 = 2 + 6(1 - d)$	
$8d + 16 - 36 = 2 + 6 - 6d$	Distribute.
$8d - 20 = 8 - 6d$	Simplify.
$8d - 20 + 6d + 20 = 8 - 6d + 6d + 20$	Add $6d$ and 20 to each side.
$(8d + 6d) + (-20 + 20) = (-6d + 6d) + (8 + 20)$	Combine like terms.
$14d = 28$	Simplify.
$\frac{14d}{14} = \frac{28}{14}$	Divide each side by 14.
$d = 2$	Simplify.

The solution set is $\{2\}$. ■

Application: Number Problem

Example 3 Twice a number is 5 more than 3 times the number. Find the number.

Solution

Step 1 Write an equation.

Let n represent the number. Here, "more than" implies addition.

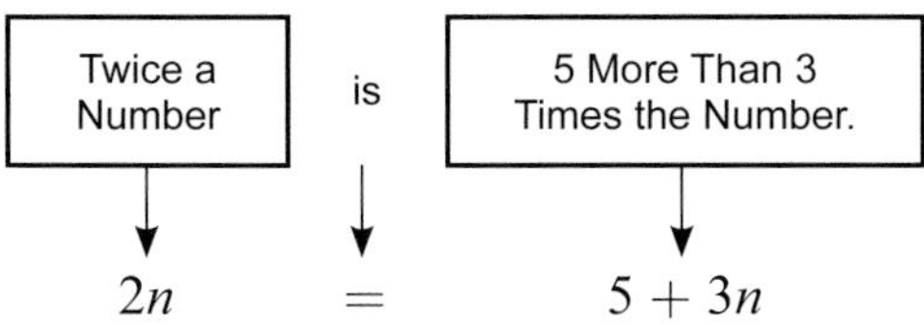

$$2n \quad = \quad 5 + 3n$$

Step 2 Solve the equation.

$$2n = 5 + 3n$$

$$2n - 3n = 5 + 3n - 3n$$ Subtract $3n$ from each side to isolate the variable terms on the left.

$$\frac{-1n}{-1} = \frac{5}{-1}$$ Divide each side by -1.

$$n = -5$$ Simplify.

Step 3 Check the solution.

$$2n = 3n + 5$$ Substitute -5 for each n in the original equation and simplify.

$$2 \cdot (-5) \stackrel{?}{=} 3 \cdot (-5) + 5$$

$$-10 \stackrel{?}{=} -15 + 5$$

$$-10 = -10 \checkmark$$

The number is -5. ■

Identifying Identities and Contradictions

Most of the equations that you have solved so far have had one or two solutions that make the equation true. But, it is possible for an equation to be true for any value of the variable or no value of the variable.

DEFINITIONS

An **identity** is an equation that is true for all values of the variable. An identity has infinitely many solutions, often represented as $\{x \mid x \in \mathbb{R}\}$.

A **contradiction** is an equation that is true for no values of the variable. A contradiction has no solutions, represented by the null set: { } or ∅.

You can recognize identities and contradictions after solving a given equation because an identity has no variables and the same quantity of constants on both sides and a contradiction has no variables and different quantities of constants on each side.

(continued)

Example 4 Identify whether each equation has zero, one, or infinitely many solutions.

A. $5x + 3 = 2(x + 3) - 3(1 - x)$

Solution Simplify each side. Then compare variables and constants.

$5x + 3 = 2(x + 3) - 3(1 - x)$	
$5x + 3 = 2x + 6 - 3 + 3x$	Distributive Property
$5x + 3 = 5x + 3$	Combine like terms and simplify.
$3 = 3$	Subtract $5x$ from each side.

This is an identity. There are infinitely many solutions. ■

B. $5x + 3 = 2(x + 3) - 3(2 - x)$

Solution

$5x + 3 = 2(x + 3) - 3(2 - x)$	
$5x + 3 = 2x + 6 - 6 + 3x$	Distributive Property
$5x + 3 = 5x$	Combine like terms and simplify.
$3 = 0$	Subtract $5x$ from each side.

This is a contradiction. There are zero solutions. ■

C. $5x + 3 = 2(x + 3) - 3(2 - 2x)$

Solution

$5x + 3 = 2(x + 3) - 3(2 - 2x)$	
$5x + 3 = 2x + 6 - 6 + 6x$	Distributive Property
$5x + 3 = 8x$	Combine like terms and simplify.
$3 = 3x$	Subtract $5x$ from each side.

Both sides have different quantities of x. This equation has one solution. (If you finish the solution, you'll find $x = 1$.) ■

THINK ABOUT IT

Example 4C is often called a *conditional equation* because it is true only for the condition that *x* is 1.

Problem Set

Identify whether each equation has zero, one, or infinitely many solutions.

1. $6\left(x + \frac{1}{3}\right) = 6x + \frac{2}{3}$
2. $3(2a + 1) - 2 = 2(a - 2) + 3(a + 1)$
3. $3(x - 2) + 2(x + 5) = 5(x + 1) + 1$
4. $4x + 2 = 2(x + 3) + 2(x - 2)$
5. $5y + 3 = 3(y - 3) - 2(y + 2)$
6. $3t - 2 = 5(t - 2) - 2(t - 4)$

Solve.

7. $3x = 16 - 5x$
8. $4y - 3 = 5y + 2$
9. $6m + 3 = \frac{2m - 4}{2}$
10. $5(a - 1) - 15 = 3(a + 2) + 4$
11. $3(p - 2) + 7 = 32 - 4(2p + 5)$
12. $7(w + 1) = 5(2w - 3) + 1$
13. $14 - x = 3x - 2$
14. $\frac{5x - 3}{2} = 3x + 8$
15. $a - 8 = \frac{6 + 5a}{3}$
16. $6n = 4n + 3$
17. $4(3 - y) = 6 - 2(1 - 3y)$
18. $7b - 20 = 3b + 12$
19. $7y + 2 = 3y - 10$
20. $\frac{2(2b + 1)}{3} = 3(b - 2)$
21. $3x + 10 = -2x$
22. $\frac{3t}{2} + 7 = 4t - 3$

*23. **Challenge** $18 - 2(3m - 1) = \frac{6 + 2(m + 3)}{2}$

Solve. For each problem:

A. Write an equation.
B. Use the equation to find the missing number.

24. Three times a number is 6 less than twice the number.
25. Three added to 4 times a number is equal to 7 less than 3 times the number.
26. Three more than twice a number is equal to the number.
27. Five more than twice a number is equal to 4 less than the number.
28. Five less than twice a number is equal to 3 added to the number.
29. Five less than one half a number is equal to 25 less than 3 times the number.

*30. **Challenge** Seven more than $\frac{2}{5}$ of a number is equal to 7 less than $\frac{3}{4}$ of the number.

Transforming Formulas

A formula is an equation that describes the relationship between two or more real-world quantities.

A formula uses variables to represent real-world quantities. Sometimes you need to rearrange the formula to make it convenient to calculate what you need.

Rewriting a Formula with One Transformation

The formula $d = rt$ relates distance d, rate or speed r, and time t. The standard formula helps you calculate distance when you know the speed and time. But, if you need to calculate the amount of time it takes to travel a given distance at a given speed, you can solve the formula for t.

Example 1 Solve the formula $d = rt$ for t.

Solution To solve for t, you need to isolate t. The expression rt indicates that t is multiplied by r. Use division to "undo" the multiplication.

$d = rt$

$\frac{d}{r} = \frac{rt}{r}$ Divide each side by r.

$\frac{d}{r} = t$ Simplify.

By the symmetric property, the transformed formula is $t = \frac{d}{r}$. ■

Rewriting a Formula with Multiple Transformations

Some formulas may require multiple transformations. For a rectangle, the formula $P = 2l + 2w$ relates the perimeter P, length l, and width w.

Example 2 Solve the formula $P = 2l + 2w$ for w.

Solution In the expression $2l + 2w$, w is first multiplied by 2 and then $2l$ is added to the product. "Undo" these operations in reverse order.

$P = 2l + 2w$

$P - 2l = 2l + 2w - 2l$ Subtract $2l$ from each side.

$P - 2l = 2w$ Simplify.

$\frac{P - 2l}{2} = \frac{2w}{2}$ Divide each side by 2.

$\frac{P - 2l}{2} = w$ Simplify.

The transformed formula is $w = \frac{P - 2l}{2}$ or $w = \frac{P}{2} - l$. ■

Applications: Perimeter and Distance

You can apply a transformed formula to a real-world application.

Example 3

A. Find the time it takes to drive 195 miles at a speed of 65 miles per hour.

Solution Use the transformed formula from Example 1.

$t = \frac{d}{r}$	Write the transformed formula.
$t = \frac{195}{65}$	Substitute 195 for d and 65 for r.
$t = 195 \cdot \frac{1}{65}$	To divide by a rate, multiply by the reciprocal.
$t = 3$	Simplify.

It takes 3 hours to drive 195 miles at 65 miles per hour.

Check Check your work by substituting the values into the original formula.

$d = rt$	Write the original formula.
$195 \stackrel{?}{=} 65 \cdot 3$	Substitute 195 for d, 65 for r, and 3 for t.
$195 = 195$ ✓	Simplify. ■

B. Find the width of a rectangle that has a perimeter of 49 inches and a length of 18 inches.

Solution Use the transformed formula from Example 2.

$w = \frac{P - 2l}{2}$	Write the transformed formula.
$w = \frac{49 - 2 \cdot 18}{2}$	Substitute 49 for P and 18 for l.
$w = \frac{49 - 36}{2}$	Multiply.
$w = \frac{13}{2}$	Subtract.
$w = 6.5$	Divide.

The width of a rectangle is 6.5 inches when the perimeter is 49 inches and the length is 18 inches.

Check

$P = 2l + 2w$	Write the original formula.
$49 \stackrel{?}{=} 2 \cdot 18 + 2 \cdot 6.5$	Substitute 49 for P, 18 for l, and 6.5 for w.
$49 \stackrel{?}{=} 36 + 13$	Multiply.
$49 = 49$ ✓	Add. ■

(continued)

You don't need to solve for the desired variable to use a formula. For instance, you can solve Example 2B by substituting the perimeter and length into the original formula and solving for w. Notice, however, that you will still subtract and then divide.

$$\begin{aligned} P &= 2l + 2w \\ 49 &= 2 \cdot 18 + 2w \\ 49 &= 36 + 2w \\ 49 - 36 &= 36 + 2w - 36 \\ 13 &= 2w \\ \frac{13}{2} &= \frac{2w}{2} \\ 6.5 &= w \end{aligned}$$

Using a transformed formula saves you from doing the same transformations over and over again.

Application: Unit Conversion

If you need to use a formula repeatedly to find the value of a particular variable, it is very helpful to solve for the desired variable first.

Example 4 The Celsius and Fahrenheit temperature scales are related by the formula $C = \frac{5}{9}(F - 32)$, where C is a temperature in degrees Celsius and F is the corresponding temperature in degrees Fahrenheit. Use the formula to find the Fahrenheit temperatures that correspond to the Celsius temperatures 0°, 25°, 50°, 75°, and 100°.

Solution

Step 1 Because you are computing several values in degrees Fahrenheit, transform the formula. To solve the formula for F, "undo" the operations on the original equation.

$$C = \frac{5}{9}(F - 32)$$

$$\frac{9}{5} \cdot C = \frac{9}{5} \cdot \frac{5}{9}(F - 32) \qquad \text{Multiply each side by } \frac{9}{5}.$$

$$\frac{9}{5}C = F - 32 \qquad \text{Simplify.}$$

$$\frac{9}{5}C + 32 = F - 32 + 32 \qquad \text{Add 32 to each side.}$$

$$\frac{9}{5}C + 32 = F \qquad \text{Simplify.}$$

Step 2 Check the transformed formula.

To check the transformed formula, substitute the new formula into the original. If the equation results in an identity, the formula is correct.

$C = \frac{5}{9}(F - 32)$ Write the original formula.

$C \stackrel{?}{=} \frac{5}{9}\left(\frac{9}{5}C + 32 - 32\right)$ Substitute $\frac{9}{5}C + 32$ for F.

$C \stackrel{?}{=} \frac{5}{9} \cdot \frac{9}{5}C$ Subtract.

$C = C\ \checkmark$ Simplify.

Step 3 Use the transformed formula. A table helps organize your work.

Temperature in Degrees Celsius (°C)	Substitute into the formula $F = \frac{9}{5}C + 32$ and simplify.	Temperature in Degrees Fahrenheit (°F)
0	$F = \frac{9}{5} \cdot 0 + 32 = 0 + 32 = 32$	32
25	$F = \frac{9}{5} \cdot 25 + 32 = 45 + 32 = 77$	77
50	$F = \frac{9}{5} \cdot 50 + 32 = 90 + 32 = 122$	122
75	$F = \frac{9}{5} \cdot 75 + 32 = 135 + 32 = 167$	167
100	$F = \frac{9}{5} \cdot 100 + 32 = 180 + 32 = 212$	212

The Celsius temperatures 0°, 25°, 50°, 75°, and 100° respectively correspond to the Fahrenheit temperatures 32°, 77°, 122°, 167°, and 212°. ■

Problem Set

Solve the formula for the indicated variable.

1. $A = lw; w$
2. $V = lwh; h$
3. $P = 2l + 2w; l$
4. $y = mx + b; x$
5. $a(b - c) = x; a$
6. $I = prt; r$
7. $C = 2\pi r; r$
8. $ax + 5 = by - 10; x$
9. $b(c - d) = y; c$
10. $\frac{x}{a} = \frac{b}{c}; c$

Solve. For each problem:

A. Solve the formula for the desired variable.

B. Use the transformed formula to solve the problem.

C. State your answer in a complete sentence.

11. Use $A = \frac{1}{2}bh$ to find the height of a triangle that has an area of 180 square inches and a base of 20 inches.

12. The simple interest formula is $I = prt$, where I represents interest, p represents principal, r represents interest rate, and t represents time in years. Determine the principal given the interest of \$10, with an interest rate of 8% for 2 years.

13. The volume of a rectangular prism can be computed by using the formula $V = lwh$. Find the width of a prism that has a volume of 200 cubic feet, length of 4 feet, and height of 25 feet.

14. Find the radius of a circle with an area of 25 square centimeters. Use $A = \pi r^2$ and round to the nearest hundredth.

15. Determine the height of a cone with a volume of 50 cubic centimeters and a radius of 10 centimeters. Use the formula $V = \frac{1}{3}\pi r^2 h$. Give your answer to four decimal places.

16. Use the formula $y = mx + b$ to compute the slope of a line m if $x = 5$, $y = 7$, and $b = 10$.

17. The surface area of a cylinder is determined by the formula $S = L + 2\pi r^2$, where S represents surface area, L represents lateral area, and r represents radius. Find the lateral area (to the nearest hundredth) of a tube with a surface area of 200 square inches and a radius of 4 inches.

18. In any triangle, the sum of the three interior angles equals 180° which is represented by the formula $x + y + z = 180$. Determine the measure of angle x if angle y measures 42° and angle z measures 53°.

19. If the odds in favor of an event is $m : n$, then the probability of the event occurring is $p = \frac{m}{m + n}$. Determine m if $n = 2$ and the probability is 25%.

20. The measures of the acute angles of an isosceles right triangle can be computed using $2(x + 45) = y$, where x represents the measure of each equal acute angle and y is the sum of the measures of all angles in the triangle. Find the measure of each acute angle if the sum of all angles equals 180°.

21. z is directly proportional to both x and y if $z = kxy$, where k is a constant. Find x if $y = 5$, $z = 40$, and $k = 2$.

22. Many teachers use weighted averages to calculate grades. If homework is worth 20%, quizzes are worth 40%, and tests are worth 40%, the formula $A = 0.20h + 0.40(q + t)$ could be used to compute a grade where A represents grade average, h represents homework points, q represents quiz points, and t represents test points. Find Aba's test points if her grade average was 95, homework points were 100, and quiz points were 90.

23. The volume of a pyramid with a rectangular base is found by using the formula $V = \frac{1}{3}lwh$, where V represents volume, l represents base length, w represents base width, and h represents height. If the volume of a pyramid is 1000 cubic feet and the width and length are each 10 feet, find the height.

24. Solve the linear equation $Ax + By = C$ for x. Then determine the value of x given $B = 4$, $C = 9$, $y = 1$, and $A = 3$.

25. The formula for the area of a trapezoid is $A = \frac{1}{2}h(b_1 + b_2)$, where h is the height and b_1 and b_2 are the base lengths. What is the second base length of the trapezoid if the height is 5 inches, one base length is 6 inches, and the area is 20 square inches?

***26.** **Challenge** If the base lengths of a trapezoid are 3 and 5, then what values of the height would give an area between 20 and 30?

***27.** **Challenge** To compute the average A of five numbers a, b, c, d, and e, divide their sum by 5. If the average of the numbers 4, b, c, 19, and 3 is 14, find the sum of b and c.

***28.** **Challenge** The volume of a cube can be found using the formula $V = s^3$, where s represents the side length of the cube. What is the side length of a cube that has a volume of 216 cubic inches?

Estimating Solutions

Not every equation needs an exact solution. When you want a solution that is close to the exact answer, but doesn't need to be precise, rounding can help.

Rounding as the Last Step

Many equations result in "messy" solutions. Use rounding to find an answer that is close to the exact solution. One simple way to use rounding is to round the answer at the last step.

Example 1 Solve each equation. Round to the nearest tenth.

A. $3.4 = 5.2x$

Solution

$3.4 = 5.2x$	
$\frac{3.4}{5.2} = \frac{5.2x}{5.2}$	Divide each side by 5.2
$0.6538461538\ldots = x$	Use a calculator to evalute $3.4 \div 5.2$.
$0.7 \approx x$	Round to the nearest tenth.

Check Because the solution is rounded, the two sides of the equation will not be exactly equal when you check. But they should be reasonably close.

$3.4 = 5.2x$	Write the original equation.
$3.4 \stackrel{?}{=} 5.2 \cdot 0.7$	Substitute 0.7 for x.
$3.4 \approx 3.64$	The two sides are approximately equal.

The solution is approximately 0.7. ■

THINK ABOUT IT

If you had to answer Example 1 with an exact solution, you could multiply to clear the decimals and then reduce the fraction.

$$\frac{3.4}{5.2} \cdot \frac{10}{10} = \frac{34}{52} = \frac{17}{26}$$

Or, if you notice that the decimal has a repeating pattern, you could use an overbar to state it exactly as $0.6\overline{538461}$.

B. $6.21(2.1 - n) = 3.5$

Solution

$6.21(2.1 - n) = 3.5$	
$13.041 - 6.21n = 3.5$	Distribute. Use a calculator to evaluate $6.21 \cdot 2.1$.
$13.041 - 6.21n - 13.041 = 3.5 - 13.041$	Subtract 13.041 from each side.
$-6.21n = -9.541$	Simplify. (Use a calculator if necessary.)
$\frac{-6.21n}{-6.21} = \frac{-9.541}{-6.21}$	Divide each side by -6.21.
$n = 1.536392915\ldots$	Use a calculator to evaluate $-9.541 \div -6.21$.
$n \approx 1.5$	Round to the nearest tenth.

(continued)

Check

$6.21(2.1 - n) = 3.5$ Write the original equation.

$6.21(2.1 - 1.5) \stackrel{?}{=} 3.5$ Substitute 1.5 for n.

$6.21 \cdot 0.6 \stackrel{?}{=} 3.5$ Simplify.

$3.726 \approx 3.5$ The two sides are approximately equal.

The solution is approximately 1.5. ■

TIP

Whenever possible, it is best that you round only in the last step of your solution so that you introduce round-off error only once.

Whenever you round a value you create round-off error. In Example 1, round-off error is introduced in the last step of each solution; that's the reason each solution does not exactly check.

Rounding as the First Step

Notice that the solutions in Example 1 require the use of a calculator or messy long division. If you don't have a calculator, you may still be able to use mental math if you first round constants and coefficients to the nearest integer. However, because you round several values, this strategy introduces more round-off error, often making your solution less accurate.

You can use a mental-math strategy for solving the same equations from Example 1.

Example 2 Estimate the solution to each equation by first rounding constants and coefficients to the nearest integer.

A. $3.4 = 5.2x$

Solution

$3.4 = 5.2x$

$3 \approx 5x$ Round to the nearest integers.

$\frac{3}{5} \approx \frac{5x}{5}$ Divide each side by 5.

$0.6 \approx x$ Use mental math. $\left(\frac{3}{5} = \frac{6}{10} = 0.6\right)$

Check This check is shown for reference only. If you round as the first step because you don't have a calculator, you'll probably skip the check.

$3.4 = 5.2x$ Write the original equation.

$3.4 \stackrel{?}{=} 5.2 \cdot 0.6$ Substitute 0.6 for x.

$3.4 \approx 3.12$ The two sides are approximately equal.

The solution is approximately 0.6. ■

B. $6.21(2.1 - n) = 3.5$

Solution

$6.21(2.1 - n) = 3.5$	
$6(2 - n) \approx 4$	Round to the nearest integers.
$12 - 6n \approx 4$	Distribute.
$12 - 6n - 12 \approx 4 - 12$	Subtract 12 from each side.
$-6n \approx -8$	Simplify.
$\frac{-6n}{-6} \approx \frac{-8}{-6}$	Divide each side by -6.
$n \approx 1.3333\ldots$	Use mental math $\left(\frac{-8}{-6} = \frac{4}{3} = 1\frac{1}{3} = 1.\overline{3}\right)$
$n \approx 1.3$	Round to the nearest tenth. (A fourth round-off error.)

Check

$6.21(2.1 - n) = 3.5$	Write the original equation.
$6.21(2.1 - 1.3) \stackrel{?}{=} 3.5$	Substitute 1.3 for n.
$6.21 \cdot 0.8 \stackrel{?}{=} 3.5$	Simplify.
$4.968 \not\approx 3.5$	The two sides are *not* approximately equal.

Because the process of this solution involved four round-off errors, 1.3 is an inaccurate estimate of the solution. If you can find a calculator, it would be best to use the method shown in Example 1B instead. ■

Application: Splitting the Total Cost

Examples 1 and 2 showed situations when it was practical to approximate solutions, because it made your solution process "easier" or your final solution "nicer." In many real-world situations, it can be convenient or necessary to round and estimate your solution.

When solving applications involving money, consider the context of the problem when deciding how to round.

Example 3 Four friends go to a restaurant and order a "family dinner" that includes appetizers, entrees, and drinks. The family dinner costs $34.96.

A. The friends want to leave a 15% tip. What is the total cost of the family dinner including the tip?

Solution

Step 1 Write an equation. Let t represent the total cost.

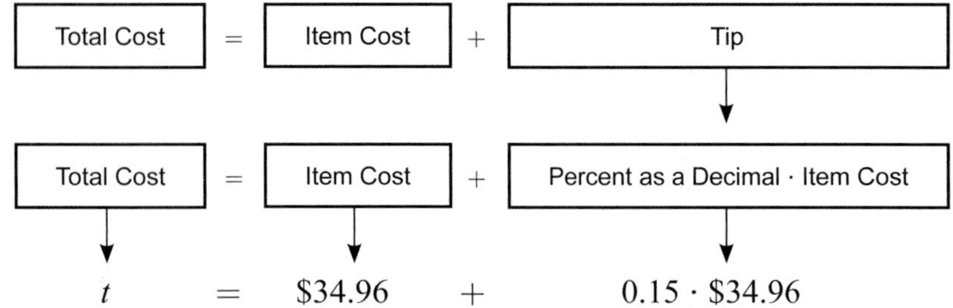

(continued)

Step 2 Simplify the right side of the equation.

$t = 34.96 + 0.15 \cdot 34.96$	
$t = 34.96 + 5.244$	Use a calculator to simplify.
$t = 40.204$	Add.
$t \approx 40.20$	Round to the nearest hundredth, or the nearest cent.

Step 3 Check the solution.

$t = 34.96 + 0.15 \cdot 34.96$	
$40.20 \stackrel{?}{=} 34.96 + 0.15 \cdot 34.96$	
$40.20 \approx 40.204$	Both sides are approximately equal.

The total cost of the family dinner with a 15% tip is \$40.20. ■

B. The four friends divide the total cost evenly. Each friend has only dollars and quarters. What is the closest estimate for the amount paid by each friend if the estimate is within one quarter per person going over the price as little as possible?

Solution

Step 1 Write an equation. Let a represent the amount each person owes.

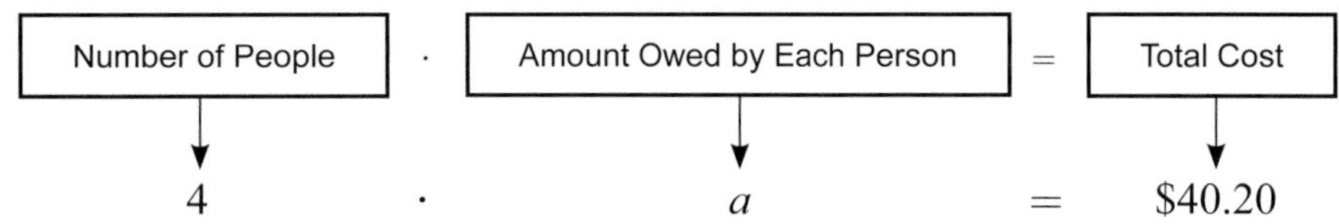

Step 2 Solve the equation.

$4a = 40.20$	Divide each side by 4.
$\frac{4a}{4} = \frac{40.20}{4}$	Use a calculator to divide.
$a = 10.05$	

THINK ABOUT IT

The friends could also decide that one would pay \$10.25, while the other three would pay \$10.

If each friend only has quarters and dollars, then they could each pay \$10.25 to cover the bill.

Step 3 Check the solution.

$4a = 40.20$	
$4 \cdot 10.25 \stackrel{?}{=} 40.20$	
$41.00 \approx 40.20$	Both sides are approximately equal.

Each friend owes \$10.25, but there will be \$0.80 left over for a bigger tip. ■

Problem Set

Solve each equation. Round your answer to the nearest tenth.

1. $1.4x = 12.7$
2. $5.9x - 1 = 12.7 + 6.2$
3. $7.25(x - 2.9) = 6.7$
4. $25.8 = 2.99x + 1$
5. $123.5x + 87.3 = -56.3$
6. $4.44(2x - 3.57) = 32.99$
7. $33.8 = 7.6 - 2.06x$
8. $1.01 = 2.03x$
9. $-11.0(x + 3.33) = 12.7$
10. $8.88(x - 3.2) = 7.93(x + 10.2)$
11. $111.78 = 67.8(2.7 - 4x)$

Estimate the solution to each equation by first rounding the constants and coefficients to the nearest integer.

12. $17.6 = -2.45x$
13. $15.67 - 23.56 = 34.18x$
14. $6.58(3.42 - x) = 19.7$
15. $11.23(75.34 - 3x) = 120.34$
16. $8.5(x + 7.8) = 90.23$
17. $22.09 = 2.01x$
18. $3.12(x + 0.2) = 5.5(x - 3.45)$
19. $10.23 = 1 - 5.07x$
20. $27.09 = 19.8(2.34 - x)$
21. $23.67(8.25 - x) = 15.4(4.45 + x)$
22. $34.89 = 2.06x - 12$

Solve. Determine if the given estimate is reasonable. Defend your decision using good estimations, and state your answer in a complete sentence.

23. Sal goes to the grocery store with $20. He buys bread for $2.05, milk for $1.99, candy for $0.99, chicken for $6.25, and cat food for $4.99. The state sales tax is 5%, and Sal expects to receive about $3 in change.

24. Gas costs $1.67 per gallon.

    A. Is $20 enough to fill a 13-gallon gas tank, if the tank was empty?

    B. If a customer receives a 2 cent per gallon rebate, how much money is saved?

25. Cleve's costume required 6 yards of fur at $8.99 per yard, and 5.25 yards of felt at $1.25 per yard. He expected to spend about $60 on his costume.

26. Skip mails three packages at the post office that weigh 10.1, 10.5, and 10.9 pounds. The post office that Skip uses rounds the weight of a package to the nearest pound to determine the price of shipment. It costs $2 to mail a package that weighs 10 pounds and $2.50 to mail a package that weighs 11 pounds.

    A. How much did Skip pay to ship each package?

    B. Was the total amount Skip spent for shipping under $10?

27. The long jump results of students in one gym class were posted on the wall. Was the average long jump for the class about 7 feet?

Student	Jump (feet)
Karla	6.56
Homer	7.56
Roberto	8.99
Al	5.67
Keisha	7.23
Morgan	8.23

28. William and three friends estimated the height of their school building.

Friend	Height (feet)
William	50
Erie	42
Juanita	35
Nowan	22

A. What is the range (the difference between the greatest and the least) of the estimates?

B. If the actual height is twice Erie's estimate decreased by Nowan's guess, what is the height of the building?

C. Were any of the estimated heights reasonable?

***29. Challenge** Simone's quarter grades are 82.5, 94.7, and 87.9. Simone thinks she needs a 95 in the last quarter to receive at least a 90% final course grade.

***30. Challenge** Ian swam the 100 meter race in 0.84 seconds. This is 0.02 seconds faster than his last race. If he finished 0.05 seconds before his closest opponent in the last race, was the race time for this opponent during the last race about 1 second?

Applications: Cost Problems

You can solve many applications involving unit prices and total cost by writing and solving an equation.

You have used multiplication and division equations to solve unit-price applications that involve one item. Now that you know how to solve equations with multiple transformations, you can solve more advanced cost problems that involve multiple items.

Mix of Products

In cost problems, your variable does not have to represent a unit price. It may represent the total cost or the quantity of an item.

Example 1 Mrs. Rivera goes to a local grocery store to buy trail mix ingredients for a hiking trip she is planning. The store sells small bags of mixed nuts for \$1.49 and small bags of dried fruit for \$0.99. Her receipt shows that she bought 17 items for a total of \$22.83. How many bags of mixed nuts and how many bags of dried fruit did Mrs. Rivera buy?

Solution Use the Problem-Solving Plan from Unit 1 to solve cost problems.

Step 1 *Identify* This problem involves two unknown quantities: the number of bags of mixed nuts and the number of bags of dried fruit.

Step 2 *Strategize* Use logic and algebra to define both quantities with just one variable.

Let m represent the number of bags of mixed nuts.

You know that Mrs. Rivera bought 17 items. So you can write an equation that helps you define the number of bags of dried fruit.

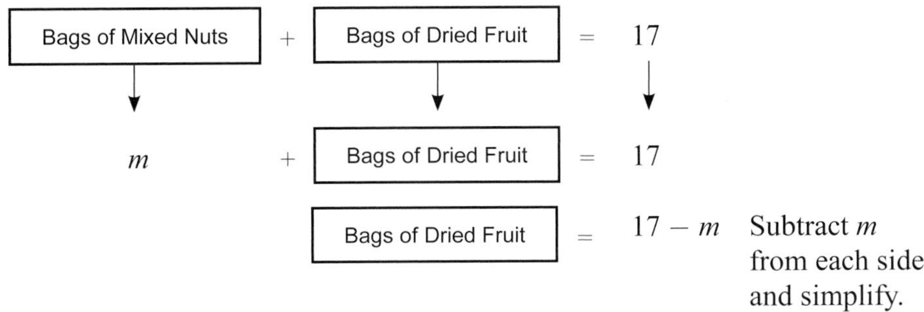

TIP

Another way to arrive at the expression 17 − *m* is to think of starting with all 17 items and taking away the *m* bags of mixed nuts. You are left with the bags of dried fruit.

Let $17 - m$ represent the number of bags of dried fruit.

(continued)

Step 3 *Set Up* Write a cost equation.

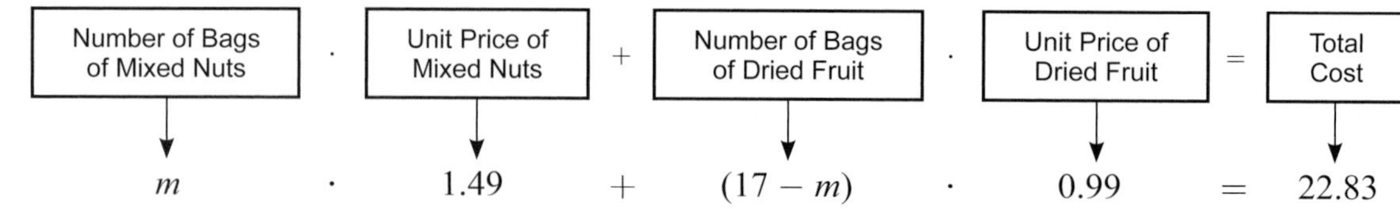

$$m \quad \cdot \quad 1.49 \quad + \quad (17 - m) \quad \cdot \quad 0.99 \quad = \quad 22.83$$

You can use the commutative property of multiplication to rewrite the equation as $1.49m + 0.99(17 - m) = 22.83$.

Step 4 *Solve*

$1.49m + 0.99(17 - m) = 22.83$	
$1.49m + 16.83 - 0.99m = 22.83$	Distribute.
$(1.49m - 0.99m) + 16.83 = 22.83$	Combine like terms.
$0.50m + 16.83 = 22.83$	Simplify.
$0.50m + 16.83 - 16.83 = 22.83 - 16.83$	Subtract 16.83 from each side.
$0.50m = 6$	Simplify.
$\frac{0.50m}{0.50} = \frac{6}{0.50}$	Divide each side by 0.50.
$m = 12$	Simplify.

If $m = 12$, then $17 - m = 17 - 12 = 5$.

So, Mrs. Rivera bought 12 bags of mixed nuts and 5 bags of dried fruit.

Step 5 *Check*

$1.49m + 0.99(17 - m) = 22.83$	Write the original cost equation.
$1.49 \cdot 12 + 0.99(17 - 12) \stackrel{?}{=} 22.83$	Substitute 12 for *m*.
$1.49 \cdot 12 + 0.99 \cdot 5 \stackrel{?}{=} 22.83$	Simplify. This step also confirms the quantity of 5.
$17.88 + 4.95 \stackrel{?}{=} 22.83$	Simplify.
$22.83 = 22.83$ ✓	The solution checks. ■

Different Wage Rates

To solve wage problems, use steps similar to those used to solve cost problems.

Example 2 Bradley tutors students in mathematics and science. Last week he tutored 8 hours in math and 15 hours in science, and he earned \$200. If Bradley earns \$10 per hour for math tutoring, how much does he earn per hour for science tutoring?

Solution

Step 1 *Identify* Find the dollar amount Bradley earns per hour tutoring science.

Step 2 *Strategize* Let *s* represent Bradley's charge per hour, in dollars, for science tutoring.

Step 3 *Set Up* Write an equation.

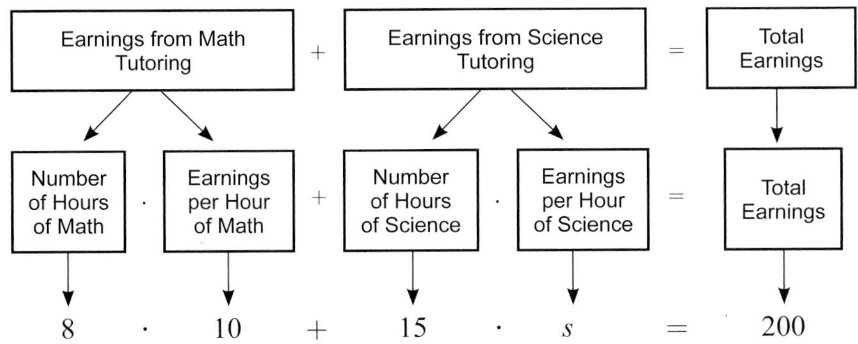

Step 4 *Solve*

$8 \cdot 10 + 15s = 200$	
$80 + 15s = 200$	Multiply to simplify the constant term on the left side.
$80 + 15s - 80 = 200 - 80$	Subtract 80 from each side.
$15s + (80 - 80) = 200 - 80$	Combine like terms.
$15s = 120$	Simplify.
$\frac{15s}{15} = \frac{120}{15}$	Divide each side by 15.

Bradley earns \$8 per hour for science tutoring.

Step 5 *Check*

$8 \cdot 10 + 15s = 200$	Write the original equation.
$8 \cdot 10 + 15 \cdot 8 \stackrel{?}{=} 200$	Substitute 8 for s.
$80 + 120 \stackrel{?}{=} 200$	Simplify.
$200 = 200$ ✓	The solution checks. ■

> **THINK ABOUT IT**
>
> **It is also possible to set up and solve this equation with units included.**
>
> $$8\text{ hr}\left(\frac{\$10}{1\text{hr}}\right) + s \cdot 15\text{ hr} = \$200$$
> $$\$80 + 15s\text{ hr} = \$200$$
> $$15s\text{ hr} = \$120$$
> $$s = \frac{\$8}{1\text{ hr}}$$

Estimating in a Cost Problem

Some cost problems may result in "messy" solutions. This happens because dollar amounts are usually rounded to the nearest cent. Apply your estimation skills in these situations.

Example 3 Nectarines cost \$2.99 per pound. Tenika buys a single nectarine for \$0.75. How much does the nectarine weigh to the nearest hundredth of a pound?

Solution

Step 1 *Identify* Find the weight of the nectarine.

Step 2 *Strategize* Let w represent the nectarine's weight in pounds.

Step 3 *Set Up* Write an equation. Total cost is the product of the unit price and the weight. $2.99w = 0.75$

(continued)

Step 4 *Solve*

$2.99w = 0.75$

$\frac{2.99w}{2.99} = \frac{0.75}{2.99}$ Divide each side by 2.99.

$w = 0.2508361204\ldots$ Use a calculator.

$w \approx 0.25$ Round to hundredths.

Tenika's nectarine weighs about 0.25 pounds.

Step 5 *Check* If the nectarine weighs exactly 0.25 pounds, the total cost would be $2.99 \cdot 0.25 = 0.7475$. The grocery store would round this number up to \$0.75. ■

Problem Set

Solve. For each problem:

A. Define variables for the unknowns.
B. Write and simplify an equation to model the problem.
C. Solve the equation.
D. Give your answer in a complete sentence.

1. A restaurant stocked up on pancake mix to accommodate its breakfast customers. Buckwheat mix costs \$2.30 per pound and whole wheat mix costs \$1.85 per pound. The restaurant bought a total of 23 pounds of mix for \$46.60. How many pounds of each mix were purchased?

2. Selma's cell phone plan charges \$0.14 per minute. The first month her total cost was \$6.72. How many minutes did she use?

3. Josh visits an organic grocery store to buy fruit. He fills a grocery bag with pomegranates and oranges that weigh 15 pounds. Pomegranates cost \$1.56 per pound and oranges cost \$1.40 per pound. If Josh's bag costs \$21.64, how much of each fruit did he buy?

4. Mr. Goldberg has \$3.30 in change in his pocket. He knows he has only dimes and quarters and that he has 5 more dimes than quarters. How many of each coin does he have?

5. Mr. Garcia hires a contractor to build a path that is 3.5 feet long. The contractor charges Mr. Garcia \$42.50. How much did Mr. Garcia pay per foot for the job?

6. Mrs. Fuller is building a deck. The composite deck material cost \$9.20 per foot and the railing cost \$6.40 per foot. If Mrs. Fuller paid \$1998 for 240 feet of materials, how much of each material did she buy?

7. A recipe for soup requires 8 ounces of broth for each serving. How many servings can be made with 144 ounces of broth?

8. Roberta uses a taxi to commute to work. Taxi A charges \$2.60 per mile and Taxi B charges \$3.25 per mile. Whenever Taxi A is busy with other commuters, Roberta uses Taxi B. Last week, Roberta rode in taxis for 26 miles and spent \$73.45 on taxi fare, excluding tip. How many miles did each taxi take her?

9. Juan chooses 4 items for his main course, 1 drink, and 1 dessert in a restaurant. The total cost of the meal is \$9.80. If each main course item costs \$1.10 and the dessert costs \$0.50 more than the drink, what are the costs of Juan's drink and dessert?

10. Shakisha earned $760 last week in a clothing store. She earns $20 per hour working the register and receives time and a half for her management training. Given that Shakisha worked 36 hours last week, how many register and management training hours did she work?

11. Suri chooses fabric at a sewing store for $7.99 per yard. She paid $1 for the amount she needed. How much fabric did she buy?

12. Uri earns $1 for each of his assigned household chores. His parents also pay him $0.70 for every extra chore completed. If he earned $24.20 last month by completing a total of 32 chores, how many extra jobs did he complete?

13. Maddie's piggy bank contains dimes, nickels, and pennies. She has 3 more nickels than dimes and 5 fewer pennies than dimes. If she has a total of $2.02, how many of each coin does she have?

14. At the store, coffee sells for $3.10 per pound. Sarah bought $3.88 worth of coffee. How much coffee did she buy?

15. Merv has two jobs. He earns a salary of $45,000 per year as an accountant and $10.50 per hour at his part-time job. Merv earned $48,570 last year. How many part-time hours did he work?

16. Ghamba is wallpapering a room in her house. Regular wallpaper rolls cost $12.99 per roll and border rolls cost $5.99 per roll. If she bought 12 rolls and paid $134.88, how many rolls of each type did she buy?

17. Lew spent $26.98 on a shirt and shorts. If the shirt cost $5 less than the shorts, how much did each item cost?

18. Ori drove 203.75 miles while on vacation. Assuming he only drove at the set speeds 55 miles per hour and 40 miles per hour, how long did he travel at each speed if he drove for 4.25 hours?

19. Uniqua invested $10,000. She invested part in a certificate of deposit (CD) that earned 9% interest per year and part in a land venture that earned 8% per year. Her annual yield was $850. How much did Uniqua invest in the CD and how much did she put in the land venture?

20. Jana burns 154 calories per hour on her exercise machine. In how many minutes will she burn 64 calories?

21. Annika bought a jar of vitamins at the health food store for $10. How much did each vitamin cost if the jar contained 125 pills?

22. Ed bought a new car with 12 accessories. Each accessory cost either $23.99 or $120.84. If he paid $675.28 for all accessories, how many of each type did he buy?

23. Bryan works at a mall phone store that received a shipment of two types of phones. Regular cell phones cost $99 and camera cell phones cost $110. If Bryan sold a total of 62 phones for a total of $6380, how many of each type did he sell?

24. Kareem bought a bag of 25 bolts and nuts at the hardware store. Bolts cost $0.10 per item and nuts cost $0.05 per item. If he paid $2.15, how many nuts and how many bolts did he buy?

25. Celia works as a store clerk in two different stores. In the video store, she earns $5.75 an hour and in the grocery store she earns $7.25 per hour. If she earned $214 last week while working a total of 32 hours, how many hours did she work at each store?

26. Twelve ears of corn cost $4.99. Sue paid $2.91. How many ears of corn did she buy?

27. Fudge costs $7.99 per pound. Brian paid $1.33 for one piece. Assuming each piece has an equal weight, what is the weight of one piece?

28. Bonita is a magazine editor. Last week she proofread for 35 hours and rewrote pages for 5 hours and earned $900. If she earned $40 per hour for rewriting, how much did she earn per hour for proofreading?

29. Gino owns a pizza place. His specialty pizza consists of 12 toppings. Vegetable toppings cost $0.90 each and meat toppings cost $0.75 each. If this pizza costs $16.99, which includes a $2 profit and the cost of other ingredients at $4.79, how many toppings of each kind were used?

30. Every week, Gisriel works in a music store for 20 hours, plays in a band for 5 hours, and teaches music for 15 hours. He earns $20 per hour at the music store and $50 per hour teaching music. If he makes $1600 per week, how much does he earn per hour playing in the band?

Inequalities

You can use inequality symbols to compare two expressions that are not equal.

REMEMBER

An inequality is a number sentence that includes one of the symbols $<$, $>$, $\leq$, or $\geq$

Translating Sentences into Inequalities

Example 1 Translate each sentence into an inequality.

A. Four plus one is greater than one minus two.

Solution

$\underbrace{\text{Four plus one}}_{4+1}\quad\underbrace{\text{is greater than}}_{>}\quad\underbrace{\text{one minus two.}}_{1-2}$

The inequality is: $4 + 1 > 1 - 2$, or $5 > -1$. ■

B. Seven and two-tenths minus three is less than two times three.

Solution

$\underbrace{\text{Seven and two-tenths minus three}}_{7.2-3}\quad\underbrace{\text{is less than}}_{<}\quad\underbrace{\text{two times three.}}_{2\cdot 3}$

The inequality is: $7.2 - 3 < 2 \cdot 3$, or $4.2 < 6$. ■

C. Two times two is less than or equal to two squared.

Solution

$\underbrace{\text{Two times two}}_{2\cdot 2}\quad\underbrace{\text{is less than or equal to}}_{\leq}\quad\underbrace{\text{two squared.}}_{2^2}$

The inequality is: $2 \cdot 2 \leq 2^2$, or $4 \leq 4$. ■

Determining the Truth of an Inequality

Example 2 Determine whether each inequality is true or false.

A. $8 > 5$

Solution Translate each inequality into a sentence and use your number sense to determine its truth.

$8 > 5 \leftrightarrow$ "Eight is greater than five."

Yes, eight is greater than five. This is a true inequality. ■

B. $2.7 < -6$

Solution

$2.7 < -6 \leftrightarrow$ "Two and seven-tenths is less than negative six."

No positive number is less than a negative number. This is a false inequality. ■

C. $-3 \geq -3$

Solution

$-3 \geq -3 \leftrightarrow$ "Negative three is greater than or equal to negative three."

Although negative three is not greater than negative three, the two numbers are equal to each other. This is a true inequality. ■

Determining Whether a Given Value Is a Solution of an Inequality

Like equations, inequalities may contain variable terms. A **solution of an inequality** is a value of the variable that makes the equation true.

Example 3 Determine whether $x = -5$ is a solution of $x \leq -9$.

Solution Substitute the value and determine the truth of the inequality.

$x \leq -9$

$-5 \overset{?}{\leq} -9$ Substitute -5 for x.

$-5 \nleq -9$ False. If necessary, use a number-line graph to see that -5 is actually greater (farther right) than -9.

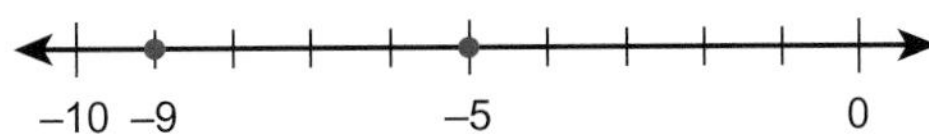

No, $x = -5$ is not a solution of the inequality $x \leq -9$. ■

An inequality frequently has infinitely many solutions. For example, the solutions of $x \geq 2$ are all real numbers greater than or equal to 2, including 2, 2.001, 3, 3000, and 1,000,000, to name a few. You could never list all of the numbers greater than or equal to 2, but you can represent the solution set of $x \geq 2$ on a number-line graph.

DEFINITION

The **graph of an inequality** is a display of all possible solutions of the inequality.

REMEMBER

A ray is part of a line that starts at an endpoint and extends infinitely in one direction.

If you try to plot all of the real numbers greater than or equal to 2, the points cover all of the number line to the right of 2. This creates a ray with endpoint 2. Because 2 is a solution to $x \geq 2$, it is shown as a closed circle.

$x \geq 2$

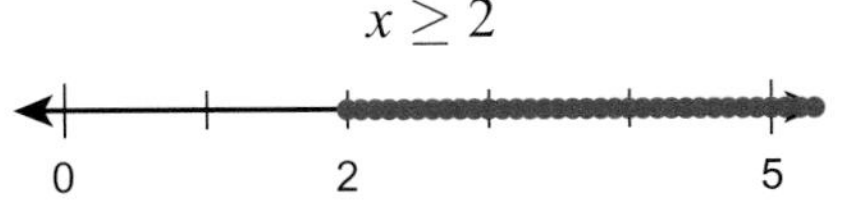

becomes

$x \geq 2$

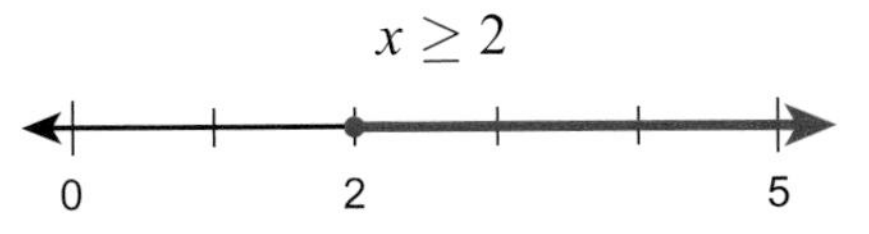

(continued)

How would you graph $x > 2$? All the solutions of $x > 2$ are solutions of $x \geq 2$. The only difference between the solutions is the endpoint since 2 is not greater than 2. Therefore, the graph of $x > 2$ is the same ray as the graph of $x \geq 2$ but the endpoint is an open circle to show that 2 is not a solution.

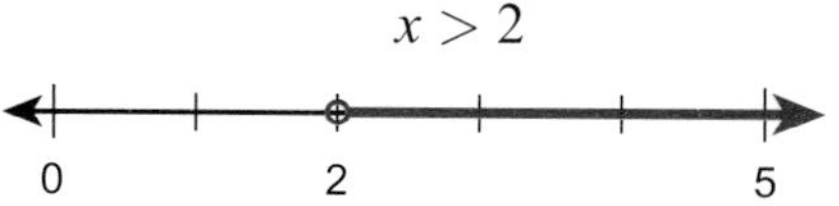

For "less than" inequalities, the ray is directed to the left.

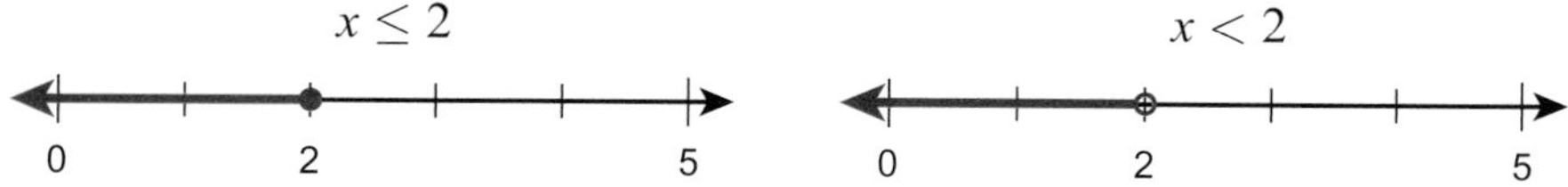

> **TIP**
>
> **When the variable is isolated on the left side of an inequality, the inequality symbol mimics the direction of the ray. That is, $x \geq 2$ and $x > 2$ have right-facing rays, $\rightarrow$. $x \leq 2$ and $x < 2$ have left-facing rays, $\leftarrow$.**

Graphing a Simple Inequality

Example 4 Graph each inequality on a number line.

A. $x < -1$

Solution To graph $x < -1$, use a left-facing ray with an open circle at -1.

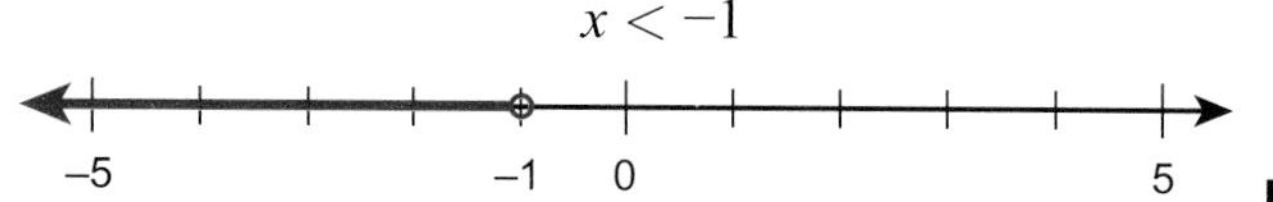

■

B. $t \geq 3.5$

Solution To graph $t \geq 3.5$, use a right-facing ray with a closed circle at 3.5. The endpoint does not fall on a tick mark, so be sure to include a label.

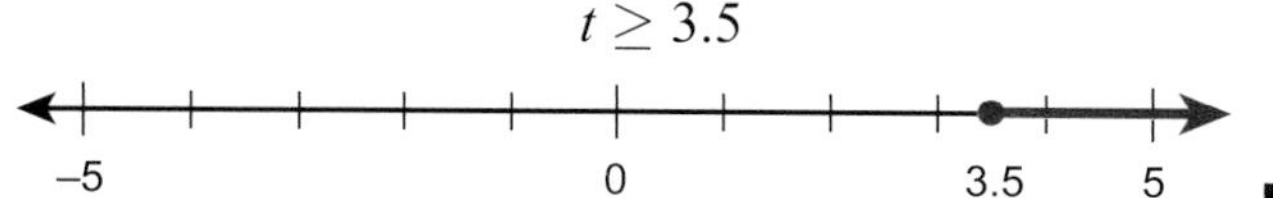

■

C. $n > 0$

Solution To graph $n > 0$, use a right-facing ray with an open circle at 0.

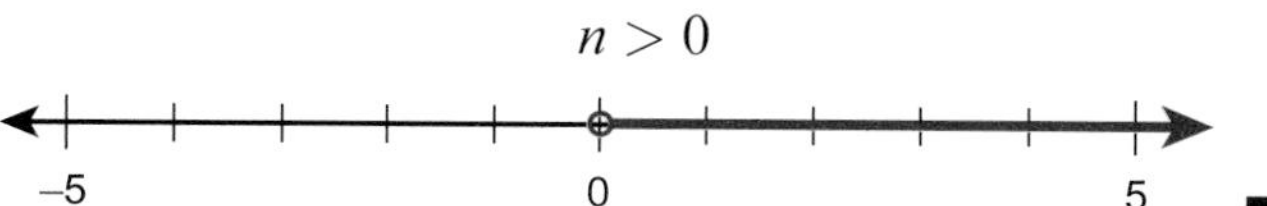

■

Graphing an Inequality with a Restricted Domain

Some inequalities have a restricted domain such as whole numbers or integers.

To graph an inequality with a restricted domain, first imagine the graph as if the domain were all real numbers. Then adjust the endpoint(s) and ray(s) or segment to represent the correct domain.

Example 5 Graph $x \geq -1.25$ over the domain $x \in \mathbb{Z}$.

Solution First imagine the graph of $x \geq -1.25$ for all real numbers.

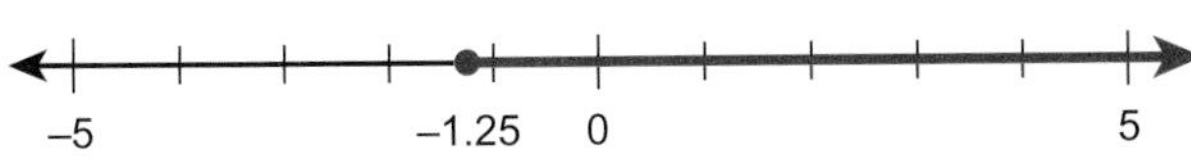

–5
–1.25
0
5

Now adjust the graph for the restricted domain of integers.

$$x \geq -1.25, x \in \mathbb{Z}$$

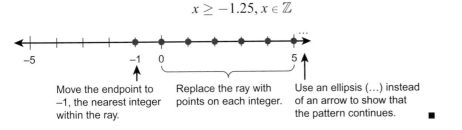

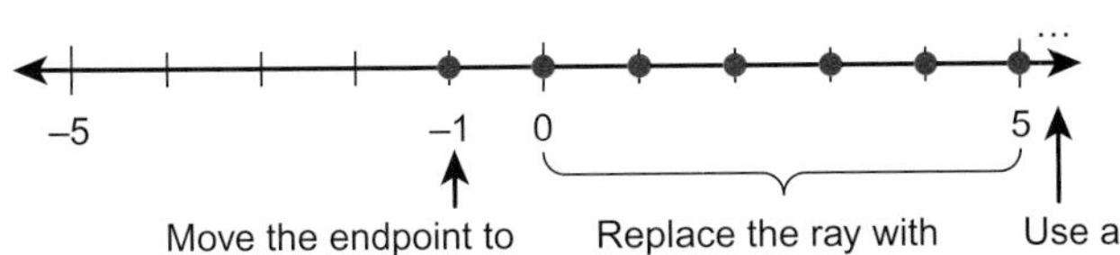

–5
–1
0
5
...
Move the endpoint to –1, the nearest integer within the ray.
Replace the ray with points on each integer.
Use an ellipsis (...) instead of an arrow to show that the pattern continues.

■

> **REMEMBER**
>
> The symbol for real numbers is $\mathbb{R}$, integers is $\mathbb{Z}$, whole numbers is $\mathbb{W}$, and natural numbers is $\mathbb{N}$.

Problem Set

Determine whether each inequality is true or false.

1. $\frac{4}{3} < \frac{1}{3}$

2. $-7 \leq -6$

3. $-14.3 > 13.4$

Translate each sentence into an inequality. Then determine whether each inequality is true or false.

4. Twenty plus four is less than twenty times four.

5. Twelve minus nine is greater than nine minus twelve.

6. Eight and one-tenth minus four is greater than or equal to two times two.

7. Four and nine-tenths divided by seven is less than one minus one-tenth.

8. One plus six is greater than three plus five.

9. Eight times two is less than or equal to four times four.

10. Two-fifths times two is greater than or equal to one minus two-fifths.

Determine whether the given value of the variable is a solution of the inequality.

11. $t > 4.2; t = 0$

12. $x \geq -2; x = -3$

13. $m < 5; m = 1$

14. $s > -2.25; s = -2.2$

15. $v \leq -\frac{17}{2}; v = 8$

16. $h > 16; h = 17$

17. $b \geq 71.182; b = 71.128$

18. $z \leq \frac{4}{81}; z = \frac{2}{9}$

Graph each inequality on a number line.

19. $y < 0$

20. $m \leq -0.5$

21. $l > -7$

22. $d \geq 2$ over the domain $\mathbb{W}$

23. $f < -6$ over the domain $\mathbb{Z}$

24. $x \geq -2$

25. $n < 5$ over the domain $\mathbb{N}$

26. $t \leq -3$ over the domain $\mathbb{R}$

27. $z > -10$

28. $a < -2.5$

***29.** **Challenge** $w > -1$ over the domain $\mathbb{Z} \cap \mathbb{N}$

***30.** **Challenge** $k \leq 4$ over the domain $\mathbb{Z} \cup \mathbb{W}$

Solving Inequalities

Similar to solving an equation, you can solve an inequality by finding a series of equivalent inequalities.

Equivalent inequalities are inequalities with the same solutions. Because most inequalities tell you that one quantity is greater or less than another, you use *properties of order* that maintain the greater/lesser relationship between the two sides of the inequality.

PROPERTIES OF ORDER

NOTE: These properties also hold for the inequality symbols $\geq$ and $\leq$.

Comparison Property of Order	If $a > b$, then $b < a$. If $a < b$, then $b > a$.
Transitive Property of Order	If $a > b$ and $b > c$, then $a > c$. If $a < b$ and $b < c$, then $a < c$.
Addition Property of Order	If $a > b$, then $a + c > b + c$. If $a < b$, then $a + c < b + c$.
Subtraction Property of Order	If $a > b$, then $a - c > b - c$. If $a < b$, then $a - c < b - c$.
Multiplication Properties of Order	
Positive Multiplier:	If $a > b$ and $c > 0$, then $ca > cb$ and $ac > bc$. If $a < b$ and $c > 0$, then $ca < cb$ and $ac < bc$.
Negative Multiplier:	If $a > b$ and $c < 0$, then $ca < cb$ and $ac < bc$. If $a < b$ and $c < 0$, then $ca > cb$ and $ac > bc$.
Division Properties of Order	
Positive Divisor:	If $a > b$ and $c > 0$, then $\frac{a}{c} > \frac{b}{c}$. If $a < b$ and $c > 0$, then $\frac{a}{c} < \frac{b}{c}$.
Negative Divisor:	If $a > b$ and $c < 0$, then $\frac{a}{c} < \frac{b}{c}$. If $a < b$ and $c < 0$, then $\frac{a}{c} > \frac{b}{c}$.

The properties of order are very similar to the properties of equality. But there is one major difference: if you multiply or divide each side of an inequality by a negative value, then you must reverse the inequality symbol.

Solving a One-Step Inequality

Example 1 Solve each inequality.

A. $x + 3 \leq 8$

Solution

$x + 3 \leq 8$

$x + 3 - 3 \leq 8 - 3$ Subtract 3 from each side. (Subtraction Property of Order)

$x \leq 5$ Simplify.

The solution is all real values less than or equal to 5. You can state the solution simply as $x \leq 5$ or display it with a graph of the inequality.

Check Choose three values to check. A value to the left of the endpoint should make a true statement. The endpoint should make a true statement. Any value to the right should make a false statement.

$x = 0$	$x = 5$	$x = 10$
$x + 3 \leq 8$	$x + 3 \leq 8$	$x + 3 \leq 8$
$0 + 3 \stackrel{?}{\leq} 8$	$5 + 3 \stackrel{?}{\leq} 8$	$10 + 3 \stackrel{?}{\leq} 8$
$3 \leq 8$ ✓	$8 \leq 8$ ✓	$13 \not\leq 8$

The solution is correct. ■

B. $-2a > 6$

Solution

$-2a > 6$

$\frac{-2a}{-2} < \frac{6}{-2}$ Divide each side by -2 and reverse the inequality symbol. (Division Property of Order, Negative Divisor)

$a < -3$ Simplify.

The solution is all real values less than -3.

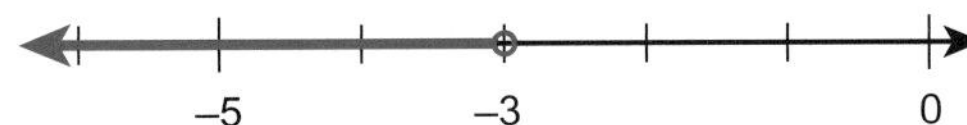

Check The inequality does not include its endpoint, so substituting -3 for a should make the original inequality false. Values to the left should make the inequality true and values to the right should make it false.

$a = -4$	$a = -3$	$a = 0$
$-2a > 6$	$-2a > 6$	$-2a > 6$
$-2 \cdot (-4) \stackrel{?}{>} 6$	$-2 \cdot (-3) \stackrel{?}{>} 6$	$-2 \cdot 0 \stackrel{?}{>} 6$
$8 > 6$ ✓	$6 \not> 6$	$0 \not> 6$

The solution is correct. ■

(continued)

C. $\frac{n}{4} \geq -3$

Solution

$$\frac{n}{4} \geq -3$$

$4 \cdot \frac{n}{4} \geq 4 \cdot (-3)$ Multiply each side by 4.(Multiplication Property of Order, Positive Multiplier)

$n \geq -12$ Simplify.

The solution is all real values greater than or equal to -12.

Check

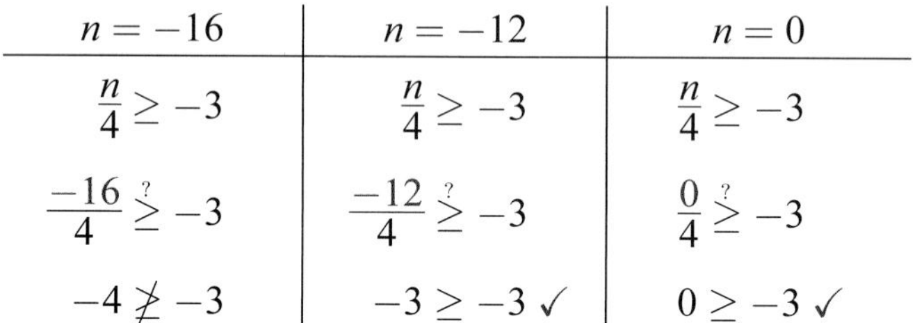

$n = -16$	$n = -12$	$n = 0$
$\frac{n}{4} \geq -3$	$\frac{n}{4} \geq -3$	$\frac{n}{4} \geq -3$
$\frac{-16}{4} \overset{?}{\geq} -3$	$\frac{-12}{4} \overset{?}{\geq} -3$	$\frac{0}{4} \overset{?}{\geq} -3$
$-4 \not\geq -3$	$-3 \geq -3$ ✓	$0 \geq -3$ ✓

The solution is correct. ■

Solving an Inequality with Multiple Transformations

Example 2 Solve each inequality. Graph the solution on a number line.

A. $-5 \geq \frac{x+1}{3}$

Solution

$$-5 \geq \frac{x+1}{3}$$

$3 \cdot (-5) \geq 3 \cdot \frac{x+1}{3}$ Multiply each side by 3. (Multiplication Property of Order, Positive Multiplier)

$-15 \geq x + 1$ Simplify.

$-15 - 1 \geq x + 1 - 1$ Subtract 1 from each side. (Subtraction Property of Order)

$-16 \geq x$ Simplify.

$x \leq -16$ Reverse the entire inequality. (Comparison Property of Order)

The solution is all real values less than or equal to -16.

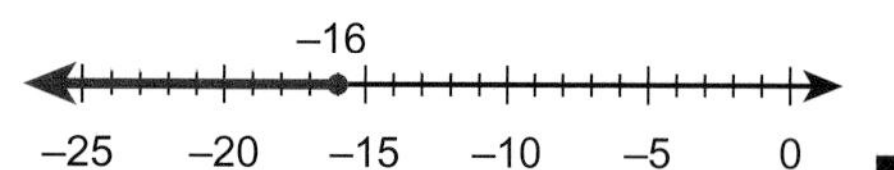

■

B. $-5 - 3(g + 7) < g + 3$

Solution Whenever possible, you should simplify first.

$-5 - 3(g + 7) < g + 3$	
$-5 - 3g - 21 < g + 3$	Distribute.
$-3g - 26 < g + 3$	Combine like terms and simplify.
$-3g - 26 - g < g + 3 - g$	Subtract g from each side. (Subtraction Property of Order)
$-4g - 26 < 3$	Combine like terms and simplify.
$-4g - 26 + 26 < 3 + 26$	Add 26 to each side. (Addition Property of Order)
$-4g < 29$	Simplify.
$\frac{-4g}{-4} > \frac{29}{-4}$	Divide each side by -4 and reverse the inequality symbol. (Division Property of Order, Negative Divisor)
$g > -7.25$	Simplify.

−10 −7.25 −5 0 ■

Application: Number Puzzle

Example 3 The sum of two consecutive integers is less than 50. Find the greatest possible pair of integers.

Solution

Step 1 Write an inequality. Let n represent the first integer. The next consecutive integer is $n + 1$.

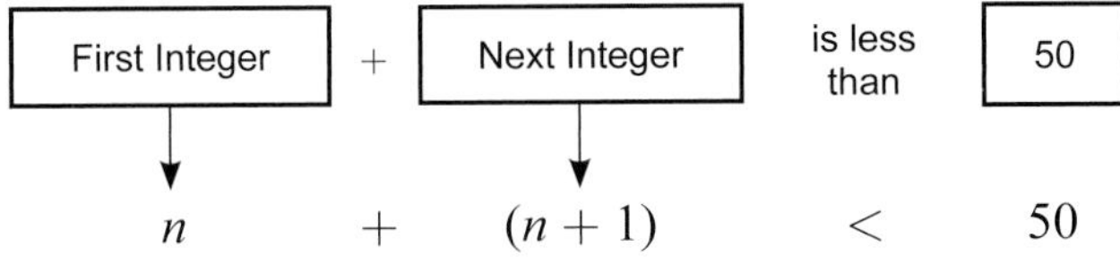

Step 2 Solve the inequality.

$n + (n + 1) < 50$	
$2n + 1 < 50$	Combine like terms.
$2n + 1 - 1 < 50 - 1$	Subtract 1 from each side. (Subtraction Property of Order)
$2n < 49$	Simplify.
$\frac{2n}{2} < \frac{49}{2}$	Divide each side by 2. (Division of Property of Order, Positive Divisor)
$n < 24.5$	Simplify.

The solution is all numbers less than 24.5. However, because n represents an integer, the domain is restricted to $n \in \mathbb{Z}$. The greatest possible integer for n is 24, so the other number is 25.

(continued)

Step 3 Check the solution.

$$n + (n + 1) < 50$$
$$24 + (24 + 1) \overset{?}{<} 50$$
$$24 + 25 \overset{?}{<} 50$$
$$49 < 50 \checkmark$$

The solution checks. The pair of consecutive integers is 24 and 25. ■

Problem Set

Solve each inequality. If a variable is in the denominator, assume is it greater than zero unless noted.

1. $x - 7 < 14$
2. $5t \leq -15$
3. $4n - 6(n + 1) > 12$
4. $3f \leq \frac{9 - f}{3}$
5. $2 \geq \frac{2}{v}$
6. $\frac{1}{-c} < 7$
7. $x + 13 > 21$
8. $1 \leq \frac{40}{h}$
9. $5 > 5(12 - a)$
10. $-8y \geq 56$
11. $\frac{m}{6} - 2 < 2$
12. $u - (2 + 3u) \geq \frac{u}{-3}$
13. $-\frac{n}{34} > 0.5$
14. $2s + 20 \leq 119 - 9s$
15. $\frac{k + 4}{k} < 13$
16. $\frac{1}{9} \geq \frac{4}{p}$
17. $-j \leq 18 - 2j$
18. $-16 \leq 14r - (19 + 13r)$
19. $52 + z > 52 - z$
20. $100l < 7$
21. $0.125 > \frac{3}{8q}$
22. $\frac{4n}{9} \geq \frac{11}{18}$

Solve.

23. The product of a whole number and -12 is no greater than -84. Find the smallest valid whole number.
24. The sum of two consecutive integers is at least 14. Find the least possible pair of integers.
25. The difference of 40 and a natural number is less than 29.5. Find the smallest valid natural number.
26. The quotient of a whole number and its square is greater than 0.2. Find the greatest valid whole number.
27. The sum of two consecutive even integers is no greater than 1249. Find the greatest pair of even integers.
28. The product of a real number and -19 is at least the difference of 423 and the real number. Find the greatest valid real number.

*29. **Challenge** The quotient of the square of a natural number and two times that number is greater than or equal to 1.8.

A. Find the smallest valid natural number.

B. How would your answer change if the number was a real number instead of a natural number?

*30. **Challenge** The sum of a whole number plus half of the whole number is less than 0.75.

A. Find the greatest valid whole number.

B. How would your answer change if the number was a natural number instead of a whole number?

Combined Inequalities

A combined inequality is a combination of two inequalities.

DEFINITIONS

A **combined inequality** is a number sentence that contains two inequalities combined by AND or OR.
A **conjunction** is any sentence that uses AND.
A **disjunction** is any sentence that uses OR.

In mathematics, a conjunction represents the intersection of two sets. So, the graph of $x > -2$ AND $x \leq 5$ shows the solutions in common, or the overlap, between the two inequalities.

REMEMBER

An intersection of two sets is the set of elements that are in both sets.

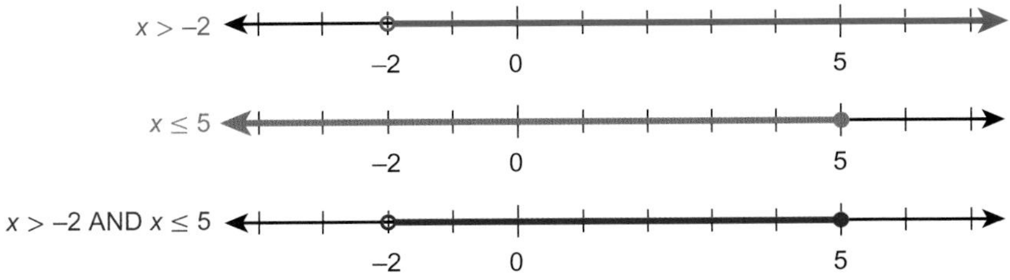

You can also use the transitive property of order to write the conjunction $x > -2$ AND $x \leq 5$ in the shorthand form $-2 < x \leq 5$. The graphical solution above is described as the interval between -2, exclusive, and 5, inclusive. The word *between* means the solution can be any real number that falls between the given points; *exclusive* and *inclusive* tell whether the endpoints are hollow or solid.

REMEMBER

A union of two sets is the set of elements that are in one or both of the sets.

In mathematics, a disjunction represents the union of two sets. So $x \leq -3$ OR $x \geq 3$ represents all of the solutions of both inequalities together.

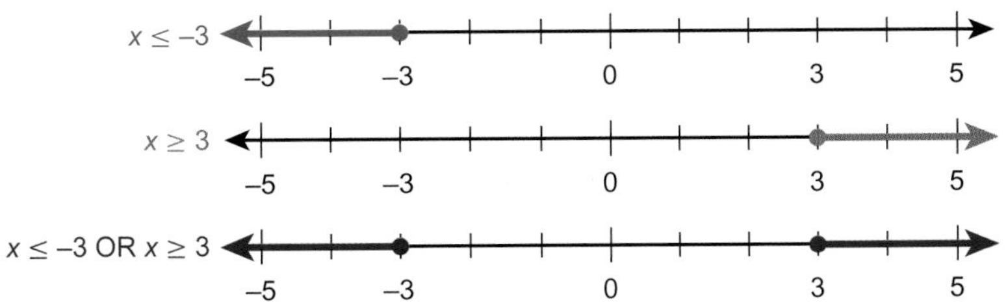

Writing a Combined Inequality to Match a Graph

Example 1 Write a combined inequality that matches the solution set shown in each graph.

A.

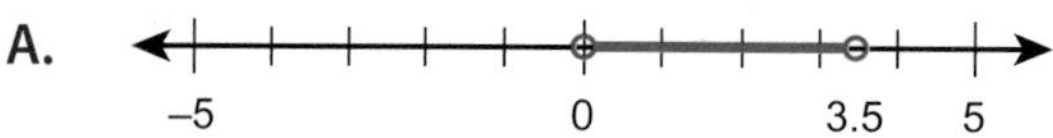

Solution This graph shows all real values between 0 and 3.5, exclusive of both endpoints. It is a conjunction that can be written two ways:

$x > 0$ AND $x < 3.5$ or $0 < x < 3.5$ ■

B.

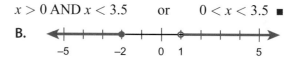

−5 −2 0 1 5

Solution This graph shows the union of all real values less than or equal to −2 or greater than 1. It is a disjunction that can be written as:

$x \leq -2$ OR $x > 1$ ■

Solving and Graphing a Conjunction

Now that you know how to solve inequalities with multiple transformations, you can also solve and graph more advanced compound inequalities.

Example 2 Solve and graph each combined inequality.

A. $39 < -3x - 18 < 9$

Solution Write and solve two separate inequalities.

$$39 < -3x - 18 < 9$$

$$\begin{array}{lcl} 39 < -3x - 18 & \text{AND} & -3x - 18 < 9 \\ 39 + 18 < -3x - 18 + 18 & & -3x - 18 + 18 < 9 + 18 \\ 57 < -3x & & -3x < 27 \\ \frac{57}{-3} > \frac{-3x}{-3} & & \frac{-3x}{-3} > \frac{27}{-3} \\ -19 > x & & x > -9 \end{array}$$

$$-19 > x > -9$$

THINK ABOUT IT

If there are no solutions in common, then a conjunction results in the empty set, ∅.

This conjunction means $x > -9$ AND $x < -19$. But the intersection of those two sets is empty. So, there is no solution, ∅.

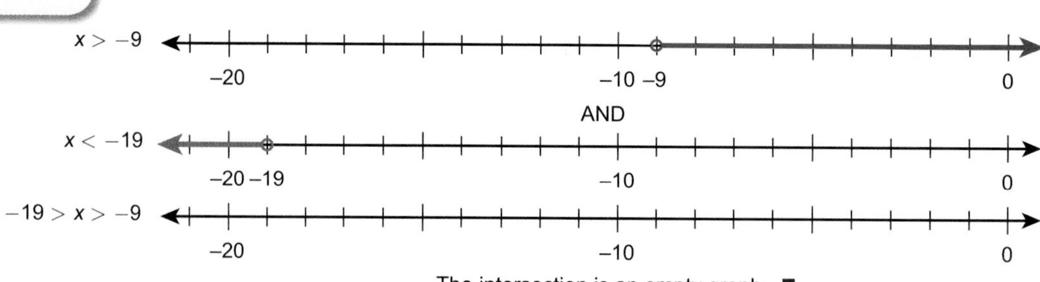

The intersection is an empty graph. ■

B. $1 - 4m \le 3 - 5m \le m - 3$

Solution When there are variables on multiple sides, use separate inequalities.

$$1 - 4m \le 3 - 5m \le m - 3$$

	AND	
$1 - 4m \le 3 - 5m$		$3 - 5m \le m - 3$
$1 - 4m + 5m \le 3 - 5m + 5m$		$3 - 5m + 5m \le m - 3 + 5m$
$1 + m \le 3$		$3 \le 6m - 3$
$1 + m - 1 \le 3 - 1$		$3 + 3 \le 6m - 3 + 3$
$m \le 2$		$6 \le 6m$
		$\frac{6}{6} \le \frac{6m}{6}$
		$1 \le m$

$$1 \le m \le 2$$

The solution is all real numbers between 1 and 2, inclusive.

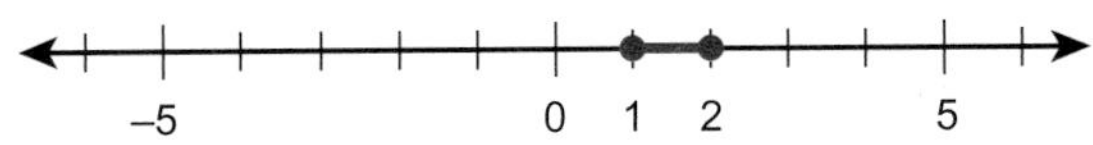

■

Solving and Graphing a Disjunction

Example 3 Solve and graph each combined inequality.

A. $2x + 3 < 5$ OR $x - 7 > -2$

Solution For disjunctions, you must solve two separate inequalities.

	OR	
$2x + 3 < 5$		$x - 7 > -2$
$2x + 3 - 3 < 5 - 3$		$x - 7 + 7 > -2 + 7$
$2x < 2$		$x > 5$
$\frac{2x}{2} < \frac{2}{2}$		
$x < 1$		

The solution is the union of all real values less than 1 or greater than 5.

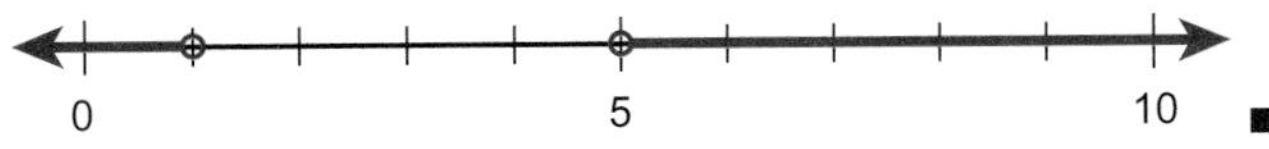

■

(continued)

B. $-4x \leq 12$ OR $x > 2x - 3$

Solution

$$-4x \leq 12 \qquad \text{OR} \qquad x > 2x - 3$$

$$\frac{-4x}{-4} \geq \frac{12}{-4} \qquad\qquad x - 2x > 2x - 3 - 2x$$

$$-x > -3$$

$$x \geq -3 \qquad\qquad \frac{-x}{-1} < \frac{-3}{-1}$$

$$x < 3$$

The solution is the union of all real values greater than or equal to –3 or less than 3. But this union includes every real value. So, the solution is all real numbers $\mathbb{R}$.

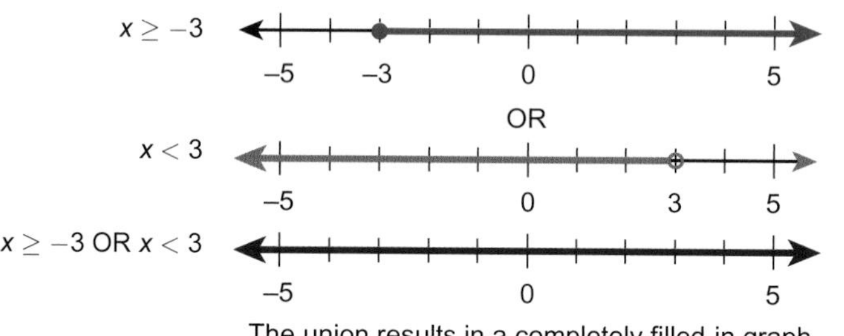

The union results in a completely filled-in graph. ■

Application: Number Puzzle

Example 4 The sum of two consecutive integers is between 50 and 60, exclusive. Find all the possible pairs of numbers.

Solution

Step 1 Write a compound inequality. Let n represent the first integer. The next consecutive integer is $n + 1$.

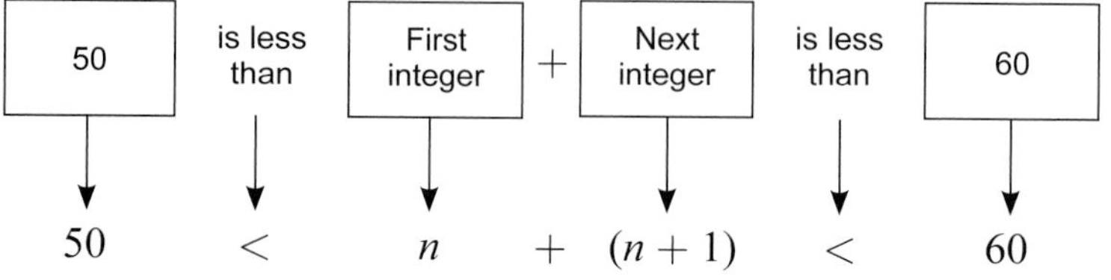

Step 2 Solve the combined inequality. Since the variables are in the middle, you can keep the inequalities together and solve by performing every operation to each of the three sides.

$$50 < n + (n + 1) < 60$$

$50 < 2n + 1 < 60$ Combine like terms.

$50 - 1 < 2n + 1 - 1 < 60 - 1$ Subtract 1 from each side. (Subtraction Property of Order)

$49 < 2n < 59$ Simplify.

$\frac{49}{2} < \frac{2n}{2} < \frac{59}{2}$ Divide each side by 2. (Division Property of Order, Positive Divisor)

$24.5 < n < 29.5$ Simplify.

The solution is all real numbers greater than 24.5 and less than 29.5. However, because n represents an integer, the domain is restricted to $n \in \mathbb{Z}$. Therefore, n is any integer between 25 and 29, inclusive.

Step 3 Check the solution. Test a few values between 25 and 29, inclusive.

$50 < n + (n + 1) < 60$	$50 < n + (n + 1) < 60$
$50 \overset{?}{<} 25 + (25 + 1) \overset{?}{<} 60$	$50 \overset{?}{<} 29 + (29 + 1) \overset{?}{<} 60$
$50 \overset{?}{<} 25 + 26 \overset{?}{<} 60$	$50 \overset{?}{<} 29 + 30 \overset{?}{<} 60$
$50 < 51 < 60$ ✓	$50 < 59 < 60$ ✓

The possible pairs of integers are: 25 and 26, 26 and 27, 27 and 28, 28 and 29, and 29 and 30. ■

Problem Set

Write a combined inequality that matches the solution set shown in each graph.

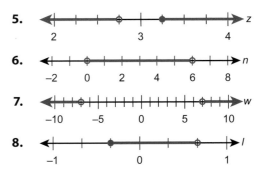

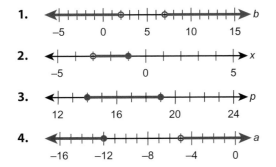

1. 

2. 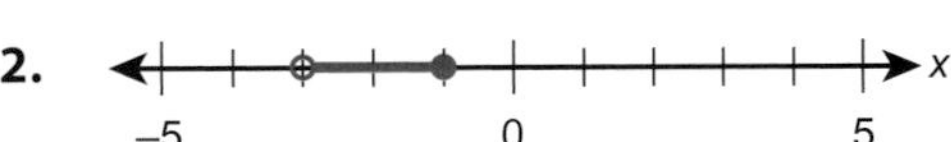

3. 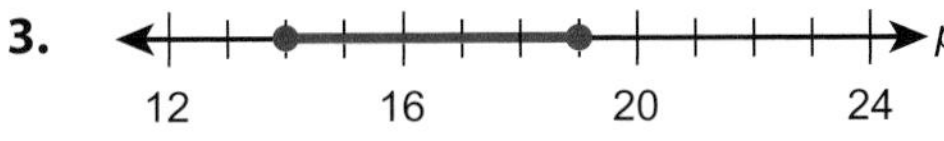

4. −16 −12 −8 −4 0 a

5. 2 3 4 z

6. 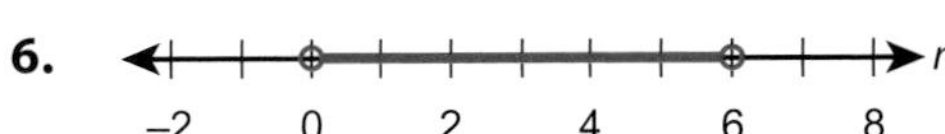

7. 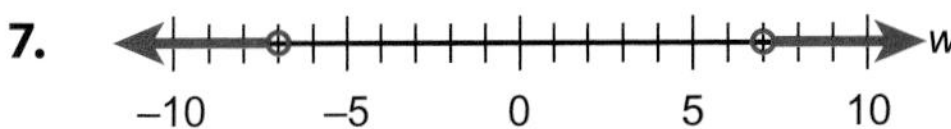

8. 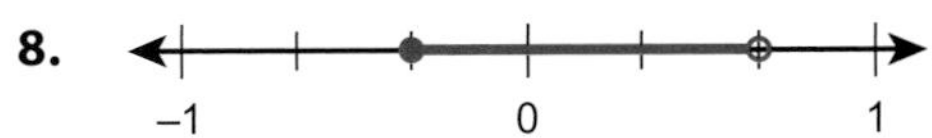

Solve and graph each combined inequality.

9. $28 \leq 2t + 26 < 32$

10. $3 + h \leq 5h - 2(h + 1) \leq 10$

11. $6f + 85 < 21$ OR $31 - f < 29$

12. $6v < 38 - 13v$ OR $v - 4 \geq 9 + 2v$

13. $-4 \leq -\frac{x}{12} < 5$

14. $17 \leq 13 + 2(g - 7) < 23$

15. $1.4 - 2c < 0.8c - 2(7 + c)$ OR $\frac{c}{-12} \leq 0.5$

16. $-1 \leq 2 - j < -5$

17. $m - 4 \leq 3 + 2m \leq 7$

18. $0.4 < y + 1.2 < 0.6$

19. $105 \leq s - 15$ OR $15s \leq 2250$

20. $q < 5q - 7$ OR $12 < \frac{3}{q}$

21. $-81 < -9d \leq -18$

22. $47 \leq -2r + 3(4r + 9)$ OR $r + 9 < 4 - 5r$

23. $7 \leq \frac{x}{11} - 2 < 8$

24. $k - 7 \leq \frac{k}{5}$ OR $k \leq 2k + 1$

Solve using combined inequalities.

25. The sum of two consecutive odd integers is between 28, exclusive, and 36, exclusive. Find all the possible pairs of consecutive odd integers.

26. The quotient of an integer and -10 is between -2 and 5, inclusive. Find all the valid integers.

*27. **Challenge** The difference of two consecutive integers divided by the lesser integer is either greater than $\frac{1}{19}$ or no greater than $\frac{1}{26}$. Find all pairs of consecutive integers that do not satisfy these requirements.

*28. **Challenge** The product of a whole number and 9 is either less than 9 or at least 45. Find all whole numbers that do not satisfy these requirements.

*29. **Challenge** The sum of a natural number and $\frac{2}{3}$ times the number is between 7 and 52, exclusive.

A. Find all the valid natural numbers.

B. If it is also true that 2 times the natural number is greater than 30 and less than 40, find all the valid natural numbers.

*30. **Challenge** The difference of 0.7 times an integer and 6 is between -14 and 21, inclusive.

A. Find all the valid integers.

B. If it is also true that the the quotient of the integer and 4 is either greater than 9 or less than -0.5, find all the valid integers.

Absolute Value Equations and Inequalities

To solve an absolute value equation or inequality, rewrite it as a conjunction or disjunction.

ABSOLUTE VALUE EQUATIONS AND INEQUALITIES

If $|x| = a$ for some positive number a, then $x = a$ OR $x = -a$.

If $|x| > a$ for some positive number a, then $x > a$ OR $x < -a$.

If $|x| \geq a$ for some positive number a, then $x \geq a$ OR $x \leq -a$.

If $|x| < a$ for some positive number a, then $x < a$ AND $x > -a$.

If $|x| \leq a$ for some positive number a, then $x \leq a$ AND $x \geq -a$.

TIP

You can remember whether an inequality is a conjunction or disjunction with this mnemonic: greater than = great OR less than = less th AND.

For the rules above, x may represent a single variable or a larger expression, such as $x + 5$ or $2x - 9$. The first step of your solution should always be to isolate the absolute value expression and rewrite the equation or inequality as a conjunction or disjunction. "Undo" any operations inside the absolute value expression only after you convert it to a conjunction or disjunction.

Solving an Absolute Value Equation

Example 1 Solve $|x + 3| = 7$. Graph the solution.

Solution The absolute value expression $|x + 3|$ is already isolated.

Convert the equation to a disjunction.

$$|x + 3| = 7$$

$x + 3 = 7$	OR	$x + 3 = -7$	Rewrite the equation as a disjunction.
$x + 3 - 3 = 7 - 3$		$x + 3 - 3 = -7 - 3$	Subtract 3 from each side.
$x = 4$		$x = -10$	Simplify.

The solution set is $\{4, -10\}$.

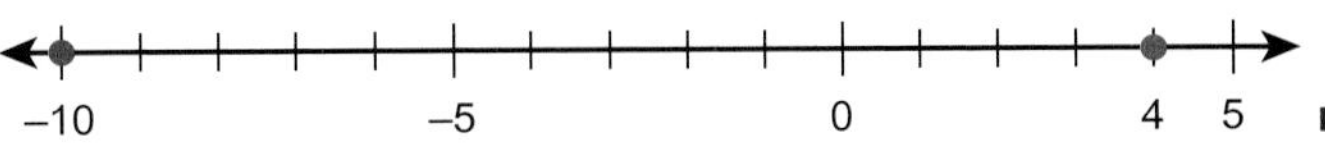

■

Solving a Greater-Than Absolute Value Inequality

Example 2 Solve each inequality. Graph the solution.

A. $|2x - 1| \geq 9$

Solution

The absolute value expression is already isolated. Your first step will be to convert to a disjunction.

$$|2x - 1| \geq 9$$

$2x - 1 \geq 9$	OR	$2x - 1 \leq -9$	Rewrite the inequality as a disjunction.
$2x - 1 + 1 \geq 9 + 1$		$2x - 1 + 1 \leq -9 + 1$	Add 1 to each side.
$2x \geq 10$		$2x \leq -8$	Simplify.
$\frac{2x}{2} \geq \frac{10}{2}$		$\frac{2x}{2} \leq \frac{-8}{2}$	Divide each side by 2.
$x \geq 5$		$x \leq -4$	Simplify.

The solution is the union of all real values greater than or equal to 5 or less than or equal to -4.

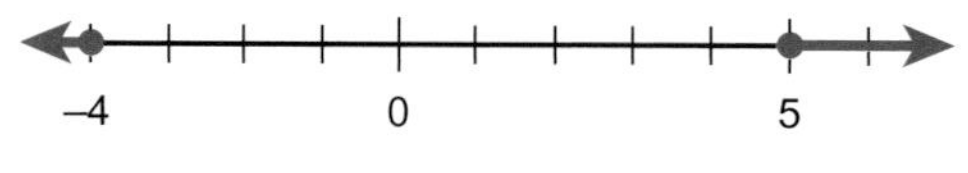

■

B. $3|k + 2| + 8 > 5$

Solution

First isolate the absolute value expression.

$3\|k + 2\| + 8 > 5$	
$3\|k + 2\| + 8 - 8 > 5 - 8$	Subtract 8 from each side.
$3\|k + 2\| > -3$	Simplify.
$\frac{3\|k + 2\|}{3} > \frac{-3}{3}$	Divide each side by 3.
$\|k + 2\| > -1$	Simplify.

The rule for converting to a disjunction says that the constant a is "some positive number." But in this inequality $a = -1$, a negative number.

Use logic to finish the solution. Because an absolute value expression is always positive, $|k + 2|$ will always be greater than -1. So, any real value of k makes the inequality true.

The solution is all real numbers, $\mathbb{R}$.

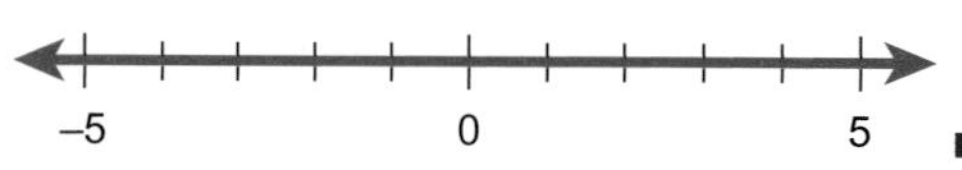

■

THINK ABOUT IT

If you continue to solve Example 2B by writing $k + 2 > -1$ OR $k + 2 < 1$, you get $k > -3$ OR $k < -1$. The union of these inequalities fills in the entire number line and is still equivalent to $\mathbb{R}$.

Solving a Less-Than Absolute Value Inequality

Example 3 Solve each inequality. Graph the solution.

A. $|x - 2| < 2$

Solution The absolute value expression is already isolated. Your first step will be to convert to a conjunction.

	$|x - 2| < 2$		
$x - 2 < 2$	AND	$x - 2 > -2$	Rewrite the inequality as a conjunction.
$x - 2 + 2 < 2 + 2$		$x - 2 + 2 > -2 + 2$	Add 2 to each side.
$x < 4$		$x > 0$	Simplify.
	$0 < x < 4$		

The solution is all real values between 0 and 4, exclusive.

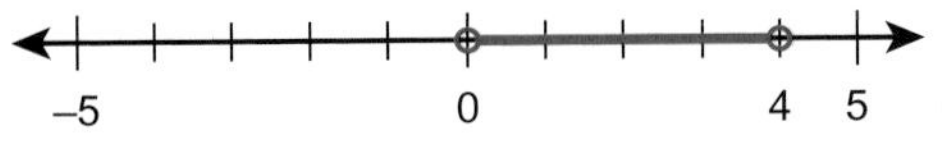

■

B. $5 - 3|r| \geq -7$

Solution This looks like a greater-than inequality with a negative constant a. Begin your solution by isolating the absolute value expression to see this is a less-than inequality.

$5 - 3|r| \geq -7$	
$5 - 3|r| - 5 \geq -7 - 5$	Subtract 5 from each side.
$-3|r| \geq -12$	Simplify.
$\frac{-3|r|}{-3} \leq \frac{-12}{-3}$	Divide each side by -3.
$|r| \leq 4$	Simplify. It is now a less-than absolute value inequality.
$r \leq 4$ AND $r \geq -4$	Rewrite the inequality as a conjunction.
$-4 \leq r \leq 4$	

The solution is all real values between -4 and 4, inclusive.

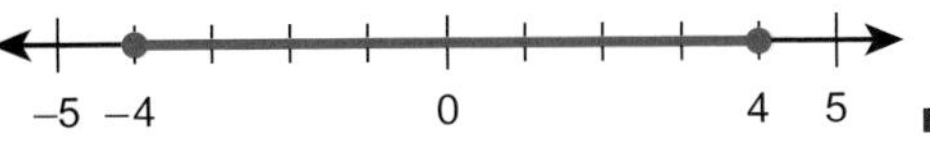

■

Problem Set

Solve. For each problem:

A. State the equation or inequality as a disjunction or conjunction.
B. Solve.
C. Graph the solution.

1. $|x + 4| = 6$
2. $5 + |2y + 1| = 12$
3. $|5 - m| \geq 7$
4. $|2m - 2| > 5$
5. $|3r| < 27$
6. $|x + 6| < 5$
7. $|2x| > 18$
8. $6 - 2|t| \geq -10$
9. $2|x - 1| + 9 > 5$
10. $5|a + 3| = 25$
11. $|p - 7| + 4 \leq 20$
12. $|3b - 2| > 7$
13. $|6 - 2y| > 3$
14. $\frac{|3s - 4|}{2} \leq 2.5$

Solve. For each problem:

A. State the equation or inequality as a disjunction or conjunction.
B. Solve each equation or inequality.

15. $|3x + 2| \geq 11$
16. $|2n - 3| < 9$
17. $6 - 4|t - 2| = -2$
18. $4 - 2|y - 1| \geq -8$
19. $5 + |a - 4| = 6$
20. $|3 + 4k| > 7$
21. $|8 - b| \leq 6$
22. $12 - 2|k + 1| \geq -4$
23. $24 - 4|2 - 5y| > 0$

*24. **Challenge** $|12 + 2m| = 3m + 5$

25. $2|3b - 1| + 6 \geq 4$

*26. **Challenge** $3|w + 5| = 33 + 12w$

Solve. For each problem:

A. Write an absolute value equation or inequality.
B. Solve.
C. Give your answer in a complete sentence.

27. The scale in the supermarket's produce department has a sign saying, "Weight may be up to 4 ounces more or less than actual weight." Jacinta has put carrots on the scale, and the scale reads 2.5 pounds. What are the possible weights w of the carrots? (1 pound = 16 ounces)

28. Trevor plans to exercise 20 hours per month, with a variation of no more than 3 hours in any month's total. For the first 3 weeks of February, his hours were 6, 3, and 5. What are the possible numbers of hours h he should exercise in the fourth week to maintain his goal?

29. Li's car gets about 26 miles per gallon of gasoline. This number of miles per gallon varies by up to 5 miles more or less, depending on the type of driving (highway, town, etc.). What is the range of miles m Li could drive on 15 gallons?

30. Belinda is creating a wooden square pattern. The length of each side of the pattern must be within 0.002 cm of 16 cm. What is the range of acceptable side lengths for this pattern?

Applications: Inequalities

You can use inequalities to write mathematical models for many real-life situations.

Algebra is a tool for solving problems. You have learned how to solve many types of applications with equations. Now you can use inequalities to solve a wider variety of applications, particularly those that involve a range of possible solutions.

Maximum Cost

Example 1 For a winter party, Noriko needs to buy a gift for one of her coworkers. According to the rules of the party, she can spend at most a total of $20, including tax. The rate of sales tax is 8%. How much can Noriko's gift cost before tax?

TIP

The phrase "at most" tells you the largest possible value, and is equivalent to "less than or equal to." The phrase "at least" tells you the smallest possible value, and is equivalent to "greater than or equal to."

Solution

Step 1 *Identify* Find the greatest price of the gift before tax.

Step 2 *Strategize* Let c represent the cost of the gift in dollars before tax. Note that Noriko can't spend negative money on the gift, so the domain of the problem is money values that are at least zero.

Step 3 *Set Up* Write an inequality.

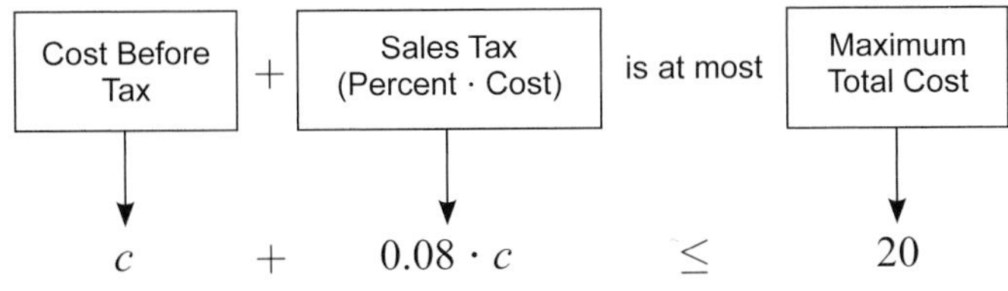

(continued)

Step 4 *Solve*

$$c + 0.08c \leq 20$$

$$1.08c \leq 20$$ Collect like terms. $c = 1c$

$$\frac{1.08c}{1.08} \leq \frac{20}{1.08}$$ Divide each side by 1.08.

$$c \leq 18.5185185\ldots$$

$$c \leq 18.51$$ Round down to the nearest cent so Noriko won't go over budget.

Noriko's gift can cost at most $18.51 before tax.

THINK ABOUT IT

The gift cannot cost less than $0, so you could also write a compound inequality: $0 \leq c + 0.08c \leq 20$

Step 5 *Check* Test prices greater than, less than, and equal to $18.51.

$c = 16.99$	$c = 18.51$	$c = 18.52$
$c + 0.08c \leq 20$	$c + 0.08c \leq 20$	$c + 0.08c \leq 20$
$16.99 + 0.08 \cdot 16.99 \stackrel{?}{\leq} 20$	$18.51 + 0.08 \cdot 18.51 \stackrel{?}{\leq} 20$	$18.52 + 0.08 \cdot 18.52 \stackrel{?}{\leq} 20$
$16.99 + 1.3592 \stackrel{?}{\leq} 20$	$18.51 + 1.4808 \stackrel{?}{\leq} 20$	$18.52 + 1.4816 \stackrel{?}{\leq} 20$
$18.3492 \leq 20$ ✓	$19.9908 \leq 20$ ✓	$20.0016 \not\leq 20$

The solution checks. ■

Profit

In business, the money spent to run the business, manufacture items, or provide services is called *cost.* The money that is earned when items or services are sold is called *revenue.* A business makes *profit* when its revenue is greater than its cost.

Example 2 Ygnacio starts a small business making video recordings of weddings and other events. His camcorder cost $953. For each event, he spends another $25 on media (tapes and DVDs). He earns $85 per event that he records. When will Ygnacio begin to make a profit?

Solution

Step 1 *Identify* Find the number of events Ygnacio must record to earn a profit.

Step 2 *Strategize* Let n represent the number of events that Ygnacio records. Assume that Ygnacio only records whole events, so the domain is restricted: $n \in \mathbb{W}$.

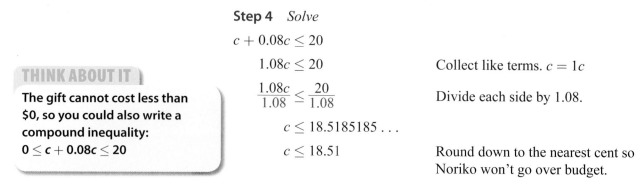

Step 3 *Set Up* Write an inequality.

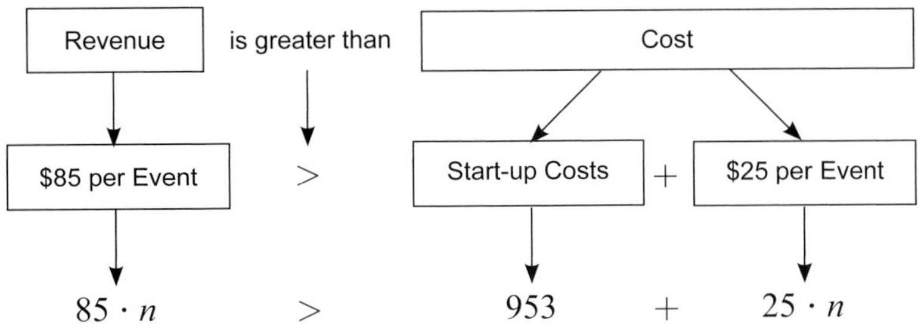

Step 4 *Solve*

$$85n > 953 + 25n$$

$$85n - 25n > 953 + 25n - 25n$$ Subtract $25n$ to collect variables on one side.

$$60n > 953$$

$$\frac{60n}{60} > \frac{953}{60}$$ Divide each side by 60.

$$n > 15.88\overline{3} \approx 15.9$$

Now adjust the solution for the restricted domain. First graph $n > 15.9$ for all real numbers, and then adjust the endpoint and ray for whole-numbers.

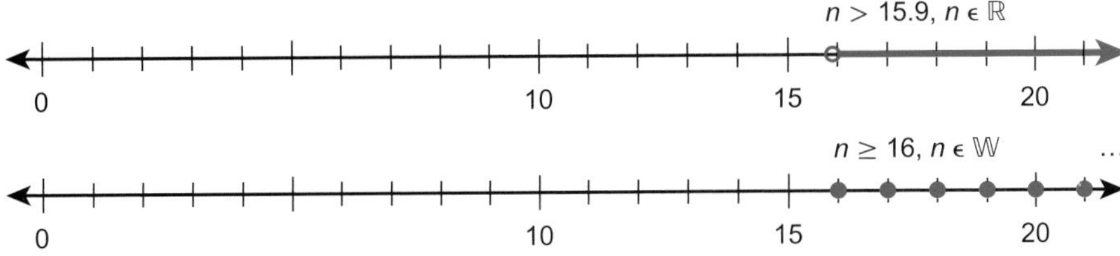

The solution is $n \geq 16$, where $n \in \mathbb{W}$. Ygnacio will make a profit with the 16th event that he records, and every event after that.

Step 5 *Check*

$n = 15$	$n = 16$	$n = 20$
$85n > 953 + 25n$	$85n > 953 + 25n$	$85n > 953 + 25n$
$85 \cdot 15 \overset{?}{>} 953 + 25 \cdot 15$	$85 \cdot 16 \overset{?}{>} 953 + 25 \cdot 16$	$85 \cdot 20 \overset{?}{>} 953 + 25 \cdot 20$
$1275 \overset{?}{>} 953 + 375$	$1360 \overset{?}{>} 953 + 400$	$1700 \overset{?}{>} 953 + 500$
$1275 \ngtr 1328$	$1360 > 1353$ ✓	$1700 > 1453$ ✓

The solution checks. ■

THINK ABOUT IT

To find how much profit Ygnacio makes, subtract cost from revenue: *profit* = *revenue* − *cost*. For example, after his 20th event, Ygancio's profit is \$1700 − \$1453, or \$247.

Calculating Grades

Many students have been in a situation where they want to do well enough on an exam so that their overall class average is within a certain range. You can use a compound inequality to do this.

REMEMBER

The *mean* is what most people commonly call the *average*. To find the mean, sum up the values and divide by the number of values.

Example 3 In Mrs. Lindley's mathematics class, a student's overall class average is the mean of the scores on four chapter exams and the final exam, which counts twice. A student who earns an overall average between 80, inclusive, and 90, exclusive, gets a B in the class.

Nico is a student in Mrs. Lindley's class. He has scored 85, 70, 73, and 79 on the four chapter exams, and he is now preparing for the final exam. Is it possible for Nico to get a B in the class? If so, what scores will result in a B?

Solution

Step 1 *Identify* Find the score Nico must get on the final exam to earn a B in the class.

Step 2 *Strategize* Let f represent Nico's score on the final exam.

Step 3 *Set Up* Write an inequality.

$$80 \leq \text{Overall average} < 90$$

$$80 \leq \frac{\text{Sum of values}}{\text{Number of values}} < 90$$

$$80 \leq \frac{85 + 70 + 73 + 79 + f + f}{6} < 90$$

$$80 \leq \frac{307 + 2f}{6} < 90$$

Because the final exam counts twice, the arithmetic mean is actually the sum of six scores.

Step 4 *Solve*

$$80 \leq \frac{307 + 2f}{6} < 90$$

$$6 \cdot 80 \leq 6 \cdot \frac{307 + 2f}{6} < 6 \cdot 90$$ Multiply each side by 6.

$$480 \leq 307 + 2f < 540$$

$$480 - 307 \leq 307 + 2f - 307 < 540 - 307$$ Subtract 307 from each side.

$$173 \leq 2f < 233$$

$$\frac{173}{2} \leq \frac{2f}{2} < \frac{233}{2}$$ Divide each side by 2.

$$86.5 \leq f < 116.5$$

Nico can get a B if he scores between 86.5, inclusive, and 116.5, exclusive, on the final exam.

THINK ABOUT IT

Unless extra credit is offered, the highest grade Nico can score on the final exam is 100.

Step 5 *Check* Test a few values.

$f = 80$	$f = 86.5$	$f = 90$
$80 \le \frac{307 + 2f}{6} < 90$	$80 \le \frac{307 + 2f}{6} < 90$	$80 \le \frac{307 + 2f}{6} < 90$
$80 \overset{?}{\le} \frac{307 + 2 \cdot 80}{6} \overset{?}{<} 90$	$80 \overset{?}{\le} \frac{307 + 2 \cdot 86.5}{6} \overset{?}{<} 90$	$80 \overset{?}{\le} \frac{307 + 2 \cdot 90}{6} \overset{?}{<} 90$
$80 \overset{?}{\le} \frac{307 + 160}{6} \overset{?}{\le} 90$	$80 \overset{?}{\le} \frac{307 + 173}{6} \overset{?}{<} 90$	$80 \overset{?}{\le} \frac{307 + 180}{6} \overset{?}{<} 90$
$80 \overset{?}{\le} \frac{467}{6} \overset{?}{<} 90$	$80 \overset{?}{\le} \frac{480}{6} \overset{?}{\le} 90$	$80 \overset{?}{\le} \frac{487}{6} \overset{?}{<} 90$
$80 \not\le 77.8\overline{3} \not< 90$	$80 \le 80 < 90$ ✓	$80 \le 81.1\overline{6} < 90$ ✓

The solution checks. ■

Problem Set

Solve. For each problem:

A. Define variables for the unknowns.
B. Write an inequality to model the problem.
C. Solve the inequality.
D. Give your answer in a complete sentence.

1. The length of a rectangle is twice its width. If the perimeter is at most 120, what is the greatest possible value for the width?

2. Sam wants to be named the greatest home run hitter of his baseball league. In the past 5 seasons he has hit 24, 20, 23, 20, and 21 home runs, respectively. To qualify for the home run trophy he must average at least 22 home runs in 6 seasons. How many home runs must he hit this season to qualify?

3. Ono opens a small seafood restaurant. Start-up costs total $24,000. Each day she spends $500 on daily operating costs. She earns $850 per day in sales. When will Ono begin to make a profit?

4. Jamie works part time at an accounting firm. He gets paid by the task: the more difficult the job, the more money he earns. Jamie needs to make $500 to pay his bills, and the company has a policy that they will not pay more than $800 per week. This week, he completed 5 tasks that paid $50, $75, $120, $100, and $80, respectively. What will he have to earn on his last task of the week to reach his goal?

5. A farmer plants 3 more acres of wheat than corn on his land. If he plants no more than 30 acres, how many acres are used for corn?

6. A local charity earns money to donate to flood victims. It receives $200 per day in cash donations and $150 in pledges but must spend $75 per day in operating costs. After how many days will the charity have enough money to make at least a $1000 donation?

7. Suki is saving for a new car. If she is considering a car that costs between $10,000 inclusive and $12,000 inclusive, how many deposits of $550 must she make in her account to afford a car?

8. Raphael is twice as old as his sister. The sum of their ages is less than 30. What is the greatest age Raphael's sister can be?

9. The west coast is in the midst of a drought. Rainfall totals for this month are 1 in., 2.5 in., 3 in., and 1.7 in., respectively. The total rainfall should be between 15 in., inclusive, and 20 in., inclusive. How many more inches of rain are needed to meet these amounts?

10. Brea invested $500 in stocks. She continues to invest the same amount every time she calls her stockbroker. For every transaction she completes, she must pay $11 to her broker. This amount is deducted from her investment. How many calls must she make to invest at least $2000?

11. The Davis family stops at one rest stop during their car trip to Florida. The family spends $\frac{1}{4}$ of the time at the stop as they did in the car during the first part of their trip. Assuming that the family rode in the car for equal amounts of time surrounding their rest, what is the greatest amount of time they stayed in the car if their trip took less than 6 hours?

12. In a factory, the production time of a sofa is 3 times as long as the production time of a chair. If the time for creating 2 sofas and 4 chairs is no more than 20 hours, find the production time of 1 chair.

13. During the swim season, Soo-Min posted the following times for her swimming events: 4.25 s, 5.75 s, 3.75 s, and 5.00 s. If she wants to finish the season with an overall average between 4.50 and 5.00 seconds, exclusive, what time must she post in her final race?

14. A car manufacturer produces 2 more than 4 times the number of engines than brake systems. If the manufacturer makes at least 100 components a week, how many brake systems do they make?

15. Jan has an equal number of quarters and dimes. If the value of her change is less than $2, what is the greatest number of quarters and dimes she can have?

16. Alan has a tutoring business. For each hour he tutors, he earns $50. In addition to a $75 newspaper ad, his expenses per session include $5 materials and $2 transportation. How many hours must Alan tutor before he makes a profit?

17. Vladimir is a serious video gamer. On his favorite game, he has earned the following points the first five times he played: 1000, 2300, 5400, 1999, and 3000. To enter the winner's circle, he must have an average between 2699 and 2901, exclusive. How many points does he have to earn on his sixth time to reach this average?

18. Charles has 6 times as many action figures as Ibeau. Together, their action figures total more than 75. How many does each have?

19. Eli started a sign printing business. His equipment costs $1200 and he pays $60 per job to the 2 employees who complete the work. He charges customers $100 per job. How many jobs must Eli obtain to make a profit?

20. A rectangle's length is 5 more than its width. If the perimeter the rectangle is at most 70, what is the greatest possible value for the width?

21. A wedding planner charges $6000 per wedding. Her initial business costs total $1200. If she spends $5500 per wedding to accommodate her clients, when will she make a profit?

22. Juno wants to earn at least a C+ in his English class. He must earn an average grade between 75 and 100, inclusive, to do this. If his previous test scores are 72, 71, 74, and 78, what must Juno earn on this last English test?

23. Gee's age is 5 less than three times Roberto's age. The sum of their ages is greater than 11. What is the youngest Roberto can be?

24. A toy company spends $20 for every doll it makes. Promotion of the dolls cost $400 and the company sells each doll for $30. How many dolls must the company sell to make a profit?

UNIT 5 Applying Fractions

Sometimes stores sell items at a fraction of the price.

What do a scale drawing, a bicycle's gears, and a sale at the local store all have in common? They all present problems that can be solved using equations with fractions.

Big Ideas

- A number is any entity that obeys the laws of arithmetic; all numbers obey the laws of arithmetic. The laws of arithmetic can be used to simplify algebraic expressions.
- Solving an equation means finding values for the variable or variables that make the equation a true statement.
- If you can create a mathematical model for a situation, you can use the model to solve other problems that you might not be able to solve otherwise. Algebraic equations can capture key relationships among quantities in the world.

Unit Topics

- Ratios
- Proportions
- Percents
- Applications: Percents
- Applications: Mixture Problems

Ratios

A **ratio** is a comparison of two quantities using division.

You can write ratios in different forms. For example, if a bag contains three pennies and five dimes, then you could write the ratio of pennies to dimes as 3 to 5, 3 : 5, $\frac{3}{5}$, or 0.6.

Like fractions, you should write ratios in simplest form. For example, if there are 15 boys and 12 girls in a classroom, then the ratio of boys to girls is $\frac{15}{12} = \frac{5}{4}$. So, the ratio of boys to girls is 5 : 4.

Writing Ratios

Example 1 Write each ratio in fraction and decimal form.

A. 6 to 20

Solution

Write the ratio 6 to 20 as $\frac{6}{20}$.

$\frac{6}{20} = \frac{3}{10}$ Simplify the fraction.

$= 0.3$ Divide to convert the fraction to a decimal.

The ratio 6 to 20 is $\frac{3}{10}$ or 0.3. ■

B. 4 : 16

Solution

Write the ratio 4 : 16 as $\frac{4}{16}$.

$\frac{4}{16} = \frac{1}{4}$ Simplify the fraction.

$= 0.25$ Divide to convert the fraction to a decimal.

The ratio 4 : 16 is $\frac{1}{4}$ or 0.25. ■

(continued)

Example 2 Write the ratio of a to b for $2a = 3b$.

Solution

$2a = 3b$

$\frac{2a}{2} = \frac{3b}{2}$ Divide each side by 2.

$a = \frac{3b}{2}$ Simplify.

$\frac{a}{b} = \frac{3b}{2b}$ Divide each side by b.

$\frac{a}{b} = \frac{3}{2}$ Simplify.

The ratio of a to b is $\frac{3}{2}$ or 1.5. ■

Solving a Number Problem

Solve number problems involving ratios by writing and solving equations.

When setting up equations to solve problems, you will want to limit the variables when possible. For example, if you have two unknown numbers, but it is stated that one is twice the value of the other, you may describe those two numbers as n and $2n$, rather than naming the numbers two different variables, n and m. Or if you are given a ratio, such as 2:3, you may naturally think of 2:3 as $x:y$. But, it would be easier to solve an equation if you write this ratio in terms of one variable. Instead, think of 2:3 as $2x:3x$.

Example 3 The ratio of two numbers is 3 to 8. The sum of the numbers is 66. Find the two numbers.

Solution

Step 1 Write variable expressions for the two numbers. Because the ratio of the numbers must simplify to $\frac{3}{8}$, write both numbers as multiples of the same number.

first number: $3x$
second number: $8x$

Step 2 Write and solve an equation.

$3x + 8x = 66$ The sum of the numbers is 66.

$11x = 66$ Combine like terms.

$x = 6$ Divide each side by 11.

Substitute 6 into each expression: $3x = 3 \cdot 6 = 18$ and $8x = 8 \cdot 6 = 48$. The two numbers are 18 and 48.

Step 3 Check. $\frac{18}{48} = \frac{3}{8}$ and $18 + 48 = 66$. ✓ ■

Application: Geometry

Example 4

A. The sides of a rectangle have a 3 to 1 length to width ratio, and the perimeter is 120 feet. Find the dimensions of the rectangle.

Solution Express the length as $3x$ and the width as x. Then use the perimeter formula to find x.

$$2l + 2w = P$$

$2 \cdot 3x + 2 \cdot x = 120$ Substitute $3x$ for l and x for w.

$6x + 2x = 120$ Simplify.

$8x = 120$ Combine like terms.

$x = 15$ Divide.

The width is $x = 15$, and the length is $3x = 3 \cdot 15 = 45$. So, the dimensions of the rectangle are 45 feet by 15 feet. ■

B. One square has an area of 36 square inches and another square has an area of 64 square inches. Write the ratio of the perimeter of the larger square to the perimeter of the smaller square.

Solution The length of a side of the larger square is $\sqrt{64 \text{ in}^2} = 8$ in., and the length of a side of the smaller square is $\sqrt{36 \text{ in}^2} = 6$ in.

$$\frac{\text{perimeter of larger square}}{\text{perimeter of smaller square}} = \frac{4 \cdot 8 \text{ in.}}{4 \cdot 6 \text{ in.}} = \frac{8}{6} = \frac{4}{3}$$

The ratio of the perimeters of the larger square to the smaller square is 4:3. ■

Problem Set

Write each ratio in fraction and decimal form.

1. 3 to 12
2. 9 to 6
3. 7:11
4. 35:42
5. 8 to 8
6. 180:108
7. 4.5:1.5
8. $\frac{2}{5}$ to $\frac{4}{5}$
9. 4:64
10. $\frac{1}{3}:\frac{1}{7}$
11. 2.1 to 2.8

Find the ratio of m to n. Give your answer in decimal and fraction form.

12. $3m = 8n$
13. $12m = n$
14. $4m = 40n$
15. $2m = 9n$
16. $\frac{1}{16}m = \frac{1}{15}n$
17. $7m = 6n$
18. $11m = 12.1n$

Solve each number problem using ratios.

For each problem:

A. Define variables for the unknowns.
B. Write an equation to model the problem.
C. Solve the equation.
D. Give your answer in a complete sentence.

19. The ratio of two numbers is 1.75. The difference of the numbers is 12. Find the two numbers.

20. The ratio of two numbers is $\frac{5}{22}$. The product of the numbers is 440. Find all possible pairs of numbers.

21. The ratio of two numbers is 11 : 12. The sum of the numbers is 207. Find the two numbers.

22. The ratio of two numbers is 2 to 1. The sum of the numbers is $\frac{9}{4}$. Find the two numbers.

23. The ratio of two numbers is 3 to 4. The difference of the numbers is −1.9. Find the two numbers.

24. The ratio of two numbers is 1.5. The difference of the numbers is 23. Find the two numbers.

25. For every 5 pages of a book that Jessica reads, Jeremy reads 4. In one hour, they read a total of 36 pages. How many pages did they each read?

***26.** **Challenge** The sides of an isosceles triangle have a 5 : 5 : 8 length ratio. The perimeter is 26 inches. Find the side lengths of the triangle.

27. An alloy has a mass ratio of aluminum to silicon of 19. How much of each element is present in 40 grams of the alloy?

Use the following information for Problems 28 and 29: The ratio of the areas of two circles is 12 : 19. The difference of the areas is 245 cm^2.

28. Calculate the area of each circle.

29. Calculate the radius of the smaller circle.

Use the following information for Problems 30 and 31: The ratio of two numbers is 17.75. Their product is 1775.

***30.** **Challenge** Find all the possible pairs of numbers.

***31.** **Challenge** How would the answer be different if the ratio was −17.75?

Use the following information for Problems 32 and 33: Using her employee discount, Rachel tried to buy two pairs of jeans that cost the same. The cashier applied her discount to only one pair of jeans, for which she paid 85% of the regular price. Her total came to $109.15.

***32.** **Challenge** Calculate the regular and discounted prices of the jeans.

***33.** **Challenge** How much will she be refunded if they correct the error?

Proportions

You can join two equivalent ratios together to form an equation called a **proportion**.

The ratio of 24 to 15 is equivalent to the ratio of 8 to 5, so the equation $\frac{24}{15} = \frac{8}{5}$ is a proportion. In general, proportions can be represented by $\frac{a}{b} = \frac{c}{d}$, where a and d are called the **extremes** and b and c are called the **means**. You can use the following properties to write proportions in equivalent forms.

TIP

The proportion $\frac{a}{b} = \frac{c}{d}$ can also be written as $a:b = c:d$.

PROPERTIES

The Means-Extremes Product Property:
If $\frac{a}{b} = \frac{c}{d}$, then $ad = bc$, given that b and d are not 0.

The Reciprocal Property:
If $\frac{a}{b} = \frac{c}{d}$, then $\frac{b}{a} = \frac{d}{c}$, given that a, b, c, and d are not 0.

The Exchange Property:
If $\frac{a}{b} = \frac{c}{d}$, then $\frac{a}{c} = \frac{b}{d}$, given that b, c, and d are not 0.

The Add-One Property:
If $\frac{a}{b} = \frac{c}{d}$, then $\frac{a+b}{b} = \frac{c+d}{d}$, given that b and d are not 0.

Using the Means-Extremes Product Property

Example 1 Solve each proportion.

A. $\frac{1}{2} = \frac{x+1}{6}$

Solution

$\frac{1}{2} = \frac{x+1}{6}$

$1 \cdot 6 = 2(x + 1)$	Means-Extremes Product Property
$6 = 2x + 2$	Multiply on the left; distribute 2 on the right.
$4 = 2x$	Subtract 2 from each side.
$2 = x$	Divide each side by 2. ■

(continued)

B. $\frac{2x - 4}{3} = \frac{x + 1}{6}$

Solution

$$\frac{2x - 4}{3} = \frac{x + 1}{6}$$

$(2x - 4)6 = 3(x + 1)$	Means-Extremes Product Property
$12x - 24 = 3x + 3$	Distribute on each side.
$9x - 24 = 3$	Subtract $3x$ from each side.
$9x = 27$	Add 24 to each side.
$x = 3$	Divide each side by 9. ■

Example 2 Find the ratio of a to b when $\frac{3}{4} = \frac{a - b}{a + b}$.

Solution

$$\frac{3}{4} = \frac{a - b}{a + b}$$

$3(a + b) = 4(a - b)$	Means-Extremes Product Property
$3a + 3b = 4a - 4b$	Distribute on each side.
$3b = a - 4b$	Subtract $3a$ from each side.
$7b = a$	Add $4b$ to each side.
$7 = \frac{a}{b}$	Divide each side by b.

The ratio of a to b is 7 to 1. ■

Applications

When solving an application problem involving proportions, it is important to set up the proportion correctly.

There are different strategies you can use to set up a proportion problem, but in every case you must identify the unknown quantity before writing the proportion. If the unknown quantity is a rate, define the variable you will use, then set up the proportion, making sure you compare units the same way on each side of the proportion. For example, if a problem states that there are 200 electronic devices manufactured every 2 hours and asks how many will be manufactured in 8 hours, you can define the variable x as the number of items that will be manufactured in 8 hours. When writing the proportion, make sure the hours are both listed in the numerators of the fractions or both listed in the denominators. In this example, two possible proportions that will give you a correct answer are $\frac{x}{8} = \frac{200}{2}$ and $\frac{8}{x} = \frac{2}{200}$.

Predicting an Outcome

Example 3 A town has 6420 registered voters. A survey of the people in the town found that 3 out of 4 people would vote for Ms. Chang for mayor. Predict the number of people who would vote for Ms. Chang if all 6420 registered voters voted.

Solution Write and solve a proportion with one ratio for the survey and one ratio for the number of voters. Let x represent the number of people who would vote for Ms. Chang.

$$\frac{3}{4} = \frac{x}{6420}$$

$3 \cdot 6420 = 4x$ Means-Extremes Product Property

$19{,}260 = 4x$ Multiply.

$4815 = x$ Divide each side by 4.

Out of 6420 voters, about 4815 would vote for Ms. Chang. ■

Using Scale

Example 4 On a map, the distance between two cities is 7.5 inches. Find the actual distance in miles between the two cities if the scale on the map is 1 inch to 35 miles.

Solution Let x represent the actual distance. Then, write and solve a proportion.

$$\frac{1}{35} = \frac{7.5}{x}$$

$1x = 35 \cdot 7.5$ Means-Extremes Product Property

$x = 262.5$ Multiply.

The actual distance between the two cities is 262.5 miles. ■

Gas Mileage

Example 5 Julio used 5 gallons of gas to drive 187 miles. How far can he drive on a full tank if his gas tank holds 12 gallons of gas?

Solution Let x represent the distance on a full tank. Then, write and solve a proportion.

$$\frac{187}{5} = \frac{x}{12}$$

$187 \cdot 12 = 5x$ Means-Extremes Product Property

$2244 = 5x$ Multiply.

$448.8 = x$ Divide each side by 5.

Julio can drive 448.8 miles using a full tank of gas. ■

Cost

Example 6 Kim bought 12 bottles of juice for $16.68. How much will it cost her to buy 30 bottles of the same juice?

Solution Let x represent the cost of 30 bottles of juice. Then, write and solve a proportion.

$$\frac{12}{16.68} = \frac{30}{x}$$

$12x = 16.68 \cdot 30$ Means-Extremes Product Property

$12x = 500.4$ Multiply.

$x = 41.7$ Divide each side by 12.

It will cost Kim $41.70 to buy 30 bottles of juice. ■

Problem Set

Solve.

1. $\frac{x+2}{8}=\frac{1}{2}$
2. $\frac{x-2}{5}=\frac{1}{5}$
3. $\frac{3x+1}{10}=\frac{x-1}{7}$
4. $x+1=\frac{x-2}{4}$
5. $\frac{1}{7}=\frac{x-3}{14}$
6. $\frac{x-10}{3}=\frac{1}{15}$
7. $x-6=\frac{2x+1}{3}$
8. $\frac{1}{9}=\frac{x+3}{2}$
9. $\frac{5x+2}{11}=\frac{x}{3}$
10. $\frac{x}{6}=\frac{7}{12}$
11. $2x+12=\frac{3(x-1)}{4}$

Find the ratio of *a* to *b*.

12. $\frac{1}{2}=\frac{a+b}{a-b}$
13. $\frac{1}{12}=\frac{3a}{a+b}$
14. $\frac{2}{5}=\frac{a-b}{a+b}$
15. $\frac{3}{8}=\frac{a}{a-b}$
16. $\frac{1}{10}=\frac{a-b}{2a}$
17. $\frac{1}{7}=\frac{a}{4a-b}$
18. $\frac{1}{11}=\frac{5a}{2a+b}$

Solve. For each problem:

A. Define variables for the unknowns.
B. Write a proportion to model the problem.
C. Solve.
D. Give your answer in a complete sentence.

19. Quaid buys 3 square feet of grass sod for \$11. If Quaid wants to buy 50 square feet, how much will he pay?
20. In a survey, 6 out of 10 customers preferred Cleanbiz laundry detergent over Zapout. If 150 customers participated in the survey, how many people preferred Cleanbiz?
21. Abraham bought 3 bottles of floor cleaner for \$12.05. How much will Abraham pay for 15 bottles?
22. A realtor earns a \$25,000 commission for selling a \$300,000 house. At the same rate, what commission would the realtor make when selling a \$250,000 house?
23. The ratio of perimeters of two triangles is 2 to 7. If the perimeter of the smaller triangle is 24 inches, what is the perimeter of the larger triangle?
24. A fourth-grade class is going on a treasure hunt. If the map scale is 1 inch to 3 feet and the treasure is 8.5 inches away from the class on the map, what is the actual distance between the class and the treasure?
25. In a television survey, 4 out of 5 people liked comedy shows more than reality shows. If 6000 people were surveyed, how many people preferred comedy shows?
26. Samir paid \$15.50 in shipping charges on a package that weighed 20 pounds. If shipping costs a certain set amount per pound, what shipping charges would Samir pay on a 50-pound package?
27. The ratio of the areas of two rectangles is 2 to 3. If the area of the larger rectangle is 600 square feet, what is the area of the smaller rectangle?
28. On a map, a housing development is represented by a rectangle with a width of 5 cm and a length of 10 cm. If the development is 2 miles wide, how long is it?

*29. **Challenge** At SaveRite, a 4-ounce carton of juice costs \$0.85 and a 16-ounce carton costs \$2.70. Which size carton would you buy to pay the least amount per ounce?

Use the following information for Problems 30 and 31: On the game show, 'Who Wants to Win Money,' 4 out of 7 people in the 434-person audience chose the correct answer to the geography question and 1 out of 2 people chose the incorrect answer to the trivia question.

*30. **Challenge** How many people answered the geography question correctly?

*31. **Challenge** How many answered the trivia question incorrectly?

Percents

A ratio that compares a number to 100 is a **percent**.

The symbol used for percent is %, and it means "per one hundred." So, 25% means "25 per 100." Since you can write every ratio as a fraction or decimal, you can also write every percent as a fraction or decimal.

NOTATION

% percent

Converting Between Fraction, Decimal, and Percent

Use the following rules to make conversions involving percents.

PROPERTIES

Percent to Fraction: To write a percent as a fraction, remove the % sign, then write the number with a denominator of 100. Simplify the fraction if necessary.

Fraction to Percent: To write a fraction as a percent, divide the numerator by the denominator and multiply by 100%.

Percent to Decimal: To write a percent as a decimal, remove the % sign, then divide by 100.

Decimal to Percent: To write a decimal as a percent, multiply by 100%.

REMEMBER

To multiply by 100, move the decimal point two places to the right. To divide by 100, move the decimal point two places to the left.

Example 1 Write each percent as a decimal.

A. 145% **B.** 0.38%

Solution Remove the % sign and divide by 100.

A. $145\% = 145 \div 100$
$= 1.45$ ■

B. $0.38\% = 0.38 \div 100$
$= 0.0038$ ■

Example 2 Write each decimal as a percent.

A. 0.003 **B.** 6.5

Solution Multiply by 100%.

A. $0.003 = 0.003 \cdot 100\%$
$= 0.3\%$ ■

B. $6.5 = 6.5 \cdot 100\%$
$= 650\%$ ■

(continued)

Example 3 Write each fraction as a percent.

A. $\frac{5}{8}$ **B.** $\frac{7}{20}$

Solution Divide the numerator by the denominator and multiply by 100%.

A. $\frac{5}{8} = (5 \div 8) \cdot 100\%$
$= 0.625 \cdot 100\%$
$= 62.5\%$ ■

B. $\frac{7}{20} = (7 \div 20) \cdot 100\%$
$= 0.35 \cdot 100\%$
$= 35\%$ ■

Using the Percent Proportion

You can use the following proportion to solve percent problems.

$$\frac{\text{part}}{\text{whole}} = \frac{\text{percent}}{100}$$

Example 4

A. Thirteen is what percent of 25?

Solution Write the percent proportion and fill in the known information.

$\frac{\text{part}}{\text{whole}} = \frac{\text{percent}}{100}$

$\frac{13}{25} = \frac{x}{100}$ Use x for the unknown percent.

$13 \cdot 100 = 25x$ Means-Extremes Product Property

$1300 = 25x$ Multiply.

$52 = x$ Divide each side by 25.

Thirteen is 52% of 25. ■

B. What is 215% of 212?

Solution Write and solve a percent proportion.

$\frac{\text{part}}{\text{whole}} = \frac{\text{percent}}{100}$

$\frac{x}{212} = \frac{215}{100}$ Use x for the unknown part.

$100x = 212 \cdot 215$ Means-Extremes Product Property

$100x = 45{,}580$ Multiply.

$x = 455.8$ Divide each side by 100.

Four hundred fifty-five and eight tenths is 215% of 212. ■

C. One hundred twenty-two is 40% of what number?

Solution

$$\frac{\text{part}}{\text{whole}} = \frac{\text{percent}}{100}$$

$\frac{122}{x} = \frac{40}{100}$ Use x for the unknown whole.

$122 \cdot 100 = x \cdot 40$ Means-Extremes Product Property

$12{,}200 = 40x$ Multiply.

$305 = x$ Divide each side by 40. ■

Application: Recycling

Example 5 During a recycling drive, the Green Club collected 125 cans and bottles. If 72% of these were cans, how many bottles were collected?

Solution Let x equal the number of bottles collected. If 72% were cans, then 28% (100% − 72% = 28%) were bottles. Use this to write and solve a percent proportion.

$$\frac{\text{part}}{\text{whole}} = \frac{\text{percent}}{100}$$

$\frac{x}{125} = \frac{28}{100}$ Note that x (the number of bottles) is an unknown part.

$x \cdot 100 = 125 \cdot 28$ Means-Extremes Product Property

$100x = 3500$ Multiply.

$x = 35$ Divide each side by 100.

A total of 35 bottles were collected during the recycling drive. ■

Problem Set

Write each percent as a decimal.

1. 8.4%

2. 215%

3. 147.3%

4. 0.09%

Write each number as a percent.

5. 2.7

6. 0.05

7. $\frac{4}{5}$

8. $\frac{3}{8}$

9. 0.7

10. 1.325

11. $\frac{27}{40}$

***12.** **Challenge** $2\frac{2}{5}$

Solve. Use the percent proportion and show your work.

13. Twenty-four is what percent of 60?
14. Seventeen is what percent of 20?
15. What is 48% of 180?
16. What is 160% of 94?
17. Twelve is 30% of what number?
18. Eighty is 125% of what number?
19. Thirty-six is 40% of what number?
20. Eighteen is what percent of 15?
21. What is 74% of 325?
22. Sixty-five is what percent of 81.25?
23. What is 30% of 25?

*24. **Challenge** Forty-one and seventy-six one hundredths is 43.5% of what number?

Set up an equation and solve it to answer each question.

25. Yoshi spent $28.80 at the supermarket. This was 36% of the cash he had in his wallet.
    - **A.** How much cash did Yoshi have before he paid his supermarket bill?
    - **B.** After shopping, Yoshi bought dinner for his family for $16.50. He gave the server a 16% tip. How much money did Yoshi have left?
26. Julia has two memory cards for her digital camera. She has used 332.8 MB of the 512 MB card, and 22.4 MB of the 32 MB card. Which card has the highest percent used, and what is the difference between the percents?
27. Marisol scored 80% on her math test. The test had 45 questions, and each question was worth the same amount of the final score. How many questions did Marisol answer correctly?
28. Three candidates were running for class president. Of the 250 students eligible to vote, 75 voted for Carlos and 32% of the students voted for LaToya. Of those who didn't vote for Carlos or LaToya, 60% voted for Stephanie and the rest of the students chose not to vote.
    - **A.** What percent of the eligible students voted for Carlos?
    - **B.** How many votes did LaToya receive?
    - **C.** How many votes did Stephanie receive?
    - **D.** Who won the election?
29. Last softball season, Tai was at bat 75 times and got 24 hits. Show Tai's batting average as a percent and as a decimal to the thousandths place.
30. In Alan's survey of his classmates, he asked if they preferred swimming, skating, or skiing. In the survey, 27.5% of Alan's classmates chose swimming.
    - **A.** If 11 classmates chose swimming, how many classmates does Alan have?
    - **B.** Seventeen classmates chose skiing. What percent was that?

Applications: Percents

A percent of change shows how much an amount increases or decreases.

PERCENT OF CHANGE

$$\text{percent of change} = \frac{\text{amount of change}}{\text{original amount}}$$

Percent Increase and Decrease

Example 1

A. On Saturday, 410 people visited a museum. On Sunday, 123 fewer people visited. What is the percent decrease in the number of visitors from Saturday to Sunday?

Solution

$$\text{percent of change} = \frac{\text{amount of change}}{\text{original amount}} = \frac{123}{410} = 0.3$$

The percent decrease is 30%. ■

REMEMBER

Multiply by 100% to change a decimal to a percent.

B. The table shows the number of students enrolled at a summer science program during the summers of 2006 and 2007. Find the percent increase in the enrollment from 2006 to 2007.

Year	2006	2007
Number of Students	240	276

Solution

$$\text{percent of change} = \frac{\text{amount of change}}{\text{original amount}} = \frac{276 - 240}{240} = \frac{36}{240} = 0.15 = 15\%$$

The percent increase was 15%. ■

Discounts and Markups

When an item at a store goes on sale, the change in price reflects a **discount**. When the price of an item is increased, the change reflects a **markup**. To solve discount and markup problems where the percent is unknown, you can use the percent of change formula.

You can write more specific equations for discount and markup:

DISCOUNT PERCENT

$$\text{Discount Percent} = \frac{\text{Discount Amount}}{\text{Original Price}}$$

(continued)

MARKUP PERCENT

$$\text{Markup Percent} = \frac{\text{Markup Amount}}{\text{Original Price}}$$

If the original or new price is unknown, you will need to use a formula that relates the original price, the new price, and a discount or markup percent.

$$\begin{aligned} \text{New Price} &= \text{Original Price} - \text{Discount Amount} \\ &= \text{Original Price} - \text{Discount Percent} \cdot \text{Original Price} \\ \text{New Price} &= \text{Original Price}\ (1 - \text{Discount Percent}) \end{aligned}$$

You can also solve this equation for the Original Price:

$$\text{New Price} = \text{Original Price}\ (1 - \text{Discount Percent})$$

$$\frac{\text{New Price}}{1 - \text{Discount Percent}} = \text{Original Price}$$

Example 2

A. A store manager buys T-shirts for \$3 each and sells them for \$10.50 each. Find the percent markup in the price of each T-shirt.

Solution The amount of markup is $\$10.50 - \$3 = \$7.50$.

$$\text{percent change} = \frac{\text{amount of increase}}{\text{original amount}} = \frac{7.50}{3.00} = 2.5$$

The percent markup is 250%. ■

B. A skateboard that regularly costs \$145 is now being sold at a 35% discount. Find the new price of the skateboard.

Solution

$$\begin{aligned} \text{New Price} &= \text{Original Price}\ (1 - \text{Discount Percent}) \\ &= 145(1 - 35\%) \\ &= 145(1 - 0.35) \\ &= 145(0.65) \\ &= 94.25 \end{aligned}$$

The new price is \$94.25. ■

C. A computer was bought at a 20% discount for \$639. Find the original price of the computer.

Solution

$$\begin{aligned} \text{Original Price} &= \frac{\text{New Price}}{(1 - \text{Discount Percent})} \\ &= \frac{639}{(1 - 20\%)} \\ &= \frac{639}{(1 - 0.20)} \\ &= \frac{639}{(0.80)} \\ &= 798.75 \end{aligned}$$

The original price was \$798.75. ■

D. Adele spent \$56 on a handbag that was originally \$80. Calculate the percent discount she received on the handbag.

Solution

$$\text{percent of change} = \frac{\text{amount of change}}{\text{original amount}} = \frac{80 - 56}{80} = \frac{24}{80} = 0.30$$

Adele received a 30% discount on the handbag. ■

Simple Interest

When a bank regularly adds money to a savings account, the account is collecting **interest**. There are different kinds of interest. **Simple interest** is earned at a fixed percent of the initial deposit, or **principal** amount.

SIMPLE INTEREST FORMULA

$I = Prt$, where I is the amount of interest, P is the principal, r is the **interest rate,** and t is time in years.

Example 3

A. Laura invests \$600 at a simple annual interest rate of 4.5%. Find the amount of interest Laura will earn over 3 years.

Solution Substitute 600 for P, 0.045 for r, and 3 for t in the simple interest formula.

$$\begin{aligned} I &= Prt \\ &= 600 \cdot 0.045 \cdot 3 \\ &= 81 \end{aligned}$$

Laura will earn \$81. ■

REMEMBER

You should change all percents to decimal or fraction form before using them in a formula.

B. Juan earned \$945 in interest by investing \$4500 at a 6% simple interest rate. For what length of time did Juan invest his money?

Solution Substitute 945 for I, 4500 for P, and 0.06 for r in the simple interest formula. Then solve for t.

$$\begin{aligned} I &= Prt \\ 945 &= 4500 \cdot 0.06 \cdot t \\ 945 &= 270t \\ 3.5 &= t \end{aligned}$$

Juan invested his money for 3.5 years. ■

Problem Set

Set up an equation or expression and solve it to answer each question.

1. In July, an average of 120 people visited the state park each day. In December, the number of visitors decreased to 45 per day. Find the percent decrease between July and December.

2. Over the past five years, the number of students attending Deirdre's high school has increased by a total of 8%. This year, 702 students attend the high school. How many attended five years ago?

3. Zoe sold her painting to an art dealer for \$325. The dealer priced the painting for retail sale at a 30% markup. During the summer art festival, he sold the painting at 10% off the retail price.

   A. Find the retail price.

   B. Find the dealer's selling price at the art festival.

4. Last year, Jason earned \$25,750. This year, he earned \$27,037.50. Find the percent increase in his income.

5. The bookstore offers a 20% discount to teachers buying books for class. What is the teachers' discount price on a book originally priced at \$28.95?

6. The specialty store marks up kitchen products at 40% over wholesale. The discount store marks up at 30%. What is the difference between the prices of a blender at the specialty and discount stores, if the wholesale price is \$52?

7. A researcher surveyed elementary school students before and after a physical fitness seminar at the school. The table shows the results.

Average Minutes Spent Per Week on Activity		
	Before seminar	After seminar
Exercise	95	120
Television	360	190

   A. What percent increase was found in the number of hours of exercise per week? Round your answer to the nearest percent.

   B. What percent decrease was found in the number of hours of television watching per week? Round your answer to the nearest percent.

8. During her first year on the math team, Fiona earned 208 points at math meets. During her second year, she earned 260 points. How much did Fiona improve, expressed as a percent increase?

9. Last month, Lauren opened a shop to sell handmade beads. In her first week, she sold 120 beads. In her fourth week, she sold 204 beads. Find the percent increase in Lauren's bead sales.

10. Erick increased a number by 20%. He then decreased the new number by 20%.

    A. If Erick's original number was 90, what was his final number?

    B. Is the final number the same as the original number? Explain.

11. The world languages club is selling candles as a fundraiser. They pay \$1.80 for each candle, and then sell them at a 75% markup. What is the selling price of each candle?

12. After a 30% increase in patients, a clinic treated 260 patients per week. How many patients did the clinic see per week before the increase?

13. Anita bought a bicycle for \$229.95 including 5% sales tax. What was the price before tax?

14. The retail price of a sweater is \$30. The sweater goes on sale at 20% off, and then goes on clearance at 25% off the sale price. What is the clearance price?

15. Omer earned \$8500 and invested 15% of his earnings in an account with a 4.5% simple interest rate. How much interest will he earn on his initial investment in 4 years?

16. The conservation club was able to find enough litter around the town to fill 65 garbage bags. After a community clean-up campaign, the club found enough litter to fill $42\frac{1}{4}$ garbage bags. What was the percent decrease in the litter that the club found?

17. The table shows yearly ticket sales and revenues for a theater.

Annual Report		
	Tickets Sold	Ticket Revenues
2005	224,500	\$1,459,250
2006	262,919	\$1,708,973.50
2007	289,080	\$1,879,020

A. What was the percent increase in revenues from 2005–2007?

B. If all other factors remain the same, including average ticket price, how many tickets must be sold in 2008 to create a 10% increase in revenues from 2007–2008?

18. Min bought two equally priced music CDs for \$17.92 at a 30%-off sale. Find the original price of each CD.

19. Tomas wanted to buy a computer priced at \$950. He waited for the store's annual clearance sale and bought the computer for \$712.50. What percent was the discount at the clearance sale?

20. In 2000, 8500 dogs lived in Emilio's town. In 2005, this number increased to 9775. What was the percent increase in dogs living in Emilio's town from 2000 to 2005?

21. Luis opened a savings account with \$250. Each month he deposited \$50. After 12 months, what was the percent increase in his savings account, not including interest?

22. A restaurant chain had 15,250 locations in 1975. By 2000, there were 21,655 locations. What was the percent increase in locations over the 25-year period?

23. In Collegetown, 6500 people attended the first football game of the season. That number increased by 35% for the homecoming game. How many people attended the homecoming game?

*24. **Challenge** When money is invested in an account that compounds annually, each year's interest is added to the principal. The next year's interest is calculated based on the new total principal (previous year's principal plus previous year's interest). Using the simple interest formula, calculate the compound interest on an initial investment of \$2000 for the first 3 years at 5% interest.

*25. **Challenge** Chang had \$5300 to invest. He invested part of it at a 5% simple interest rate, and the rest at a 4% simple interest rate. In the first year he earned a total of \$244 interest. How much did he invest at each rate?

Use the formula $I = prt$ to solve.

26. Basir earned \$631.40 in 7 years on an investment at a 5.5% simple interest rate. How much was Basir's investment?

27. Benito invested \$750 at a simple interest rate of 5.5%. Find the amount of interest Benito will earn after 5 years.

28. Aisha earned \$2484 in interest on a \$9200 investment at a 4.5% simple interest rate. How long was Aisha's money invested?

29. A charity received a donation of \$20,500, and invested it at a 6% simple interest rate.

A. How long would it take for the charity to earn \$5,535 interest?

B. What is the minimum number of full years the charity should allow the investment to mature to double the original investment?

30. Jennifer earned \$249.60 in $6\frac{1}{2}$ years on a \$640 investment. What was the simple interest rate?

Applications: Mixture Problems

Word problems that involve a mixture of two or more items of different value are mixture problems.

On many occasions, you can describe one variable in terms of another variable to simplify solving for unknown quantities. For example, if a number is twice a second number and five more than three times a third number, you can write each of the three numbers in terms of one variable.

Let x, y, and z represent the three unknown numbers. Then $x = 2y$ and $x = 3z + 5$. After solving the equations for y and z, you end up with three unknown quantities in one variable: x, $\frac{1}{2}x$, and $\frac{x - 5}{3}$.

Trail Mix

Example 1

A. Ted made trail mix for the school field trip by mixing together Sunshine Mix, which costs \$2.50 per pound, Fruit Mix, which costs \$1.50 per pound, and Nut Mix, which costs \$2 per pound. Ted used twice as much Fruit Mix and half as much Nut Mix as he did Sunshine Mix. How many pounds of each mix did he use if the total cost for all the trail mix was \$19.50?

Solution Let x equal the number of pounds of Sunshine Mix, then complete the table. Notice that the last column is found by multiplying the previous two columns.

TIP

The first two columns are for set-up purposes only. The equation comes from the last column.

	Number of Pounds	Cost per Pound	Total Cost
Sunshine Mix	x	2.50	$2.50x$
Fruit Mix	$2x$	1.50	$3x$
Nut Mix	$0.5x$	2	x
Total			\$19.50

Write and solve an equation.

$2.50x + 3x + x = 19.50$ Use the last column to write the equation.

$6.50x = 19.50$ Combine like terms.

$x = 3$ Divide each side by 6.50.

Substitute $x = 3$ into the expressions for the number of pounds to find the number of pounds of each mix:

Sunshine Mix: $x = 3$

Fruit Mix: $2x = 2 \cdot 3 = 6$

Nut Mix: $0.5x = 0.5 \cdot 3 = 1.5$

Ted used 3 pounds of Sunshine Mix, 6 pounds of Fruit Mix, and 1.5 pounds of Nut Mix. ■

B. How much Crackle Mix, which costs \$3.50 per pound, should be mixed with Lake Mix, which costs \$2 per pound, to make 5 pounds of trail mix costing \$3.05 per pound?

Solution Let x represent the number of pounds of Crackle Mix. The total amount of Crackle Mix and Trail Mix is 5 pounds, so $5 - x$ represents the number of pounds of Lake Mix.

	Number of Pounds	Cost per Pound	Total Cost
Crackle Mix	x	3.50	$3.5x$
Lake Mix	$5 - x$	2	$2(5 - x)$
Total	5	5.50	15.25

Write and solve an equation.

$3.5x + 2(5 - x) = 15.25$ Use the last column to write the equation.

$3.5x + 10 - 2x = 15.25$ Distribute 2.

$1.5x + 10 = 15.25$ Combine like terms.

$1.5x = 5.25$ Subtract 10 from each side.

$x = 3.5$ Divide.

Crackle Mix: $x = 3.5$

Lake Mix: $5 - x = 5 - 3.5 = 1.5$

Three and a half pounds of Crackle Mix should be mixed with 1.5 pounds of Lake Mix. ■

Acid Solution

An acid solution is a liquid solution, of which a percentage is acid. For example, if you mix 4 ounces of acid with 4 ounces of water, you make 8 ounces of a 50% acid solution.

Example 2 A chemist has 12 liters of a 40% acid solution. How many liters of a 15% acid solution should he mix with it to make it a 35% acid solution?

Solution Let x represent the amount of 15% acid solution. Since the amount of 15% solution is added to the 12 liters of the 40% solution, let $x + 12$ represent the amount of 35% acid solution.

	Liters of Solution	Percent Acid	Liters of Acid
40% solution	12	0.40	4.8
15% solution	x	0.15	$0.15x$
35% solution	$x + 12$	0.35	$0.35(x + 12)$

(continued)

Write and solve an equation.

$4.8 + 0.15x = 0.35(x + 12)$	Use the last column to write the equation.
$4.8 + 0.15x = 0.35x + 4.2$	Distribute 0.35.
$0.6 + 0.15x = 0.35x$	Subtract 4.2 from each side.
$0.6 = 0.2x$	Subtract $0.15x$ from each side.
$3 = x$	Divide each side by 0.2.

Three liters of the 15% solution should be added to the 40% solution. ■

Coin Problems

Example 3 A bag containing 116 dimes and quarters is worth \$23. How many of each type of coin are in the bag?

Solution Let x represent the number of dimes. The total number of coins is 116, so subtract the number of dimes from the total number of coins to get the number of quarters. Let $116 - x$ represent the number of quarters.

	Number of Coins	Value of Each Coin	Total Value
Dimes	x	0.10	$0.10x$
Quarters	$116 - x$	0.25	$0.25(116 - x)$
Total			23

Write and solve an equation.

$0.10x + 0.25(116 - x) = 23$	Use the last column to write the equation.
$0.10x + 29 - 0.25x = 23$	Distribute 0.25.
$-0.15x + 29 = 23$	Combine like terms.
$-0.15x = -6$	Subtract 29 from each side.
$x = 40$	Divide.

dimes: $x = 40$

quarters: $116 - x = 116 - 40 = 76$

There are 40 dimes and 76 quarters. ■

Problem Set

Solve. For each problem:

A. Prepare a table to set up the problem.
B. Write and solve an equation to model the problem.
C. Solve for the components of the mixture.
D. Give your answer in a complete sentence. If necessary, round your answer to the nearest tenth.

1. Iris made a quilt using 200 rectangular pieces of fabric. Each red piece covers 16 square inches and each white piece covers 64 square inches. How many pieces of each color did she use if the quilt covers 5600 square inches?

2. How much yellow coneflower seed, which costs \$12 per ounce, should be mixed with purple coneflower seed, which costs \$6.50 per ounce, to make a pound of flower seed mix costing \$10 per ounce?

3. A contractor purchased boxes of three types of nails at the hardware store. The clipped head nails cost \$32, the large round head nails cost \$40, and the small round head nails cost \$34. She bought twice as many boxes of clipped head nails and three times as many boxes of small round head nails as she bought large round head nails. How many boxes of each nail did she buy if the total cost for all the nails was \$824?

4. Horatio bought 15 pieces of pottery to decorate shelves in his living room. He bought several large vases which cost \$11 each and several small vases which cost \$7 each. How many of each size did he buy if the total cost was \$129?

5. To make 2 pounds of organic mixed nuts that cost \$10 per pound, how many pounds of organic almonds at \$14 per pound and organic cashews at \$8 per pound should be mixed together? Give your answer using fractions.

6. Emma broke open her piggy bank and found 254 pennies, nickels, and dimes worth \$10.96. She found twice as many pennies as dimes. How many of each coin did she find?

7. Raouf spent \$77 renting 20 movies over three months. How many classic movies, which cost \$3.50, and new releases, which cost \$4.50, did he rent?

8. Traci bought 15 candles for a centerpiece. She bought twice as many scented candles, which cost \$4 each, as small candles, which cost \$1 each. She also bought large candles, which cost \$2 each. If she spent \$42 for the candles, how many of each did she buy?

9. Karthik is preparing a song playlist from his collection of 2.5-minute and 3-minute songs. How many of each song length should he use to make a 1-hour playlist of his 22 favorite songs?

10. Jorge is buying 8 fish for his aquarium. How many Fancy Male Blue Guppies, which cost \$3.75 each, and Platies, which cost \$1.75, can Jorge buy if he has \$20 to spend?

11. Vernon wants to make a breakfast smoothie of skim milk, which has 300 mg of calcium per cup, nonfat plain yogurt, which has 490 mg of calcium per cup, and banana, which has 7 mg of calcium per cup. How much of each should he mix to get 400 mg of calcium in a cup of smoothie if he wants to use half as much banana as milk?

12. How much white tea, which costs \$14.80 per pound, should be mixed with mint tea, which costs \$9 per pound, to make 2 pounds of tea blend that costs \$11 per pound?

13. A chemist has 10 liters of a 50% acid solution. How many liters of a 20% acid solution should he mix with it to make a 35% acid solution?

14. Ezekiel has 1 liter of a solution that is 3 parts water and 1 part vinegar. How much should he add of a 1 part water and 3 parts vinegar solution to make a solution that is 3 parts water and 2 parts vinegar?

15. A jewelry supply store owner wants to package a mixture of 22-mm beads, which cost \$4.25 each, and 21-mm beads, which cost \$2.75 each. How many of each type should the owner mix to make a bag of 30 that costs \$105?

16. Kim wants to make a fruit juice blend from pineapple juice, which has 44% RDA Vitamin C per cup, and orange juice, which has 133% RDA Vitamin C per cup. How much of each should she mix to get 100% RDA Vitamin C per cup?

17. Brad took a jar of 192 quarters and dimes that he had saved and poured it into the change converter machine in the grocery store. The total value was \$29.55. How many of each coin were in the jar?

18. Cuong made a patio using 274 6-inch square stones and 12-inch square stones. How many of each square did he use if the stones cover 91 square feet?

*19. **Challenge** Zoe bought 20 picture frames of various sizes. She bought 3 times as many 5×7 frames, which cost \$7 each, as 8×10 frames, which cost \$10 each. She bought the same number of 8×10 frames as she bought 11×14 frames, which cost \$15 each. Each 4×6 frame she bought cost \$5. How many of each size did she buy if the total cost was \$142?

*20. **Challenge** Claudia spent \$244 last year on movies at \$7 per ticket, concerts at \$15 per ticket, high school baseball games at \$5 per ticket, and high school football games at \$6 per ticket. If she attended 34 total events, 3 times as many movies as concerts, and 2 times as many baseball games as concerts, how many of each event did she attend?

UNIT 6 Linear Equations and Inequalities

The yellow lines are parallel.

You've probably heard the phrase, "That's where I draw the line!" In algebra, you can take this expression literally. Linear equations and their graphs play an important role in the never-ending quest to model the real world.

Big Ideas

- Expressions, equations, and inequalities express relationships between different entities.
- The laws of arithmetic can be used to simplify algebraic expressions and equations. Solving an equation means finding values for the variable or variables that make the equation a true statement.
- If you can create a mathematical model for a situation, you can use the model to solve other problems that you might not be able to solve otherwise. Algebraic equations can capture key relationships among quantities in the world.

Unit Topics

- Equations in Two Variables
- Graphs
- Lines and Intercepts
- Slope
- Slope-Intercept Form
- Point-Slope Form
- Parallel and Perpendicular Lines
- Equations From Graphs
- Applications: Linear Models
- Graphing Linear Inequalities
- Inequalities From Graphs

Equations in Two Variables

An equation in the form $Ax + By = C$ is a linear equation in two variables.

Checking Solutions to Equations in Two Variables

A solution to a linear equation in two variables is an ordered pair (x, y). You can determine if an ordered pair is a solution to an equation in two variables by substituting the values of x and y into the equation. If a true statement results, the ordered pair is a solution to the equation.

Example 1 Determine if each ordered pair is a solution to the equation $4x - y = 8$.

A. $(0, 8)$

Solution Substitute 0 for x and 8 for y in the equation $4x - y = 8$.

$$\begin{aligned} 4x - y &= 8 \\ 4 \cdot 0 - 8 &\stackrel{?}{=} 8 \\ 0 - 8 &\stackrel{?}{=} 8 \\ -8 &\neq 8 \end{aligned}$$

The ordered pair $(0, 8)$ is not a solution to the equation $4x - y = 8$. ■

B. $(-1, -12)$

Solution Substitute -1 for x and -12 for y in the equation $4x - y = 8$.

$$\begin{aligned} 4x - y &= 8 \\ 4 \cdot (-1) - (-12) &\stackrel{?}{=} 8 \\ -4 + 12 &\stackrel{?}{=} 8 \\ 8 &= 8 \checkmark \end{aligned}$$

The ordered pair $(-1, -12)$ is a solution to the equation $4x - y = 8$. ■

Finding Solutions to an Equation in Two Variables

To find solutions to an equation in two variables, first solve the equation for y in terms of x. Once you have the equation solved for y, choose some values of x and substitute them to find values of y.

Example 2 Find four solutions of the equation $6x + 3y = 9$.

(continued)

Solution

Step 1 Solve the equation for y.

$$6x + 3y = 9$$

$$6x + 3y - 6x = 9 - 6x \quad \text{Subtract } 6x \text{ from each side.}$$

$$3y = 9 - 6x \quad \text{Simplify.}$$

$$\frac{3y}{3} = \frac{9 - 6x}{3} \quad \text{Divide each side by 3.}$$

$$y = \frac{9}{3} - \frac{6x}{3} \quad \text{Simplify.}$$

$$y = 3 - 2x \quad \text{Simplify.}$$

Step 2 Using the values for x in the table below, find each value of y.

x	−2	0	4	8
y				

When $x = -2$:

$$\begin{aligned} y &= 3 - 2x \\ &= 3 - 2 \cdot (-2) \\ &= 3 + 4 \\ &= 7 \end{aligned}$$

When $x = 0$:

$$\begin{aligned} y &= 3 - 2x \\ &= 3 - 2 \cdot 0 \\ &= 3 - 0 \\ &= 3 \end{aligned}$$

When $x = 4$:

$$\begin{aligned} y &= 3 - 2x \\ &= 3 - 2 \cdot 4 \\ &= 3 - 8 \\ &= -5 \end{aligned}$$

When $x = 8$:

$$\begin{aligned} y &= 3 - 2x \\ &= 3 - 2 \cdot 8 \\ &= 3 - 16 \\ &= -13 \end{aligned}$$

The table below shows the values for y.

x	−2	0	4	8
y	7	3	−5	−13

Four solutions are (−2, 7), (0, 3), (4, −5), and (8, −13). There are infinitely many other solutions to this equation. ■

Application: Admission Prices

You can use equations in two variables to solve real-world applications.

Example 3 At an art museum, admission tickets cost \$12 for adults and \$8 for children. On Sunday, 65 child tickets were sold and a total of \$1780 was collected for admission. How many adult tickets were sold?

Solution

Step 1 *Identify* Find the number of adult tickets sold.

Step 2 *Strategize* Let T represent the total amount collected, a represent the number of adult tickets sold, and c represent the number of child tickets sold.

Step 3 *Set Up* Write an equation to model the problem.

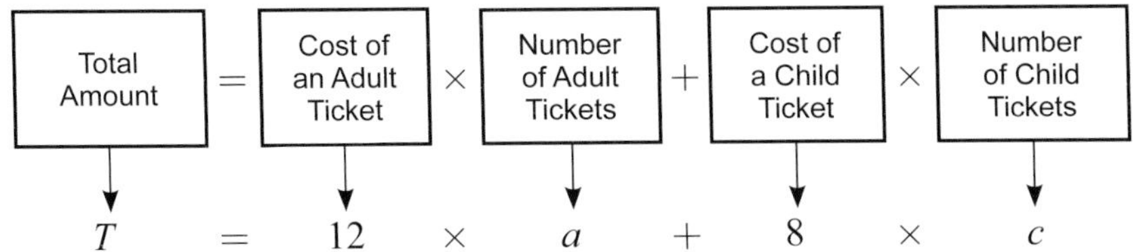

The problem is modeled by the equation $T = 12a + 8c$.

Step 4 *Solve* Substitute 1780 into the equation for T and 65 into the equation for c.

$T = 12a + 8c$

$1780 = 12a + 8 \cdot 65$

Solve the equation for a.

$1780 = 12a + 8 \cdot 65$	Write the equation.
$1780 = 12a + 520$	Multiply.
$1260 = 12a$	Subtract 520 from each side.
$105 = a$	Divide each side by 12.

105 adult tickets were sold.

Step 5 *Check*

$T = 12a + 8c$	Write the original equation.
$1780 \stackrel{?}{=} 12 \cdot 105 + 8 \cdot 65$	Substitute 1780 for T, 105 for a, and 65 for c.
$1780 \stackrel{?}{=} 1260 + 520$	Multiply.
$1780 = 1780$ ✓	Add. ■

Problem Set

Determine if the ordered pair is a solution to the equation $3x + 2y = 6$.

1. (10, –12) **2.** (8, –5) **3.** (–2, 0) **4.** (4, –3)

Determine if the ordered pair is a solution to the equation $3x - 3y = 21$.

5. (12, –5) **6.** (5, –2) **7.** (–1, 3) **8.** (–3, –10)

Determine if the ordered pair is a solution to the equation $2x - \frac{y}{2} = -8$.

9. (3, 28) **10.** (–5, –36)

Solve the equation for y and then find the value of y for the given x-value.

11. $5x + y = 10$

A. $x = -2$

B. $x = 3$

12. $2x + 5y = 5$

A. $x = 15$

B. $x = -5$

13. $3y - 8x = 2$

A. $x = 2$

B. $x = -1$

C. $x = \frac{1}{2}$

14. $3y - 6x = -3$

A. $x = -4$

B. $x = 2$

15. $2(x - 3) + 5 = 4y - 3(x + y)$

A. $x = -2$

B. $x = 3$

16. $3x + 4y = 12$

A. $x = 8$

B. $x = -4$

17. $5x + 4y = 8$

A. $x = -4$

B. $x = 0$

C. $x = -3$

18. $4x - 2y = 10$

A. $x = -2$

B. $x = 5$

19. $2(2x - y) + 2 = y - 4$

A. $x = -3$

B. $x = 9$

20. $3x - 2y = -7$

A. $x = 3$

B. $x = -1$

21. $2(x + y) - 3(2x - 4) = 4(y - 2)$

A. $x = 3$

B. $x = -1$

C. $x = -\frac{1}{3}$

***22.** **Challenge** $\frac{1}{3}x - \frac{2}{5}y = 4$

A. $x = 12$

B. $x = -6$

C. $x = 3$

***23.** **Challenge** $\frac{x}{2} + \frac{2}{3}y = x - 2$

A. $x = -8$

B. $x = 6$

Solve using an equation with two variables. For each problem:

A. Define variables for the unknowns.
B. Write an equation to model the problem.
C. Solve the equation.
D. Give your answer in a complete sentence.

24. An amusement park charges $21 for adults and $17 for children ages 12 and under. The Anderson family reunion included a trip to the amusement park, which cost a total of $706. If 8 adults and 7 teens were included in the trip, how many children ages 12 and under were included?

25. A wholesaler is packing books for shipping. A certain box will contain 24 novels, weighing 28 ounces each, and reference books weighing 52 ounces each. The total weight of the books is 984 ounces. How many reference books will be packed?

26. Lina bought 5 pounds of grapes at \$2.59 per pound. She also bought peanuts at \$1.95 per pound, and the total cost for peanuts and grapes was \$26.60. How many pounds of peanuts did she buy?

27. In one week, a shirt shop sold 68 embroidered shirts and 97 silk-screened shirts, for a total of \$2767.75 in sales. If the embroidered shirts sell for \$17.95 each, what is the price of each silk-screened shirt?

28. Tickets to the junior class charity fundraising dance cost \$15 for juniors and \$18 for other students. Eighty juniors bought tickets, and total ticket sales were \$2532. How many other students bought tickets?

29. Jake and Suki made a collage of photos for the yearbook. They used 30 large photos, each measuring 1.5 by 2 inches, and a number of small photos, each measuring 1.2 by 1.5 inches. The total area of the photos was 162 square inches. How many small photos did they use?

*30. **Challenge** A designer has pleated 6 yards of fabric. Each large pleat decreases the total length of the fabric by 2.5 inches. Each small pleat decreases the length by 1.75 inches. After pleating, the fabric is 92.25 inches long. If the designer made 25 large pleats, how many small pleats did he make?

Graphs

You have seen that you can use a number line to graph numbers. To graph an ordered pair, you need two number lines that form a coordinate plane.

DEFINITIONS

An **ordered pair** is a pair of numbers in which the first number is the ***x*-coordinate,** or **abscissa,** and the second number is the ***y*-coordinate,** or **ordinate,** of a point's location.

The **Cartesian coordinate system** is a method of locating points in a plane in which the coordinates of the points are its distances from two intersecting perpendicular lines called axes. The horizontal line, often called the ***x*-axis,** and the vertical line, often called the ***y*-axis,** intersect at the **origin.** The ordered pair at the origin is (0, 0) and is labeled *O*.

Graphing Points on a Coordinate Plane

HOW TO GRAPH A POINT ON A COORDINATE PLANE

1. Start at the origin.
2. Move left or right along the *x*-axis according to the *x*-coordinate of the ordered pair. Move right for positive numbers and left for negative numbers.
3. Move up or down according to the *y*-coordinate. Move up for positive numbers and down for negative numbers.

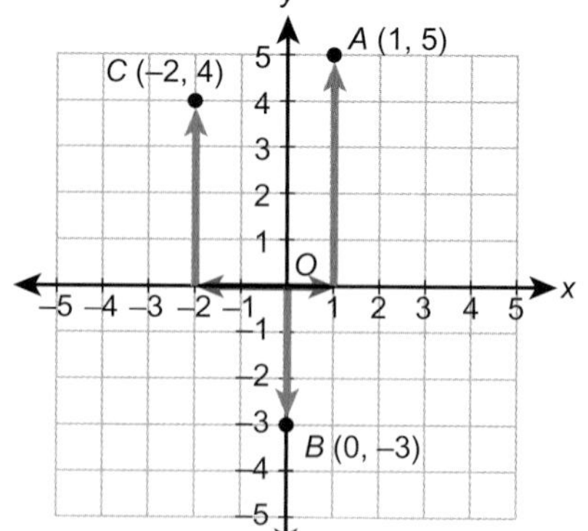

Example 1 Graph the points $A(1, 5)$, $B(0, -3)$, and $C(-2, 4)$ on the coordinate plane.

Solution

To graph $A(1, 5)$, start at the origin and move 1 unit to the right along the x-axis and 5 units up parallel to the y-axis.

To graph $B(0, -3)$, start at the origin. Since the x-coordinate is 0, you do not move any distance along the x-axis. Move 3 units down along the y-axis.

To graph $C(-2, 4)$, start at the origin and move 2 units to the left and 4 units up. ■

Identifying Points on a Coordinate Plane

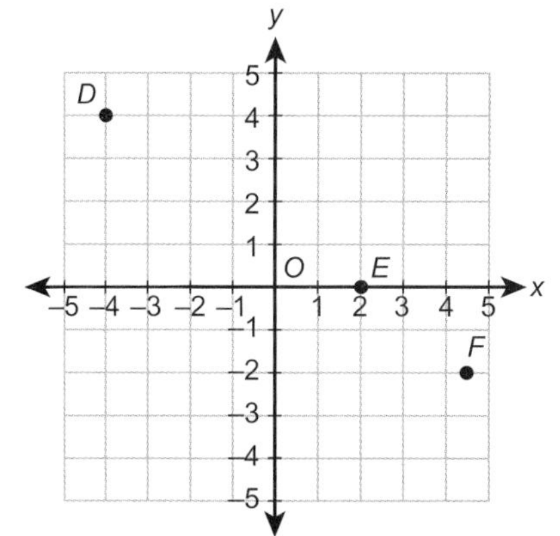

Example 2 Identify the coordinates of points D, E, and F.

Solution

Point D is 4 units to the left of the origin and 4 units up. The coordinates are $(-4, 4)$.

Point E is 2 units to the right of the origin and 0 units up. The coordinates are $(2, 0)$.

Point F is 4.5 units to the right of the origin and 2 units down. The coordinates are $(4.5, -2)$. ■

Identifying Quadrants

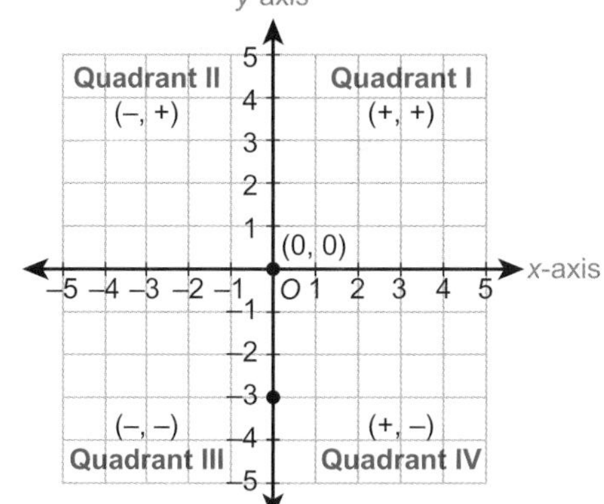

The coordinate plane is divided into four regions called **quadrants.** The quadrants are labeled using the Roman numerals I, II, III, and IV. Points in Quadrant I have a positive x-coordinate and a positive y-coordinate. In Quadrant II, points have a negative x-coordinate and a positive y-coordinate. Points in Quadrant III have a negative x-coordinate and a negative y-coordinate. In Quadrant IV, points have a positive x-coordinate and a negative y-coordinate. Points that lie on one of the axes are not in any quadrant.

Example 3 Identify the quadrant in which each point lies.

A. $Q(-2, 8)$

Solution The x-coordinate is negative and the y-coordinate is positive, so the point lies in Quadrant II. ■

B. $Z(0, 2)$

Solution The x-coordinate is zero and the y-coordinate is positive, so the point lies on the y-axis. ■

C. $B(4, -3)$

Solution The x-coordinate is positive and the y-coordinate is negative, so the point lies in Quadrant IV. ■

D. $(4, 3)$

Solution The x-coordinate is positive and the y-coordinate is positive, so the point lies in Quadrant I. ■

Application: City Map

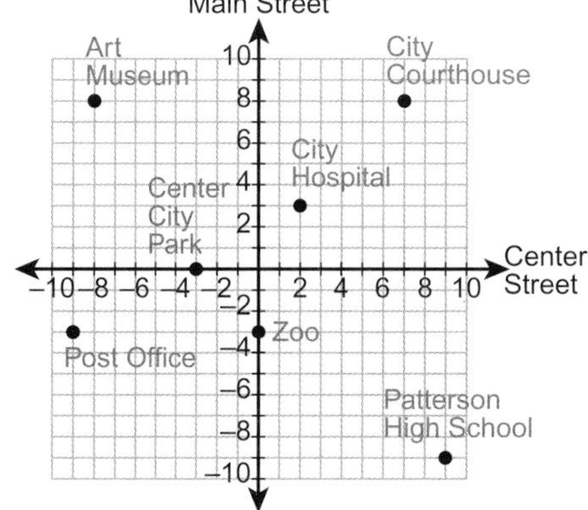

Example 4 A city planner uses the coordinate plane to identify locations in the city. Use the map to identify the coordinates of each of the following locations.

A. The Post Office

B. Center City Park

C. Patterson High School

D. The City Courthouse

(continued)

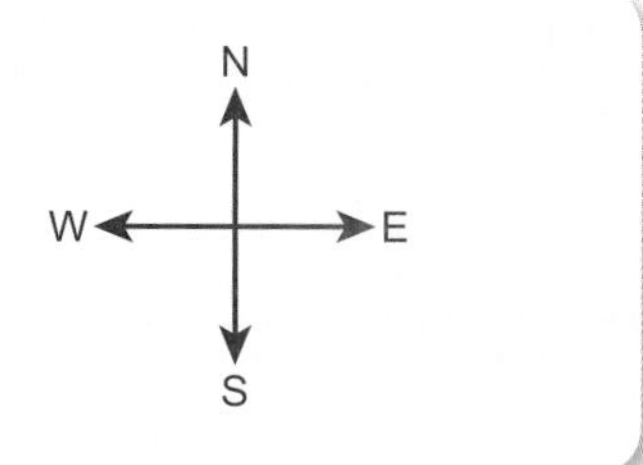

Solution

A. The Post Office is located 9 blocks west of Main Street and 3 blocks south of Center Street. Its coordinates are $(-9, -3)$. ■

B. Center City Park is on Center Street, 3 blocks west of Main Street. Its coordinates are $(-3, 0)$. ■

C. Patterson High School is located 9 blocks east of Main Street and 9 blocks south of Center Street. Its coordinates are $(9, -9)$. ■

D. The City Courthouse is located 7 blocks east of Main Street and 8 blocks north of Center Street. Its coordinates are $(7, 8)$. ■

Problem Set

Graph the points on the coordinate plane.

1. $A(3, -2), B(0, 5), C(-2, -1)$
2. $D(4, 1), E(3, -4), F(-2, 3)$
3. $R(-3, 0), S(0, -3), T(2, 5), U(5, 2)$
4. $K(-3, 1), L(0, 3), M(2, -2), N(-2, -4)$
5. $F(-2, -5), G(1, 2.5), H(1, -2), J(-3.5, 0)$
6. $A(2, -2.5), B(-1, 4), C(0.5, -3), D(-4, -4)$
7. $Q(1, 1), R(1, -1), S(-6, -4), T(-3, 2), U(-6, 0), V(8, 9)$

*8. **Challenge** $A(-8, -7), B(-6, 1.5), C(2.5, 9.5), D(7, 3), E(4, -3.5), F(0, -6.5)$

Identify the coordinates for each point.

9.

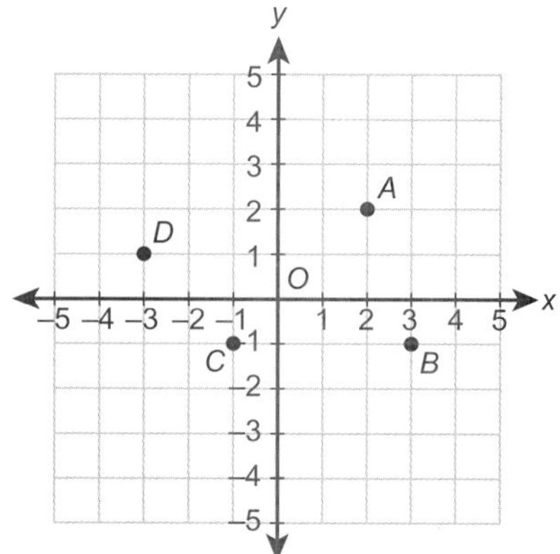

10.

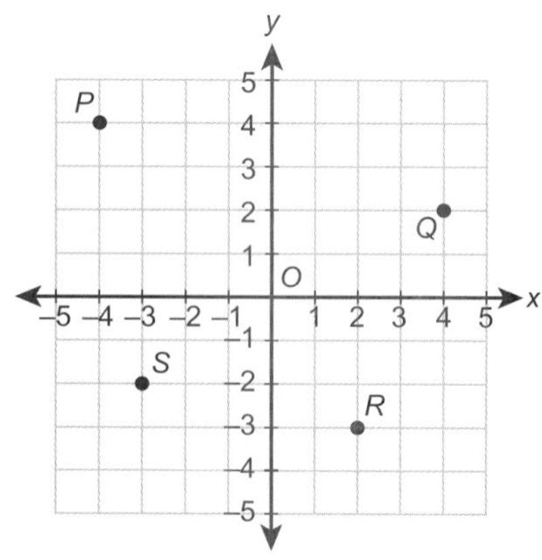

11.

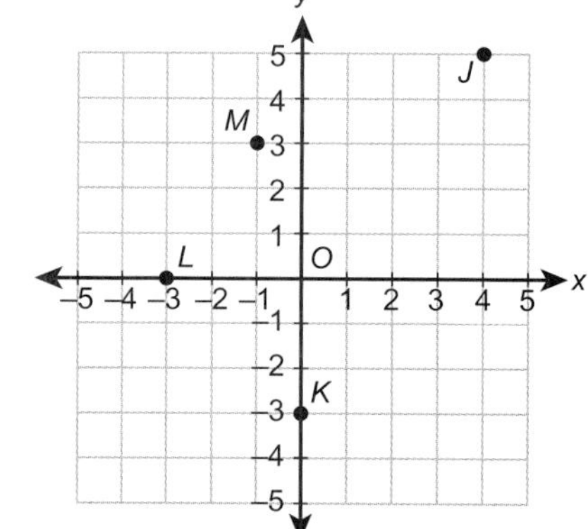

12.

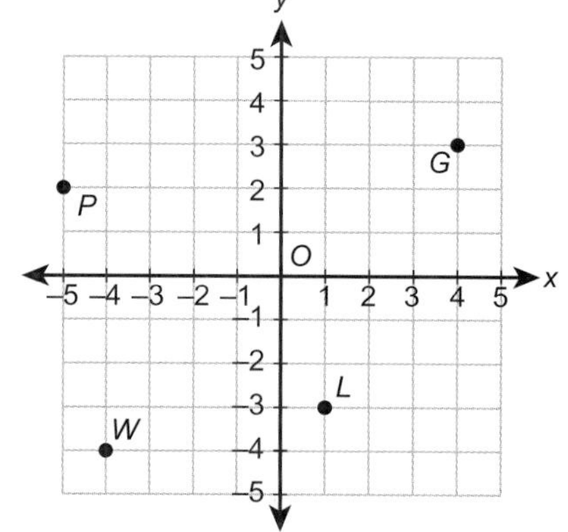

13.

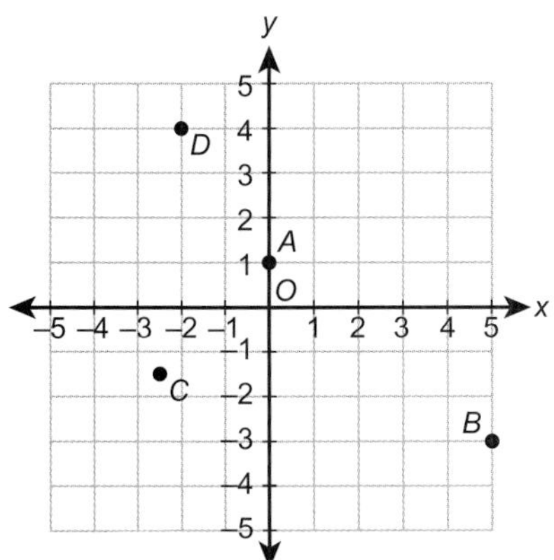

15.

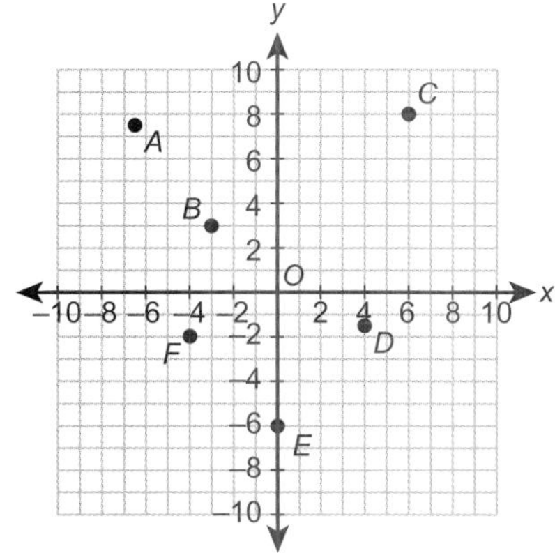

14.

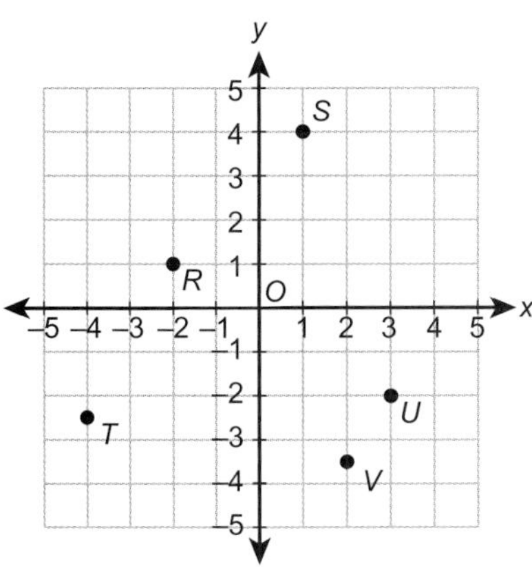

16.

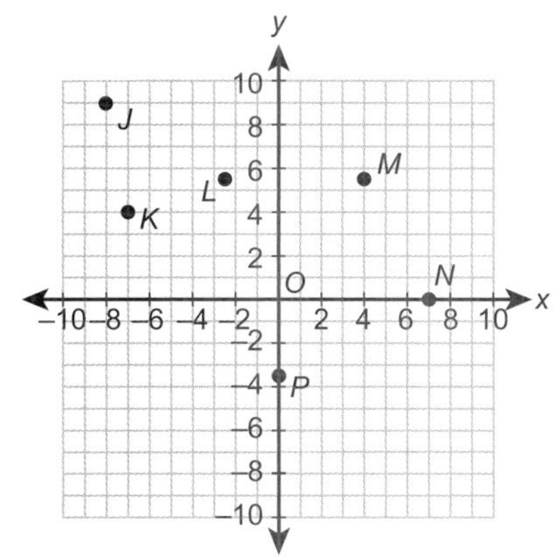

Identify the quadrant in which each point with the given coordinates lies. If the point lies on an axis, name the axis.

17. (−3, −1)

18. (−5, 0)

19. (3.4, 9)

20. (6, −4)

21. (−4, 6)

Give the coordinates and quadrant for each point.

22. **A.** Point P

B. Point M

23. **A.** Point H

B. Point J

24. **A.** Point T

B. Point Z

25. **A.** Point L

B. Point N

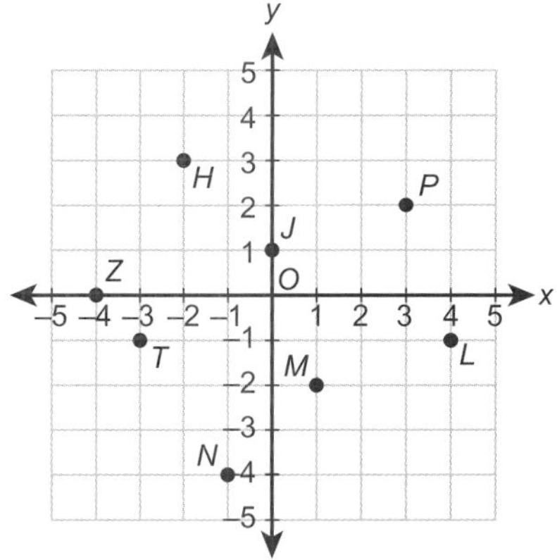

Use the maps to answer the questions.

26.

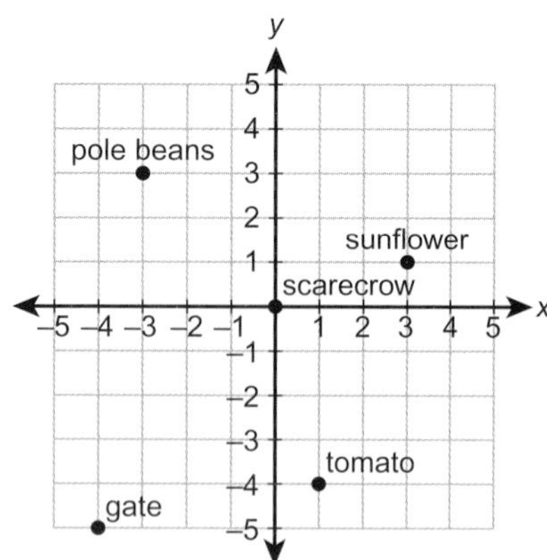

A. Name the plants that appear at each set of coordinates on the garden map: (–3, 3), (3, 1), (1, –4).

B. Give the coordinates for the gate and the scarecrow.

27. Create a map of a town with the following locations:

A. Main Street on the x-axis and Elm Street on the y-axis.

B. City Hall at (–4, –6), a High School at (8, 9), and a Supermarket at (–6, 1).

C. A rectangular park whose northwest corner is located 6 squares west and 2 squares south of the High School, and whose southeast corner is located 9 squares east and 8 squares north of the City Hall.

28. Kevin made this map of the trees around his house.

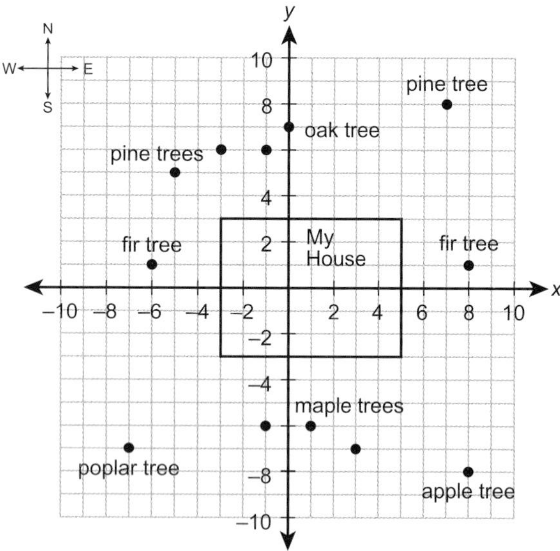

A. Give the coordinates for the oak tree.

B. Give the coordinates for the 3 maple trees.

***29. Challenge**

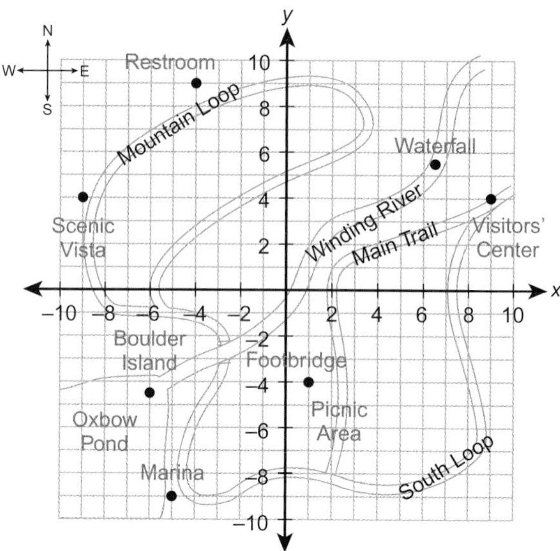

A. Use the map of Mountainview Nature Center to give coordinates for the following features: Picnic Area, Scenic Vista, Marina, Restroom, Waterfall, Boulder Island, and the southwest corner of the Visitors' Center building.

B. Tell where you would be at each of these points on the map: (9, –6), (–8, –7), (4, 4), (–2.5, –2.5), (–5, 7).

***30. Challenge** Jacinta made this map of the approximate locations of stars she saw in the winter sky.

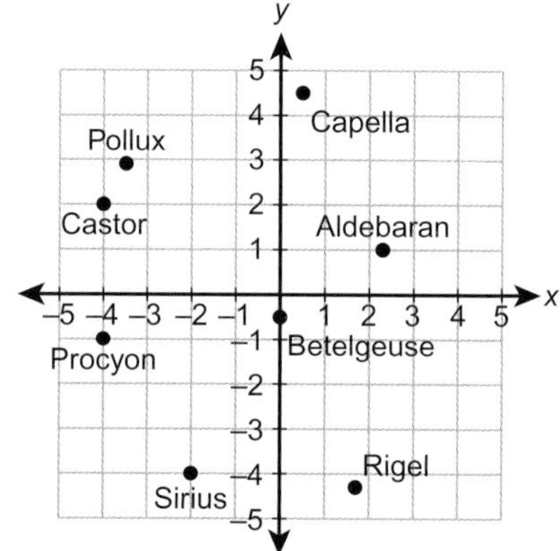

A. Give the coordinates for Castor, Procyon, Sirius, and Betelgeuse.

B. Name the star that is closest to each set of coordinates: (–3.5, 3), (0.5, 4.5), (1.7, –4.3), (2.3, 1).

Lines and Intercepts

The graph of a linear equation is a line.

DEFINITION

The **standard form** of a linear equation is $Ax + By = C$, where A, B, and C are integers and A and B are not both zero.

Writing Equations in Standard Form

Example 1 Write each equation in standard form.

A. $4x = y + 12$

Solution

Subtract y from both sides.

$$4x = y + 12$$
$$4x - y = y + 12 - y$$
$$4x - y = 12$$

The equation in standard form is $4x - y = 12$. ■

B. $y = 3x - 18$

Solution

Subtract $3x$ from both sides.

$$y = 3x - 18$$
$$y - 3x = 3x - 18 - 3x$$
$$y - 3x = -18$$
$$-3x + y = -18$$

The equation in standard form is $-3x + y = -18$. ■

Graphing Lines on the Coordinate Plane

You can use ordered pairs to graph a line on the coordinate plane. If you graph any two points on the plane, there is exactly one line that passes through both points. So, to graph a line you need to know at least two points on the line.

TIP

Though two points determine a line, it is often helpful to graph three points as a way of checking your work.

Example 2 Graph the line containing the points (0, 2), (1, 5), and (−2, −4).

Solution Graph each point. Then draw the line connecting the three points.

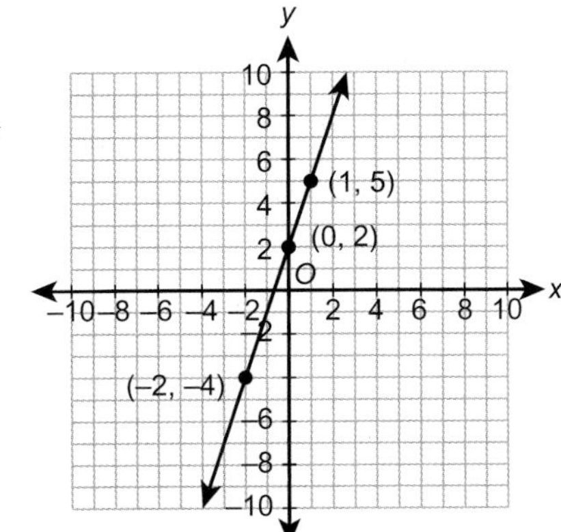

Collinear Points

Points are **collinear** if they lie on the same line.

Example 3 Are the points (4, 0), (6, 2), and (−1, −1) collinear?

Solution Graph each point. Then try to draw a line connecting the three points.

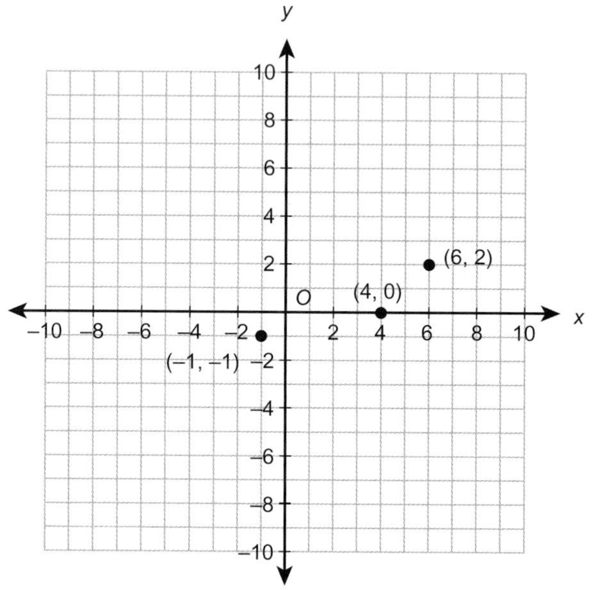

A line cannot be drawn connecting the three points. The points are not collinear. ■

To Graph Lines Using Intercepts

When the equation of a line is in standard form, it is convenient to use the x- and y-intercepts to graph the line.

DEFINITION

The ***x*-intercept** of a graph is the x-coordinate of the point where the graph intersects the x-axis. The ***y*-intercept** is the y-coordinate of the point where the graph intersects the y-axis.

Any point that lies on the x-axis has a y-coordinate of 0 and any point that lies on the y-axis has an x-coordinate of 0. So, to find the x-intercept of a line, find the value of x when $y = 0$, and to find the y-intercept, find the value of y when $x = 0$.

Example 4 Graph the line $5x - 4y = 20$ by finding its x- and y-intercepts.

Solution

Step 1 Find the x- and y-intercepts.

To find the x-intercept, substitute 0 into the equation for y. Then solve for x.

$5x - 4y = 20$ Write the equation of the line.

$5x - 4 \cdot 0 = 20$ Substitute 0 for y.

$5x - 0 = 20$

$5x = 20$ Solve for x.

$\frac{5x}{5} = \frac{20}{5}$

$x = 4$

The x-intercept is 4, so the line intersects the x-axis at the point (4, 0).

To find the y-intercept, substitute 0 into the equation for x. Then solve for y.

$5x - 4y = 20$ Write the equation of the line.

$5 \cdot 0 - 4y = 20$ Substitute 0 for x.

$0 - 4y = 20$

$-4y = 20$ Solve for y.

$\frac{-4y}{-4} = \frac{20}{-4}$

$y = -5$

The y-intercept is -5, so the line intersects the y-axis at the point $(0, -5)$.

Step 2 Graph the x- and y-intercepts and connect the points to draw the line.

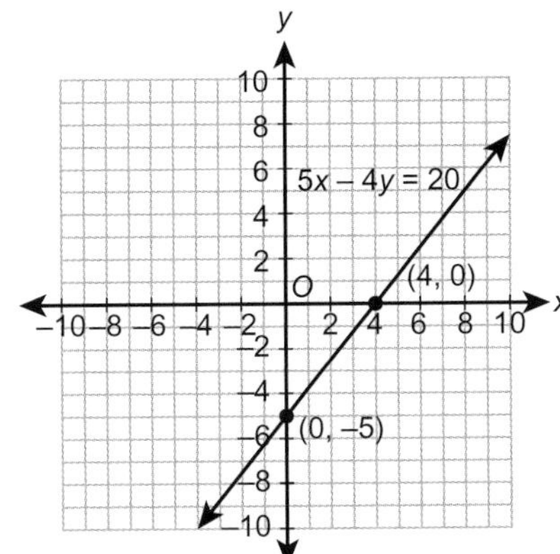

■

Application: Purchase

Example 5 You are buying food for a family reunion and have purchased 120 hot dogs. Hot dog rolls come in packages of 8 and packages of 10. The situation can be modeled by the linear equation

$$8x + 10y = 120$$

where x is the number of packages containing 8 rolls and y is the number of packages containing 10 rolls.

A. Find the x- and y-intercepts and graph the equation $8x + 10y = 120$.

B. What is the domain for this problem?

C. Name all possible choices for the number of packages of each quantity of hot dog rolls you could buy.

(continued)

Solution

A. To find the x-intercept, substitute 0 into the equation for y. Then solve for x.

$$\begin{aligned} 8x + 10y &= 120 \\ 8x + 10 \cdot 0 &= 120 \\ 8x &= 120 \\ x &= 15 \end{aligned}$$

The x-intercept is 15.

To find the y-intercept, substitute 0 into the equation for x. Then solve for y.

$$\begin{aligned} 8x + 10y &= 120 \\ 8 \cdot 0 + 10y &= 120 \\ 10y &= 120 \\ y &= 12 \end{aligned}$$

The y-intercept is 12.

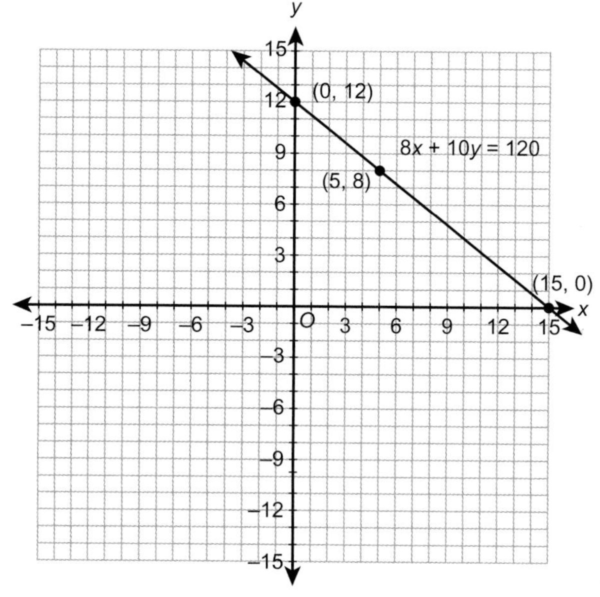

■

B. Since only a whole number of packages can be purchased, only the whole number solutions are meaningful. The domain is all whole numbers greater than or equal to 0 and less than or equal to 15.

C. Use a table to list all the whole number coordinates the line passes through.

x	0	5	10	15
y	12	8	4	0

From the table, read the four possible choices: 0 packages of 8 rolls and 12 packages of 10 rolls, 5 packages of 8 rolls and 8 packages of 10 rolls, 10 packages of 8 rolls and 4 packages of 10 rolls, and 15 packages of 8 rolls and 0 packages of 10 rolls. ■

Problem Set

Write each equation in standard form.

1. $x = 14 - 2y$
2. $6y - 12 = -3x$
3. $\frac{x}{3} + 4 = \frac{3}{4}y$
4. $10 - 2(x - y) = 3x + 1$
5. $4(x - 2) = 3(2y - 1)$

*6. **Challenge**
$3(x - y) - \frac{x}{2} - 4 = 5y - 2(2y - 3x) - 6$

Find the *x*- and *y*-intercepts.

7.

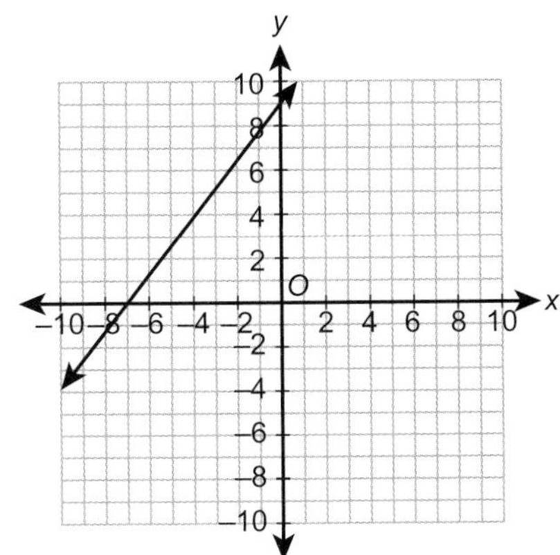

8. $3x - 2y = 18$

9.

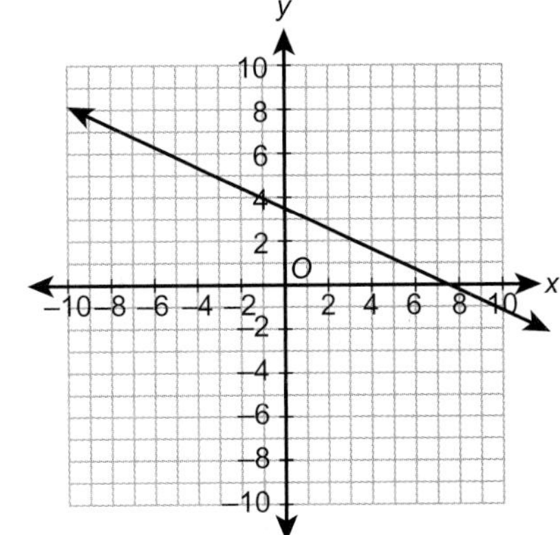

10. $-6x + 4y = 96$

Graph the points and determine if they are collinear.

11. (1, 0), (3, 4), (−2, −3)
12. (8, −5), (−6, 2), (0, −1)
13. (−3, 8), (2, 4), (9, −1)

Graph the line containing each set of points.

14. (−3, −3), (9, 7), (−9, −8)
15. (7, −2), (0, 4), (−7, 10)
16. (−7, −2), (7, 0), (−1, −1)
17. (−5, 4), (1, −4), (−8, 8)
18. (2, 8), (−1, 2), (−7, −10)
19. (5, 7.5), (9, 7), (−7, 9)

For each problem:

A. Find the *x*- and *y*-intercepts.
B. Use the intercepts to graph the line.

20. $3x + 2y = 12$
21. $x - 3y = -9$
22. $4x - 3y = -24$
23. $2(x - 3y) + 2 = 2(5 - y)$

Challenge

*24. $3\left(3x - \frac{y}{2}\right) - 3 = 15$

*25. $\frac{x}{2} - 3 = 2(x - y)$

For each problem:

A. Write an equation to model the situation.
B. Find the x- and y-intercepts.
C. Graph the line.
D. Use the graph to find 3 possible solutions.

26. A florist is making flower arrangements and each arrangement will include either 6 or 9 daisies. He is using 108 daisies in all. How many of each type of arrangement could he make?

27. Aleksandra is buying nuts for a large party. She has $112, and wants to buy cashews at $7 per pound and pistachios at $8 per pound. How many pounds of each kind of nut could she buy?

28. The senior class trip will include 180 students who will ride in taxis in groups of 5 or 6 students. How many of each size group could the students make?

29. Malachi is pouring punch into cups that hold 3 or 4 ounces. He has 72 ounces of punch in all; how many of each size cup could he fill?

Slope

The steepness of a line is its slope.

The **slope** of a line is the ratio of the vertical change, or **rise,** between any two points on the line to the horizontal change, or **run,** between the same two points.

$$\text{slope} = \frac{\text{vertical change}}{\text{horizontal change}} = \frac{\text{rise}}{\text{run}}$$

SLOPE FORMULA

The slope m of a line containing the two points (x_1, y_1) and (x_2, y_2) can be found using the formula

$$m = \frac{y_2 - y_1}{x_2 - x_1}.$$

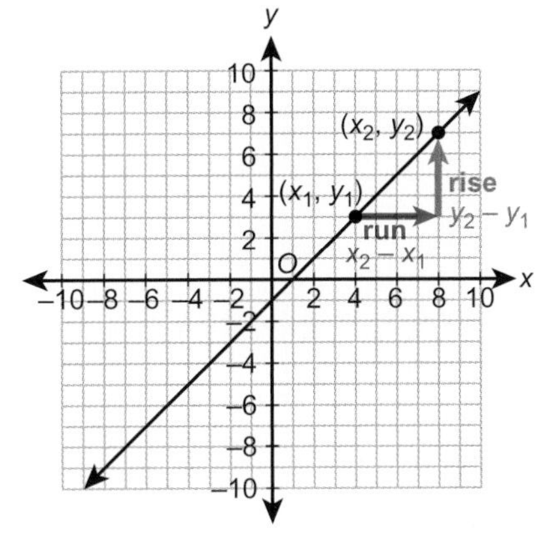

THINK ABOUT IT

$y_2 - y_1$ is the vertical change and $x_2 - x_1$ is the horizontal change.

Finding the Slope of a Line

To find the slope of a line, you can use the graph of the line to find the rise and run or you can use the slope formula if you know two points that lie on the line.

Example 1

A. Find the slope of the line shown in the graph using the ratio of rise to run.

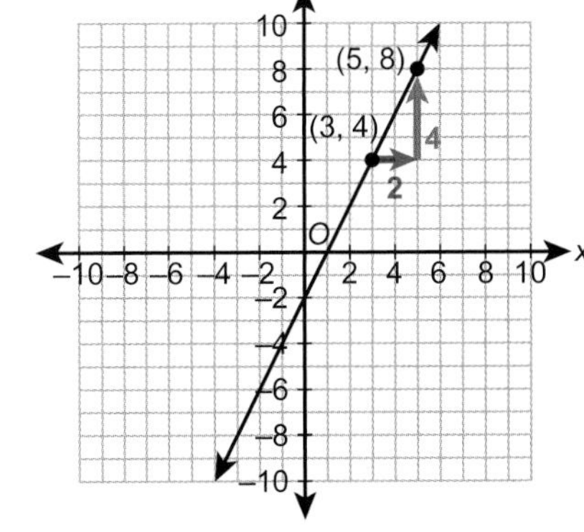

Solution The vertical change between the two points is 4 units. The horizontal change between the two points is 2 units.

$$\text{slope} = \frac{\text{rise}}{\text{run}} = \frac{4}{2} = 2$$

The slope of the line is 2. ■

(continued)

B. Find the slope of the line passing through the points $(-3, 7)$ and $(1, 2)$.

Solution Use the slope formula. Choose either point to be (x_1, y_1).

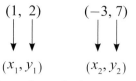

$$\begin{array}{cc} (1,\ 2) & (-3,\ 7) \\ \downarrow\ \downarrow & \downarrow\ \downarrow \\ (x_1, y_1) & (x_2, y_2) \end{array}$$

Substitute values into the slope formula for x_1, x_2, y_1, and y_2.

$$m = \frac{y_2 - y_1}{x_2 - x_1} = \frac{7 - 2}{-3 - 1} = \frac{5}{-4} = -\frac{5}{4}$$

The slope of the line is $-\frac{5}{4}$. ■

Finding the Slope of Horizontal and Vertical Lines

Example 2 Find the slope of each line.

A.

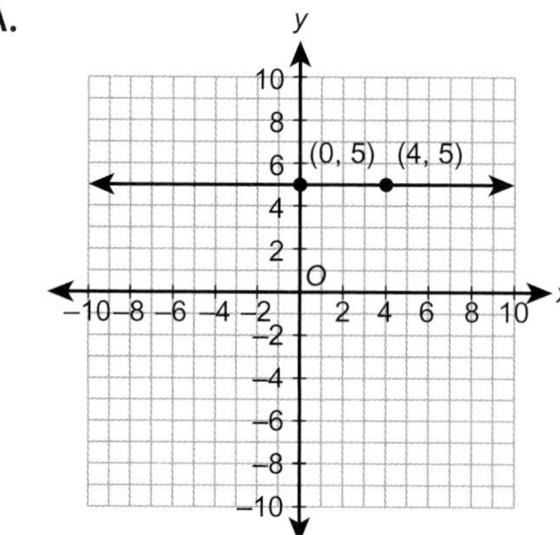

B.

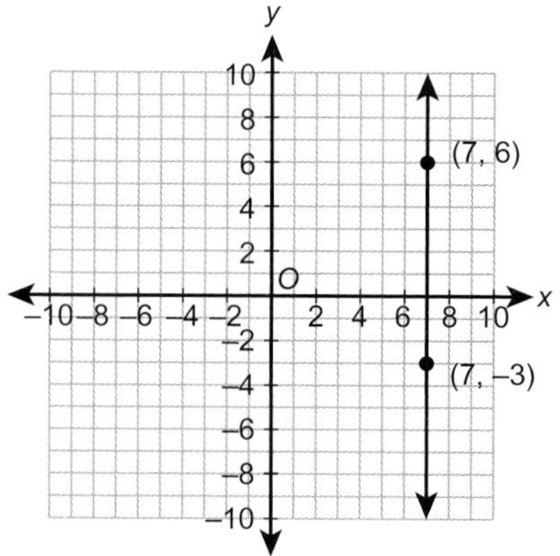

Solution

A. The points $(0, 5)$ and $(4, 5)$ lie on the line. Use the slope formula.

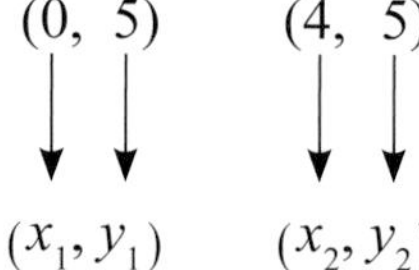

Substitute values into the slope formula for x_1, x_2, y_1, and y_2.

$$m = \frac{y_2 - y_1}{x_2 - x_1} = \frac{5 - 5}{4 - 0} = \frac{0}{4} = 0$$

The slope of the line is 0. All horizontal lines have a slope of 0. ■

B. The points $(7, 6)$ and $(7, -3)$ lie on the line. Use the slope formula.

$$\begin{array}{cc} (7,\ 6) & (7,\ -3) \\ \downarrow\ \downarrow & \downarrow\ \downarrow \\ (x_1, y_1) & (x_2, y_2) \end{array}$$

Substitute values into the slope formula for x_1, x_2, y_1, and y_2.

$$m = \frac{y_2 - y_1}{x_2 - x_1} = \frac{-3 - 6}{7 - 7} = \frac{-9}{0}$$

undefined

Division by zero is undefined, so the slope of the line is undefined. All vertical lines have an undefined slope. ■

SLOPES

Lines can be classified by their slopes.

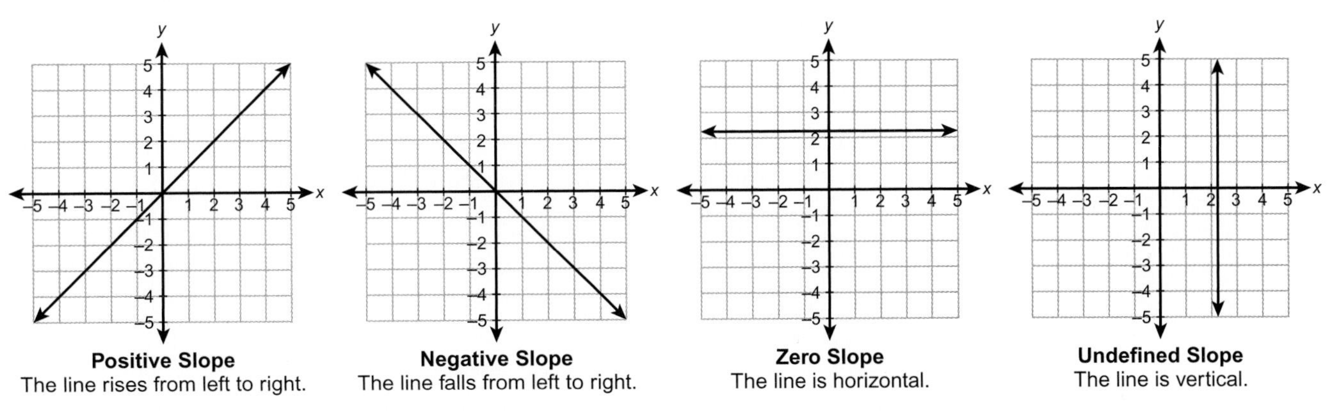

Positive Slope The line rises from left to right.

Negative Slope The line falls from left to right.

Zero Slope The line is horizontal.

Undefined Slope The line is vertical.

Using the Equation of a Line to Determine the Slope

Example 3 Find the slope of the line $3x + 5y = 30$.

Solution

Step 1 You need two points to find the slope of the line. Intercepts are easy points to find, so use them to compute the slope.

Find the x- and y-intercepts of the line.

To find the x-intercept, substitute 0 into the equation for y. Then solve for x.

$$3x + 5y = 30$$
$$3x + 5 \cdot 0 = 30$$
$$3x = 30$$
$$x = 10$$

The x-intercept is 10.

To find the y-intercept, substitute 0 into the equation for x. Then solve for y.

$$3x + 5y = 30$$
$$3 \cdot 0 + 5y = 30$$
$$5y = 30$$
$$y = 6$$

The y-intercept is 6.

The points (10, 0) and (0, 6) lie on the line $3x + 5y = 30$.

Step 2 Use the intercepts to find the slope of the line.

$$m = \frac{y_2 - y_1}{x_2 - x_1} = \frac{6 - 0}{0 - 10} = \frac{6}{-10} = -\frac{3}{5}$$

The slope of the line $3x + 5y = 30$ is $-\frac{3}{5}$. ■

Graphing a Line Using a Point on the Line and the Slope

Example 4 Graph the line that contains the point (1, 6) and has a slope of $\frac{2}{3}$.

Solution The slope of the line is $\frac{2}{3}$, so the vertical change, $y_2 - y_1$, is 2 and the horizontal change, $x_2 - x_1$, is 3. Since you know (1, 6) is a point on the line, you can set up and solve the two equations:

$$\begin{aligned} y_2 - y_1 &= 2 \\ y_2 - 6 &= 2 \\ y_2 - 6 + 6 &= 2 + 6 \\ y_2 &= 8 \end{aligned} \qquad \begin{aligned} x_2 - x_1 &= 3 \\ x_2 - 1 &= 3 \\ x_2 - 1 + 1 &= 3 + 1 \\ x_2 &= 4 \end{aligned}$$

A second point on the line is (4, 8). Now plot the two points, (1, 6) and (4, 8), and draw the line.

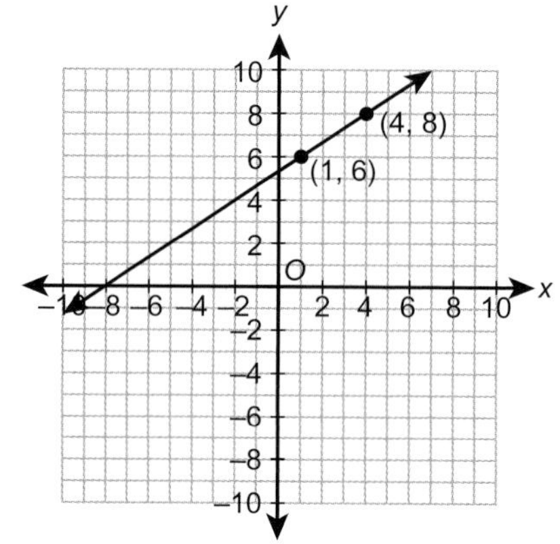

■

Application: Rate of Change

A **rate of change** is the ratio of a change in one quantity to a change in a second quantity. A linear equation models a constant rate of change.

Example 5 The table shows the total late fee for a movie rental. Find the rate of change of late fee to time.

Time (days late)	2	4	6
Total Late Fee (dollars)	1.50	3	4.50

Solution Write the rate of change as a ratio. Start by picking two ordered pairs.

$$\text{rate of change} = \frac{\text{change in late fee}}{\text{change in time}} = \frac{3 - 1.50}{4 - 2} = \frac{1.50}{2} = 0.75$$

Choose two more ordered pairs to see that the rate of change is constant.

$$\text{rate of change} = \frac{\text{change in late fee}}{\text{change in time}} = \frac{4.50 - 3}{6 - 4} = \frac{1.50}{2} = 0.75$$

The rate of change is \$0.75 per day. ■

Problem Set

Find the slope of the line using the ratio of rise to run.

1.

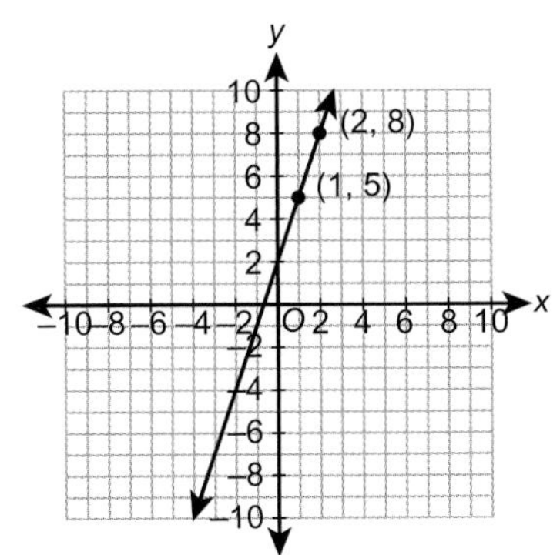

2.

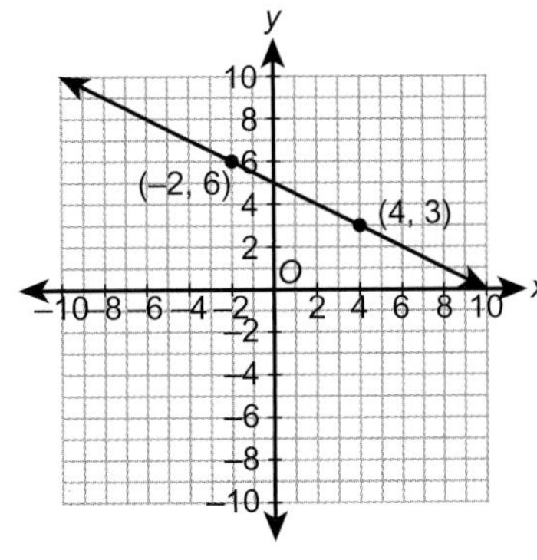

3.

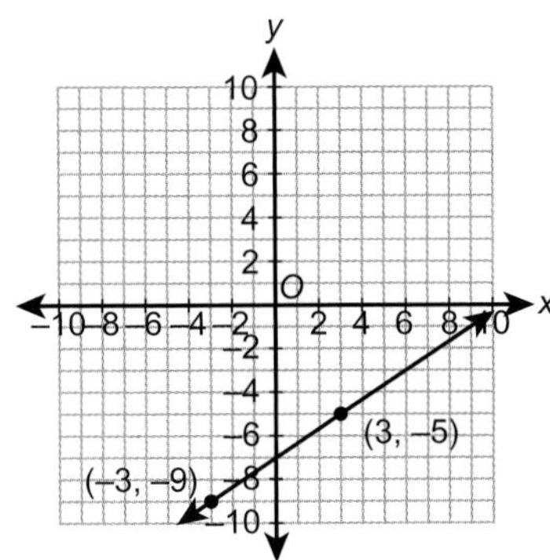

Use the slope formula to find the slope of the line passing through the given points.

4. (4, 8) and (1, 6)

5. (0, 2) and (0, 9)

6. (–4, 0) and (7, 0)

7. (–2, 9) and (–10, 33)

8. (12, 5) and (18, 14)

9. (–4, 7) and (0, 8)

Determine if the slope of the line is positive, negative, zero, or undefined.

10.

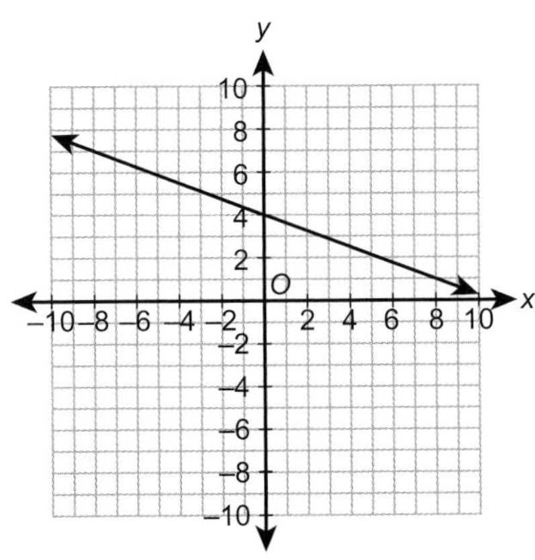

11.

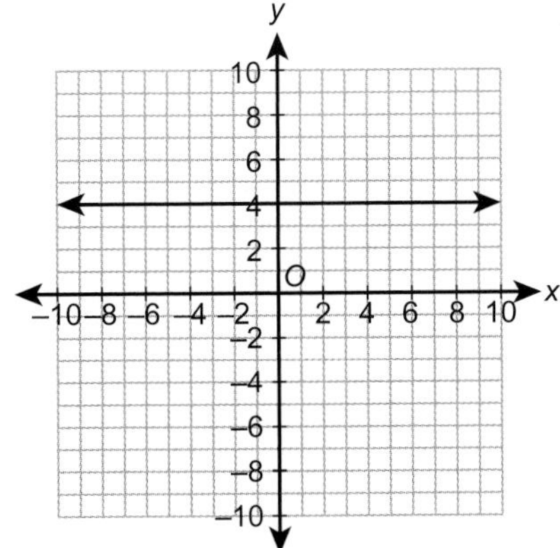

12.

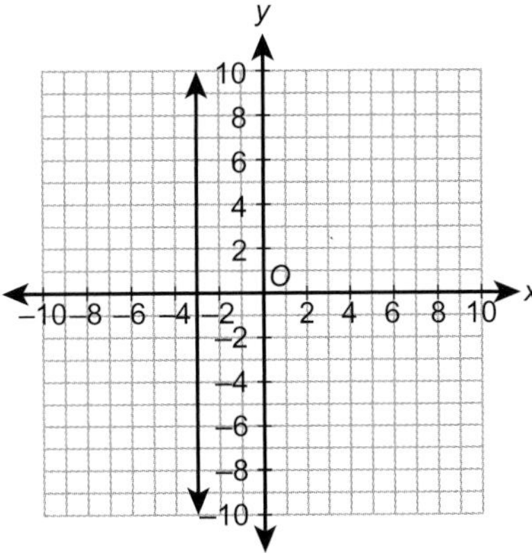

13.

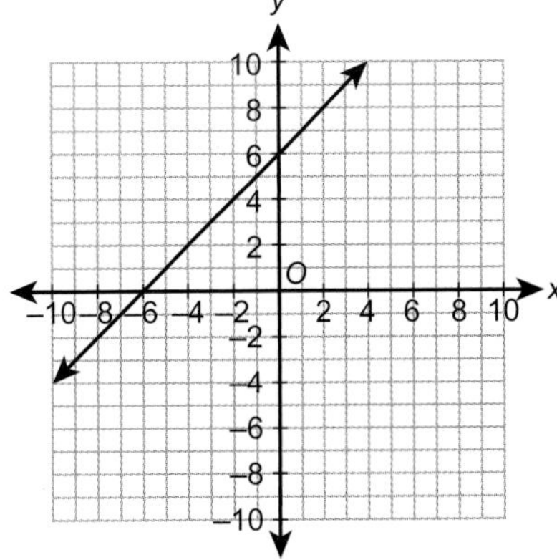

14.

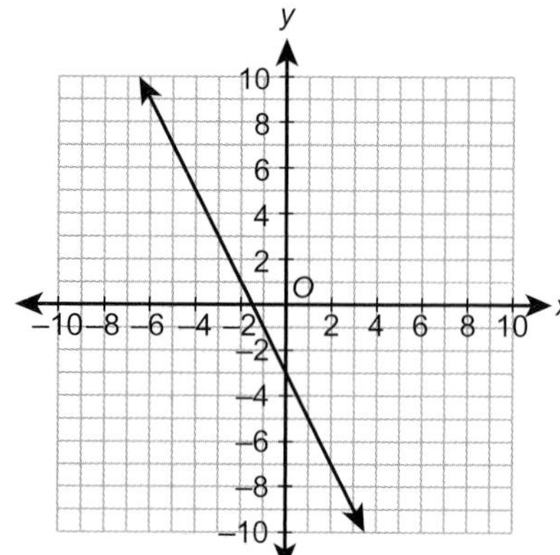

15.

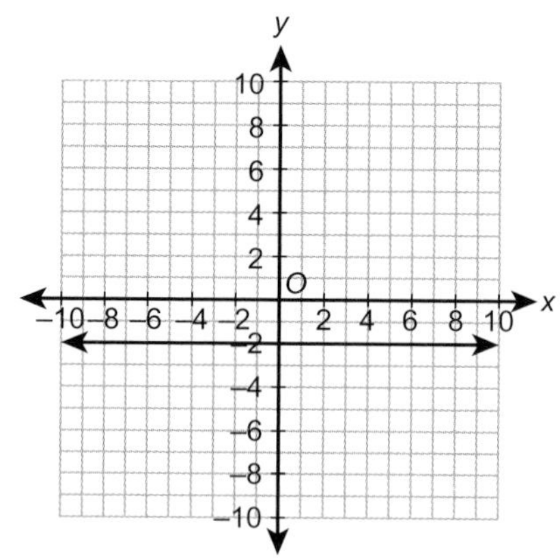

For each problem:

A. Find two points that lie on the line.
B. Use the slope formula to find the slope of the line.

16. $4x - 4y = 16$

17. $-3x + 5y = 30$

18. $-7x - 2y = 56$

19. $-12x + 3y = -72$

20. $13x - 5y = -130$

Graph the line that contains the given point and has the given slope.

21. $(3, 1); m = \frac{1}{3}$

22. $(-4, 7); m = 0$

23. (9, 1); slope is undefined

24. $(-5, 4); m = -\frac{3}{4}$

Solve. For each problem:

A. Find the rate of change between each set of points.
B. Use your answer from part A to determine if the relation is linear.
C. Explain why or why not.

25. The table shows the cost for movie tickets. Find the rate of change of price to number of tickets.

Number of Tickets	1	3	5
Price	\$6.50	\$19.50	\$32.50

26. The table shows the total number of miles that Juanita has driven this week to work. Find the rate of change of miles driven to time.

Number of Days	3	4	5
Miles	48	64	80

27. The table shows the total profit that Domingo's Barber Shop has earned this month. Find the rate of change of profit earned to the number of haircuts.

Haircuts	13	27	55
Profit	\$45.50	\$94.50	\$192.50

28. The table shows the cost for ride tickets for the local carnival. Find the rate of change of price to number of tickets.

Number of Tickets	15	30	60
Price	\$30	\$54	\$105

***29. Challenge** The table shows the total amount of minutes that Katarina has spent grocery shopping this year. Find the rate of change of minutes spent shopping to time.

Month	June	September	November
Total Minutes	480	720	880

***30. Challenge** The table shows the total amount of hours that Marta has studied for the upcoming College Entrance Exam. Find the rate of change of hours spent studying to time.

Date	16th	17th	18th
Total Hours	12	18	24

Slope-Intercept Form

You can write the equation of a line in various forms including standard form and slope-intercept form.

The different forms of the equation of a line are equivalent. That is, even though they are written differently, they represent the same line so they will have the same graph and the same solutions.

The different forms can help identify characteristics of a line more easily. For example, the slope-intercept form of a linear equation can help you identify the slope and y-intercept, while the slope may not be easily identifiable from the same equation written in standard form.

DEFINITION

The **slope-intercept form** of a linear equation is $y = mx + b$, where m is the slope of the line and b is the y-intercept.

Identifying the Slope and *y*-Intercept

Example 1 Identify the slope and y-intercept of each line.

A. $y = 3x + 4$

B. $y = -5x - \frac{1}{2}$

Solution

A. The equation of the line is in slope-intercept form. m is the slope of the line and b is the y-intercept.

$$y = mx + b$$

$$\downarrow \quad \downarrow$$

$$y = 3x + 4$$

The slope of the line is 3 and the y-intercept is 4. ■

B. Write the equation as $y = -5x + \left(-\frac{1}{2}\right)$.

$$y = mx + b$$

$$\downarrow \quad \downarrow$$

$$y = -5x + \left(-\frac{1}{2}\right)$$

The slope of the line is -5 and the y-intercept is $-\frac{1}{2}$. ■

REMEMBER

A linear equation is in standard form when it is in the form:

$Ax + By = C$.

Converting a Line from Standard to Slope-Intercept Form

Example 2 Write the equation of the line $2x + 5y = 15$ in slope-intercept form.

Solution Solve the equation for y.

$2x + 5y = 15$

$5y = -2x + 15$ Subtract $2x$ from each side of the equation.

$y = -\frac{2}{5}x + 3$ Divide each side by 5.

The equation in slope-intercept form is $y = -\frac{2}{5}x + 3$. ■

Using Slope-Intercept Form to Graph a Line

Example 3 Graph the line $3x + y = 5$.

Solution

Step 1 Write the equation in slope-intercept form.

$3x + y = 5$

$y = -3x + 5$ Subtract $3x$ from each side of the equation.

Step 2 Use the equation to identify the slope and y-intercept of the line.

$y = mx + b$

↓ ↓

$y = -3x + 5$

The slope of the line is -3 and the y-intercept is 5.

Step 3 Use the y-intercept to graph a point on the line. The line intersects the y-axis at the point (0, 5).

Step 4 Use the slope of the line to graph a second point on the line. The slope of the line is -3 or $\frac{-3}{1}$. The rise is -3 and the run is 1. Start at the point (0, 5). Move 3 units down and 1 unit to the right. A second point on the line is (1, 2). Draw a line through the points (0, 5) and (1, 2).

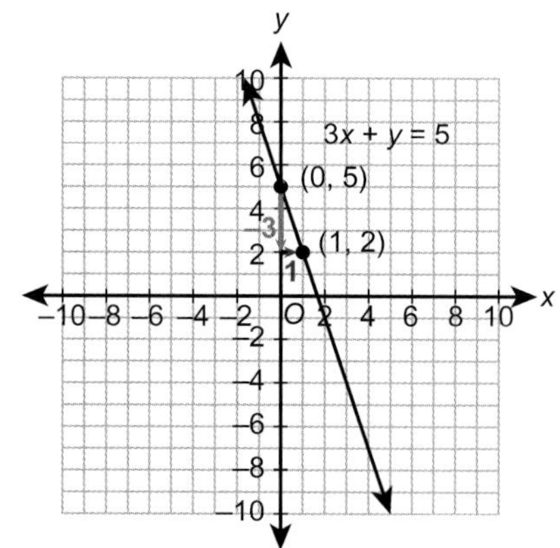

■

Application: Profit

Example 4 You are selling items on an online auction site. Each item sells for \$2.50 and there is a one-time listing fee of \$8.

A. Write an equation to model your profit, P.

B. Graph the equation.

C. What does each intercept represent?

D. What is the domain of the problem?

Solution

A.

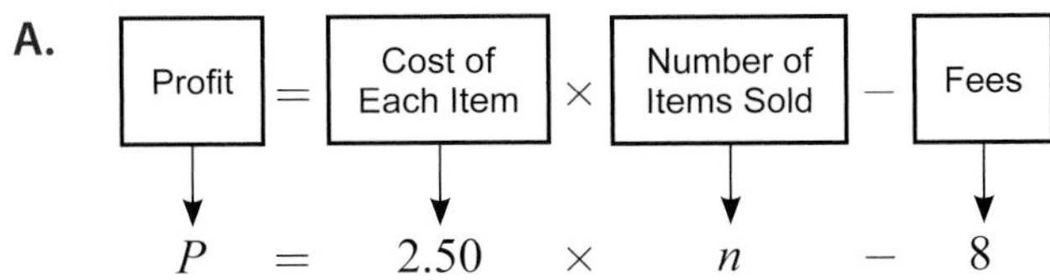

$$P = 2.50 \times n - 8$$

The problem is modeled by the equation $P = 2.5n - 8$.

B. Find the slope and y-intercept of the line.

$$y = mx + b$$

$$P = 2.5n + (-8)$$

The slope of the line is 2.5 and the y-intercept is -8. Use the slope of the line to graph a second point on the line. Write the slope of the line as $\frac{2.5}{1}$. The rise is 2.5 and the run is 1. Start at the point $(0, -8)$. Move 2.5 units up and 1 unit to the right. A second point on the line is $(1, -5.5)$. Draw a line through the points $(0, –8)$ and $(1, -5.5)$.

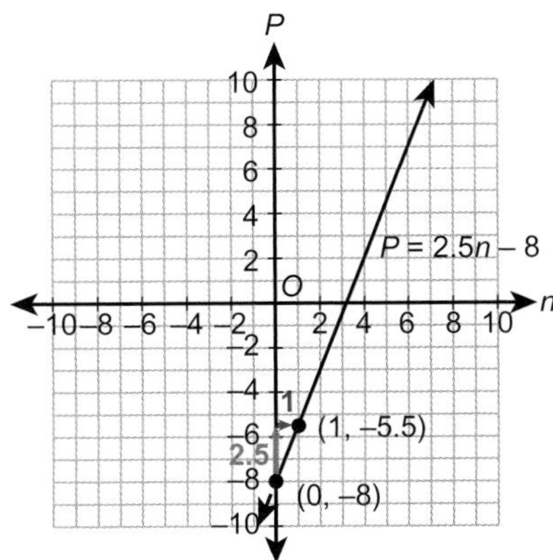

C. The vertical axis represents P, the dollar amount of your profit. The P-intercept, $(0, -8)$ represents the greatest amount of money you can lose, or the greatest negative profit amount. If you sell 0 items, you will still have to pay the listing fee of \$8. Your profit will be $-\$8$. The horizontal axis represents n, the number of items sold. The line crosses the n-axis between 3 and 4, at the point (3.2, 0). If you sold 3.2 items, you would break even. Any n-value greater than that number signifies a positive profit amount. Since you can sell only whole items, you must sell 4 items to make a profit.

D. Since you can only sell whole items, the domain of the problem is all whole numbers. ■

Problem Set

Identify the slope and y-intercept.

1. $y = 2x - 8$
2. $y = -\frac{1}{2}x + 7$
3. $y = \frac{1}{4}x - \frac{3}{4}$
4. $y = 5x + 12$
5. $y = -7x + \frac{7}{2}$
6. $y = 2x - 8$

Write each equation in slope-intercept form.

7. $4x - 7y = 14$
8. $3x + 4y = 24$
9. $9x - 2y = -36$
10. $8x + 4y = 48$
11. $-3x - 2y = 30$
12. $-6x - 9y = -36$

Graph the line.

13. $2x + y = 9$
14. $-4x + y = 5$
15. $-6x - y = 3$
16. $\frac{1}{2}x + y = 4$
17. $x + y = 7$
18. $x - 2y = 10$
19. $-3x + y = -2$
20. $x + 5y = 15$
21. $-x - y = 1$

Solve. For each problem:

A. Write an equation to model the problem.
B. Graph the equation.
C. Describe the practical meaning of the y-intercept.
D. Answer the question.

22. You are selling items at a fair for \$6.50 each. Renting the booth at the fair cost \$25. How many items do you need to sell to make a profit?

23. Manya is selling charm bracelets at the school flea market. Each bracelet sells for \$3 and there is a charge of \$0.25 per charm. How much does a bracelet cost with five charms?

24. Olayinka is participating in a bowl-a-thon to benefit the local hospital. Each sponsor will pay Olayinka \$2 plus \$0.10 per pin that she knocks down. How much will Olayinka raise per sponsor for knocking down 52 pins?

25. Zain is getting her pictures printed at the local photo shop. The cost to print digital pictures is a set \$5.50 fee per order plus an additional \$0.05 per print. How much will Zain pay to have 25 pictures printed?

26. Moving Video charges a one-time membership fee of \$9.99 plus \$3.99 to rent each movie. How much will renting 22 movies cost?

*27. **Challenge** Carlos is selling dried fruit bars for the football team. Each bar sells for \$0.50 and the cost of ordering the box of 100 bars was \$12. How many candy bars must Carlos sell to make a profit of \$30?

*28. **Challenge** You are selling items on an online auction site. Each item sells for \$3.25 and there is a one-time listing fee of \$14. How many items must you sell to make a profit of \$100?

Point-Slope Form

You can write the equation of a line in point-slope form if you know the slope of the line and *any* point that lies on the line.

DEFINITION

The **point-slope form** of the equation of a line that passes through the point (x_1, y_1) and has a slope of m is $y - y_1 = m(x - x_1)$.

You can see how the point-slope form is derived using the slope formula.

$m = \frac{y_2 - y_1}{x_2 - x_1}$	Write the slope formula.
$m(x_2 - x_1) = \frac{y_2 - y_1}{x_2 - x_1}(x_2 - x_1)$	Multiply each side by $(x_2 - x_1)$.
$m(x_2 - x_1) = y_2 - y_1$	Simplify.
$y_2 - y_1 = m(x_2 - x_1)$	Symmetric Property
$y - y_1 = m(x - x_1)$	Substitute y for y_2 and x for x_2.

Writing the Equation of a Line in Point-Slope Form

Example 1 Use point-slope form to write an equation of the line that passes through the given point and has the given slope.

A. $(3, 5)$; slope $= -\frac{1}{2}$

B. $(-1, -6)$; slope $= 5$

Solution

A. $(3, 5)$; slope $= -\frac{1}{2}$

$y - y_1 = m\ (x - x_1)$

$\downarrow \quad \downarrow \quad \downarrow$

$y - 5 = -\frac{1}{2}(x - 3)$

The equation of the line in point-slope form is $y - 5 = -\frac{1}{2}(x - 3)$. ■

B. $(-1, -6)$; slope $= 5$

$y - y_1 = m(x - x_1)$

$\downarrow \quad \downarrow \quad \downarrow$

$y - (-6) = 5[x - (-1)]$

$y + 6 = 5(x + 1)$

The equation of the line in point-slope form is $y + 6 = 5(x + 1)$. ■

Using the Graph of a Line to Write the Equation in Point-Slope Form

Example 2

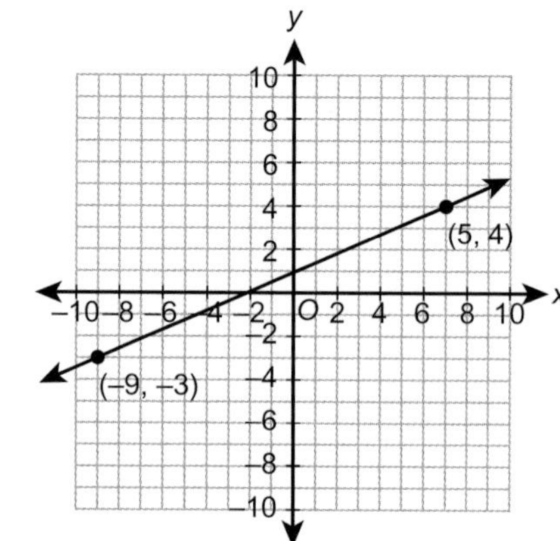

A. Write the equation of the line shown in the graph using the coordinates (5, 4).

B. Write the equation of the line shown in the graph using the coordinates (−9, −3).

C. Determine if the two equations are equivalent.

Solution

A.

Step 1 Find the slope of the line using the slope formula.

$$m = \frac{y_2 - y_1}{x_2 - x_1} = \frac{4 - (-3)}{5 - (-9)} = \frac{4 + 3}{5 + 9} = \frac{7}{14} = \frac{1}{2}$$

Step 2 Write the equation in point-slope form. Use point (5, 4) in the point-slope equation.

Use the point (5, 4).

$$y - y_1 = m(x - x_1)$$

$$\downarrow \quad \downarrow \quad \downarrow$$

$$y - 4 = \frac{1}{2}(x - 5)$$

B.

Step 1 Use the slope found in part A: $\frac{1}{2}$.

Step 2 Write the equation in point-slope form. Use the point (−9, −3).

$$y - y_1 = m(x - x_1)$$

$$\downarrow \quad \downarrow \quad \downarrow$$

$$y - (-3) = \frac{1}{2}[x - (-9)]$$

$$y + 3 = \frac{1}{2}(x + 9)$$

C. Show that the equations in Step 2 are equivalent by writing each in slope-intercept form.

Solve the first equation for y.

$$y - 4 = \frac{1}{2}(x - 5)$$
$$y - 4 = \frac{1}{2}x - \frac{5}{2}$$
$$y = \frac{1}{2}x - \frac{5}{2} + 4$$
$$y = \frac{1}{2}x - \frac{5}{2} + \frac{8}{2}$$
$$y = \frac{1}{2}x + \frac{3}{2}$$

Solve the second equation for y.

$$y + 3 = \frac{1}{2}(x + 9)$$
$$y + 3 = \frac{1}{2}x + \frac{9}{2}$$
$$y = \frac{1}{2}x + \frac{9}{2} - 3$$
$$y = \frac{1}{2}x + \frac{9}{2} - \frac{6}{2}$$
$$y = \frac{1}{2}x + \frac{3}{2}$$

The equations are equivalent. ■

REMEMBER

The slope-intercept form of the equation of a line is:

$$y = mx + b$$

where m is the slope of the line and b is its y-intercept.

Application: Writing a Linear Equation

Example 3 Corbin is buying concert tickets for some of his friends. The table shows the cost when purchasing different amounts of tickets. The total cost includes a parking fee of $12.

Number of Tickets (x)	2	4	6	8
Total Cost (y)	$29	$46	$63	$80

A. Write the equation that gives the total cost y in terms of the number of tickets purchased x in point-slope form.

B. Convert the equation from part A to slope-intercept form.

C. What is the meaning of the y-intercept?

D. What is the meaning of the slope?

Solution

A.

Step 1 Use the table to find the slope of the line. Choose any two data pairs in the table.

Let $(x_1, y_1) = (2, 29)$ and $(x_2, y_2) = (4, 46)$.

$$m = \frac{y_2 - y_1}{x_2 - x_1} = \frac{46 - 29}{4 - 2} = \frac{17}{2}$$

The slope of the line is $\frac{17}{2}$.

Step 2 Write the equation in point-slope form, using the data point (2, 29).

$$y - y_1 = m(x - x_1)$$
$$y - 29 = \frac{17}{2}(x - 2)$$

(continued)

B. Write the equation in slope-intercept form.

$$y - 29 = \frac{17}{2}(x - 2)$$

$$y - 29 = \frac{17}{2}x - 17 \qquad \text{Distributive Property}$$

$$y = \frac{17}{2}x - 17 + 29 \qquad \text{Add 29 to each side.}$$

$$y = \frac{17}{2}x + 12 \qquad \text{Simplify.}$$

C. The y-intercept represents the cost of parking.

D. The cost of each ticket is the slope of the line. Write $\frac{17}{2}$ as a decimal.

$\frac{17}{2} = 8.5$. The cost of each ticket is \$8.50. ■

Problem Set

Find the slope.

1. $y - 2 = -3(x + 1)$
2. $y + 6 = \frac{1}{3}(x - 4)$
3. $y + 7 = -\frac{3}{4}(x - 4)$

Use point-slope form to write the equation of the line that passes through the given point and has the given slope.

4. $(1, 2)$; $m = -5$
5. $(-3, 4)$; $m = 7$
6. $(0, 5)$; $m = \frac{1}{3}$
7. $(0, 0)$; $m = \frac{3}{4}$
8. $(-1, -4)$; $m = 3$
9. $(7, -8)$; $m = \frac{1}{7}$

For each problem:

A. Find the slope of the line.
B. Write two equations of the line in point-slope form—one for each of the points given on the graph.

10.

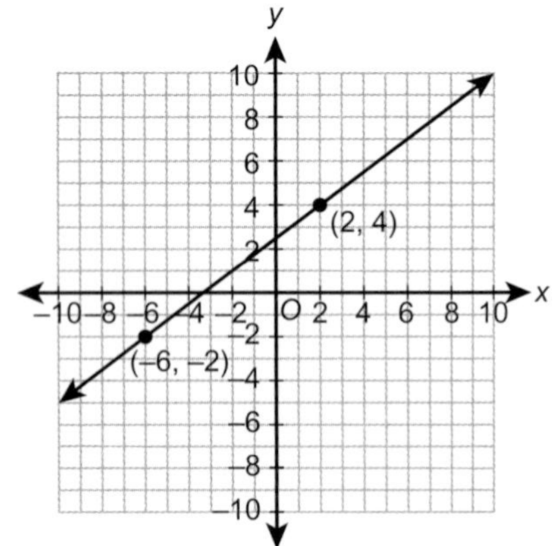

11.

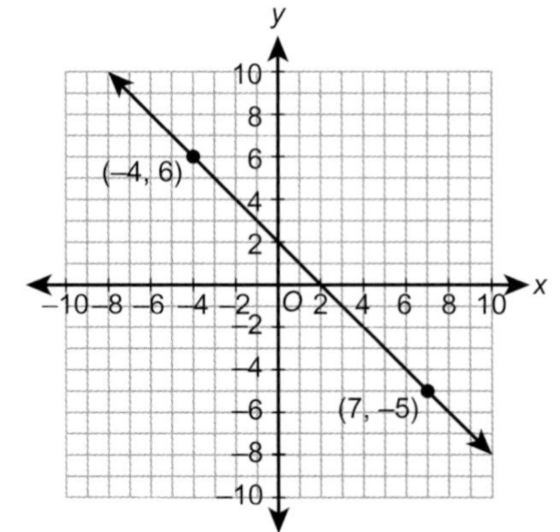

12.

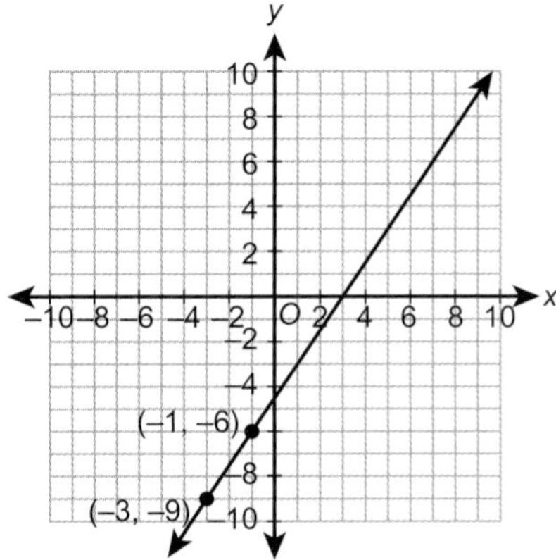

14.

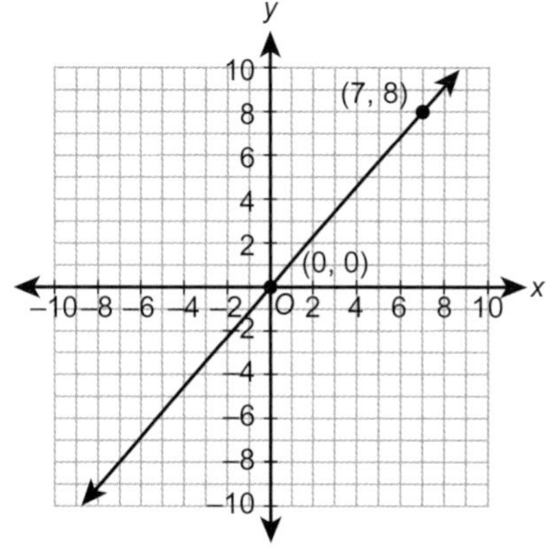

13.

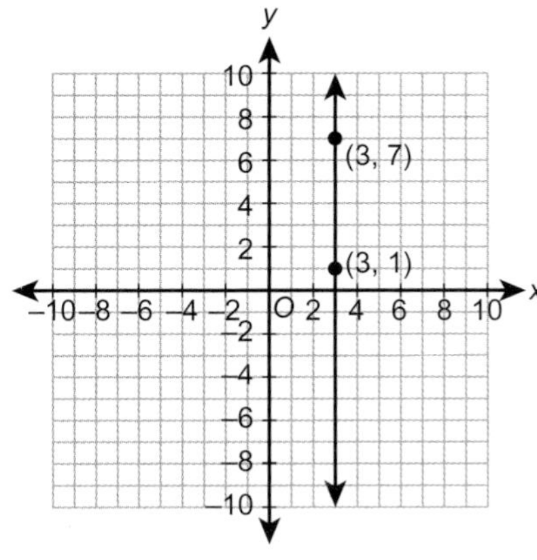

15.

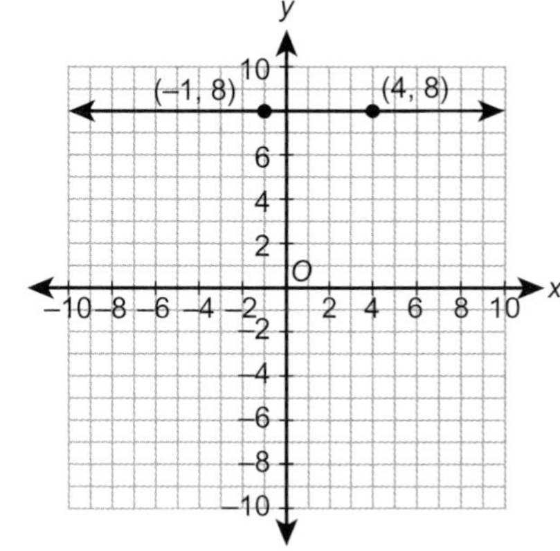

Graph the line.

16. $y - 2 = 3(x - 1)$

17. $y + 4 = \frac{1}{3}(x + 2)$

18. $y - 3 = -\frac{1}{2}(x + 1)$

19. $y + 2 = -4x$

20. $y = 2(x + 6)$

21. $y + 1 = \frac{1}{6}(x - 4)$

Solve.

22. Mr. Gonzales drives a toll road every day to reach his job. The table below shows the total cost for the miles driven.

A. Write an equation that gives the total cost y in terms of the number of miles traveled x.

B. How much will Mr. Gonzales pay if he drives 32 miles?

Number of Miles	10	20	30	40
Cost	\$7.60	\$15.10	\$22.60	\$30.10

23. Soo-Min has been practicing her jumping for years. The table below shows her jumping height at four ages.

A. Write an equation that gives the total jumping height y in terms of her age x.

B. How high should Soo-Min be able to jump at age $17\frac{1}{2}$ if she continues progressing at the same rate?

Age	10	12	14	16
Jumping Height	3″	5″	7″	9″

24. Dweezil has a piggie bank with pennies and quarters. As he adds more quarters to the bank, he makes a table that shows the value of all of the coins in the bank given a specific number of quarters.

A. Write an equation that gives the total value of coins y in terms of the number of quarters x.

B. How many pennies are in the bank?

C. What will the value of the collection be when the bank contains 20 quarters?

Number of Quarters	5	8	11	14
Value of Coins	$10.25	$11	$11.75	$12.5

25. Alonzo saves $50 a month from money earned at his job. His grandparents also give him $\frac{1}{2}$ of that amount each month. The table below shows his total savings.

A. Write an equation that gives his savings y in terms of the number of months he works x.

B. How much will Alonzo have in his account after 2 years?

Months	1	6	11	16
Savings	$75	$325	$575	$825

26. The company NewDisks manufactures CDs. The table shows the total production cost y for x CDs which includes materials and labor.

A. Write an equation that gives the total production cost y in terms of the number of CDs manufactured x.

B. Can the company manufacture 2000 CDs for under $130?

Number of CDs	100	200	300	400
Production Cost	$15	$20	$25	$30

27. Lamar has started walking for exercise. His results for the last week are in the table below.

A. Write an equation that gives the time y in terms of the distance walked x.

B. How long will it take Lamar to walk 10 miles?

Distance (miles)	1	2	3	4
Time (minutes)	15	30	45	60

28. Farmer Cal plants corn every year. The table shows the total cost of producing a corn crop given the number of acres available.

A. Write an equation that gives the total cost y in terms of the number of available acres x.

B. Can 1000 acres of corn be farmed for less than $1700?

Number of Acres	100	200	300	400
Cost of Crop	$195	$370	$545	$720

***29. Challenge** The Hermitage Car Company recorded the sales of its new special edition sports car for one month. The results are in the table below.

A. Write an equation that gives the sales y in terms of the number of available sports cars on the lot x.

B. Write in words what the data point (75, 5) means in this application.

C. As the number of sports cars on the lot increases what happens to demand?

Number of Sports Cars on the Lot	25	50	75	100
Sales	9	7	5	3

***30. Challenge** The average price of gas increases each year as indicated in the table below.

A. Write an equation that gives the average cost in terms of the year x.

B. Find the missing values for years 2 and 4.

C. Assuming a constant rate of increase, what year would the average cost of gas be $4.60?

Year	1	2	3	4
Average Cost	$2.20		$2.60	

Parallel and Perpendicular Lines

You can use the slope of a line to determine characteristics of the line. You can also use the slopes of two (or more) lines to determine if the lines are parallel or perpendicular.

PROPERTY

Slopes of Parallel Lines

If two lines have the same slope, then the lines are parallel.
If two lines are parallel, then the lines have the same slope.

REMEMBER

Two lines that lie in the same plane are parallel if they never intersect.

Writing the Equation of a Line Parallel to Another Line

Example 1 Find the equation of the line that passes through the point $(2, -1)$ and is parallel to the line $8x + 2y = 10$. Write the equation of the parallel line in slope-intercept form.

Solution

Step 1 Find the slope of the line $8x + 2y = 10$. Start by writing the equation in slope-intercept form.

$$8x + 2y = 10$$
$$2y = -8x + 10$$
$$y = -4x + 5$$

The slope of the line is -4.

Step 2 The slope of the parallel line is -4 and a point on the line is $(2, -1)$. Use point-slope form to find the equation of the line.

$y - y_1 = m(x - x_1)$	Use point-slope form.
$y - (-1) = -4(x - 2)$	Substitute -1 for y_1, -4 for m, and 2 for x_1.
$y + 1 = -4x + 8$	Simplify.
$y + 1 - 1 = -4x + 8 - 1$	Subtract 1 from each side.
$y = -4x + 7$	Simplify.

The equation of the parallel line is $y = -4x + 7$. ■

REMEMBER

Two lines that lie in the same plane are perpendicular if they intersect at right angles.

PROPERTY

Slopes of Perpendicular Lines

If two lines have slopes that are negative reciprocals, then the lines are perpendicular.

If two lines are perpendicular, then their slopes are negative reciprocals.

Writing the Equation of a Line Perpendicular to Another Line

Example 2 Find the equation of the line that passes through the point (1, 3) and is perpendicular to the line $12x + y = 6$. Write the equation of the perpendicular line in slope-intercept form.

Solution

Step 1 Find the slope of the line $12x + y = 6$. Write the equation in slope-intercept form.

$$12x + y = 6$$

$$y = -12x + 6$$

The slope of the line is -12.

REMEMBER

If the product of two numbers is -1, the two numbers are negative reciprocals.

Step 2 The slope of the perpendicular line is the negative reciprocal of -12 which is $\frac{1}{12}$. Find the equation of the line that passes through the point (1, 3) and has a slope of $\frac{1}{12}$. Use point-slope form to find the equation of the line.

$y - y_1 = m(x - x_1)$	Use point-slope form.
$y - 3 = \frac{1}{12}(x - 1)$	Substitute 3 for y_1, $\frac{1}{12}$ for m, and 1 for x_1.
$y - 3 = \frac{1}{12}x - \frac{1}{12}$	Distributive Property
$y - 3 + 3 = \frac{1}{12}x - \frac{1}{12} + 3$	Add 3 to each side.
$y = \frac{1}{12}x - \frac{1}{12} + \frac{36}{12}$	Rename 3 as $\frac{36}{12}$.
$y = \frac{1}{12}x + \frac{35}{12}$	Simplify.

The equation of the perpendicular line is $y = \frac{1}{12}x + \frac{35}{12}$. ■

Determining Whether Lines are Parallel, Perpendicular, or Neither

To determine if lines are parallel or perpendicular, find the slope of each line. If the slopes are the same, the lines are parallel. If the slopes are negative reciprocals, the lines are perpendicular.

Example 3 Determine whether each pair of lines is parallel, perpendicular, or neither.

A. $4x + 3y = 1$

$8x + 6y = 12$

Solution Write each line in slope-intercept form to identify its slope.

Line 1:

$$4x + 3y = 1$$
$$3y = -4x + 1$$
$$y = \frac{-4x + 1}{3}$$
$$y = -\frac{4}{3}x + \frac{1}{3}$$

Line 2:

$$8x + 6y = 12$$
$$6y = -8x + 12$$
$$y = \frac{-8x + 12}{6}$$
$$y = -\frac{8}{6}x + \frac{12}{6}$$
$$y = -\frac{4}{3}x + 2$$

The slope of both lines is $-\frac{4}{3}$, so the lines $4x + 3y = 1$ and $8x + 6y = 12$ are parallel. ■

B. $y = -2x + 7$

$2x + 5y = 10$

Solution

Line 1:

The line is in slope-intercept form.

$$y = -2x + 7$$

The slope is -2.

Line 2:

$$2x + 5y = 10$$
$$5y = -2x + 10$$
$$y = \frac{-2x + 10}{5}$$
$$y = -\frac{2}{5}x + 2$$

The slope of the line is $-\frac{2}{5}$.

The slopes of the lines are different and are not negative reciprocals, so the lines $y = -2x + 7$ and $2x + 5y = 10$ are neither parallel nor perpendicular. ■

C. $y = -4x + 7$

$x - 4y = 3$

Solution

Line 1:

$$y = -4x + 7$$

The slope of the line is -4.

Line 2:

$$x - 4y = 3$$
$$-4y = -x + 3$$
$$y = \frac{1}{4}x - \frac{3}{4}$$

The slope of the line is $\frac{1}{4}$.

(continued)

The slopes of the lines are negative reciprocals of each other, so the lines $y = -4x + 7$ and $x - 4y = 3$ are perpendicular. ■

Application: City Map

Example 4 The diagram shows streets on a coordinate grid. Is Park Avenue parallel to Ohio Avenue?

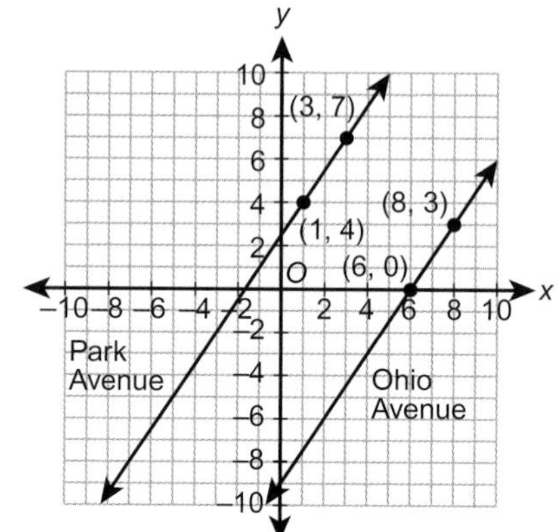

Solution Find the slope of each line using the slope formula.

Park Avenue:

Let $(x_1, y_1) = (3, 7)$ and $(x_2, y_2) = (1, 4)$.

$$m = \frac{y_2 - y_1}{x_2 - x_1} = \frac{4 - 7}{1 - 3} = \frac{-3}{-2} = \frac{3}{2}$$

Ohio Avenue:

Let $(x_1, y_1) = (8, 3)$ and $(x_2, y_2) = (6, 0)$.

$$m = \frac{y_2 - y_1}{x_2 - x_1} = \frac{0 - 3}{6 - 8} = \frac{-3}{-2} = \frac{3}{2}$$

The slopes are equal, so Park Avenue is parallel to Ohio Avenue. ■

Problem Set

For each problem:

A. Find the slope of the given line.

B. Find the slope of the line that passes through the given point and is parallel or perpendicular to the given line.

C. Write the equation of the line from part B in slope-intercept form.

1. (2, 3), parallel to $4x - 2y = 8$
2. (−1, 5), parallel to $3x + 2y = 4$
3. (4, 7), perpendicular to $6x + 3y = 12$
4. (−2, 15), perpendicular to $2x - 3y = 4$
5. (−4, −2), parallel to $10x - 5y = 15$
6. (7, 0), perpendicular to $x + y = 6$
7. (−1, 1), perpendicular to $6x - 7y = -8$
8. (0, 6), parallel to $y = 7x + 12$
9. (−2, −9), perpendicular to $24x + 3y = 0$
10. (3, −8), parallel to $x + y = 10$

11. (3, −4), perpendicular to $-40x - 8y = 16$

12. (0, 0), parallel to $-4x - 6y = 9$

13. (8, 1), perpendicular to $x = 20$

14. (−9, 0), parallel to $-3x + 3y = 11$

15. (10, 10), perpendicular to $y = 2x + 10$

16. (0, −3), perpendicular to $3x - 9y = 12$

17. (6, 10), parallel to $x = -5$

Determine whether each pair of lines is parallel, perpendicular, or neither.

18. $2x - y = -1$

    $4x - 2y = 6$

19. $y = \frac{1}{3}x + 6$

    $2x - 3y = 12$

20. $x + 10y = -20$

    $y = 10x - 1$

21. $7x - y = -5$

    $14x - 2y = 18$

22.

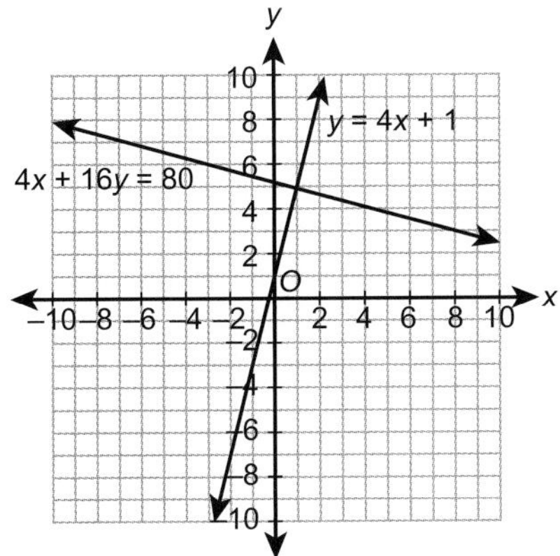

23.

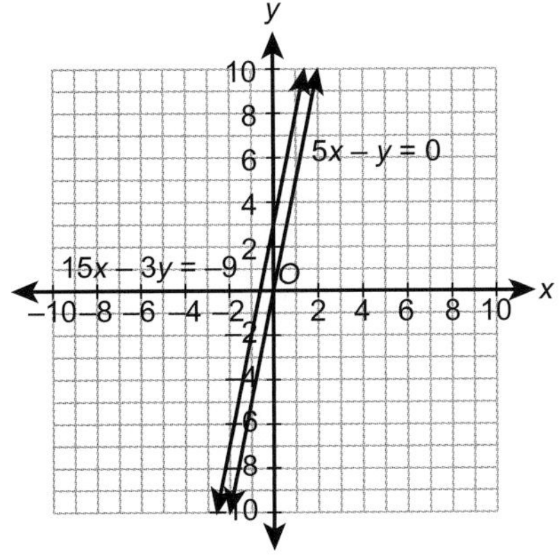

24.

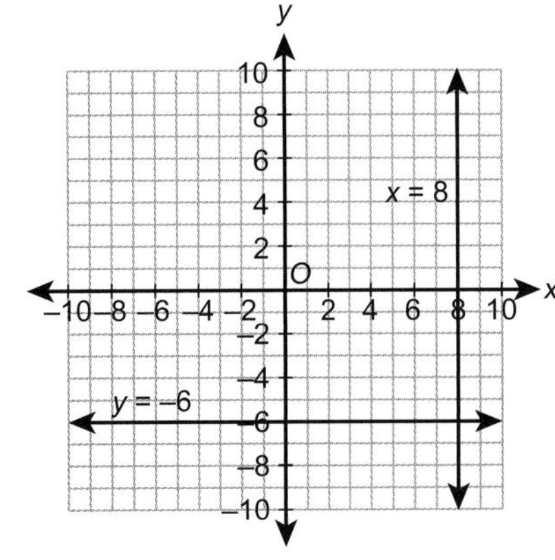

25.

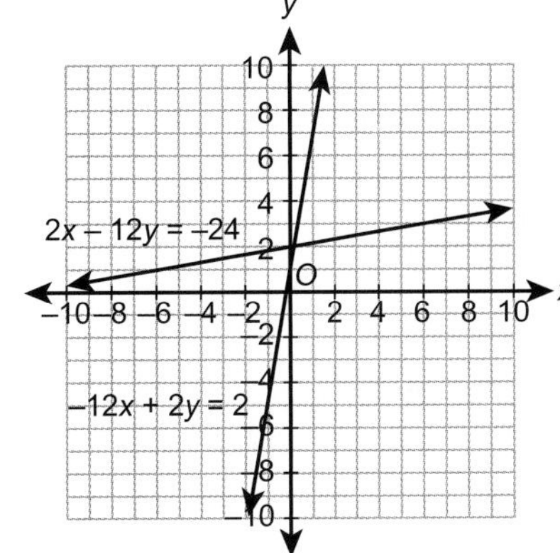

26.

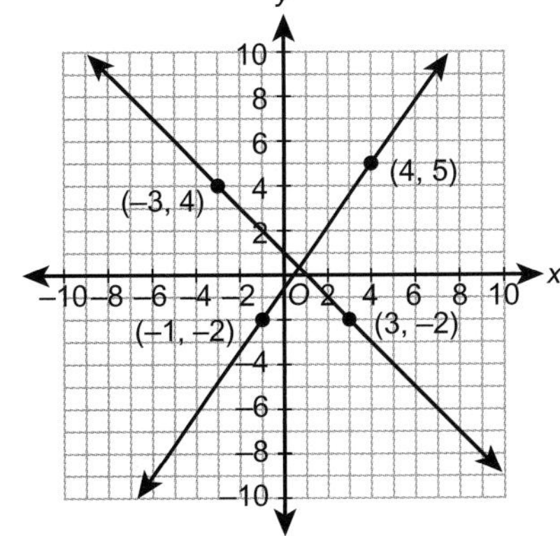

27.

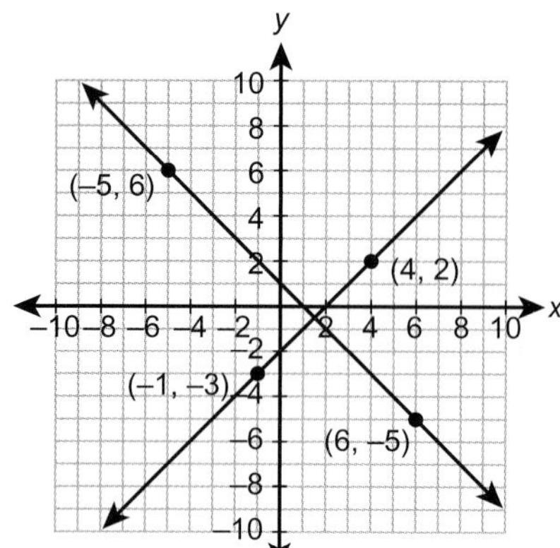

28.

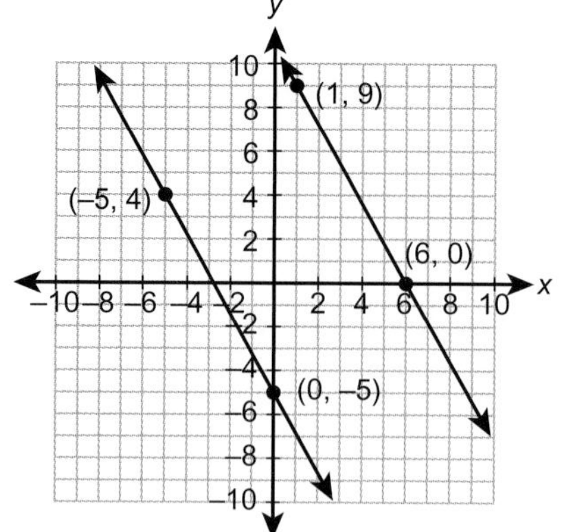

Solve.

***29.** **Challenge** Bing, Plaid, Croon, and Nod are parallel streets in the city. A new street called Duncan is constructed to run perpendicular to the four streets. Find the equation of Duncan street if it intersects Nod street at the point (6, 4). Write the equation in slope-intersect form.

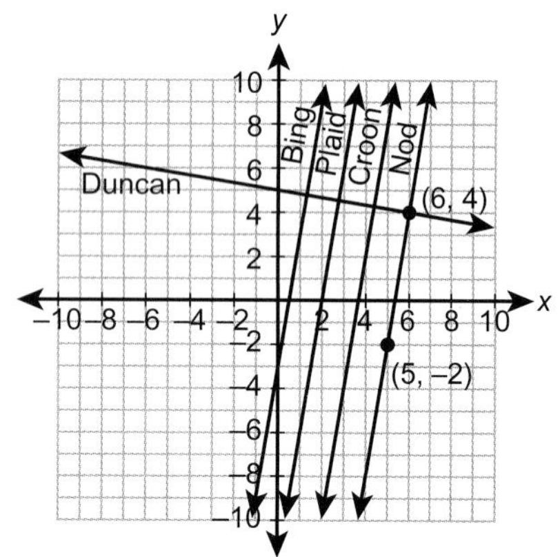

***30.** **Challenge** A square is formed by four lines. Opposite sides of the square are parallel and adjacent sides are perpendicular. Using the slope formula, find the y-coordinate of point C so that figure $ABCD$ is a square.

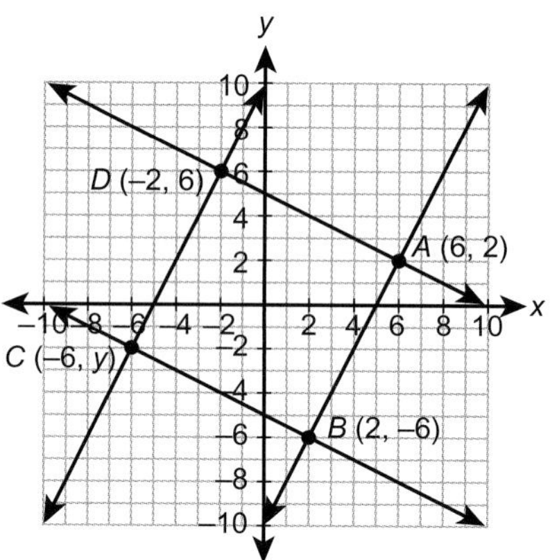

Equations from Graphs

You know how to graph a line when given an equation. You will now use the graph of a line to determine the equation of the line.

Writing the Equation of a Line in Point-Slope Form Using a Graph

When you know two points that lie on a line, you can write the equation of the line using point-slope form.

Example 1 Write the equation of the line shown in the graph.

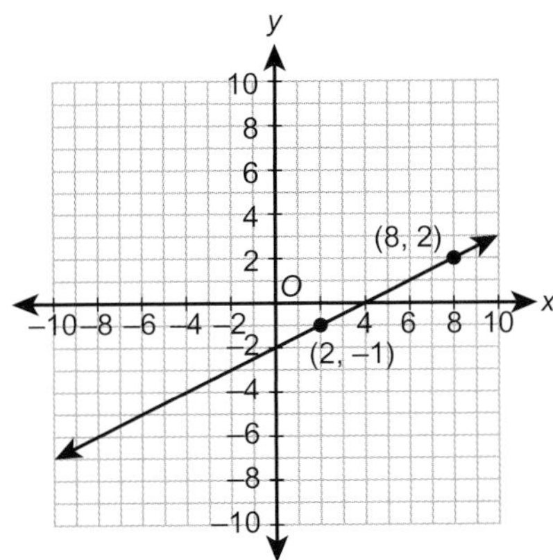

Solution

Step 1 Use the slope formula to find the slope of the line.

$$m = \frac{y_2 - y_1}{x_2 - x_1} = \frac{2 - (-1)}{8 - 2} = \frac{3}{6} = \frac{1}{2}$$

Step 2 Write the equation in point-slope form. You can use either point in the point-slope equation. Using the point (8, 2):

$y - y_1 = m(x - x_1)$ Point-slope form

$y - 2 = \frac{1}{2}(x - 8)$ Substitute 2 for y_1, $\frac{1}{2}$ for m, and 8 for x_1.

The equation of the line in point-slope form is $y - 2 = \frac{1}{2}(x - 8)$. ■

Using a Graph to Write the Equation of a Line in Standard Form

Example 2 Write the equation of the line from Example 1 in standard form.

Solution Rewrite the equation $y - 2 = \frac{1}{2}(x - 8)$ in standard form.

$y - 2 = \frac{1}{2}(x - 8)$	Equation in point-slope form
$y - 2 = \frac{1}{2}x - 4$	Distributive Property
$y = \frac{1}{2}x - 2$	Add 2 to each side of the equation.
$-\frac{1}{2}x + y = -2$	Subtract $\frac{1}{2}x$ from each side.
$2\left(-\frac{1}{2}x + y\right) = 2(-2)$	Multiple each side by 2.
$-x + 2y = -4$	Simplify.

The equation of the line in standard form is $-x + 2y = -4$. ■

Using a Graph to Write the Equation of a Line in Slope-Intercept Form

When you know two points that lie on a line and one of those points is the y-intercept, you can write the equation of the line using slope-intercept form.

Example 3 Write the equation of the line shown in the graph.

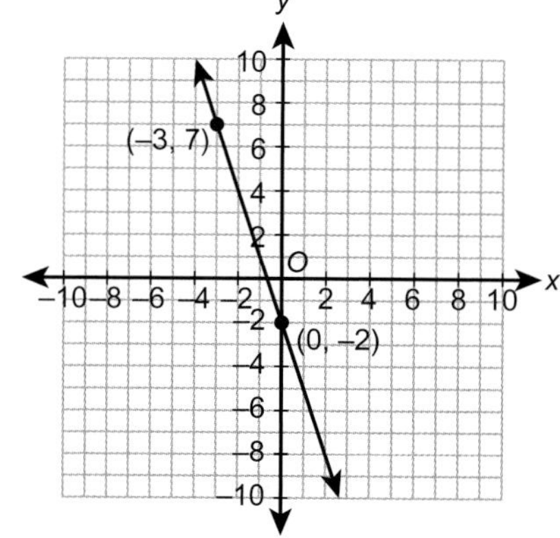

Solution

Step 1 Use the slope formula to find the slope of the line.

$$m = \frac{y_2 - y_1}{x_2 - x_1} = \frac{7 - (-2)}{-3 - 0} = \frac{9}{-3} = -3$$

Step 2 Write the equation in slope-intercept form. The line intersects the y-axis at the point $(0, -2)$ so the y-intercept is -2.

$y = mx + b$	Slope-intercept form
$y = -3x + (-2)$	Substitute -3 for m and -2 for b.
$y = -3x - 2$	Simplify.

The equation of the line in slope-intercept form is $y = -3x - 2$. ■

Writing the Equation of a Horizontal and a Vertical Line

Example 4 Write the equation of each line shown in the graph.

A. the horizontal line **B.** the vertical line

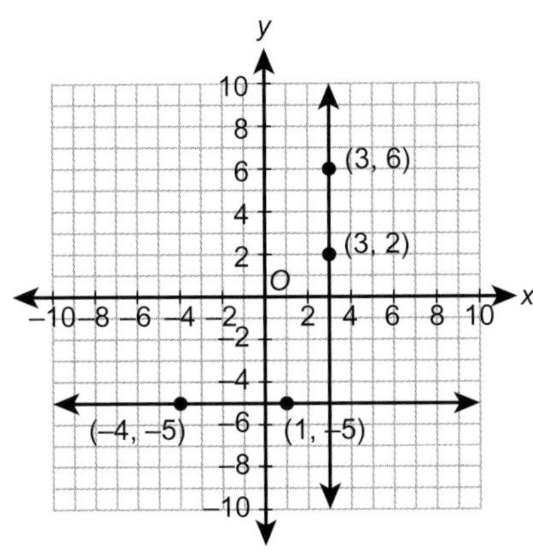

Solution

A. The y-coordinate of every point on the horizontal line is -5. The equation of the line is $y = -5$.

Another way to solve the problem is to find the slope of the line and use slope-intercept form to write the equation of the line. The line crosses the y-axis at $(0, -5)$ so the y-intercept is -5.

$$m = \frac{y_2 - y_1}{x_2 - x_1} = \frac{-5 - (-5)}{1 - (-4)} = \frac{0}{5} = 0$$

$$y = mx + b$$
$$y = 0 \cdot x + (-5)$$
$$y = -5 \ ■$$

B. The x-coordinate of every point on the vertical line is 3. The equation of the line is $x = 3$. ■

REMEMBER

The slope of a vertical line is undefined, so you can't use the point-slope or slope-intercept formulas to find the equation.

Problem Set

Write the equation of the line in point-slope form.

1. 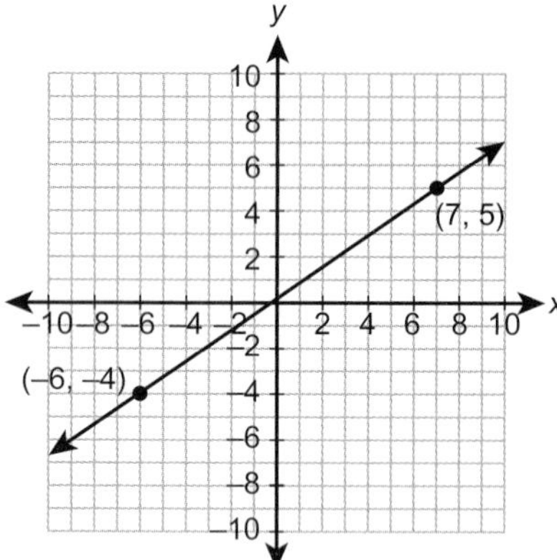

2. 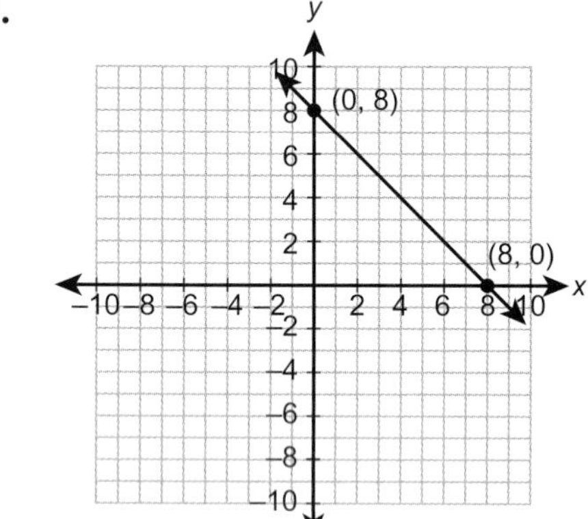

3. 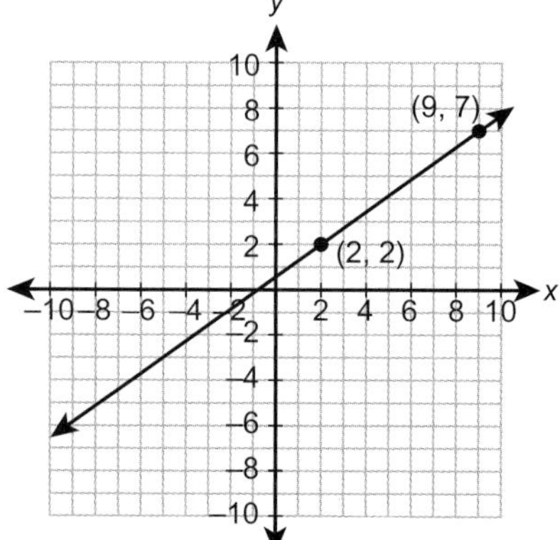

4. 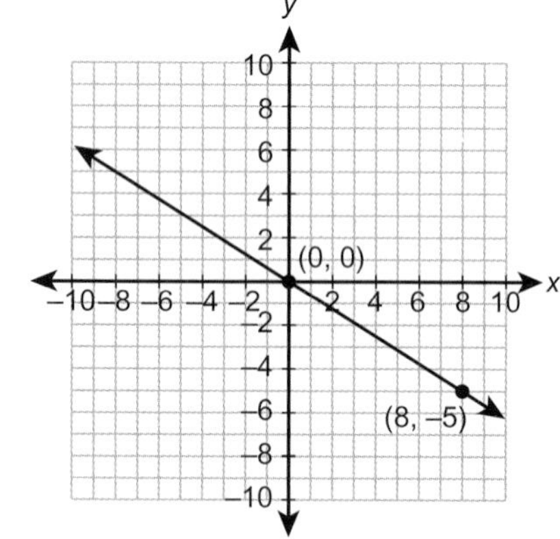

5. 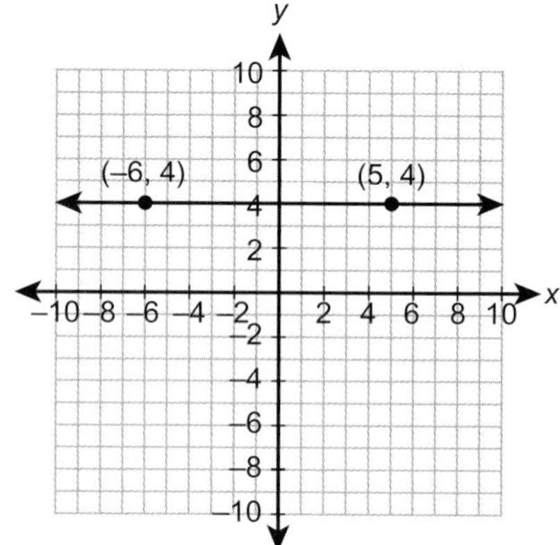

6. 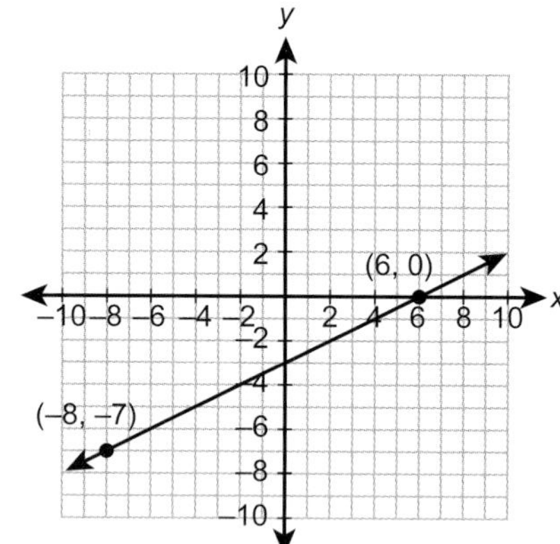

7. 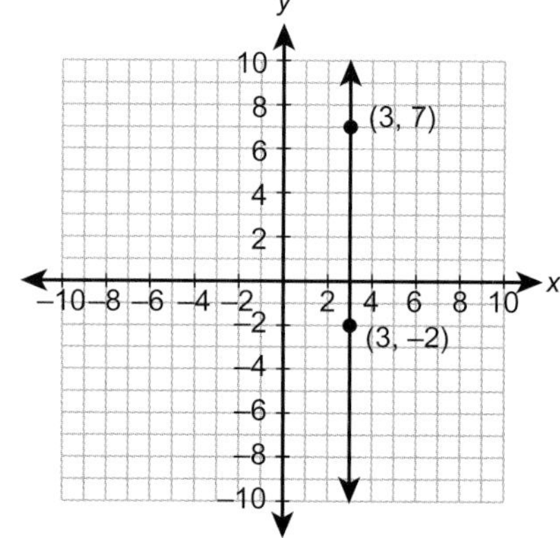

8. 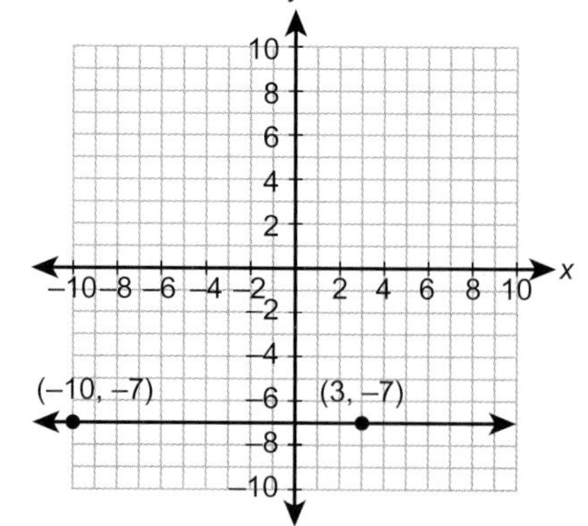

Use point-slope form to write the equation of the line in standard form.

9.

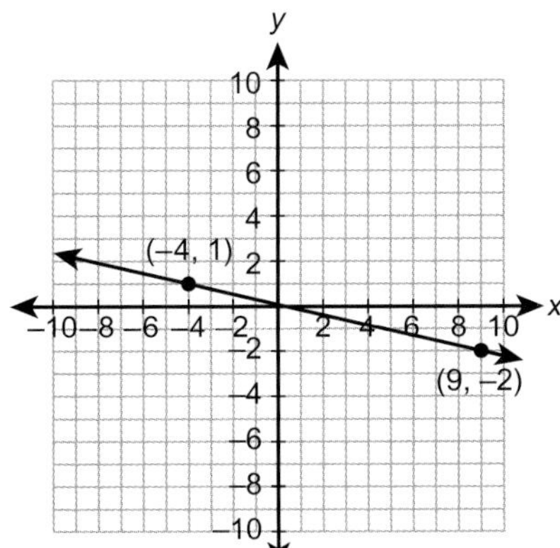

10.

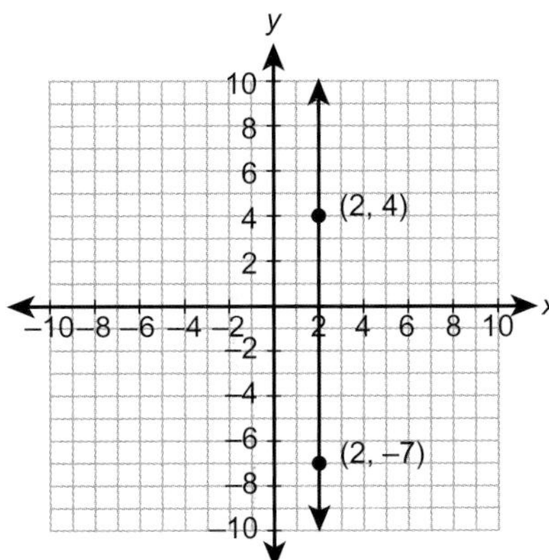

11.

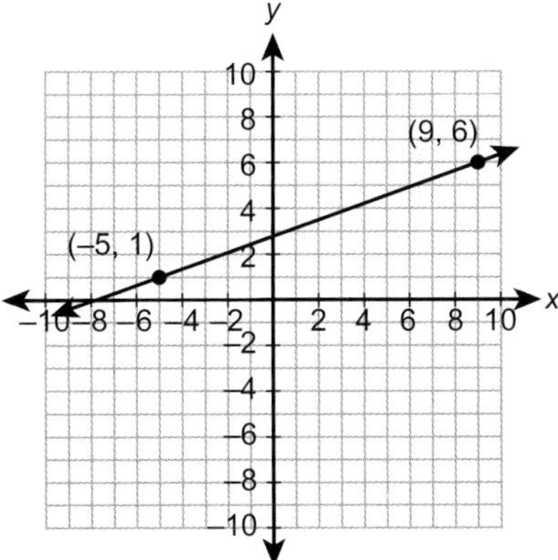

12.

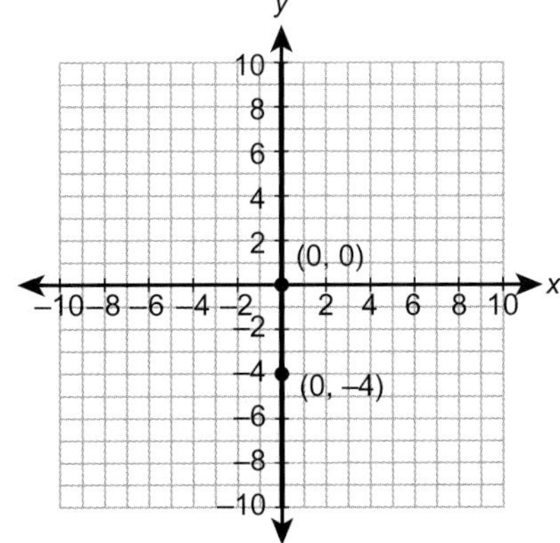

13.

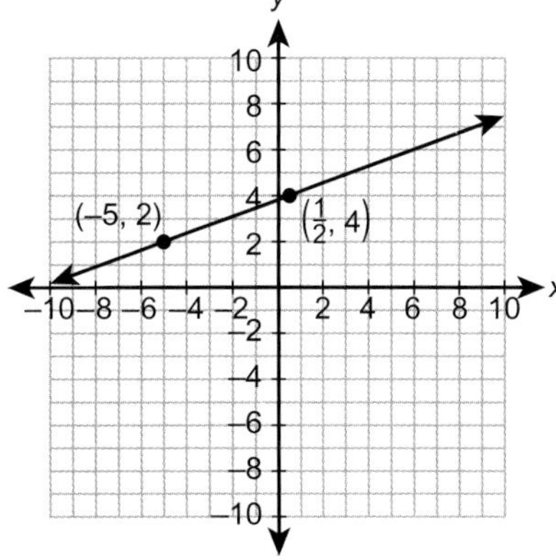

14.

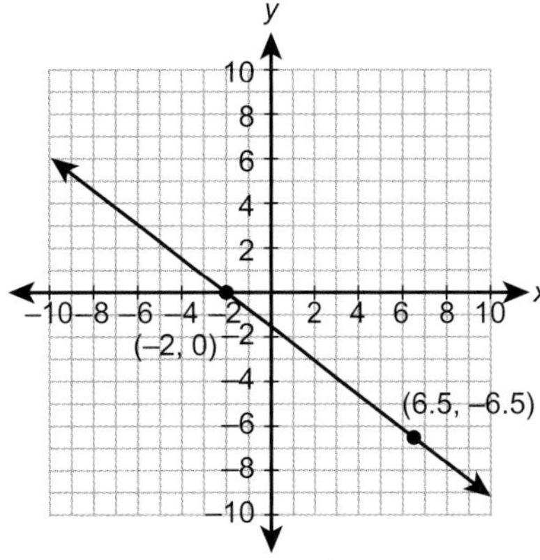

15.

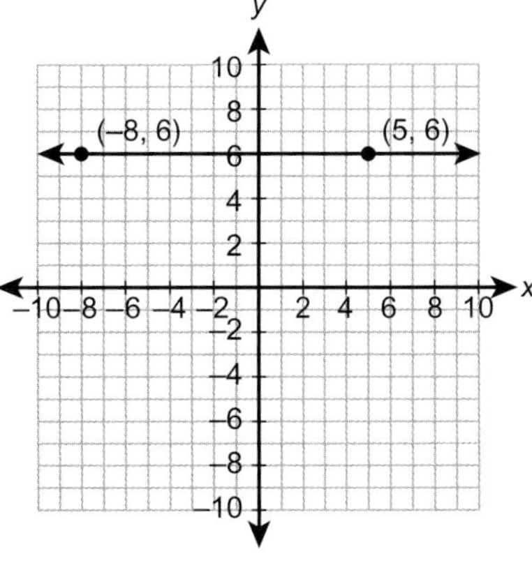

16.

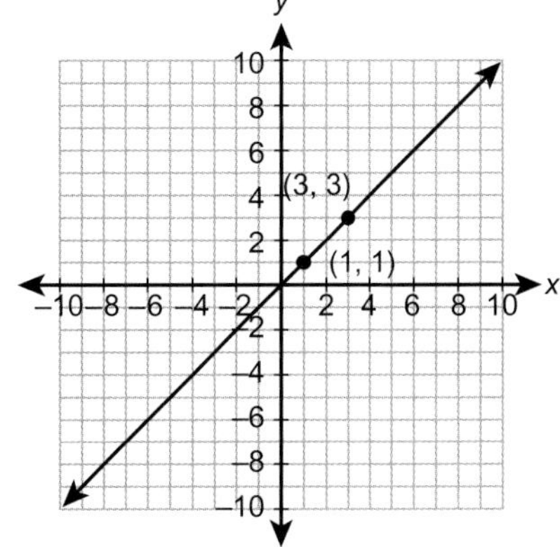

Write the equation of the line in slope-intercept form.

17.

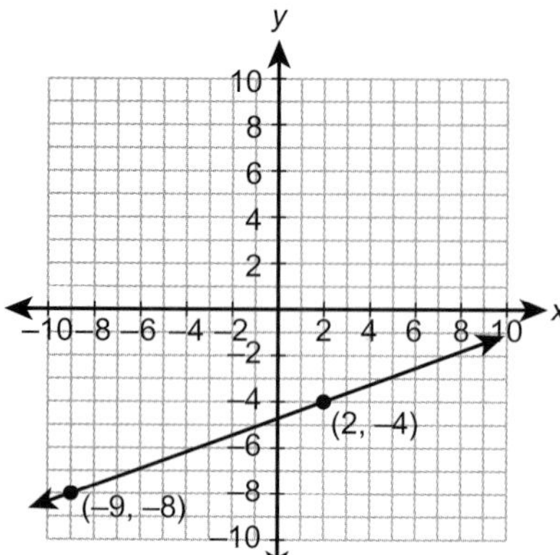

18.

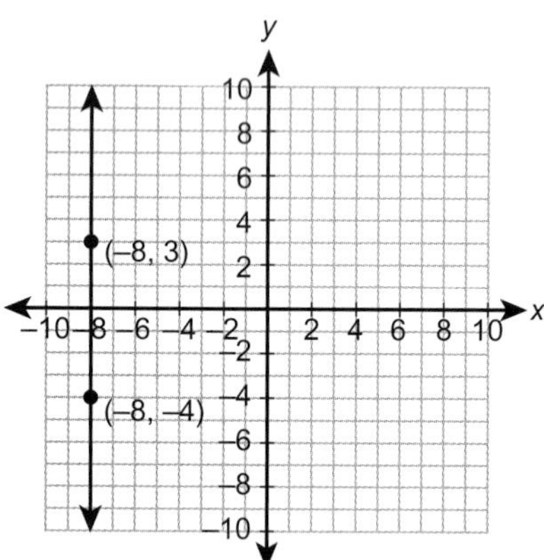

19.

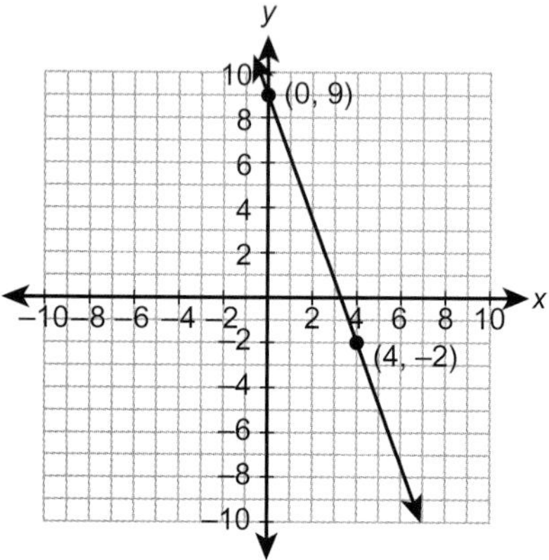

20.

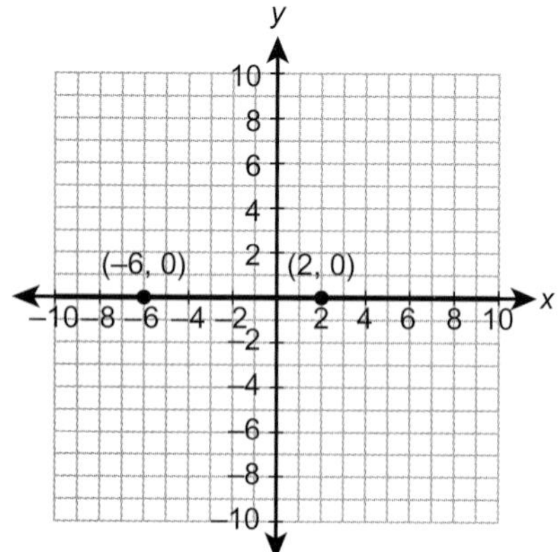

21.

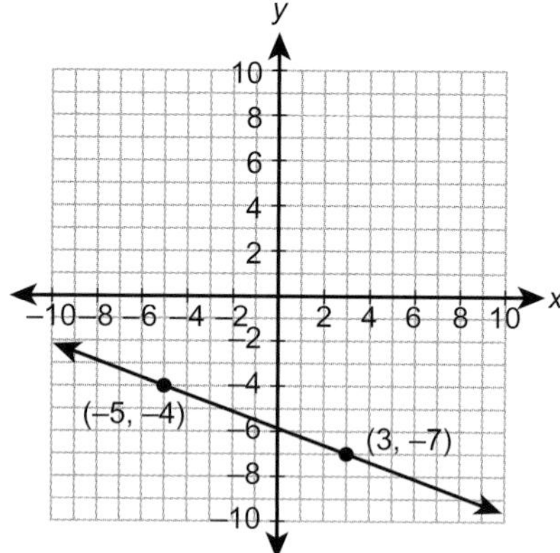

22.

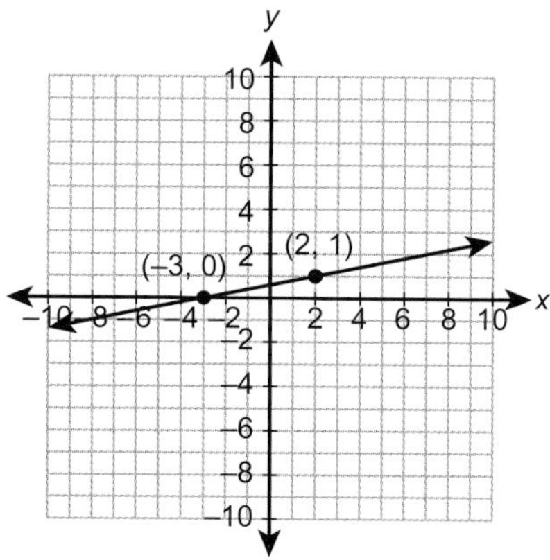

23.

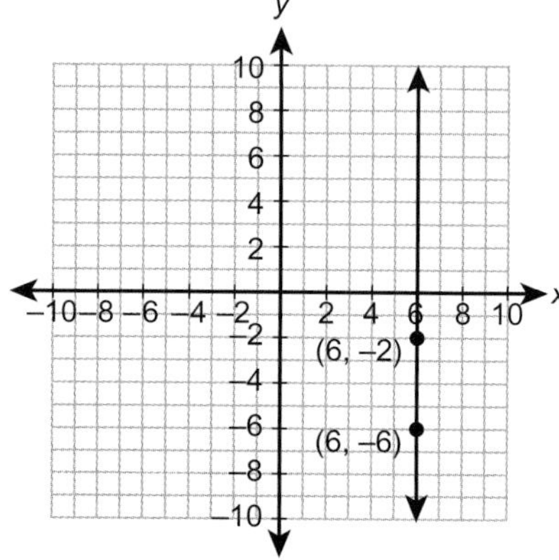

24.

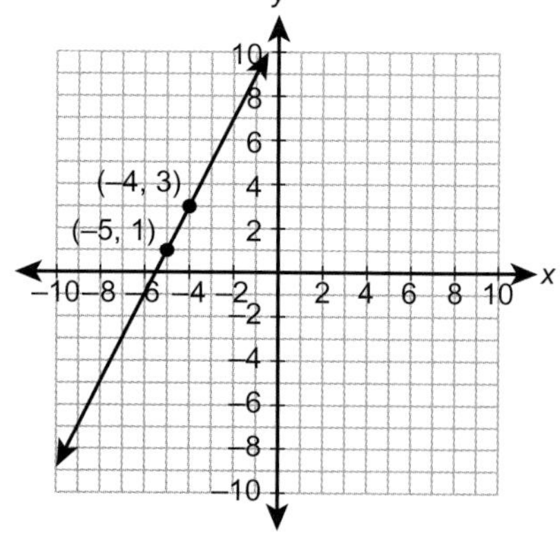

Applications: Linear Models

Use a table of values to help you understand and solve application problems involving constant rates.

Distance

Example 1 The distance d that Cosimo can walk is given by the linear equation $d = 3.5t$, where t is the time in hours. Make a table showing the values for d when $t = 1, 2, 3$, and 4. Then graph the linear equation.

Solution

Step 1 Make a table. Substitute each value of t into the equation and solve for d.

t	1	2	3	4
d	$d = 3.5t$ $= 3.5 \cdot 1$ $= 3.5$	$d = 3.5t$ $= 3.5 \cdot 2$ $= 7$	$d = 3.5t$ $= 3.5 \cdot 3$ $= 10.5$	$d = 3.5t$ $= 3.5 \cdot 4$ $= 14$

Step 2 Plot the ordered pairs (1, 3.5), (2, 7), (3, 10.5), and (4, 14). Then draw the line. Since distance and time cannot be negative, the graph of the line is restricted to quadrant I.

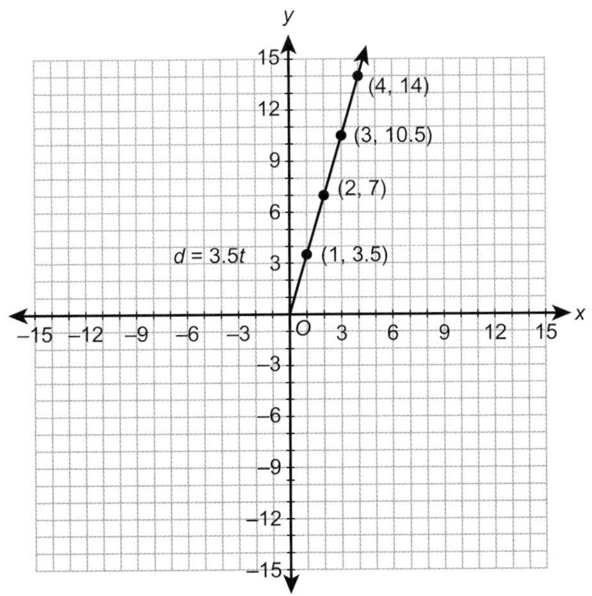

■

Cost

Example 2 An online movie rental company charges customers \$5 to sign up and a monthly fee of \$10. The total cost C for n months can be modeled by the equation $C = 10n + 5$.

A. Complete a table of values. What is the total cost for 1 month? 5 months? 7 months? 1 year?

B. Is this a linear model? Explain.

Solution

A. Substitute each value of n into the equation and solve for C.

n	1	5	7	12
C	$C = 10n + 5$ $= 10 \cdot 1 + 5$ $= 10 + 5$ $= 15$	$C = 10n + 5$ $= 10 \cdot 5 + 5$ $= 50 + 5$ $= 55$	$C = 10n + 5$ $= 10 \cdot 7 + 5$ $= 70 + 5$ $= 75$	$C = 10n + 5$ $= 10 \cdot 12 + 5$ $= 120 + 5$ $= 125$

When n is 1, C is 15, so the total cost for 1 month is \$15. When n is 5, C is 55, so the total cost for 5 months is \$55. When n is 7, C is 75, so the total cost for 7 months is \$75. The variable n is time in months, so change 1 year to 12 months. When n is 12, C is 125, so the total cost for 12 months is \$125. ∎

B. Examine the rate of change between values.

(1, 15) and (5, 55) rate of change $= \frac{y_2 - y_1}{x_2 - x_1} = \frac{55 - 15}{5 - 1} = \frac{40}{4} = 10$

(5, 55) and (7, 75) rate of change $= \frac{y_2 - y_1}{x_2 - x_1} = \frac{75 - 55}{7 - 5} = \frac{20}{2} = 10$

(7, 75) and (12, 125) rate of change $= \frac{y_2 - y_1}{x_2 - x_1} = \frac{125 - 75}{12 - 7} = \frac{50}{5} = 10$

The rates of change are equal. Therefore, the model is linear. Another way to determine if the model is linear is to look at the equation $C = 10n + 5$. Notice the equation is in slope-intercept form where the slope of the line is 10 and the y-intercept is 5. Only linear equations are written in slope-intercept form. ∎

Problem Set

For each problem:

A. Make a table of values.
B. Graph the linear equation.

1. The time t that it takes Hal to read a lesson and complete the practice problems is given by the linear equation $t = 30 + 3p$, where p is the number of practice problems. Determine the time when $p = 5$, 10, 15, and 20.

2. Jacob is mowing grass for the summer and his fee is given by the linear equation $f = 0.01a + 10$, where a is the yard area in square feet. Determine the fee when $a = 500$, 1000, 1500, and 2000.

3. Stephania is ordering sandwiches for a luncheon and to determine the number of sandwiches that she must order, she uses the linear equation $s = 3g + 3$, where g is the number of guests she expects to join her. Determine the number of sandwiches when $g = 0, 2, 4,$ and 6.

4. Hao bought a membership at a golf course, and the price he pays per month to golf is shown by the linear equation $p = 30 + 20r$, where r is the number of rounds of golf he plays. Determine the price when $r = 0, 1, 2,$ and 3.

5. For a fundraiser, elementary school students are selling a \$5 discount card for a local restaurant. The savings from buying and using the card is shown by the linear equation $s = 5d - 25$, where d is the number of dinners purchased at the restaurant with the card. Determine the savings when $d = 0, 3, 6,$ and 9.

6. A computer salesman is paid a base salary plus commission for each computer sold. Her hourly wage is shown by the linear equation $w = 5 + 2c$, where c is the number of computers sold in a given hour. Determine the wage when $c = 1, 2, 3,$ and 4.

7. The total amount a cable customer pays for cable is shown by the linear equation $c = 75 + 50m$, where m is the number of months subscribed. Determine the cost when $m = 6, 12, 18,$ and 24.

8. During deceleration, a car's speed can be shown by the linear equation $s = 55 - 5t$, where t is the time in seconds that the car decelerated. Determine the speed when $t = 2, 4, 6,$ and 8.

9. Temperature in degrees Celsius can be converted to degrees Fahrenheit using the linear equation $F = 1.8C + 32$, where C is the temperature in degrees Celsius. Determine the degrees Fahrenheit when $C = 0, 10, 20,$ and 30.

10. In Texas, sales tax is calculated using the linear equation $T = 0.0825P$, where P is the total taxable purchase amount in dollars. Determine the values for T when $P = 25, 50,$ 75, and 100.

For each problem:

A. Make a table using reasonable input values.

B. Is this a linear model? Explain. If so, give the slope and y-intercept.

11. During deceleration, a car's speed can be shown by the equation $s = 35 - 2t^2$, where t is the time in seconds that the car decelerated.

12. Two years after the purchase, if Manuel's gift card is unused, the automatic decrease on Manuel's gift card balance is given by the equation $b = 50 - 5m$, where m is the number of months beyond two years.

13. The number of customers that come to a fruit stand during the week can be modeled by the equation $c = 0.3x$, where x is the temperature in degrees Fahrenheit.

14. The total deposit and rent collected by an apartment manager for one resident are given by the equation $t = 350 + 700m$, where m is the number of months the resident has lived there.

15. At a local restaurant, the number of meal orders that can be filled in five minutes is given by the equation $m = -(n - 4)^2 + 10$, where n is the number of employees working in the kitchen.

16. The total amount in Sakura's savings account is given by the equation $P = 500 \cdot (1.1)^t$, where t is the number of years the money is in the account.

17. The total amount Ebony paid for house paint is given by the equation $T = 24.99c + 0.07 \cdot 24.99c$, where c is the number of cans of paint that she bought.

18. The amount Leon pays for electricity each month is given by the equation

$$E = 9.99 + \frac{11.07w}{100} + 4.99,$$ where w is the number of kilowatt-hours he uses. For the table, show the cost of electricity when $w = 700, 800,$ 900, and 1000.

19. A car salesman's daily pay is given by the equation $S = 48 + 0.005v$, where v is the value of the cars he sold that day. For the table, show values for S when $v = 15{,}000$, 20,000, 25,000, and 30,000.

20. The amount of a 400 g sample of a radioactive substance that remains over time is given by the equation $A = 400 \cdot \left(\frac{1}{4}\right)^d$, where d is the number of days since the sample weight was 400 g.

For each problem:

A. Make a table using the given input values.
B. Is this a linear model? Explain using rates of change.

21. At its top speed, the distance a cheetah can run in meters is given by the equation $d = 1850t$, where t is the number of minutes. Determine the distance when $t = 1, 2, 3$, and 4.

22. Hannah charges an hourly babysitting fee of $6 for two children, $7 for three children, and $8 for four or five children.

23. The monthly fee at Teresa's gym is given by the equation $f = 30 + 15c$, where c is the number of fitness classes for which she is registered. Determine the fee when $c = 0, 1, 2$, and 3.

24. At a predicted growth rate of 0.9%, Canada's population in millions of people is given by the equation $P = 33(1 + 0.009)^t$, where t is the number of years since 2006. Determine the population, in millions, for $t = 5, 10, 15$, and 20.

25. The total cost T of admission to the zoo is given by the equation $T = 13.50p$, where p is the number of people. Determine the cost when $p = 2, 4, 6$, and 8.

26. The amount Audrey pays to order digital photos online is given by the equation $A = 0.2p + 5$, where p is the number of photos she orders. Determine the amount paid when $p = 5, 10, 15$, and 20.

27. An online distributor sells couscous for $2.99 per pound and charges a shipping fee of $1.50 per pound. Determine the total amount paid A when the number of pounds purchased p is 1, 3, 5, and 7.

Solve.

***28.** **Challenge** An auto club membership provides 3 free oil changes, then charges $20 per oil change after that.

A. Make a table to show the amount paid as a function of the total number of oil changes for 1, 2, 3, 4, and 5 oil changes.

B. Explain how this problem involves linear models and define them and the ranges in which they are valid.

***29.** **Challenge** Asher works in a stockroom and gets paid $8 per hour for up to 40 hours per week. He gets paid $12 per hour for any additional hours that week.

A. Make a table to show his pay as a function of hours worked for 20, 30, 40, 50, and 60 hours in a week.

B. Explain how this problem involves linear models and define them and the ranges in which they are valid.

Graphing Linear Inequalities

You know how to graph linear equations. It is also possible to graph linear inequalities.

Solutions to Linear Inequalities in Two Variables

An ordered pair (x, y) is a solution to an inequality in two variables if substituting the values of x and y into the inequality yields a true statement.

Example 1 Determine if each ordered pair is a solution to the inequality $y < 4x - 8$.

A. $(0, 0)$ **B.** $(2, -10)$

Solution Test each ordered pair. Substitute the values of x and y into the inequality $y < 4x - 8$. Then simplify. If the resulting statement is true, the ordered pair is a solution.

A. $(0, 0)$

$$y < 4x - 8$$
$$0 \stackrel{?}{<} 4 \cdot 0 - 8$$
$$0 \stackrel{?}{<} 0 - 8$$
$$0 \not< -8$$

$(0, 0)$ is not a solution to the inequality $y < 4x - 8$. ■

B. $(2, -10)$

$$y < 4x - 8$$
$$-10 \stackrel{?}{<} 4 \cdot 2 - 8$$
$$-10 \stackrel{?}{<} 8 - 8$$
$$-10 < 0 \checkmark$$

$(2, -10)$ is a solution to the inequality $y < 4x - 8$. ■

Graphing a Linear Inequality in Two Variables

The graph of a linear inequality is a region of the coordinate plane called a half-plane.

A **boundary line** divides the coordinate plane into two half-planes. One of the half-planes contains all the points that are solutions to the inequality. The boundary line is dashed if the boundary is not part of the solution, so the inequality uses the operator $<$ or $>$. The boundary is a solid line if it is part of the solution, so it uses the operator $\leq$ or $\geq$.

REMEMBER

The graph of a linear equation is a line in the coordinate plane. Each point that is a solution to the equation lies on the line.

(continued)

To graph a linear inequality in two variables, first graph the boundary line. Then determine which half-plane contains the solutions to the inequality and shade that half-plane. The shaded region represents all the solutions to the inequality.

GRAPHING A LINEAR INEQUALITY

Step 1 Graph the boundary line. If the boundary is included in the solution, use a solid line. If the boundary is not included in the solution, use a dashed line.

Step 2 Test a point that does not lie on the boundary line to determine if the ordered pair is a solution to the inequality.

Step 3 If the ordered pair is a solution, shade the half-plane that contains the point. Otherwise shade the other half-plane.

TIP

If the boundary line does not pass through the origin, use the origin to test the solution of an inequality. If substituting the point (0, 0) results in a true statement, shade toward the origin. If not, shade away from the origin.

Example 2 Graph the inequality.

A. $y > 2x - 1$

Solution

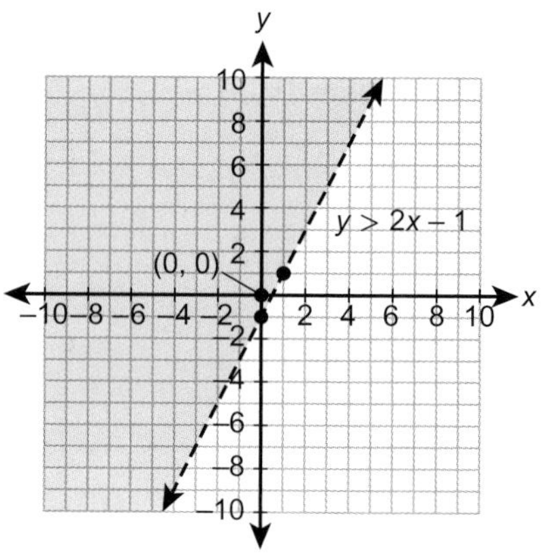

Step 1 Graph the boundary line $y = 2x - 1$. Since the inequality contains the operator $>$ the boundary line is a dashed line.

y
x
10
8
6
4
2
−10 −8 −6 −4 −2
2 4 6 8 10
−2
−4
−6
−8
−10
(0, 0)
$y > 2x - 1$

Step 2 Test a point that does not lie on the boundary line to determine if the ordered pair is a solution to the inequality. Test the point (0, 0).

$y > 2x - 1$

$0 \overset{?}{>} 2 \cdot 0 - 1$

$0 > -1$ ✓

$0 > -1$ is a true statement.

Step 3 Since (0, 0) is a solution, shade the half-plane that contains the point (0, 0). ■

B. $3x - 4y \geq 8$

Solution

Step 1 To graph the boundary line, first write the inequality in slope-intercept form.

$3x - 4y \geq 8$

$-4y \geq -3x + 8$ Subtract $3x$ from each side of the inequality.

$\frac{-4y}{-4} \leq \frac{-3x}{-4} + \frac{8}{-4}$ Divide each side of the inequality by -4. Since you are dividing an inequality by a negative number, switch the direction of the inequality.

$y \leq \frac{3}{4}x - 2$ Simplify.

Now, graph the boundary line $y = \frac{3}{4}x - 2$. Since the inequality contains the operator $\leq$, the boundary line is a solid line.

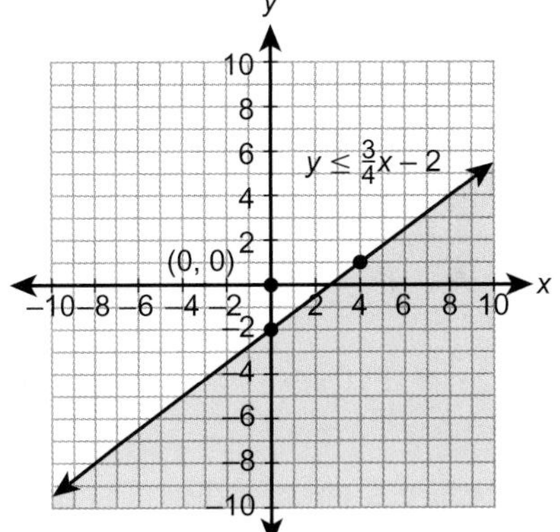

Step 2 Test a point that does not lie on the boundary line to determine if the ordered pair is a solution to the inequality. Test the point (0, 0).

$y \leq \frac{3}{4}x - 2$

$0 \overset{?}{\leq} \frac{3}{4} \cdot 0 - 2$

$0 \nleq -2$

$0 \leq -2$ is a false statement.

Step 3 Since (0, 0) is not a solution, shade the half-plane that does not contain the point (0, 0). ■

Application: Mixture

Example 3 Audrina wants to create a blend of birdseed containing millet seed and sunflower seed. Millet seed costs \$3.50 per pound and sunflower seed costs \$2 per pound. She has \$28 to spend on the birdseed.

A. Write an inequality to model the problem.

B. Graph the inequality.

C. What does the shaded area of the graph represent?

Solution

A. Write an inequality which can be used to model the problem.

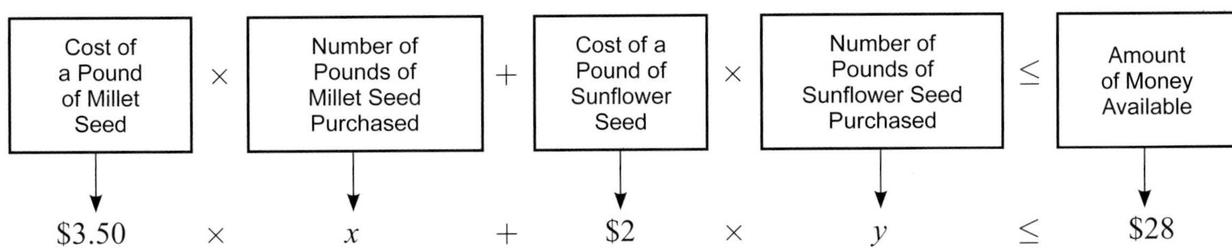

The problem is modeled by the inequality $3.5x + 2y \leq 28$. ■

(continued)

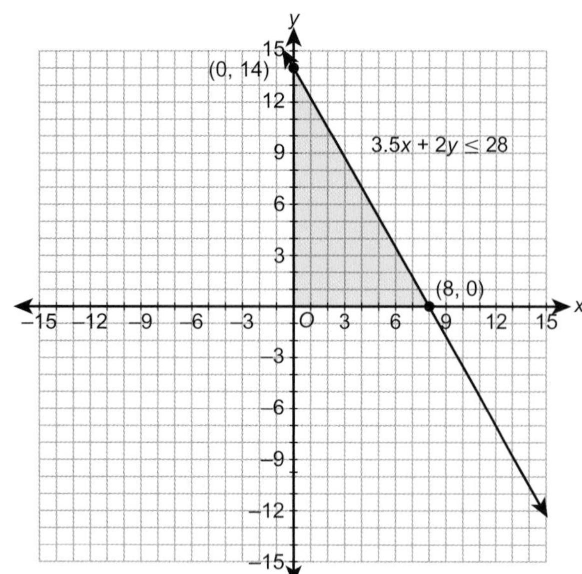

B. Graph the boundary line $3.5x + 2y = 28$. Since the inequality contains the operator $\leq$, the boundary line is a solid line. The points (8, 0) and (0, 14) are the x- and y-intercepts of the boundary line.

Test the point (2, 2) to determine which side of the boundary line to shade.

$$3.5x + 2y \leq 28$$
$$3.5 \cdot 2 + 2 \cdot 2 \overset{?}{\leq} 28$$
$$7 + 4 \overset{?}{\leq} 28$$
$$11 \leq 28 \checkmark$$

Since $11 \leq 28$ is a true statement, shade the half-plane containing the point (2, 2). The number of pounds of millet and sunflower seed purchased must always be greater than or equal to zero, so the graph is restricted to quadrant I. ■

C. The shaded area of the graph represents all the possible ordered pairs that are solutions to the inequality $3.5x + 2y \leq 28$. ■

Problem Set

Determine if each ordered pair is a solution to the given inequality.

1. $y \geq 1 - x$
 A. (4, 3)
 B. (−2, 8)

2. $y < 0.5x + 9$
 A. (−7, 1)
 B. (−6, 6)

3. $2y - 3x > 12$
 A. (−4, −17)
 B. (12, 3)

4. $\frac{1}{4}x \leq \frac{7}{3}y + 2$
 A. (48, 9)
 B. (36, −3)

5. $y \geq 11x - 119$
 A. (9, 20)
 B. (−9, −20)

6. $20y > 15 - 50x$
 A. (−0.5, 0.75)
 B. (1.2, −0.25)

7. $-y \leq -4 + x$
 A. (13, −11)
 B. (−7, 3)

8. $x + 3y < -17$
 A. (−1, −5)
 B. (−29, 4)

9. $2y > 14 - 7x$
 A. $\left(\frac{2}{7}, 7\right)$
 B. $\left(-\frac{4}{7}, 9\right)$

Graph the inequality.

10. $y \leq 10 - 3x$

11. $y - 2x > -8$

12. $x < 17 + y$

13. $2y \geq 6x + 6$

14. $5x + 4y < 2$

15. $x - y \geq 70$

16. $-5y < 10 + x$

17. $2y + 1 \geq -3 - \frac{3}{2}x$

18. $y \leq 6x - 13$

19. $y - 0.25 < 0.5x$

20. $8x \geq 12 - 2y$

21. $y < 19 - 6x$

22. $3 - \frac{1}{3}y \leq \frac{2}{9}x$

23. $y - x > 50$

Solve. For each problem:

A. Write an inequality to model the problem.
B. Graph the inequality.
C. Explain any restrictions on the graph.

24. Ciara budgeted \$30 per month for entertainment. Movies cost \$7 and sports games cost \$5.

25. A company prepares a graph of its profit forecast. The annual budget predicts monthly income of at least \$5000 more than expenditures.

26. Ameesh wants to calculate the amount of fuel used by his car on the highway versus the amount of fuel used by his car on back roads over the same distance. He knows that his car uses less than twice as many gallons of fuel per mile on the back roads as it uses on the highway.

27. Neyrchel wants to arrange a bouquet of roses and tulips that is worth at least \$20. Roses cost \$5 each and tulips cost \$4 each.

28. A salad dressing recipe requires at least 8 ounces of oil to be combined with some combination of vinegar and lemon juice in a 16-ounce container.

***29. Challenge** Braeden has a bag of 200 coins. More than 50 of them are quarters and at least 75 of them are dimes. How many of the coins are quarters or dimes?

***30. Challenge** A bean soup mix is made from lentils, which cost \$4 per pound, kidney beans, which cost \$3 per pound, and navy beans and black-eyed peas, which each cost \$10 per pound. The soup mix has half as many navy beans as kidney beans and twice as many black-eyed peas as kidney beans. What combination of lentils and kidney beans can be used to make a soup mix that costs less than \$20?

Inequalities from Graphs

Just as you can use the graph of a line to determine the equation of the line, you can use the graph of an inequality to write the inequality.

Writing an Inequality Given a Graph

Example 1 Write the inequality shown in the graph.

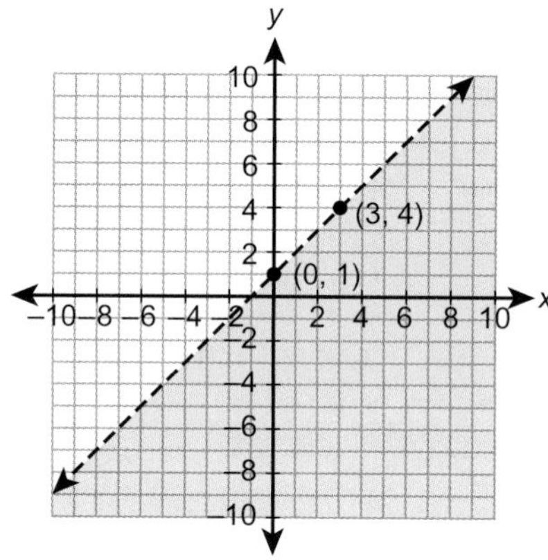

Solution

Step 1 Find the equation of the boundary line.

You know several methods for finding the equation of a line from a graph. Since you know the y-intercept of the line, use slope-intercept form. First find the slope of the line using the slope formula.

$$m = \frac{y_2 - y_1}{x_2 - x_1} = \frac{4 - 1}{3 - 0} = \frac{3}{3} = 1$$

Write the equation in slope-intercept form. The line intersects the y-axis at the point (0, 1) so the y-intercept is 1.

$y = mx + b$ Slope-intercept form

$y = 1x + 1$ Substitute 1 for m and 1 for b.

$y = x + 1$ Simplify.

The equation of the boundary line is $y = x + 1$.

Step 2 Choose a point in the half-plane that contains the solutions of the inequality. Substitute the x- and y-coordinates of the point into the equation of the boundary line, replacing the equal sign with an inequality operator that makes a true statement.

Use the point (4, 0).

$y \; \square \; x + 1$

$0 \; \square \; 4 + 1$ Substitute 4 for x and 0 for y.

$0 \; \square \; 5$ Simplify.

$0 < 5$ The less than operator makes the statement true. Since the boundary line is a dashed line, the operator is <.

The inequality is $y < x + 1$. ■

Writing an Inequality in One Variable From a Graph

Example 2 Write the inequalities shown in each graph.

A.

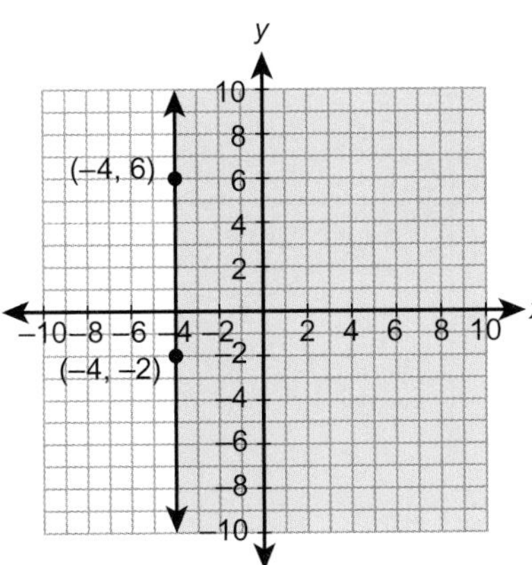

B.

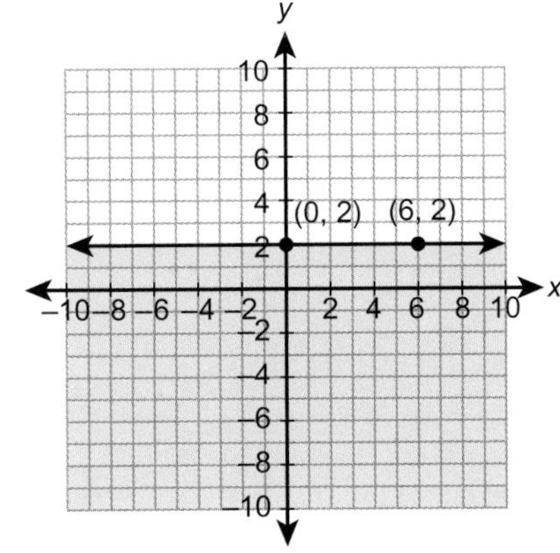

Solution

A. The equation of the boundary line is $x = -4$.

Test the point (0, 0).

$0 \geq -4$

Since the boundary line is solid the operator is $\geq$. The inequality is $x \geq -4$. ■

B. The equation of the boundary line is $y = 2$.

Test the point (0, 0).

$0 \leq 2$

Since the boundary line is solid the operator is $\leq$. The inequality is $y \leq 2$. ■

Problem Set

Write the inequality shown in the graph.

1.

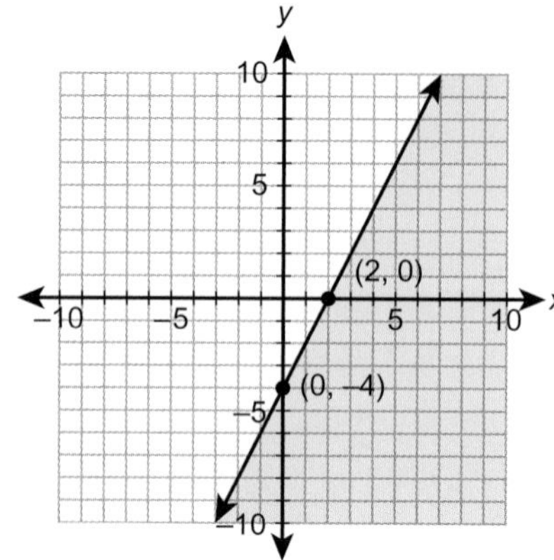

2.

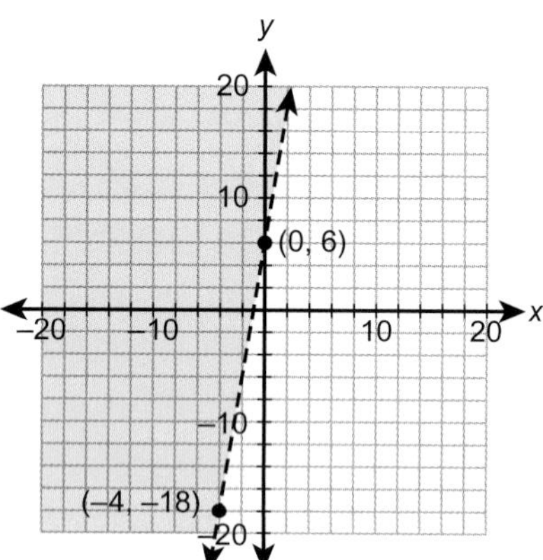

3.

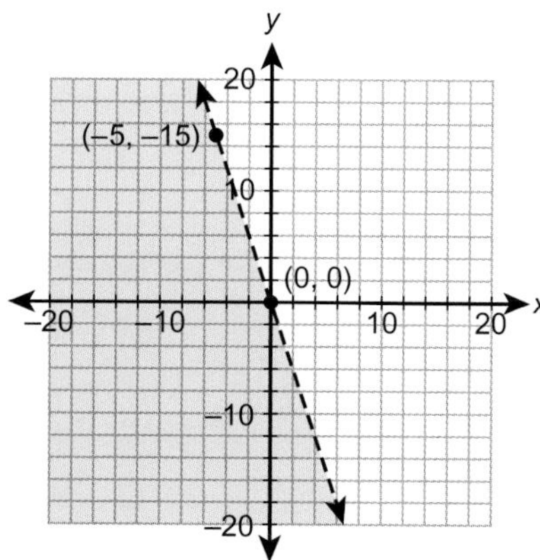

4.

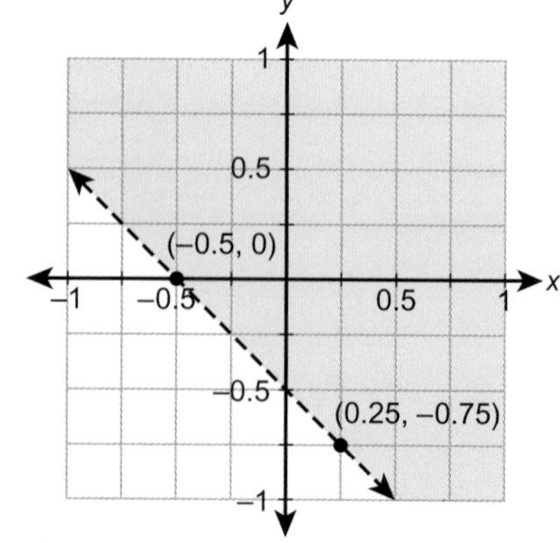

5.

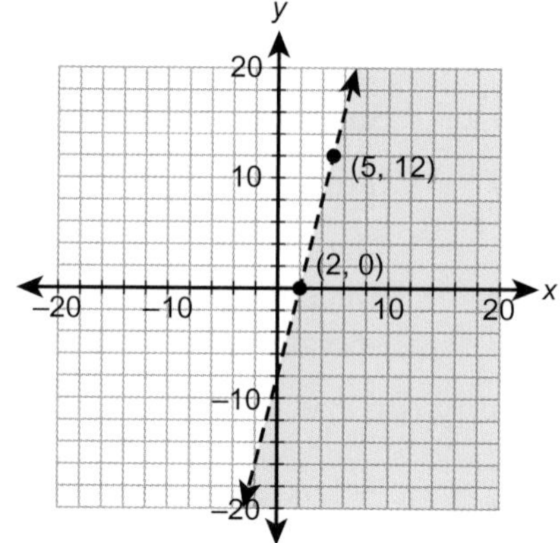

6.

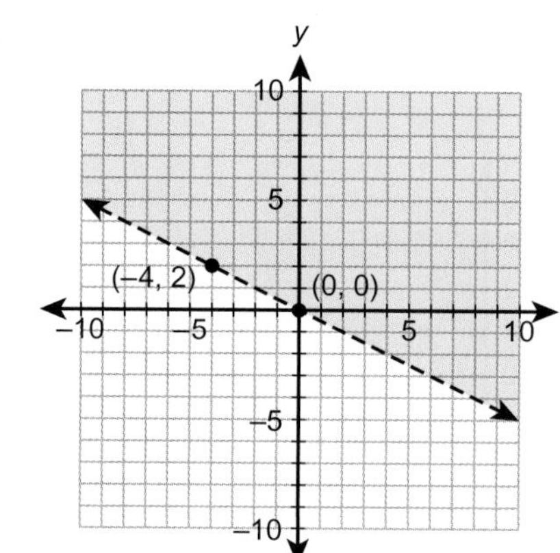

7.

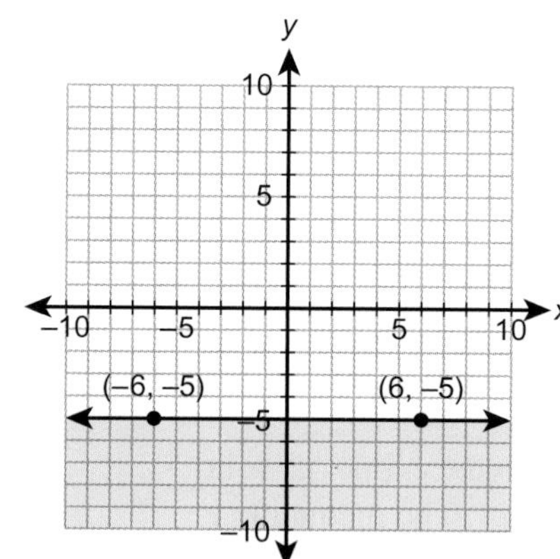

8.

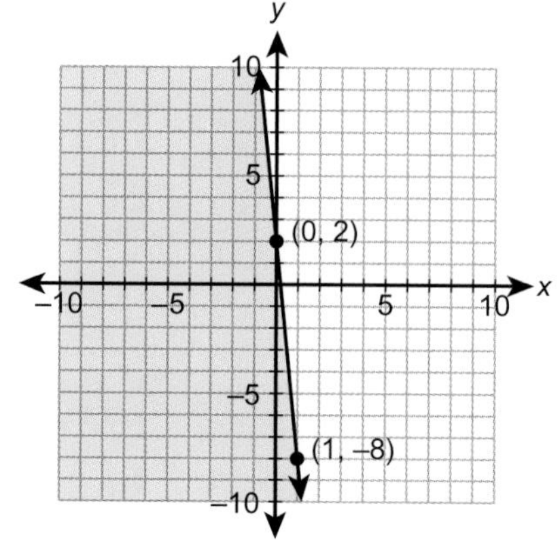

9.

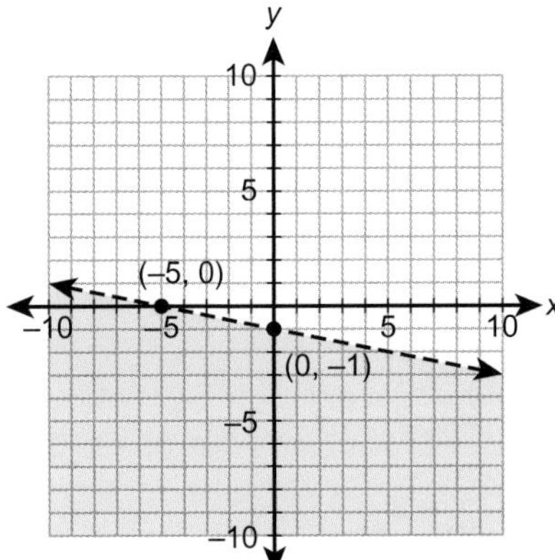

10.

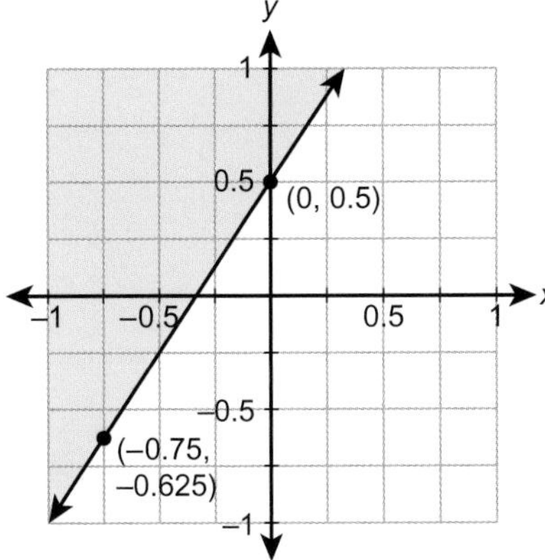

11.

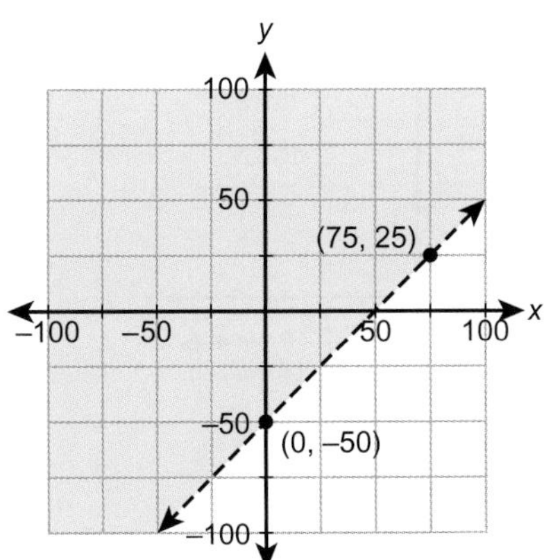

12.

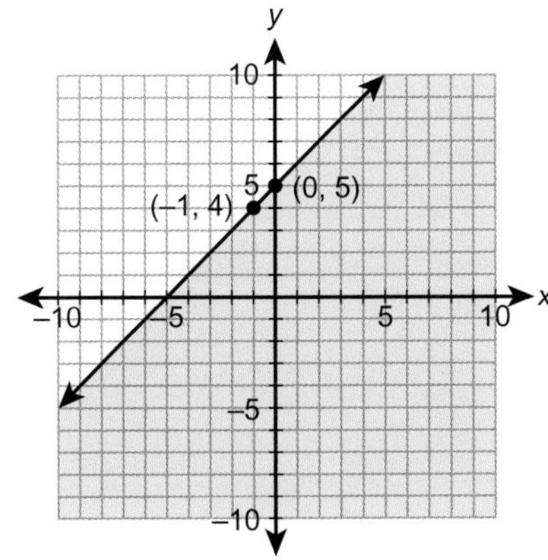

13.

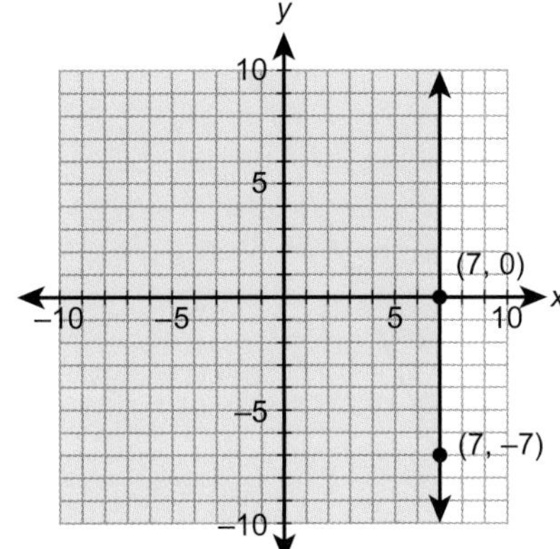

14.

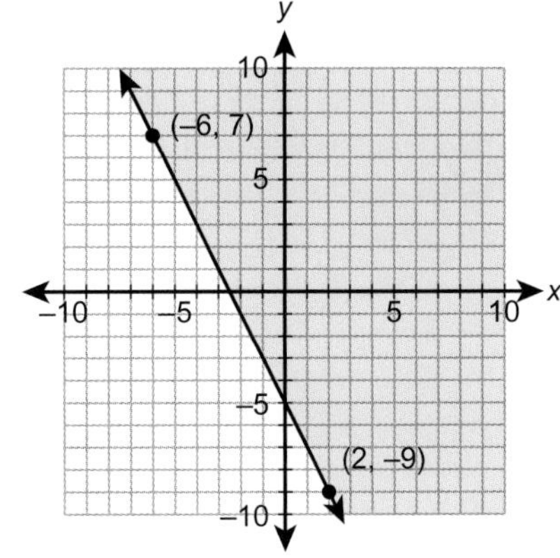

15.

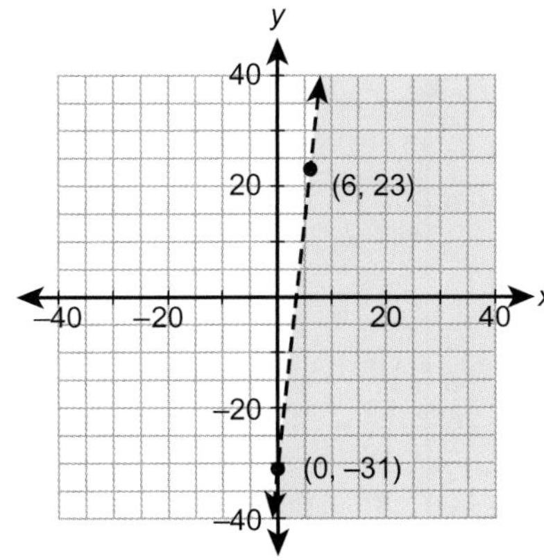

16.

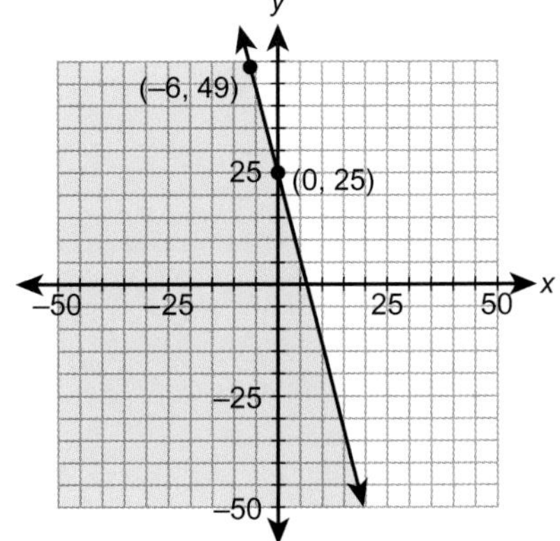

17.

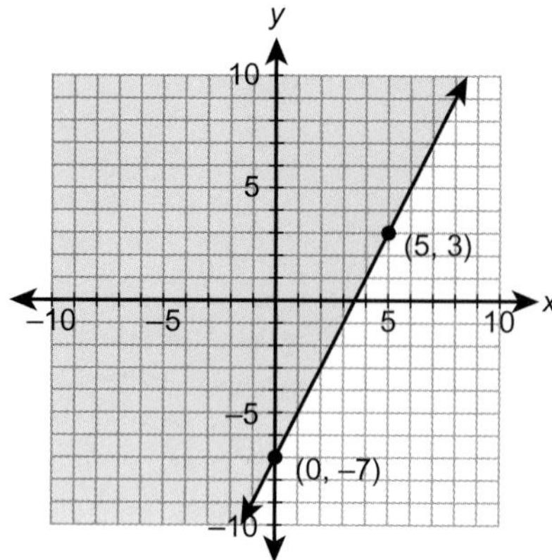

18.

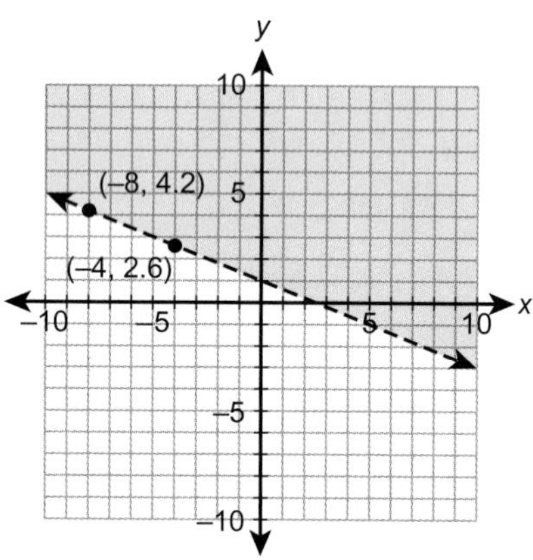

19.

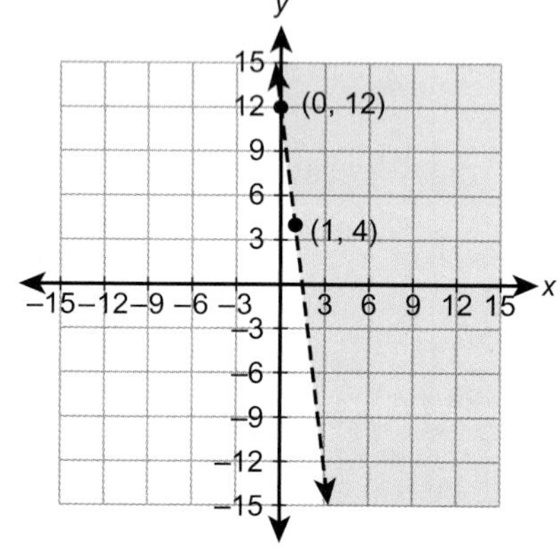

20.

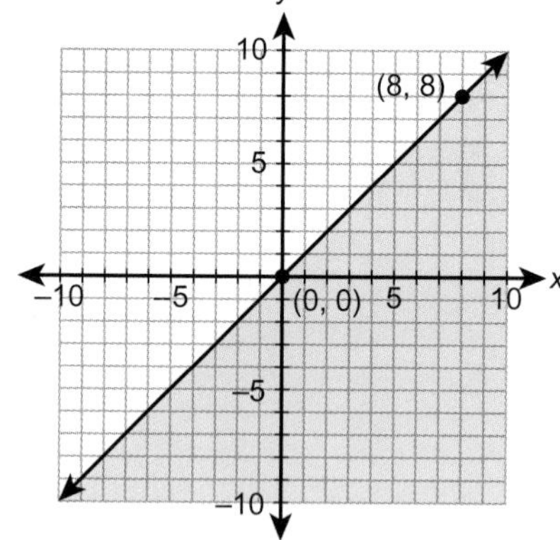

21.

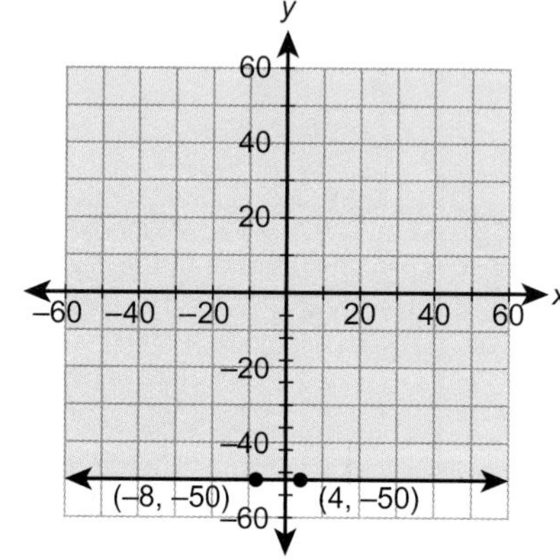

22.

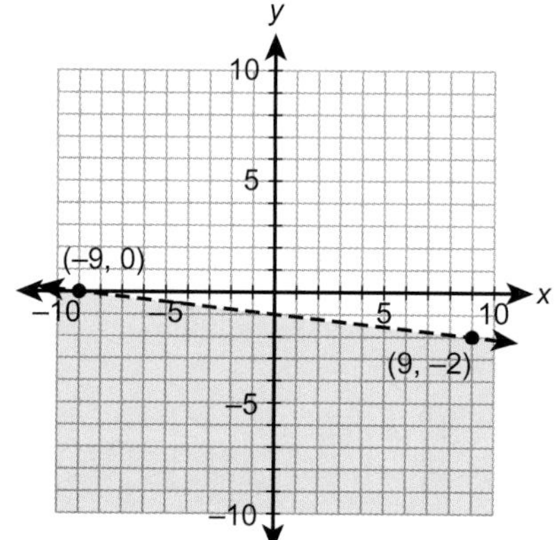

Using the graphs below, determine the operator for a matching inequality of the form y ▒ $mx + b$. Explain.

***23. Challenge**

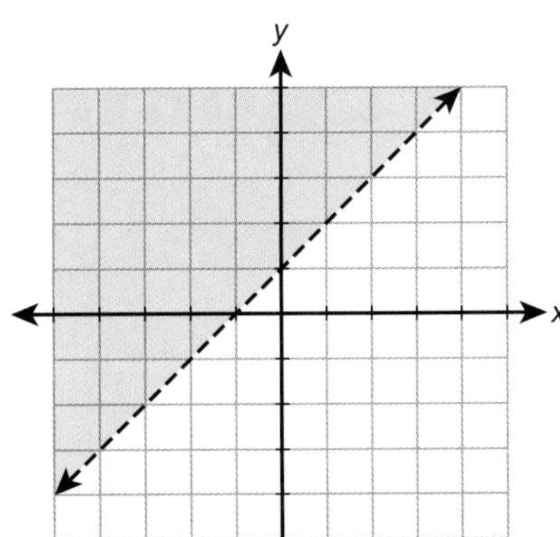

***24. Challenge**

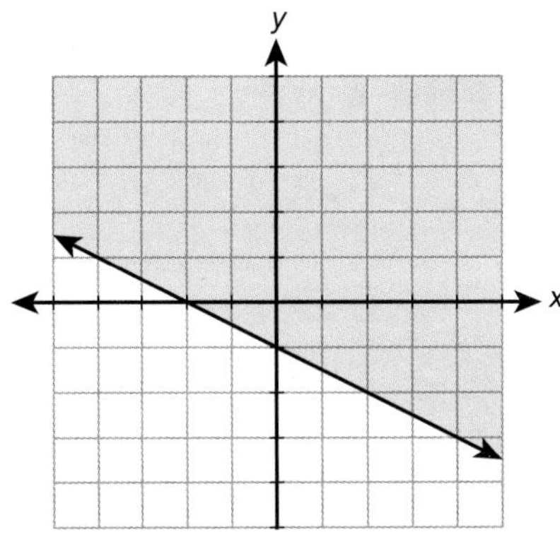

UNIT 7 Systems of Equations

The streets meet at an intersection.

When two people meet, they often shake hands or say hello to each other. Once they start talking to each other, they can find out what they have in common. What happens when two lines meet? Do they say anything? Probably not, but whenever two lines meet, you know they have at least one point in common. Finding the point at which they meet can help you solve problems in the real world.

Big Idea

- To solve a system of equations or inequalities, find the values for the variables that make all the equations or inequalities true statements.

Unit Topics

- Systems of Equations
- Substitution Method
- Linear Combination
- Linear Combination with Multiplication
- Applications: Systems of Equations
- Systems of Linear Inequalities

Systems of Equations

Two or more equations in the same variables create a system of equations.

Using a Graph to Solve a System of Equations

A solution to a system is the point of intersection of the graphs in the system. Algebraically, a solution to a system is an ordered pair that is a solution to each equation in the system.

Example 1 Solve the system by graphing. Then check the solution algebraically.

$xy = 1$
$y = 4x$

Solution Graph each equation in the coordinate plane. The intersection points appear to be $\left(\frac{1}{2}, 2\right)$ and $\left(-\frac{1}{2}, -2\right)$.

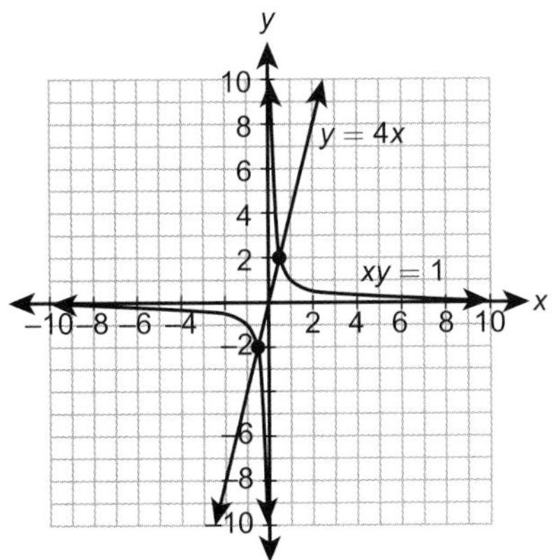

Check to determine if $\left(\frac{1}{2}, 2\right)$ and $\left(-\frac{1}{2}, -2\right)$ are solutions to the equations by substituting.

(continued)

Check the point $\left(\frac{1}{2}, 2\right)$.

Substitute $\frac{1}{2}$ for x and 2 for y in each equation.

$$xy = 1 \qquad y = 4x$$
$$\frac{1}{2} \cdot 2 \stackrel{?}{=} 1 \qquad 2 \stackrel{?}{=} 4 \cdot \frac{1}{2}$$
$$1 = 1 \checkmark \qquad 2 = 2 \checkmark$$

Check the point $\left(-\frac{1}{2}, -2\right)$.

Substitute $-\frac{1}{2}$ for x and -2 for y in each equation.

$$xy = 1 \qquad y = 4x$$
$$-\frac{1}{2} \cdot (-2) \stackrel{?}{=} 1 \qquad -2 \stackrel{?}{=} 4 \cdot \left(-\frac{1}{2}\right)$$
$$1 = 1 \checkmark \qquad -2 = -2 \checkmark$$

The points $\left(\frac{1}{2}, 2\right)$ and $\left(-\frac{1}{2}, -2\right)$ are solutions to the system of equations. ■

Using a Graph to Solve a System of Linear Equations

When both the equations in a system of equations are lines, it is a system of linear equations.

DEFINITION

A **system of linear equations** is two or more linear equations with the same variables.

THINK ABOUT IT

Not all systems of equations are systems of linear equations.

Example 2 Solve the system by graphing. Then check the solution algebraically.

$x + 2y = 4$
$4x - 2y = 16$

Solution Graph each line in the coordinate plane. The intersection of the two lines appears to be the point (4, 0).

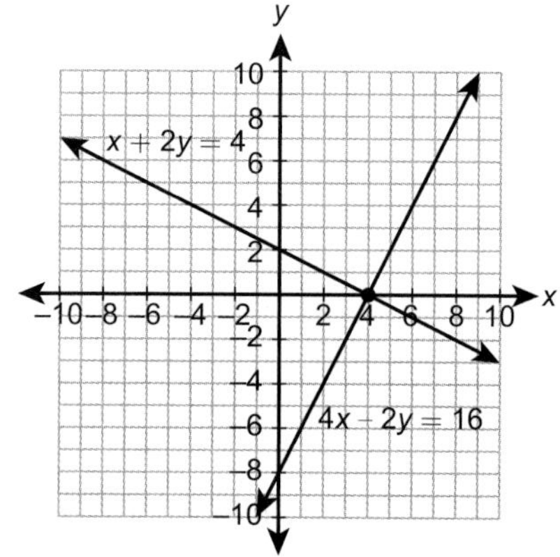

Check to determine if (4, 0) is a solution to each equation by substituting 4 for x and 0 for y in each equation.

$$x + 2y = 4 \qquad 4x - 2y = 16$$
$$4 + 2 \cdot 0 \stackrel{?}{=} 4 \qquad 4 \cdot 4 - 2 \cdot 0 \stackrel{?}{=} 16$$
$$4 = 4 \checkmark \qquad 16 = 16 \checkmark$$

The point (4, 0) is the solution to the system of equations. ■

Classifying Systems of Linear Equations

A system of linear equations is **consistent** if it has exactly one solution or infinitely many solutions. A consistent system with exactly one solution is a **consistent independent** system. A consistent system with infinitely many solutions is a **consistent dependent** or a **coincident** system. Coincident linear systems contain equations whose graphs are the same line. When the lines of a system of linear equations are parallel there is no solution to the system. A system of equations with no solution is an **inconsistent** system.

Example 3 Classify each linear system below as consistent or inconsistent. If the system is consistent, determine if it is coincident.

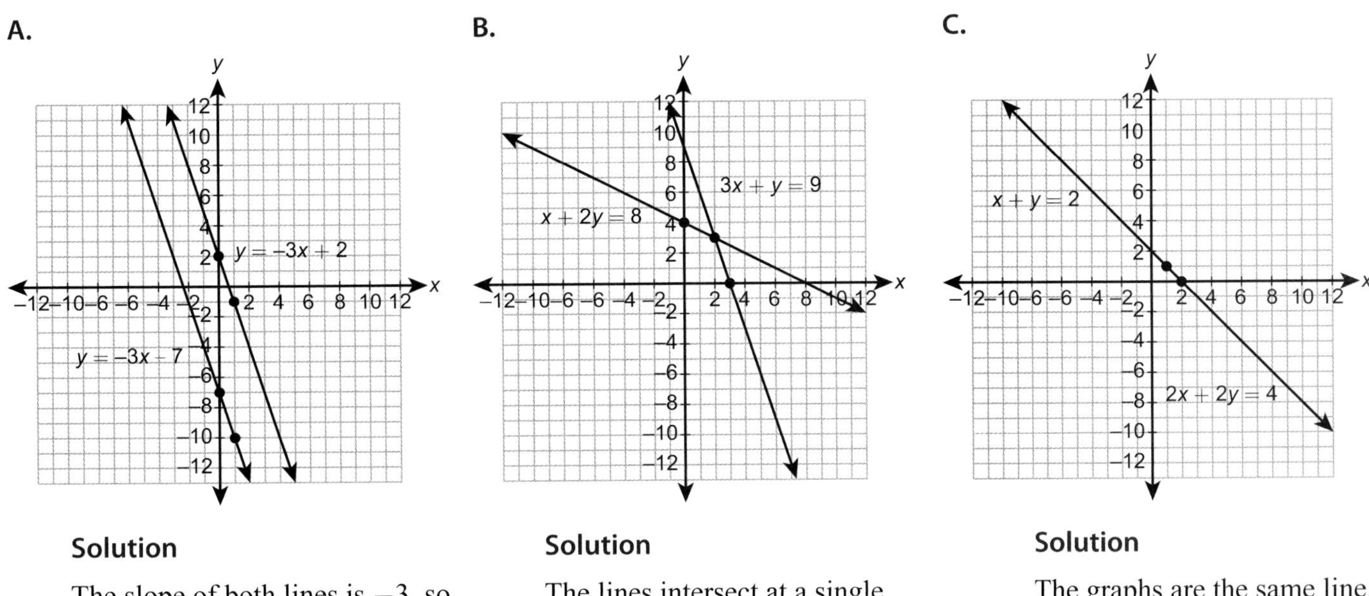

A. Solution

The slope of both lines is -3, so the lines are parallel. The system is *inconsistent.* ■

B. Solution

The lines intersect at a single point. The system is *consistent independent.* ■

C. Solution

The graphs are the same line. The system is *coincident.* ■

Application: Coin Problems

Example 4 Lucia has 10 dimes and nickels worth a total of \$0.60.

A. Write a system of equations that represents this situation.

B. Use a graph to classify the system as inconsistent, consistent independent, or coincident.

C. Use the graph from Part B to complete a table of values for each line to determine the solution of the system.

D. Use the graph to find the number of dimes and nickels that Lucia has.

(continued)

Solution

A. Let d represent the number of dimes and n represent the number of nickels. Lucia has 10 coins, so one equation in the system is $d + n = 10$. Also, the value in cents of d dimes is $0.10d$, and the value in cents of n nickels is $0.05n$. So, the other equation is $0.10d + 0.05n = 0.60$. The system that represents this situation is

$$\begin{aligned} d + n &= 10 \\ 0.10d + 0.05n &= 0.60 \end{aligned}$$

TIP

Place the independent (input) variable on the horizontal axis and the dependent (output) variable on the vertical axis.

When it is not clear if a variable is independent or dependent, place the letter that occurs first in the alphabet on the horizontal axis.

B.

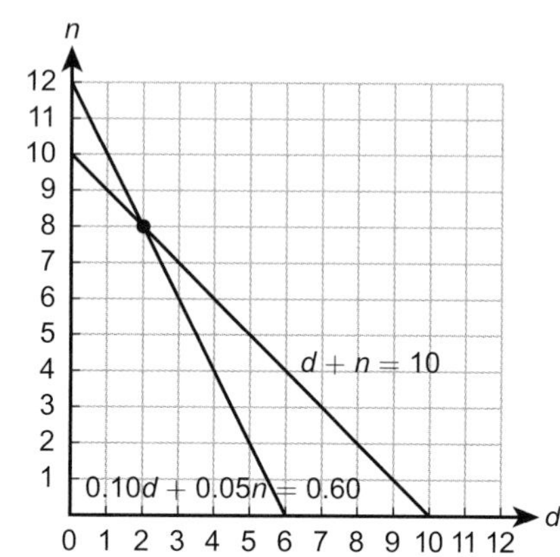

The system has one solution, so it is consistent independent.

C. The graphs intersect at the point (2, 8), which can be checked algebraically. Complete a table of values for each line.

$d + n = 10$

d	0	2	6	10
n	10	8	4	0

$0.10d + 0.05n = 0.60$

d	0	2	4	6
n	12	8	4	0

The point (2, 8) is the solution to the system of equations.

D. Since (2, 8) is the solution to the system of equations, Lucia has 2 dimes and 8 nickels. ■

Problem Set

Solve the system by graphing. Then check the solution algebraically.

1. $x + 3y = 8$
$x - 4y = -6$

2. $6m + n = -1$
$2m + 3n = -19$

3. $h = 3g + 5$
$h = g + 7$

4. $y = -2$
$y = 4x + 8$

5. $3a + b = 0$
$5a - b = 2$

6. $3r + 6s = 6$
$r = -5$

7. $y = |x|$
$2x - y = 2$

8. $y = \begin{cases} 4 \text{ if } -1 \leq x < 0 \\ 2 \text{ if } 0 \leq x < 1 \end{cases}$
$4x - 5y = 20$

Classify each linear system below as consistent independent, coincident, or inconsistent.

9.

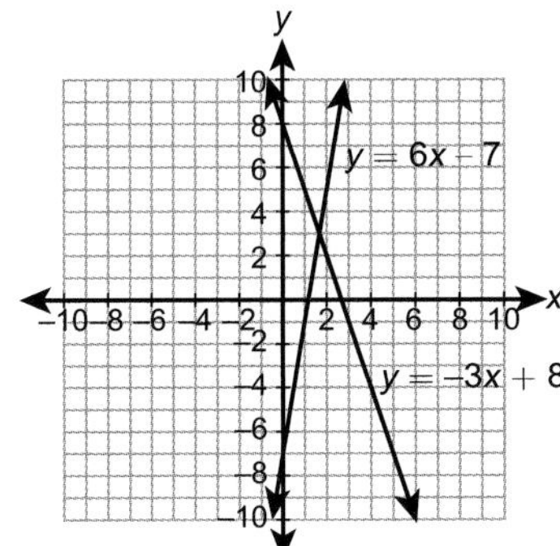

11.

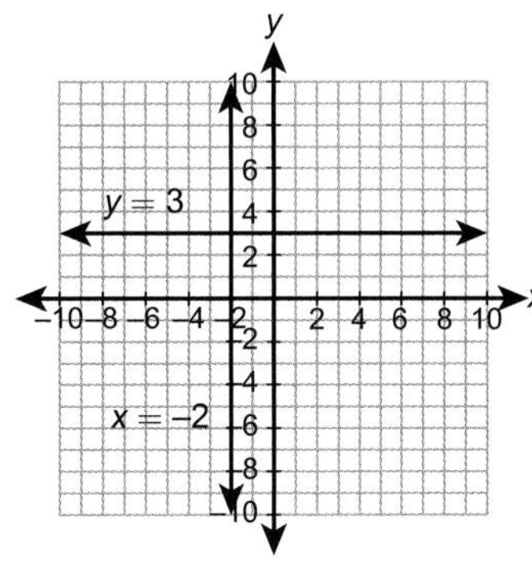

10.

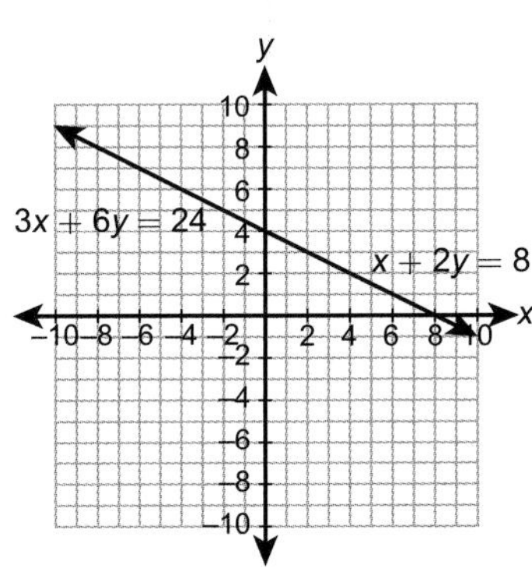

12.

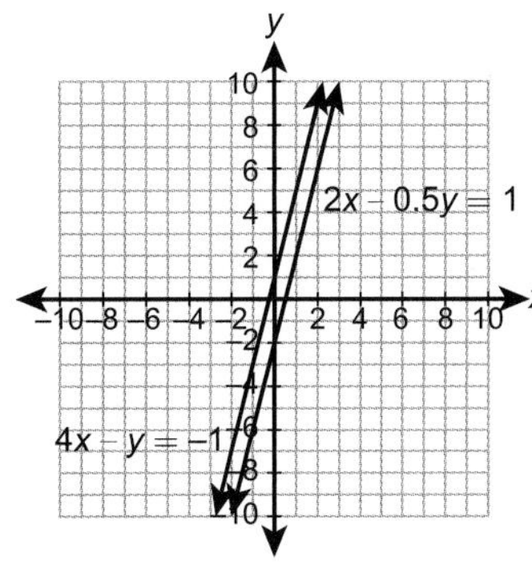

For each problem:

A. Solve the system by graphing. Round your answer to the nearest hundredth if necessary.
B. Classify the system as consistent independent, inconsistent, or coincident.

13. $5a + 4b = 16$
$3a - 5b = 15$

14. $-2x + 8y = 20$
$x - 4y = -10$

15. $n = -10m + 6$
$10m + n = -4$

16. $y = \frac{1}{3}x + 2$
$2x - 6y = -12$

17. $x = 3$
$y = 4$

18. $d = -\frac{1}{5}c + 8$
$c + d = 5$

19. $y = |x - 2|$
$y = |x - 4|$

Solve by graphing. For each problem:

A. Define variables for the unknowns.
B. Write a system of equations to model the problem.
C. Graph the system of equations.
D. Give your answer in a complete sentence.

20. Upstart High School prom tickets were sold for \$75 to juniors and \$50 to seniors. If 200 tickets were sold for \$12,750, how many juniors and seniors attended the prom?

21. Sooni invests \$5000 in two funds that pay simple interest of 6% and 7%. If she receives yearly interest of \$340, how much did she invest in each fund?

22. Lamar Lazoff hires two workers to clean his office. Lucinda can clean 2 cabinets and 3 desks in one day. Kalechi can clean 1 cabinet and 4 desks in one day. Lucinda earns \$30 a day and Kalechi earns \$25 a day. How much money do they earn per desk and per cabinet?

23. The Booksmart Company sells two types of pencils to its distributors. Mechanical pencil packs sell for 40 cents and lead pencil packs sell for 20 cents. If Maureen ordered 400 pencil packs at a cost of \$117, how many pencil packs of each type did she order?

***24.** **Challenge** A rectangle has a perimeter of 29 inches and an area of 34.5 square inches. Find the dimensions of the rectangle.

***25.** **Challenge** Koichi purchases a fence to enclose his rectangular yard. If the fence is used on only three sides of the yard and the yard's length is 80 feet, how much fence does Koichi use to enclose his 3600 square foot yard?

***26.** **Challenge** A drop-leaf table is constructed using one rectangle and one semicircle. The semicircle leaf is placed along the edge and its diameter is equal to the width of the rectangular portion. If the distance around the table is 65.7 feet and the area of the rectangle is 200 square feet, find the length and width of the rectangular portion of the table. (Use 3.14 for π and round your final answer to the nearest tenth.)

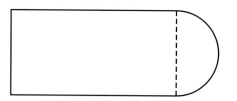

Substitution Method

The substitution method is a way to solve a system of linear equations algebraically.

THE SUBSTITUTION METHOD FOR SOLVING SYSTEMS OF EQUATIONS

Step 1 Solve one of the equations for one of the variables.

Step 2 Substitute the expression obtained in Step 1 into the other equation. Solve the resulting equation.

Step 3 Substitute the value of the variable found in Step 2 into the equivalent equation from Step 1 and solve for the variable.

REMEMBER

Equivalent equations have the same solution. Use the properties of equality to write equivalent equations.

Using the Substitution Method to Solve a System of Equations

Example 1 Solve the system.

$4x + y = 14$
$x - 2y = 8$

Solution

Step 1 Solve the first equation for y. (You could also solve the second equation for x.)

$4x + y = 14$

$y = -4x + 14$ Subtract $4x$ from each side of the equation.

Step 2 Substitute $-4x + 14$ for y in the second equation.

$x - 2y = 8$

$x - 2(-4x + 14) = 8$ Substitute $-4x + 14$ for y.

$x + 8x - 28 = 8$ Use the distributive property.

$9x - 28 = 8$ Combine like terms.

$9x = 36$ Add 28 to each side.

$x = 4$ Divide each side by 9.

(continued)

TIP

Whenever possible, solve for a variable with a coefficient of 1 or -1.

Step 3 Substitute 4 for x in the equivalent equation from Step 1.

$y = -4x + 14$

$y = -4 \cdot 4 + 14$ Substitute 4 for x.

$y = -16 + 14$ Simplify.

$y = -2$

The solution to the system is (4, −2).

Check

Substitute 4 for x and −2 for y into each original equation in the system.

$4x + y = 14$	$x - 2y = 8$
$4 \cdot 4 + (-2) \stackrel{?}{=} 14$	$4 - 2 \cdot (-2) \stackrel{?}{=} 8$
$16 + -2 \stackrel{?}{=} 14$	$4 + 4 \stackrel{?}{=} 8$
$14 = 14$ ✓	$8 = 8$ ✓

The solution (4, −2) is correct. ■

What Happens When the Variables Disappear?

You may sometimes eliminate a variable when using the substitution method, leaving either a statement that is always true (an identity) or a statement that is always false (a contradiction.) If the statement is an identity, then the system is consistent and coincident. If the statement is a contradiction, then the system is inconsistent.

Example 2 Solve the system.

A.
$$-x + 5y = 3$$
$$-3x + 15y = 9$$

Solution

Step 1 Solve the first equation for x.

$-x + 5y = 3$

$-x = -5y + 3$ Subtract $5y$ from each side.

$x = 5y - 3$ Multiply each side by −1.

Step 2 Substitute $5y - 3$ for x in the second equation.

$-3x + 15y = 9$

$-3(5y - 3) + 15y = 9$ Substitute $5y - 3$ for x.

$-15y + 9 + 15y = 9$ Use the distributive property.

$9 = 9$ Simplify.

Since the statement is an identity, the system is consistent and coincident. There are infinitely many solutions to the system. If you graph these lines, you will see that they have the same graph. ■

B. $y = -5x + 10$
$5x + y = 3$

Solution

Step 1 The first equation is already solved for y.

Step 2 Substitute $-5x + 10$ for y in the second equation.

$$5x + y = 3$$

$$5x + (-5x + 10) = 3 \quad \text{Substitute } -5x + 10 \text{ for } y.$$

$$5x - 5x + 10 = 3 \quad \text{Remove parentheses.}$$

$$10 = 3 \quad \text{Simplify.}$$

The final statement is a contradiction. The system is inconsistent, so there is no solution. Graph the equations to see that they are parallel and thus never intersect. ■

REMEMBER

If a system of linear equations is inconsistent, then the lines are parallel.

Application: Solving a Mixture Problem

Example 3 How many quarts of pure water should be combined with an unknown amount of solution containing 50% ammonia to obtain 5 quarts of a solution that contains 10% ammonia?

Solution Use the Problem-Solving Plan.

Step 1 *Identify* Find the number of quarts of pure water and the number of quarts of the 50% ammonia solution that would make 5 quarts of a 10% ammonia solution.

Step 2 *Strategize* Let p equal the number of quarts of pure water and a equal the number of quarts of the 50% ammonia solution.

Step 3 *Set Up* Write a system of equations to model the problem.

Equation 1: The total number of quarts of the cleaning solution mixture is represented by the equation $p + a = 5$.

Equation 2: If you keep in mind that 50% ammonia is the same as 50% water and that 10% ammonia is the same as 90% water, then the total amount of water in the cleaning solution can be represented as follows.

p Quarts of Pure Water	+	a Quarts of 50% Water	=	5 Quarts of 90% Water
$1 \cdot p$	+	$0.5 \cdot a$	=	$0.9 \cdot 5$
p	+	$0.5a$	=	4.5

The system of equations is
$$\begin{aligned} p + a &= 5 \\ p + 0.5a &= 4.5 \end{aligned}$$

(continued)

Step 4 *Solve* Use the substitution method.

Solve Equation 1 for p.

$$p + a = 5$$
$$p = 5 - a$$

Substitute $5 - a$ into the second equation for p.

$$p + 0.5a = 4.5$$
$$(5 - a) + 0.5a = 4.5$$
$$-0.5a = -0.5$$
$$a = 1$$

Substitute 1 for a into the equation $p = 5 - a$.

$$p = 5 - a$$
$$p = 5 - 1$$
$$p = 4$$

So, 4 quarts of water should be mixed with 1 quart of 50% ammonia solution to make 5 quarts of a 10% ammonia solution.

Step 5 *Check* Substitute 1 for a and 4 for p in the original equations.

$$p + a = 5 \qquad p + 0.5a = 4.5$$
$$4 + 1 \stackrel{?}{=} 5 \qquad 4 + 0.5 \cdot 1 \stackrel{?}{=} 4.5$$
$$5 = 5 \checkmark \qquad 4 + 0.5 \stackrel{?}{=} 4.5$$
$$4.5 = 4.5 \checkmark$$

The answer is correct. ■

Problem Set

Use the substitution method to solve each system of equations. Then check your solution.

1. $3x + y = 10$
   $y = 6x + 1$

2. $b = -4a + 5$
   $a - b = 5$

3. $6x - y = -15$
   $x + 2y = 17$

4. $x = 10$
   $y = 2x - 6$

5. $n = -7m - 4$
   $14m + 2n = -8$

6. $11c - 2d = -2$
   $c + 8d = 8$

7. $x - 3y = 7$
   $-2x + 6y = 6$

8. $4x - 7y = 10$
   $y = -1$

9. $f - 7g = 6$
   $-4f + 28g = -24$

10. $y = -3x + 6$
    $y = 5x + 38$

11. $y = 9x$
    $x + 2y = -3$

12. $x + y = -11$
    $2x - 3y = 3$

13. $w = -v + 10$
    $3v + 3w = 9$

14. $2k - 4l = 8$
    $6k + 3l = 12$

15. $y = 4$
    $y = \frac{3}{x}$

16. $3m - n = 2$
$2m + n = -7$

17. $y = -\frac{1}{x}$
$2x = 10$

18. $b = -6a$
$b = 9a$

19. $x - 3y = 2$
$-x + 3y = -2$

20. $9x - 18y = -9$
$2x + 2y = 4$

21. $d = 2c - 13$
$-2c + d = 7$

22. $y = 5$
$xy = -4$

Solve. For each problem:

A. Define variables for the unknowns.
B. Write a system of equations to model the problem.
C. Solve the system using substitution.
D. Give your answer in a complete sentence.

23. A piggy bank contains 50 coins worth $2.30. If the bank holds nickels, quarters, and pennies, and there are twice as many pennies as nickels, how many coins of each type are in the bank?

24. Sunflower seeds selling for 70¢ per pound are mixed with finch food selling for 90¢ per pound to create a 13.5-pound mixture worth $11.05. How many pounds of each seed should be used to make the mixture?

25. Sumika's lunch box contains 15 cent cheese slices mixed with 25 cent salami slices to make a lunch of 8 slices. If the total cost of the eight slices is $1.70, how many slices of salami and cheese are in the box?

26. How many liters of water should be combined with a disinfectant containing 40% bleach to make 6 liters of a 5% bleach solution?

27. How many quarts of water should be added to 100% pure cranberry juice to make an 8 quart mixture of a 20% cranberry drink?

***28.** **Challenge** Lan, Ian, and Juki have $44. Find the amount of money each has if Lan has $4 more than Ian and Juki combined and Ian and Lan's sum equals $32.

***29.** **Challenge** A chemist creates 20 kilograms of aluminum alloy with 50% aluminum. To do this, she uses two metals: one containing 40% aluminum and the other containing 60% aluminum. How much of each metal should she use?

Linear Combination

You can use the linear combination method to solve a system of linear equations algebraically.

THINK ABOUT IT

The linear combination method is also called the elimination method.

THE LINEAR COMBINATION METHOD FOR SOLVING SYSTEMS OF EQUATIONS

Step 1 Add or subtract the equations to eliminate one of the variables.

Step 2 Solve the resulting equation for the remaining variable.

Step 3 Substitute the value of the variable found in Step 2 into either of the original equations to obtain the value of the other variable.

TIP

When using the linear combination method, be sure to put both equations in standard form and line up like terms in the equations vertically.

Using the Linear Combination Method to Solve a System of Equations

Example 1 Solve each system.

A.
$$\begin{aligned} 2x + y &= 5 \\ -2x - 7y &= 13 \end{aligned}$$

Solution

Step 1 Since the coefficients of the x terms, 2 and -2, are opposites, add the equations to eliminate x.

$$\begin{array}{r} 2x + y = 5 \\ \underline{+\,(-2x - 7y = 13)} \\ -6y = 18 \end{array}$$

Step 2 Solve the resulting equation for y.

$$-6y = 18$$

$$y = -3 \qquad \text{Divide each side by } -6.$$

Step 3 Substitute -3 for y in the first equation and solve for x. Remember that you can use either of the original equations for this step.

$$\begin{aligned} 2x + y &= 5 \\ 2x + (-3) &= 5 && \text{Substitute } -3 \text{ for } y. \\ 2x &= 8 && \text{Add 3 to each side.} \\ x &= 4 && \text{Divide each side by 2.} \end{aligned}$$

The solution to the system is $(4, -3)$.

B. $4x + 5y = -5$
$x + 5y = 10$

Step 1 Since the coefficients of the y terms are equal, you can subtract the equations to eliminate y.

$$\begin{array}{rl} 4x + 5y = & -5 \\ -(\ x + 5y = & 10) \\ \hline 3x \qquad = & -15 \end{array}$$

THINK ABOUT IT

When using subtraction, be sure to subtract every term in the second equation from the corresponding term in the first.

Step 2 Solve the resulting equation for x.

$3x = -15$

$x = -5$ Divide each side by 3.

Step 3 Substitute -5 for x in the second equation and solve for y. Remember that you can use either of the original equations for this step.

$x + 5y = 10$

$-5 + 5y = 10$ Substitute -5 for x.

$5y = 15$ Add 5 to each side.

$y = 3$ Divide each side by 5.

The solution to the system is $(-5, 3)$. ■

Application: Geometry

You can apply the linear combination method to solve systems of linear equations that model situations in geometry.

Example 2 The perimeter of a rectangle is 44 feet. The length of the rectangle is 1 more than twice the width. Find the dimensions of the rectangle.

Step 1 Write a system of equations to model the problem.

Equation 1: This equation represents the perimeter of the rectangle. Use the formula $P = 2l + 2w$.

$2l + 2w = 44$

Equation 2: The length of the rectangle is 1 more than twice the width. Write an equation to model this statement.

$l = 2w + 1$

Write this linear equation in standard form by subtracting $2w$ from each side: $l - 2w = 1$.

The system of equations is $\begin{array}{r} 2l + 2w = 44 \\ l - 2w = 1 \end{array}$.

(continued)

Step 2 Solve the system of equations.

1. Add the equations.

$$\begin{array}{r} 2l + 2w = 44 \\ +\ (\ l - 2w = \ \ 1) \\ \hline 3l \qquad\quad = 45 \end{array}$$

2. Solve the equation $3l = 45$ for l.

$$3l = 45$$
$$l = 15$$

3. Substitute 15 for l in the equation $2l + 2w = 44$ and solve for w.

$$2l + 2w = 44$$
$$2 \cdot 15 + 2w = 44$$
$$30 + 2w = 44$$
$$2w = 14$$
$$w = 7$$

The length of the rectangle is 15 feet and the width is 7 feet.

Step 3 Check. Substitute 15 for l and 7 for w in each of the original equations in the system.

$2l + 2w = 44$	$l - 2w = 1$
$2 \cdot 15 + 2 \cdot 7 \stackrel{?}{=} 44$	$15 - 2 \cdot 7 \stackrel{?}{=} 1$
$30 + 14 \stackrel{?}{=} 44$	$15 - 14 \stackrel{?}{=} 1$
$44 = 44$ ✓	$1 = 1$ ✓ ■

Problem Set

Use the linear combination method to solve each system of equations.

1. $2x + 3y = -5$
   $2x - 5y = 19$
2. $2x + 4y = 6$
   $x - 4y = -21$
3. $6x - 3y = 6$
   $4x + 3y = -1$
4. $x + 3y = 3$
   $x - 2y = -12$
5. $3x + \frac{1}{3}y = 28$
   $2x - \frac{1}{3}y = 12$
6. $4x - 3.5y = 10$
   $4x + 1.5y = 0$
7. $5x - 3y = 8$
   $-5x - 2.5y = 25$
8. $2x + 7y = 25$
   $2x - y = 1$
9. $-7x + 3y = 38.5$
   $5x - 3y = -30.5$
10. $15x - 2y = 32$
    $10x + 2y = -22$
11. $3x - 3y = -21$
    $3x + 3y = 15$
12. $3x + y = 19$
    $4x + y = 17$
13. $x + y = -3$
    $x - y = -10$
14. $-2x - 6y = -12$
    $2x + 8y = 2$
15. $4x - 2y = 14$
    $2x - 2y = 11$
16. $9x + 3y = -6$
    $4x + 3y = 4$
17. $3x - 2y = 41$
    $3x + y = 2$

Challenge

***18.** $x + 3y = 13$
$2x - 4y = 6$

***19.** $\frac{3}{2}x - \frac{2}{3}y = -3$
$\frac{3}{2}x - \frac{5}{6}y = 0$

***20.** $\frac{2}{5}x + \frac{3}{4}y = 5.45$
$\frac{1}{5}x - \frac{3}{4}y = -0.65$

***21.** $6x + 3y = 9$
$3x - \frac{y}{2} = 18.5$

***22.** $4x + 0.2y = 4.4$
$2x + 0.2y = 3$

Solve. For each problem:

A. Define variables for the unknowns.
B. Write a system of equations to model the problem.
C. Solve the system using the linear combination method.
D. Give your answer in a complete sentence.

23. Walker and Kim each went with their family and friends to an art museum. Walker's group included 2 adult and 11 youth admissions, for a total price of \$90.50. Kim's group of 2 adult and 8 youth admissions totaled \$71. What were the prices for adult and youth admission?

24. A ballerina spends 235 minutes per day either dancing or cross-training. The time she spends dancing is 10 minutes less than 6 times the time she spends cross-training. How much time does she spend per day on each activity?

25. Ezra told a friend to choose any number, double it, and then subtract 6 to find a second number. He then asked his friend to add the two numbers. The sum was 45. What were the two numbers?

26. In one evening, Mel spent 4.5 hours studying for her chemistry and biology final exams. She studied biology 1.5 hours less than twice the time she studied chemistry. How long did she study each subject?

27. A hot cocoa manufacturer has mixed chocolate syrup that is 50% cocoa with some 100% powdered cocoa, to make 20 ounces of 80% cocoa. How much syrup and powdered cocoa did she mix?

28. The width of Cameron's rectangular garden is 9 feet less than twice the length. The perimeter is 96 feet. What are the length and width?

29. Three notebooks and 6 pens cost \$18.51. Three notebooks and 10 pens cost \$24.87. Find the price of 1 notebook and of 1 pen.

Linear Combination with Multiplication

If you are solving a system using the linear combination method and the corresponding variables in the equations do not have equal or opposite coefficients, you must create an equivalent equation for one or both of the equations in the system.

THE LINEAR COMBINATION METHOD WITH MULTIPLICATION FOR SOLVING SYSTEMS OF EQUATIONS

Step 1 Multiply one or both of the equations by a constant so that one of the variables will be eliminated when the equations are added or subtracted.

Step 2 Add or subtract the equations to eliminate one of the variables.

Step 3 Solve the resulting equation for the remaining variable.

Step 4 Substitute the value for the variable found in Step 3 into either of the original equations to obtain the value of the other variable.

REMEMBER

You can multiply each side of an equation by the same nonzero number to create an equivalent equation.

Using the Linear Combination Method with Multiplication to Solve a System of Equations

Example 1 Solve each system.

A. $2x + 3y = 2$
$x + y = 4$

Solution

Step 1 Multiply the second equation by -2 on each side, so the coefficients of x will be opposite.

$$\begin{aligned} 2x + 3y &= 2 \\ -2(x + y &= 4) \end{aligned} \longrightarrow \begin{aligned} 2x + 3y &= 2 \\ -2(x + y) &= -2 \cdot 4 \end{aligned} \longrightarrow \begin{aligned} 2x + 3y &= 2 \\ -2x - 2y &= -8 \end{aligned}$$

Step 2 The x terms are opposites, so add the equations to eliminate x.

$$\begin{aligned} 2x + 3y &= 2 \\ +(-2x - 2y &= -8) \\ \hline y &= -6 \end{aligned}$$

Step 3 The equation is already solved for y.

Step 4 Substitute -6 for y in the original second equation and solve for x. Remember you can use either original equation for this step.

$$x + y = 4$$

$$x + (-6) = 4 \quad \text{Substitute } -6 \text{ for } y.$$

$$x = 10 \quad \text{Add 6 to each side.}$$

The solution to the system is $(10, -6)$.

Check Substitute 10 for x and -6 for y in each original equation in the system.

$$2x + 3y = 2 \qquad x + y = 4$$

$$2 \cdot 10 + 3 \cdot (-6) \stackrel{?}{=} 2 \qquad 10 - 6 \stackrel{?}{=} 4$$

$$20 - 18 \stackrel{?}{=} 2 \qquad 4 = 4 \checkmark$$

$$2 = 2 \checkmark \blacksquare$$

B. $3x + 5y = 6$
$4x - 2y = 8$

Step 1 Multiply the first equation by 2 and the second equation by 5. This makes 10 the coefficient of y, the least common multiple of 2 and 5.

$$\begin{matrix} 2(3x + 5y = 6) \\ 5(4x - 2y = 8) \end{matrix} \longrightarrow \begin{matrix} 2(3x + 5y) = 2 \cdot 6 \\ 5(4x - 2y) = 5 \cdot 8 \end{matrix} \longrightarrow \begin{matrix} 6x + 10y = 12 \\ 20x - 10y = 40 \end{matrix}$$

TIP

When choosing a value to multiply by, pick a value that will allow you to add the equations. Adding equations is usually easier than subtracting.

Step 2 Add the equations to eliminate y.

$$\begin{array}{r} 6x + 10y = 12 \\ + (20x - 10y = 40) \\ \hline 26x \qquad = 52 \end{array}$$

Step 3 Solve the equation for x.

$$26x = 52$$

$$x = 2$$

Step 4 Substitute 2 for x in the original second equation and solve for y. Remember you can use either original equation for this step.

$$4x - 2y = 8$$

$$4 \cdot 2 - 2y = 8 \quad \text{Substitute 2 for } x.$$

$$8 - 2y = 8 \quad \text{Simplify.}$$

$$-2y = 0 \quad \text{Subtract 8 from each side.}$$

$$y = 0 \quad \text{Divide each side by } -2.$$

The solution to the system is $(2, 0)$. ■

Application: Team Dinner

Example 2 A coach ordered 10 pizzas for a team party. Some of the pizzas were cheese and some were veggie. Cheese pizzas cost \$8 and veggie pizzas cost \$10. The total cost for the pizzas was \$86. How many of each kind of pizza did the coach order?

Step 1 Write a system of equations to model the problem.

Equation 1: This equation represents the total number of pizzas ordered. Let c be the number of cheese pizzas and v be the number of veggie pizzas.

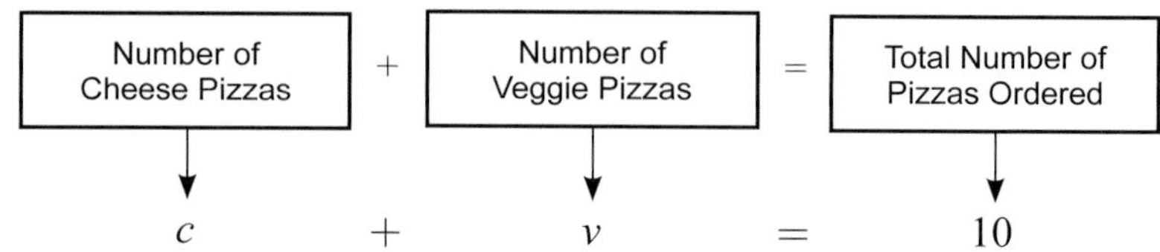

Equation 2: This equation represents the total cost.

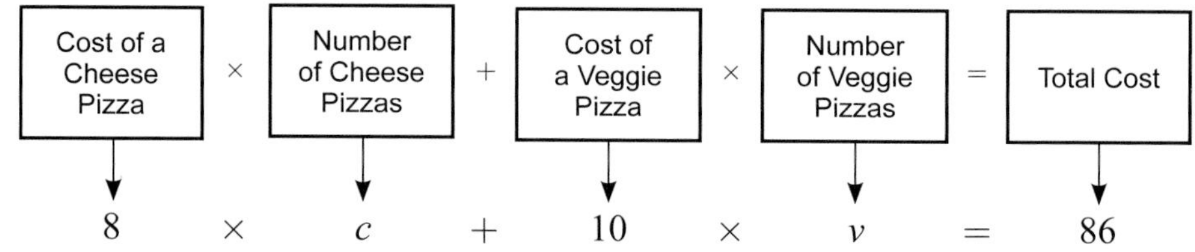

The system of equations is $\begin{array}{r} c + v = 10 \\ 8c + 10v = 86 \end{array}$.

Step 2 Solve the system of equations.

1. Multiply the first equation by -8 on each side.

$$\begin{array}{l} -8(c + v = 10) \\ 8c + 10v = 86 \end{array} \longrightarrow \begin{array}{l} -8(c + v) = -8 \cdot 10 \\ 8c + 10v = 86 \end{array} \longrightarrow \begin{array}{r} -8c - 8v = -80 \\ 8c + 10v = 86 \end{array}$$

2. Add the equations to eliminate c.

$$\begin{array}{r} -8c - 8v = -80 \\ +(\ 8c + 10v = 86) \\ \hline 2v = 6 \end{array}$$

3. Solve the equation for v.

$$2v = 6$$
$$v = 3$$

4. Substitute 3 for v in the original first equation and solve for v. Remember you can use either original equation for this step.

$c + v = 10$

$c + 3 = 10$ Substitute 3 for v.

$c = 7$ Subtract 3 from both sides and simplify.

The coach ordered 7 cheese pizzas and 3 veggie pizzas.

Step 3 Check. Substitute 7 for c and 3 for v in each equation in the system.

$$c + v = 10 \qquad 8c + 10v = 86$$
$$7 + 3 \stackrel{?}{=} 10 \qquad 8 \cdot 7 + 10 \cdot 3 \stackrel{?}{=} 86$$
$$10 = 10 \checkmark \qquad 56 + 30 \stackrel{?}{=} 86$$
$$86 = 86 \checkmark \blacksquare$$

Problem Set

Use the linear combination method with multiplication to solve each system of equations.

1. $2x + 3y = 11$
   $x + 2y = 8$

2. $3x - 2y = 6$
   $2x + 4y = 20$

3. $-14x - 8y = 9$
   $2x + 3y = -5$

4. $6x - 3y = -12$
   $5x - 2y = -13$

5. $-3x + 12y = -27$
   $5x + 20y = 15$

6. $\frac{2}{3}x - 4y = 30$
   $4x + 3y = -9$

7. $3x - 12y = 60$
   $x + 2y = 14$

8. $3x - 4y = -32$
   $2x + y = -3$

9. $x + y = 550$
   $3x - 2y = 150$

10. $4(x - y) = 4.2$
    $2(4x + y) = 0.4$

11. $x + y = 50$
    $0.05x + 0.06y = 2.8$

12. $5x + 7y = 53$
    $-3x + 2y = 24$

13. $\frac{3}{5}x + y = 3$
    $\frac{4}{5}x - 3y = 30$

14. $6x - 3y = -24$
    $-8x - 2y = 14$

15. $x + y = 5$
    $3x + 2y = 90$

16. $\frac{2x + 2y}{3} = 4$
    $\frac{3x + 5y}{2} = 6$

17. $2x - y = 65$
    $x + 4y = 10$

18. $14x - 8y = 47$
    $7x + 2y = -6.5$

19. $-4x - 5y = 1$
    $-6x + 12y = -18$

Challenge

*20. $\frac{x + 2}{3} + \frac{y - 2}{2} = 5$
    $5x - 6y = 8$

*21. $8x - 3y = 12.6$
    $2x + 7y = -35.6$

*22. $\frac{5x}{2} - 8y = -22.7$
    $\frac{3x}{5} - 10y = -0.6$

Solve using the linear combination method.

23. Caroline's cell phone plan allows unlimited cell-to-cell calls and 100 minutes of calls to land lines for a basic monthly rate, plus a per-minute rate for any additional calls to land lines. Last year, Caroline averaged 150 minutes in additional calls to land lines per month, and paid a total of \$288 for six months. José switched to the same plan, and paid \$198 for four months, averaging 225 minutes in additional land calls per month. What are the basic monthly rate and per-minute charge for the cell phone plan?

24. Three times one side s of this isosceles triangle is equal to 5 less than twice the base b. The perimeter is 62 cm. What are the measurements of the equal sides and base?

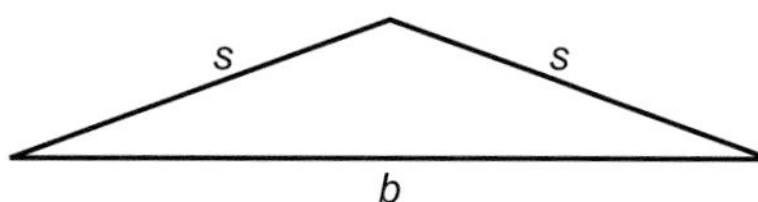

25. The Morse and Wong families attended a baseball game together. At the concession stand, the Morse family bought 9 hot dogs and 7 drinks and paid \$30.75. The Wong family bought 12 hot dogs and 8 drinks and paid \$39. Find the price of a hot dog and the price of a drink.

26. Henry filled an empty aquarium with 65° water and 70° water. The full aquarium contained 10 gallons of water with a temperature of 68°. How much of each kind of water did he add?

27. Jeff's town had a carnival with rides. The mini-coaster cost \$1.50 for each ride, and the bumper boats cost \$0.60 for each ride. Jeff took 11 rides and spent \$12. How many times did he ride on each?

28. Ginny's test had 28 problems worth a total of 100 points. Fill-in questions were worth 3 points each, and essay questions were worth 5 points each. How many of each type of question were on the test?

29. Julian invested \$3200 in two stocks, p and q. Twice the amount he invested in stock p was \$100 less than 3 times his investment in stock q. His total investment was \$3200. How much did he invest in each stock?

*30. **Challenge** A theater sells tickets at three rates: A seats for \$25, B seats for \$20, and C seats for \$15. For a certain concert, the theater sold 350 tickets for \$6450. Twice as many B seats were sold as A seats. How many of each type of seat were sold?

Applications: Systems of Equations

Systems of linear equations can model many real-world situations.

Food Service

Example 1 At a concession stand at a fair, a small cup of lemonade costs \$1.50 and a large cup costs \$2. The concession stand workers collected a total of \$6600 from the sale of lemonade. They sold twice as many large cups as small cups. How many cups of each size were sold?

Step 1 Write a system of equations to model the problem.

Equation 1: Let s be the number of small cups of lemonade sold and l be the number of large cups of lemonade sold. You are told that twice as many large cups were sold.

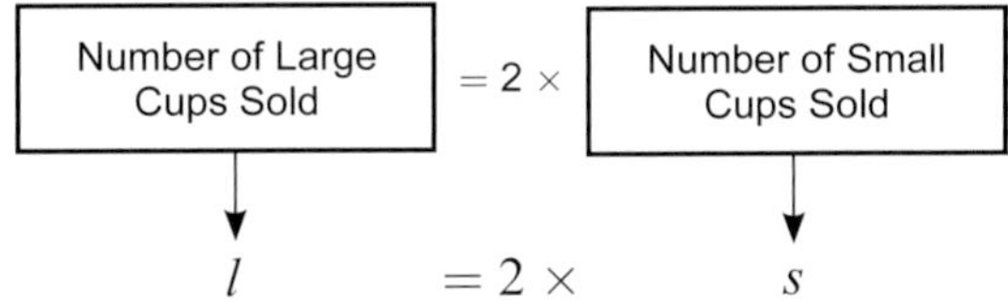

Equation 2: Total sales were \$6600 and you know the price of each type of cup, so you can write an equation to represent the total sales.

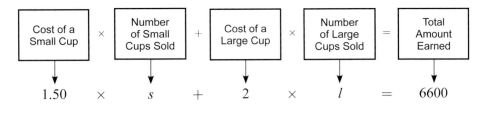

Cost of a Small Cup × Number of Small Cups Sold + Cost of a Large Cup × Number of Large Cups Sold = Total Amount Earned

$$1.50 \times s + 2 \times l = 6600$$

The system of equations is $\begin{matrix} l = 2s \\ 1.5s + 2l = 6600 \end{matrix}$

(continued)

Step 2 Solve the system of equations. Since the first equation is already solved for l, use the substitution method.

1. Substitute $2s$ for l in the second equation and solve for s.

$$1.5s + 2l = 6600$$

$$1.5s + 2 \cdot 2s = 6600 \quad \text{Substitute } 2s \text{ for } l.$$

$$1.5s + 4s = 6600 \quad \text{Simplify.}$$

$$5.5s = 6600 \quad \text{Combine like terms.}$$

$$s = 1200 \quad \text{Divide each side by 5.5.}$$

One thousand two hundred small cups of lemonade were sold.

2. Substitute 1200 for s in the first equation and solve for l.

$$l = 2s$$

$$l = 2 \cdot 1200 \quad \text{Substitute 1200 for } s.$$

$$l = 2400 \quad \text{Multiply.}$$

Two thousand four hundred large cups of lemonade were sold.

Step 3 Check. Substitute 1200 for s and 2400 for l in each equation in the system.

$$l = 2s \qquad 1.5s + 2l = 6600$$

$$2400 \stackrel{?}{=} 2 \cdot 1200 \qquad 1.5 \cdot 1200 + 2 \cdot 2400 \stackrel{?}{=} 6600$$

$$2400 = 2400 \checkmark \qquad 1800 + 4800 \stackrel{?}{=} 6600$$

$$6600 = 6600 \checkmark$$

The solution is correct. ■

Cellular Phone Service

Example 2 A cellular service plan for Company A has unlimited minutes for \$40 per month and a text message rate of \$0.10 per message. A cellular service plan for Company B has unlimited minutes for \$30 per month and a text message rate of \$0.10 per message. When is it cheaper to use Company B's plan?

Step 1 Write a system of equations to model the problem. Let t be the number of text messages per month and let c be the total monthly cost.

Equation 1: This equation models the total cost per month for Company A.

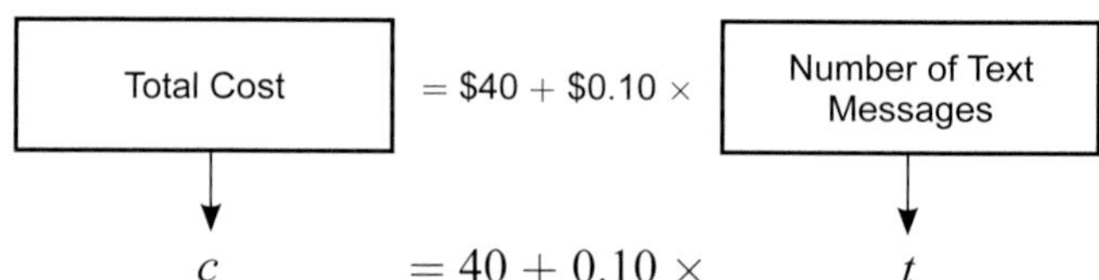

Equation 2: This equation models the total cost per month for Company B.

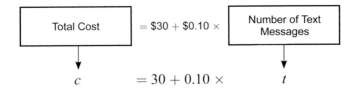

Total Cost	$= \$30 + \$0.10 \times$	Number of Text Messages
↓		↓
c	$= 30 + 0.10 \times$	t

The system of equations is $\begin{array}{l} c = 40 + 0.10t \\ c = 30 + 0.10t \end{array}$ or $\begin{array}{l} -0.10t + c = 40 \\ -0.10t + c = 30 \end{array}$.

Step 2 Solve the system of equations. Use the linear combination method and subtract the equations.

$$\begin{array}{r} -0.10t + c = 40 \\ \underline{-\,(-0.10t + c = 30)} \\ 0 = 10\ \chi \end{array}$$

Since the equation $0 = 10$ is false, the lines are parallel and there is no solution to the system. The cost is never the same for both services and it is always cheaper to use Company B's plan. ■

Mixture

Example 3 Juan wants to make a juice drink that contains 80% orange juice and 20% grapefruit juice. How many cups of pure orange juice (100% orange juice) should be combined with a mix of 60% orange juice and 40% grapefruit juice to make 3 cups of the 80% orange juice/20% grapefruit juice mixture?

Step 1 Write a system of equations to model the problem. The two unknowns in the problem are the number of cups of pure orange juice and the number of cups of the 60% orange juice/40% grapefruit juice mix. Let p represent the number of cups of pure orange juice and m represent the number of cups of the 60% orange juice/40% grapefruit juice mix.

Equation 1: This equation represents the total number of cups of Juan's juice mixture.

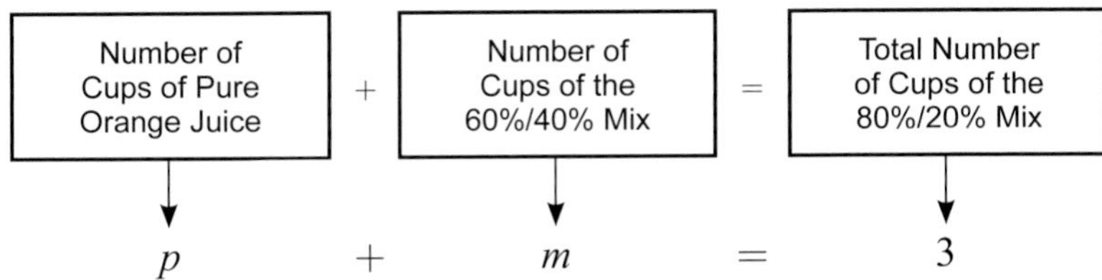

(continued)

Equation 2: This equation represents the amount of orange juice in each juice.

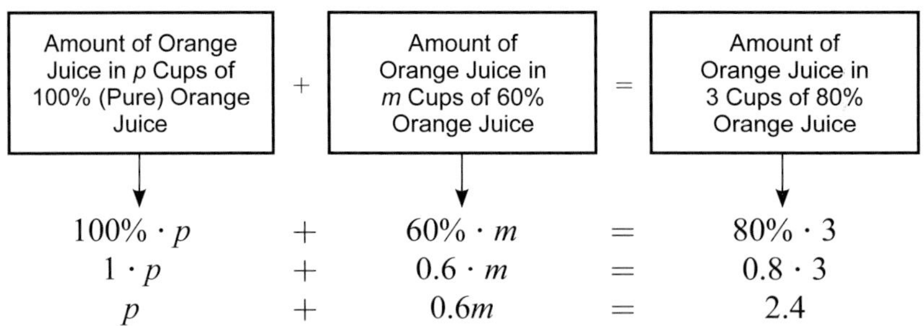

$$100\% \cdot p + 60\% \cdot m = 80\% \cdot 3$$
$$1 \cdot p + 0.6 \cdot m = 0.8 \cdot 3$$
$$p + 0.6m = 2.4$$

The system of equations is $\begin{matrix} p + m = 3 \\ p + 0.6m = 2.4 \end{matrix}$.

Step 2 Solve the system of equations.

1. Solve the first equation for p.

$$p + m = 3$$
$$p = 3 - m$$

2. Substitute $3 - m$ into the second equation for p.

$$p + 0.6m = 2.4$$
$$3 - m + 0.6m = 2.4$$
$$-0.4m = -0.6$$
$$m = 1.5$$

3. Substitute 1.5 for m into the equation $p = 3 - m$.

$$p = 3 - m$$
$$p = 3 - 1.5$$
$$p = 1.5$$

Combine 1.5 cups of pure orange juice and 1.5 cups of 60% orange juice/40% grapefruit juice mix to make 3 cups of the 80% orange juice/20% grapefruit juice mix.

Step 3 Check. Substitute 1.5 for p and 1.5 for m in each equation in the system.

$$p + m = 3$$
$$1.5 + 1.5 \stackrel{?}{=} 3$$
$$3 = 3 \checkmark$$

$$p + 0.6m = 2.4$$
$$1.5 + 0.6 \cdot 1.5 \stackrel{?}{=} 2.4$$
$$1.5 + 0.9 \stackrel{?}{=} 2.4$$
$$2.4 = 2.4 \checkmark$$

The solution is correct. ■

Problem Set

Solve. For each problem:

A. Define variables for the unknowns.
B. Write a system of equations to model the problem.
C. Solve the system.
D. Give your answer in a complete sentence.

1. While installing a sprinkler system, Ethel wants to cut a 20-foot length of plastic tubing into two pieces. The longer piece is to be 2 feet longer than twice the shorter piece. Find the length of each piece.
2. The admission fee at the fair is \$1.50 for children and \$4 for adults. On a certain day, 2200 people enter the fair and \$5050 is collected. How many children and how many adults attended?
3. The sum of two numbers is 95. One number is 16 less than twice the other. Find both numbers.
4. A-1 Rental rents a car at a rate of \$29.95 plus 15 cents per mile. Another company rents a car for \$24.95 plus 20 cents per mile. For what mileage is the cost the same?
5. Dr. Patel wants his chemistry class to prepare a 10mL mixture of 80% fluoride/20% peroxide. The class is divided into pairs and assigned to stations in the lab. At each station, he places a solution mixture that is 60% flouride/40% peroxide and a solution that is 100% fluoride. How much of the 100% fluoride do the students in Dr. Patel's class need to add to the 60%/40% mixture in order to get the desired mixture of 80%/20%?
6. A collection of quarters and nickels is worth \$3.70. There are 22 coins in all. How many of each coin are there?
7. A CD costs 3 times as much as a book at a garage sale. Yuri bought 3 books and 2 CDs for \$18. What is the price of a CD? What is the price of a book?
8. Car A costs \$25.95 to rent and 35 cents per mile to drive. Car B costs \$19.95 to rent and 55 cents per mile to drive. How many miles would one have to drive before the total cost of driving each car would be the same?
9. Jenny mailed 30 postcards and letters. The bill at the post office was \$9.28. The postcards cost \$0.23 each to mail, and the letters cost \$0.37 each. How many of each kind did she mail?
10. Eleni's landscaping company placed two orders. The first order was for 13 bushes and 4 trees, and totaled \$487. The second order was for 6 bushes and 2 trees, and totaled \$232. What is the price of one bush? What is the price of one tree?
11. Breana is selling tickets to a choral performance. On the first day of ticket sales she sold 3 senior citizen tickets and 1 child ticket for a total of \$38. Breana took in \$52 on the second day by selling 3 senior citizen tickets and 2 child tickets. Find the price of a senior citizen ticket and the price of a child ticket.
12. Tarziah is having a birthday brunch and wants to make fresh squeezed juice for her guests. She has 3 gallons of 100% fresh squeezed orange juice and 3 gallons of a mixture of 60% fresh squeezed pineapple juice and 40% fresh squeezed orange juice. How much of the 100% orange juice does she need to add to the mixture in order to make 2 gallons of 50% orange and 50% pineapple juice?
13. A farmer raises 5 times as many cows as horses. If he has 168 animals, how many cows does he have?
14. One catcher mitt and 10 outfielder gloves cost \$239.50. How much does each cost if 1 catcher mitt and 5 outfielder gloves cost \$134.50?
15. An electrician needs to cut a 49-foot piece of wire into two pieces so that one is 5 feet longer than the other. How long should each piece be?

16. Maria and Susan earned \$250,000 this year from their new company. They agree that Susan should get \$50,000 more than Maria, because she worked longer hours. How much will each woman get?

17. Tom gave his son Ferris a gift of \$10,000 more than twice as much as he gave his daughter Jeanie. If Tom gave them a total of \$497,500, how much did Jeanie get?

18. A 30-minute World War I show was divided into two segments: the causes of the war and the outcome. The segment on the causes of war was 4 times as long as the segment dedicated to the outcome of the war. How long was each part of the show?

19. The salaries of the manager and assistant manager of the local restaurant total \$371,500 a year. If the manager makes \$28,500 more than the assistant manager, what are their individual salaries?

20. A rectangle is 3 times as long as it is wide and its perimeter is 80 centimeters. Find its dimensions.

21. A Cool-Eze air-conditioning unit costs \$2250 and an average of \$412 per year to operate. A Chill-Out air-conditioning unit costs only \$1710 but \$466 per year to operate. When will the total cost of owning the two brands of air-conditioning units be the same?

22. A manufacturer uses two methods for producing one item. One method has a setup cost of \$60 and the other a setup cost of \$110. The cost to produce an item using the first method is \$1.50, and the cost to produce an item using the second method is \$1.30. Find the number of items that will make the cost of either method the same.

*23. **Challenge** The local drive-in movie theater's rectangular screen has a width 26 feet less than its length. If the perimeter of the screen is 332 feet, find its area.

*24. **Challenge** The length of a rectangle is 4 times its width. Find the area of the rectangle if its perimeter is 30 feet.

Systems of Linear Inequalities

A system of linear inequalities is two or more linear inequalities in the same variables.

Geometrically, the solution to a system of linear inequalities is the graph of all the points that are solutions of the system. Every point in the solution region must make all the inequalities true.

Graphing a System of Linear Inequalities

GRAPHING A SYSTEM OF LINEAR INEQUALITIES

Step 1 Graph each inequality in the system.

Step 2 Shade the intersection of the half-planes that are the solutions to each inequality. The intersection is the solution to the system.

Step 3 Test a point in the intersection of the half-planes to determine if the ordered pair is a solution to the system.

TIP

To graph an inequality, look in the topic "Graphing Linear Inequalities" found in the unit "Linear Equations and Inequalities."

Example 1 Graph the solution of the system of inequalities.

$y \geq x - 2$
$y < 2x + 1$

Solution

Step 1 Graph each inequality in the system.

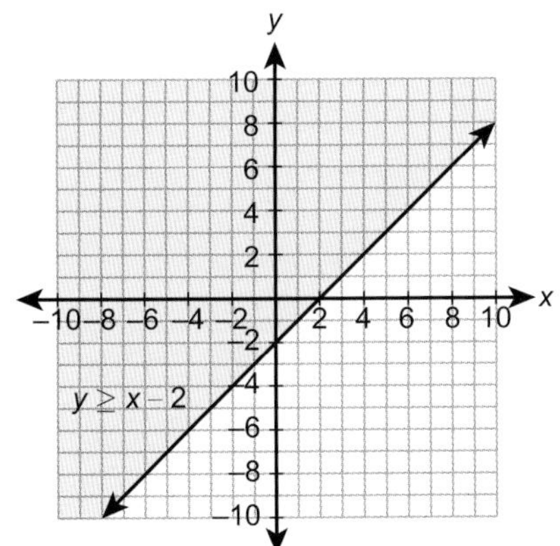

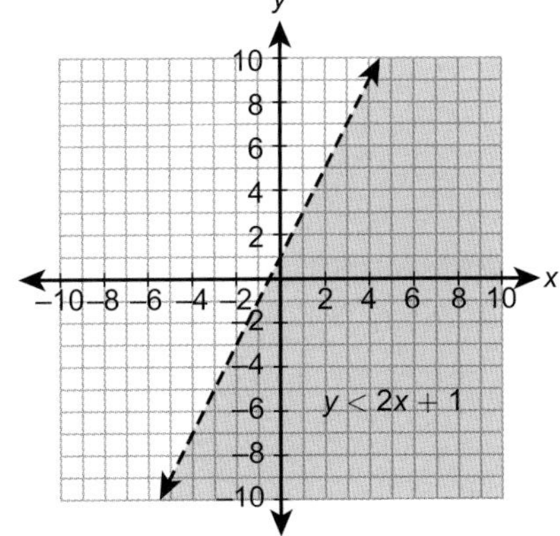

(continued)

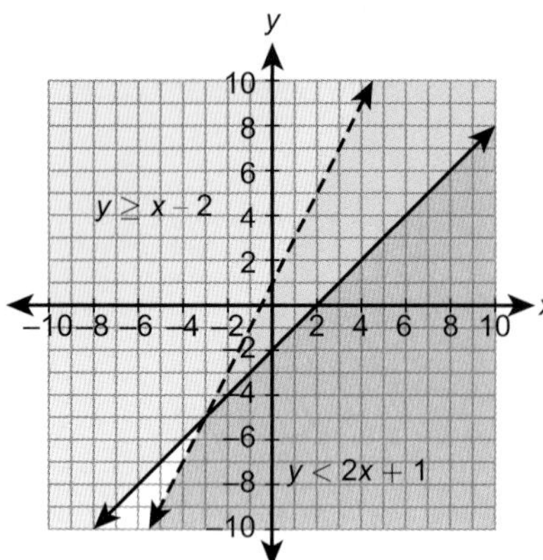

Step 2 Shade the intersection of the half-planes. Here, the shaded triangular region is the intersection of the half-planes. This triangular region is the solution to the system of inequalities.

Step 3 Test a point in the intersection of the half-planes to determine if the ordered pair is a solution to the system. Test the point (2, 3).

Substitute 2 for x and 3 for y in each inequality in the system.

$y \geq x - 2$	$y < 2x + 1$
$3 \overset{?}{\geq} 2 - 2$	$3 \overset{?}{<} 2 \cdot 2 + 1$
$3 \geq 0$ ✓	$3 \overset{?}{<} 4 + 1$
	$3 < 5$ ✓ ■

Example 2 Graph the solution of the system of inequalities.

$$y > \frac{1}{2}$$

$$y > 5x + \frac{1}{4}$$

Solution

Step 1 Graph each inequality in the system.

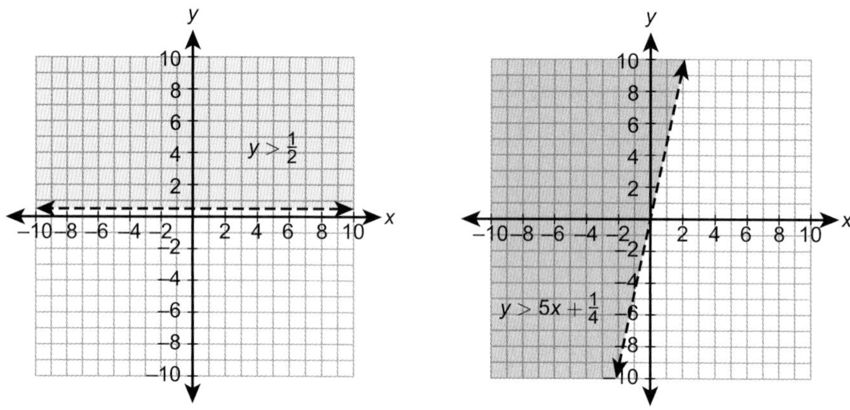

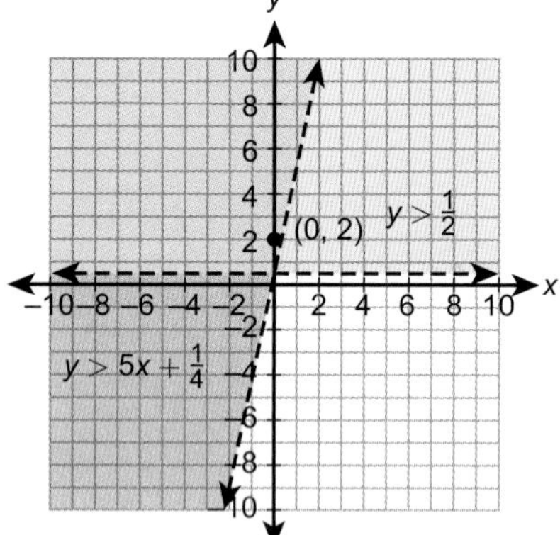

Step 2 Shade the intersection of the half-planes. In the graph, the green region is the intersection of the half-planes. This green region is the solution to the system of inequalities.

Step 3 Test a point in the intersection of the half-planes to determine if the ordered pair is a solution to the system. Test the point (0, 2).

Substitute 0 for x and 2 for y in each inequality in the system.

$y > \frac{1}{2}$	$y > 5x + \frac{1}{4}$
$2 \overset{?}{>} \frac{1}{2}$ ✓	$2 \overset{?}{>} 5 \cdot 0 + \frac{1}{4}$
	$2 \overset{?}{>} 0 + \frac{1}{4}$
	$2 > \frac{1}{4}$ ✓ ■

Example 3 Graph the solution of the system of inequalities.

$y > 2x + 4$
$y < 2x + 1$

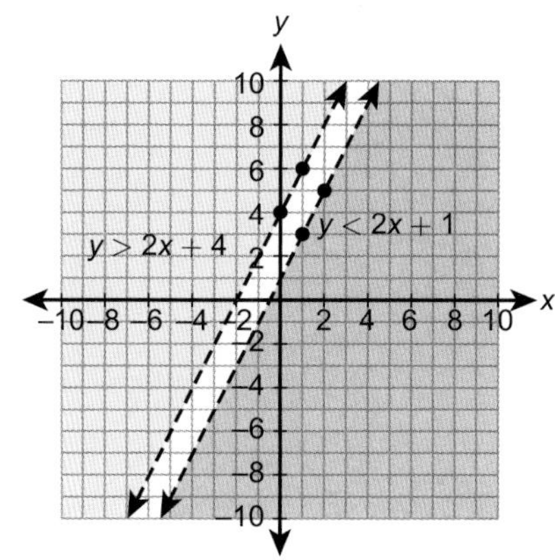

Solution

Step 1 Graph each inequality in the system.

Step 2 The boundary lines have the same slope, 2, so they are parallel. The half-planes do not intersect, so this system of inequalities has no solution. ■

Writing a System of Linear Inequalities

Example 4 Write a system of inequalities that corresponds to the green shaded region of the graph.

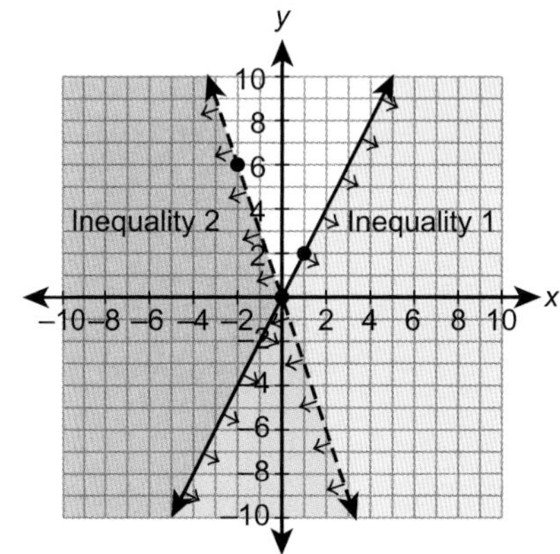

Solution

Inequality 1: The points (0, 0) and (1, 2) lie on the boundary line of Inequality 1. Find the slope of the boundary line and, since you know the y-intercept is zero, use slope-intercept form to write its equation.

Slope: Equation:

$m = \frac{2-0}{1-0} = 2$ $\quad y = mx + b$

$y = 2x + 0$

$y = 2x$

Since the region below the line is shaded and the boundary line is solid, the first inequality in the system is $y \leq 2x$.

Inequality 2: The points (0, 0) and (−2, 6) lie on the boundary line of Inequality 2. Find the slope of the boundary line and, since you know the y-intercept, use slope-intercept form to write its equation.

Slope: Equation:

$m = \frac{6-0}{-2-0} = -3$ $\quad y = mx + b$

$y = -3x + 0$

$y = -3x$

Since the region below the line is shaded and the boundary line is dashed, the second inequality in the system is $y < -3x$.

The system of inequalities is $\begin{matrix} y \leq 2x \\ y < -3x \end{matrix}$. ■

TIP

You can use the small arrows when graphing inequalities to show which half-plane should be shaded.

Application: Snack Mix

Example 5 You are making a snack mix consisting of granola and peanuts. Granola has 3 grams of fiber per ounce and peanuts have 2 grams of fiber per ounce. You want the snack mix to have at least 16 grams of fiber and weigh no more than 8 ounces.

A. Write and graph the system of linear inequalities that models the problem.

B. Name two possible combinations of granola and peanuts that can be used to make the mix.

Solution

A.

Step 1 Write the system of linear inequalities. Let x represent the number of ounces of granola in the mix and y represent the number of ounces of peanuts in the mix. Using the information in the problem, you can create the following system of inequalities.

$x > 0$ and $y > 0$	The number of ounces of granola and peanuts must each be greater than zero.
$x + y \leq 8$	The total weight of the snack mix is less than or equal to 8 ounces.
$3x + 2y \geq 16$	The number of grams of fiber must be greater than or equal to 16 grams.

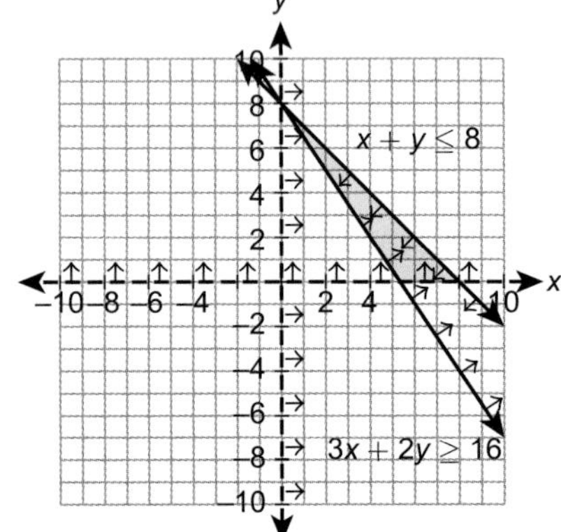

Step 2 Graph the system. Graph each inequality in the system. The intersection of all the half-planes is the green triangular region on the graph.

B. Find two solutions. Choose two points in the solution region and check that they satisfy each equation. Two possible choices are (4, 3) and (5, 2).

For the point (4, 3):

$x > 0$	$y > 0$	$x + y \leq 8$	$3x + 2y \geq 16$
$4 > 0$ ✓	$3 > 0$ ✓	$4 + 3 \overset{?}{\leq} 8$	$3 \cdot 4 + 2 \cdot 3 \overset{?}{\geq} 16$
		$7 \leq 8$ ✓	$12 + 6 \overset{?}{\geq} 16$
			$18 \geq 16$ ✓

For the point (5, 2):

$x > 0$	$y > 0$	$x + y \leq 8$	$3x + 2y \geq 16$
$5 > 0$ ✓	$2 > 0$ ✓	$5 + 2 \overset{?}{\leq} 8$	$3 \cdot 5 + 2 \cdot 2 \overset{?}{\geq} 16$
		$7 \leq 8$ ✓	$15 + 4 \overset{?}{\geq} 16$
			$19 \geq 16$ ✓

Two possible combinations for the snack mix are 4 ounces of granola and 3 ounces of peanuts or 5 ounces of granola and 2 ounces of peanuts. ■

Problem Set

Graph the solution of each of the given systems of inequalities.

1. $y < x + 1$
   $y > 3x - 2$

2. $y \geq 2x - 4$
   $y > -x + 6$

3. $y > -3x + 5$
   $y < -3x - 2$

4. $y > \frac{1}{2}x - 4$
   $y \leq -3x + 5$

5. $y \leq -\frac{1}{2}x + 8$
   $y > -4x + 6$

6. $y < x$
   $y \geq -4$

7. $y \geq x$
   $y < 2x - 3$

8. $y \leq -\frac{2}{3}x + 4$
   $y \geq -\frac{2}{3}x - 7$

9. $y \leq -\frac{1}{2}x - 8$
   $y \geq -\frac{1}{2}x + 5$

10. $y < 6$
    $y \geq -3x - 1$

11. $y \leq 8$
    $y \geq -2$

12. $y \leq -x$
    $y \geq x$

Challenge

*13. $y \geq 0$
   $y < 2x + 5$
   $y > -2x$

*14. $y \leq 5$
   $y < x$
   $y > -5$

Write a system of inequalities that corresponds to the given graph.

15.

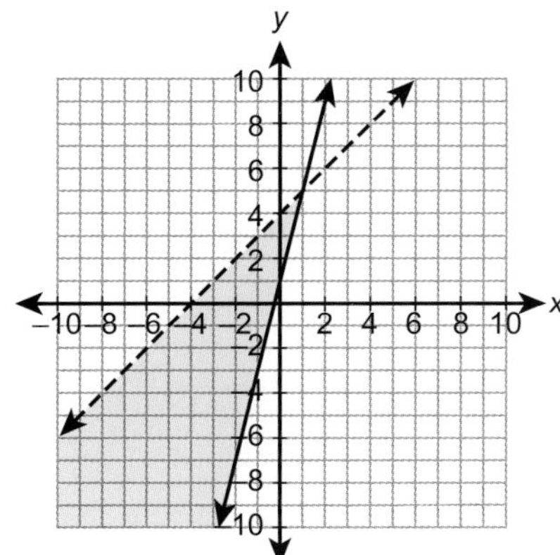

16.

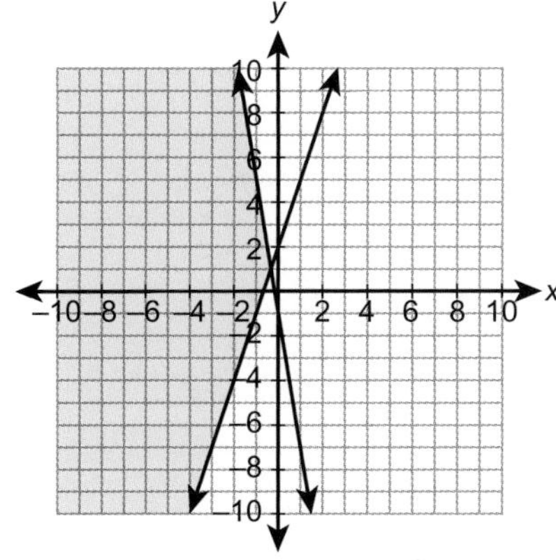

17.

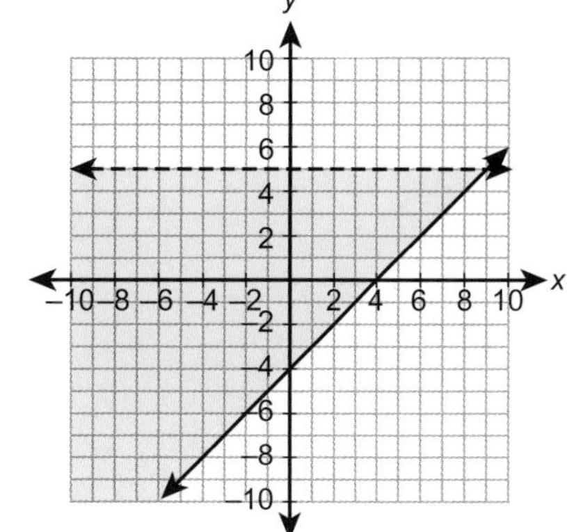

18.

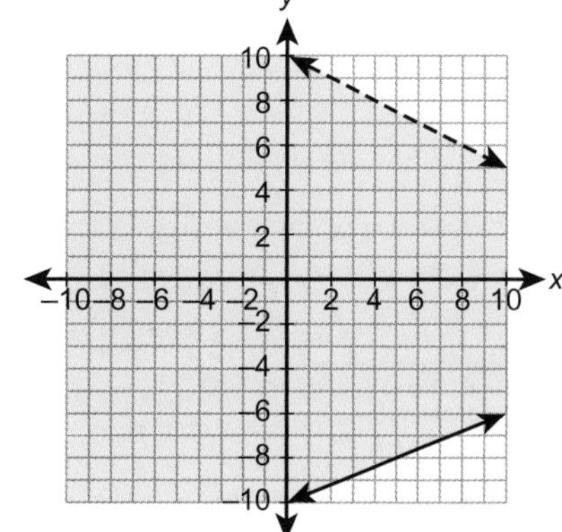

19.

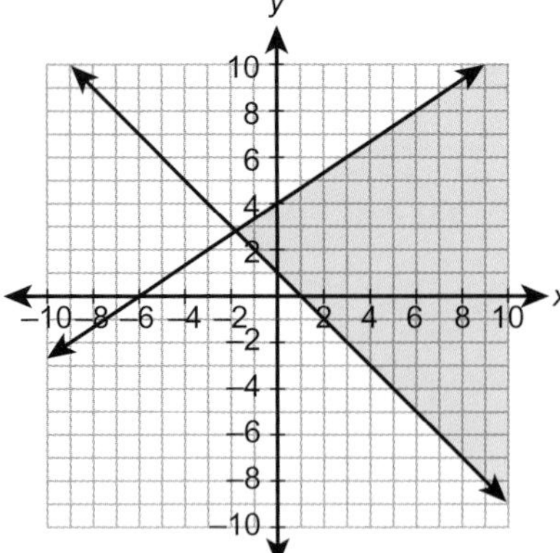

20.

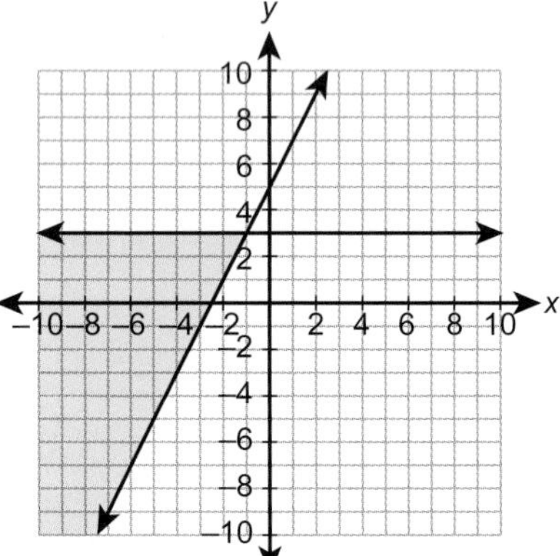

21.

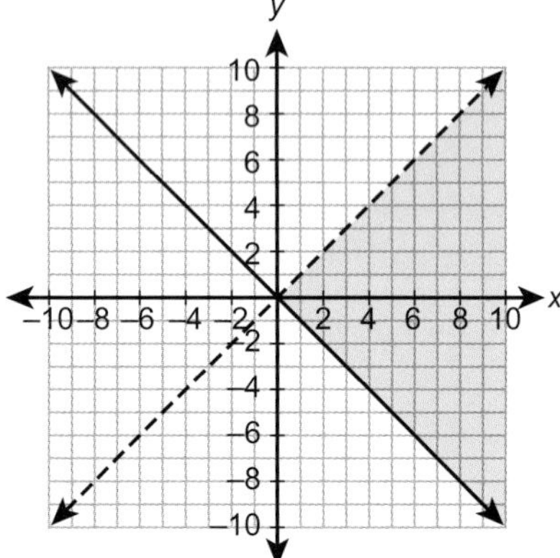

22.

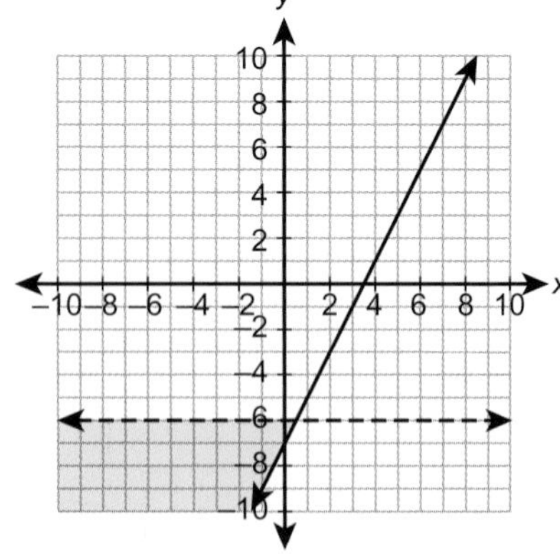

23.

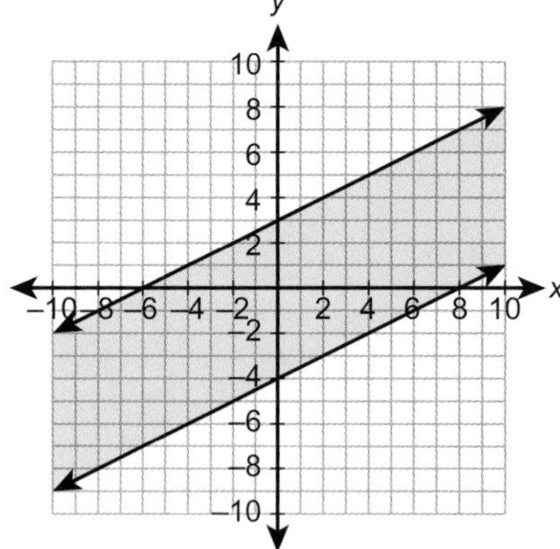

24.

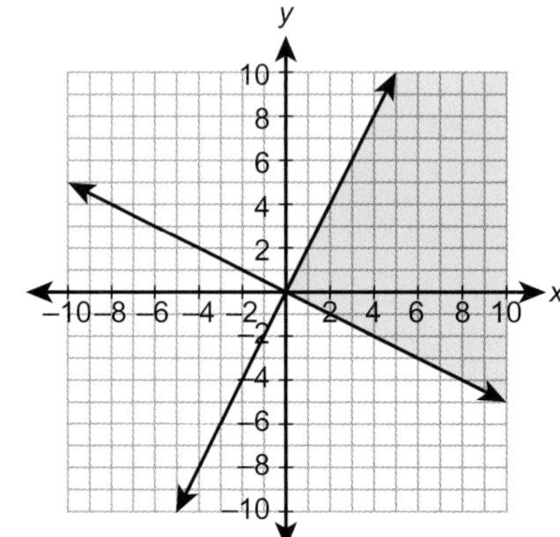

25.

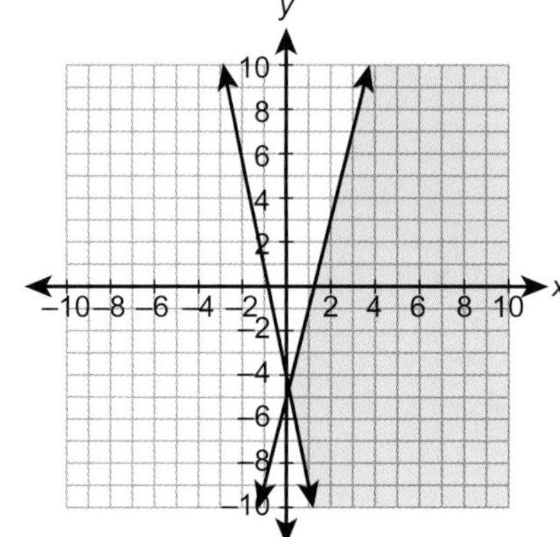

26.

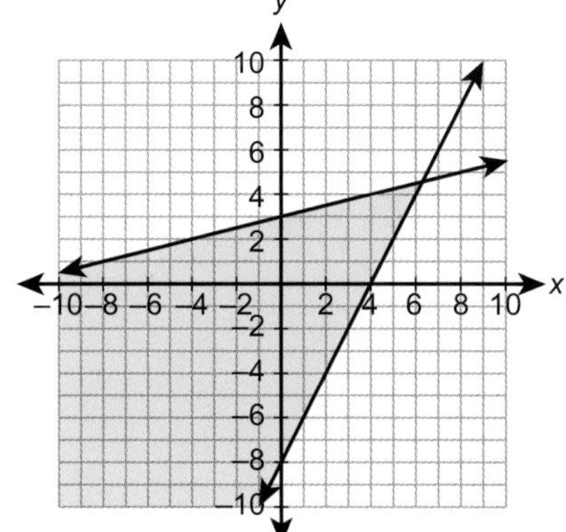

Solve. For each problem:

A. Write a system of linear inequalities to model the problem.

B. Graph the system to determine the region that has all the possible solutions.

27. You are creating a collage of black-and-white and color photographs. Each black-and-white photo costs $3 to print and each color photo costs $2 to print. You want the collage to have at least 12 photographs, but cannot afford to spend more than $36.

28. You are baking pretzels for your sister's party. She has asked you to bake at least 18 dozen regular and whole grain pretzels. You have 20 cups of flour. Each dozen of whole grain pretzels requires 2 cups of flour and each dozen of regular pretzels requires 1 cup.

29. You have been put in charge of ordering at least 10 soccer balls for your little brother's soccer team. Practice soccer balls cost $6 and game soccer balls cost $8. The coach gave you $96 to spend.

30. You are shopping at the mall for gifts for 17 friends. Boys' gifts are $2.50 each and girls' gifts are $4.25 each. The most money you can spend is $100.

***31. Challenge** You are training for the local marathon in the spring. Today you will walk and run at least 15 miles altogether. Your walking rate is 9 minutes per mile, and your running rate is 6 minutes per mile. You have to finish in less than 2 hours.

***32. Challenge** You are planting flowers for the spring season. You need at least 20 flowers, and only want mums and peonies. This year, mums are $12 each and peonies are $4 each. You must spend less than $200 on the flowers.

UNIT 8 Relations and Functions

A solar cell panel uses sunlight to produce electricity.

A solar cell is a little machine that takes in solar energy and puts out electricity. A mathematical function is a machine that takes in a number as an input and produces another number as an output. There are many kinds of functions. Some have graphs that look like lines, while others have graphs that curve like a parabola. Functions can take other forms as well. Not every function has a graph that looks like a parabola. Not every function has an equation. The important thing to remember is that if you put any valid input into a function, you will get a single result out of it.

Big Idea

- A function is a correspondence between two sets, the domain and the range, that assigns to each member of the domain exactly one member of the range. Many events in the physical world can be modeled as functions. Many functions can be described by algebraic expressions.

Unit Topics

- Relations
- Functions
- Function Equations
- Absolute Value Functions
- Direct Linear Variation
- Quadratic Variation
- Inverse Variation
- Translating Functions

Relations

In math, a relationship that shows a pairing between two sets is a *relation.*

DEFINITION

A **relation** is a mapping from a set of inputs to a set of outputs.

Representing Relations in Different Ways

You can use a set of ordered pairs to represent a relation. The x-coordinates of the ordered pairs are the inputs and the y-coordinates are the outputs. You can also display a relation using an arrow diagram, table, and graph.

Example 1 In the relation $\{(8, 3), (8, 4), (10, 5), (12, 8), (13, 9)\}$, each x-coordinate represents a student's age and each y-coordinate represents the student's grade level in school. Display the relation in an arrow diagram, table, and graph.

Solution

Arrow Diagram

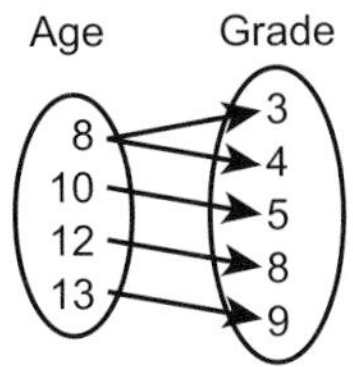

Table

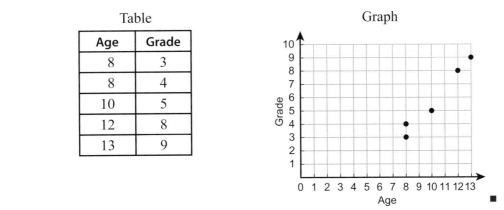

Age	Grade
8	3
8	4
10	5
12	8
13	9

Graph

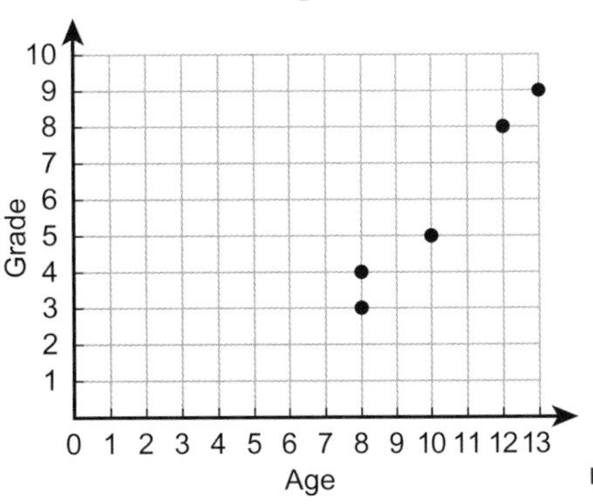

■

Finding the Domain and Range of a Relation

The **domain** of a relation is the set of allowable inputs and the **range** is the set of possible outputs.

Example 2 Find the domain and range of each relation.

A. $\{(-2, -4), (0, 3), (2, -4), (4, 1)\}$.

Solution The domain is the set of x-coordinates: $\{-2, 0, 2, 4\}$. The range is the set of y-coordinates: $\{-4, 1, 3\}$.

(continued)

TIP

When writing the domain and range, list each number in each set only once.

> **TIP**
>
> On a graph, the horizontal axis represents the values of the domain, which are the values of the independent (input) variable.
>
> The vertical axis represents the values of the range, which are the values of the dependent (output) variable.

> **THINK ABOUT IT**
>
> Inequalities are often used to represent the domain and range of some relations.

B.

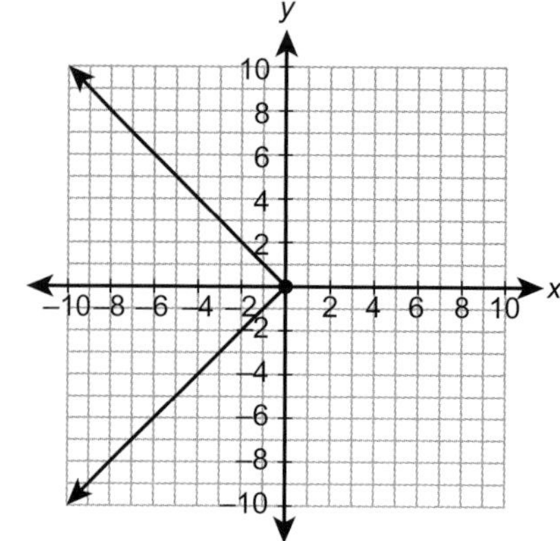

Solution The graph extends horizontally from 0 towards the negative numbers without end, and it extends vertically without beginning or end. So, the domain is all numbers less than or equal to zero, $\{x | x \leq 0\}$ and the range is all real numbers, $\{y | y \in \mathbb{R}\}$. ■

Application: Fuel Consumption

> **TIP**
>
> The inputs and outputs in a relation do not have to be numeric.

Example 3 The relation between four vehicles and their fuel consumption in miles per gallon is shown in the table. Write the relation as a set of ordered pairs. Then write the domain and range of the relation.

Vehicle (2008 model)	Average Fuel Consumption (mpg)
Ford Fusion	27
Lincoln Navigator	16
Toyota Camry	26
Honda Element	21

Solution The relation can be written as {(Ford Fusion, 27), (Lincoln Navigator, 16), (Toyota Camry, 26), (Honda Element, 21)}.

The domain is {Ford Fusion, Lincoln Navigator, Toyota Camry, Honda Element}. The range is {16, 21, 26, 27}. ■

Problem Set

Display each relation in an arrow diagram, table, and graph.

1. $\{(-4, -2), (-3, 1), (0, 4), (1, -1), (3, 3)\}$
2. $\{(-2, 0), (-1, 3), (1, -3), (2, 0), (2, 2)\}$
3. $\{(-2, 3), (-1, -1), (0, 3), (2, -2), (3, -1)\}$
4. $\{(-2, 4), (-1, 2), (0, 0), (2, -2), (2, 2)\}$
5. $\{(-4, 1), (-2, -1), (1, 2), (3, 0), (4, 3)\}$
6. $\{(-1, 0), (3, -1), (3, 1), (4, -3), (4, 3)\}$
7. $\{(1, 1), (3, 2), (5, 3), (7, 5)\}$
8. $\{(-3, 2), (-1, 6), (2, -5), (2, 7), (3, -3)\}$
9. $\{(-3, -6), (-3, 6), (2, 5), (5, -6), (5, 5)\}$
10. $\{(-6, 5), (0, -7), (2, -1), (4, 5), (5, 8)\}$
11. $\{(-8, 0), (-2, -5), (0, 0), (0, 6), (6, 9)\}$
12. $\{(-8, -4), (-3, -2), (4, 2), (4, 8), (8, 8)\}$

Find the domain and range of each relation.

13. $\{(-5, 4), (3, -2), (3, 4), (4, 3)\}$

14. $\{(-4.5, 0), (-3, 9), (0.9, 0), (4, -7.8), (4, 0), (17, 3)\}$

15. $\{(2, 5), (2, 7), (5, 5), (5.8, -6), (9, 7), (10.5, -5.8)\}$

16.

x	y
−5	−9
−1	9
−1	−9
0	0
5	9

17.

x	y
−7	3
−2	5
0	7
3	7
3	5

18.

x	y
−1.6	6
−1.6	11
3.5	5
8	5
8	6

19.

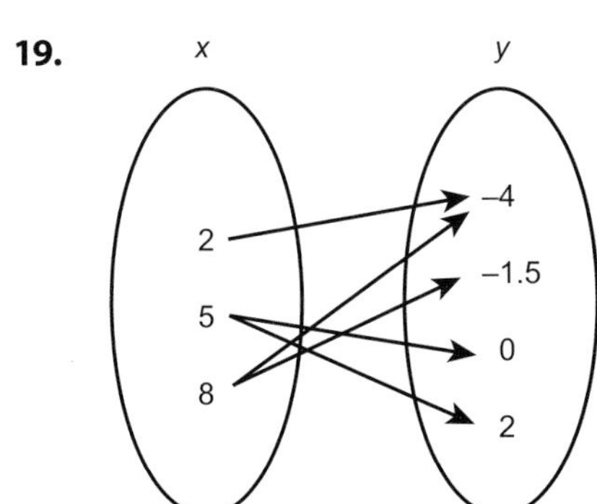

20.

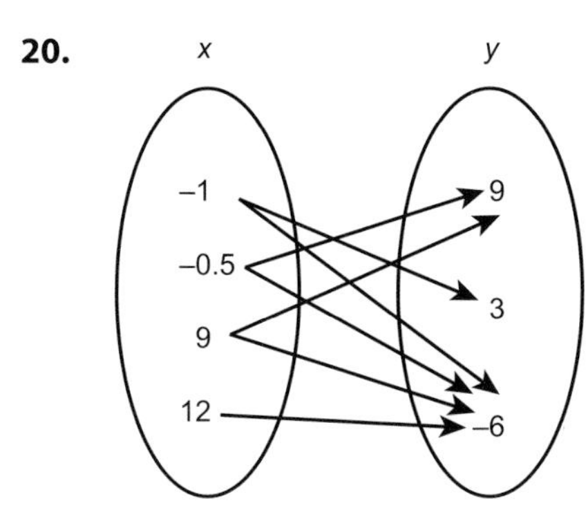

21.

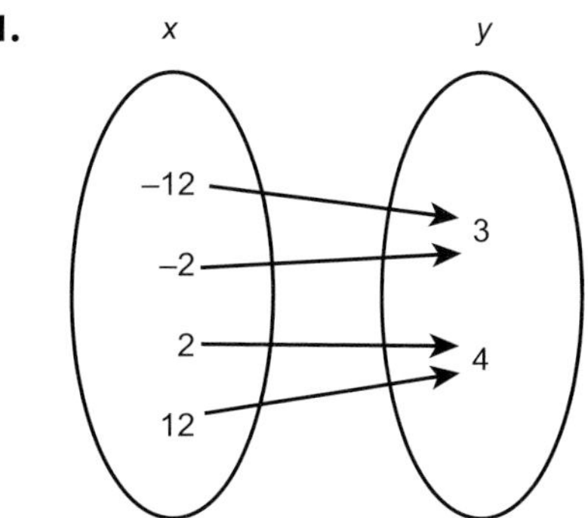

22.

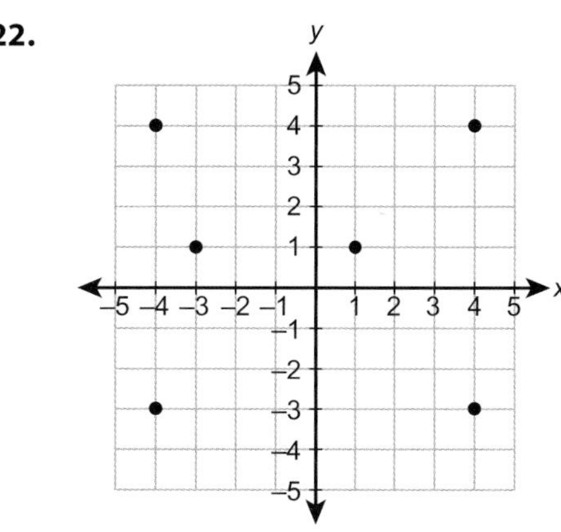

23.

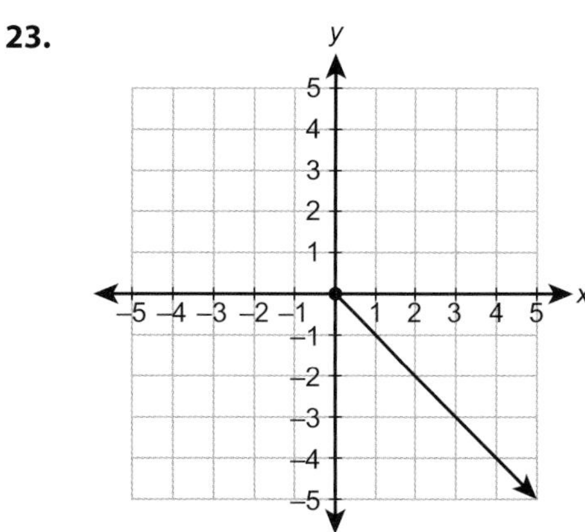

24.

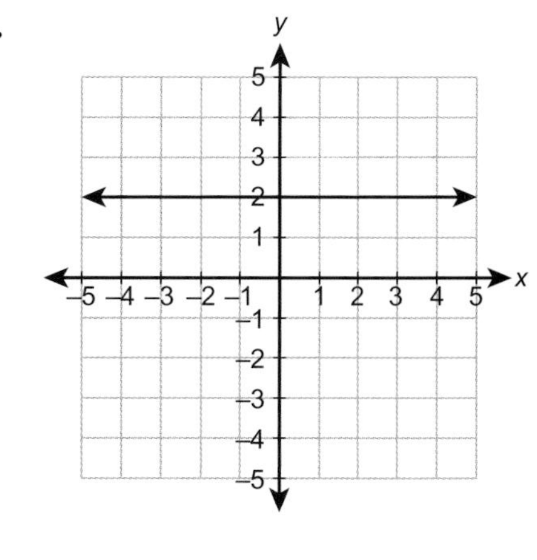

Solve.

25. Lia threw a pair of number cubes 20 times and added the number of dots that came up with each roll. She got these results: 7, 6, 6, 8, 8, 7, 7, 8, 9, 5, 7, 12, 3, 8, 10, 7, 3, 7, 2, 9.

A. Write the relation as a set of ordered pairs, using each possible resulting sum as the input and the number of times it appeared on the dice as the output.

B. Find the domain and range for the relation in Part A.

26. The table shows the number of hours 75 students reported that they had done homework in a certain week.

Number of Hours	Number of Students
2	4
3	12
4	20
6	16
7	12
9	7
12	4

A. Write the relation as a set of ordered pairs.

B. Graph the relation in a single-quadrant graph.

27. Rivka is comparing the amount of memory and the hard drive capacities of new laptop computers. She has found laptops with 1 GB memory with hard drives of 80, 100, 120, and 160 GB, and laptops with 2 GB memory with hard drives of 120, 160, 200, and 250 GB.

A. Display the relation as a set of ordered pairs, with memory size as the input and hard drive size as the output.

B. Create a table to display the relation.

28. A college published the ages of its entering students. The youngest entering student was 17 and the oldest was 31. The number of students who entered at each age is shown in this set of ordered pairs: {(17, 112), (18, 390), (19, 160), (20, 8), (21, 3), (24, 1), (31, 1)}.

A. Create a table to show the relation, using age as the input and number of students as the output.

B. Write the domain and range of the relation.

29. Bashir kept this driving log for the first eight weeks he had his driver's permit.

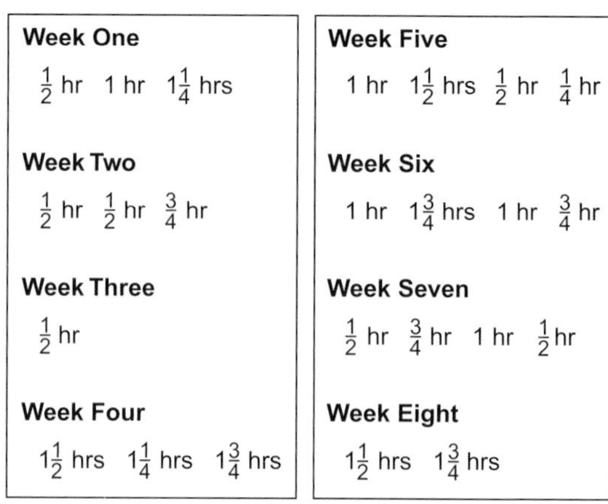

Week One
$\frac{1}{2}$ hr 1 hr $1\frac{1}{4}$ hrs

Week Two
$\frac{1}{2}$ hr $\frac{1}{2}$ hr $\frac{3}{4}$ hr

Week Three
$\frac{1}{2}$ hr

Week Four
$1\frac{1}{2}$ hrs $1\frac{1}{4}$ hrs $1\frac{3}{4}$ hrs

Week Five
1 hr $1\frac{1}{2}$ hrs $\frac{1}{2}$ hr $\frac{1}{4}$ hr

Week Six
1 hr $1\frac{3}{4}$ hrs 1 hr $\frac{3}{4}$ hr

Week Seven
$\frac{1}{2}$ hr $\frac{3}{4}$ hr 1 hr $\frac{1}{2}$ hr

Week Eight
$1\frac{1}{2}$ hrs $1\frac{3}{4}$ hrs

A. Write a set of ordered pairs, using the numbered weeks as the input and the total hours for each week as the output.

B. Write the domain and range of the relation.

30. Melinda grows peas to sell at a farmer's market. She wanted to choose a pea variety that produced a high number of peas in each pod, so she counted the peas that she found in each pod in one basket of her harvest. The graph shows her results.

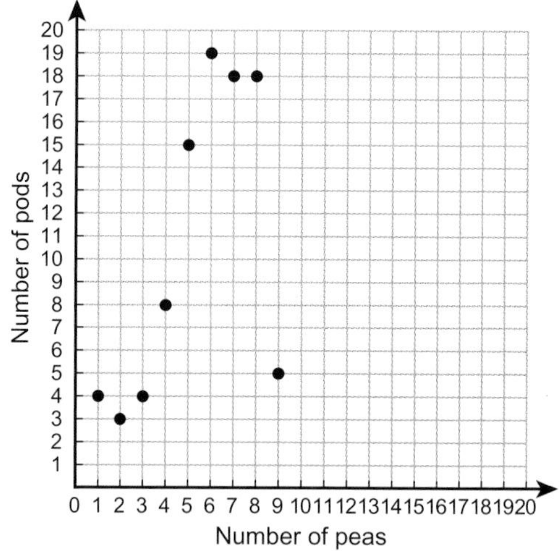

A. Write ordered pairs to show the relation.

B. Write the domain and range.

Functions

A function is a relation in which each input can have only one output.

DEFINITION

A **function** is a relation in which every element of the domain is assigned to exactly one element of the range.

The relation between people and their heights is a function because no person can have more than one height. For example, George cannot be 58 inches and 60 inches tall at the same time. However, George and Maria can both have the same height.

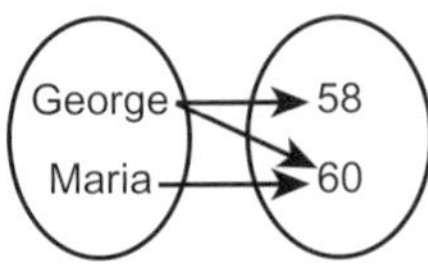

Not a Function

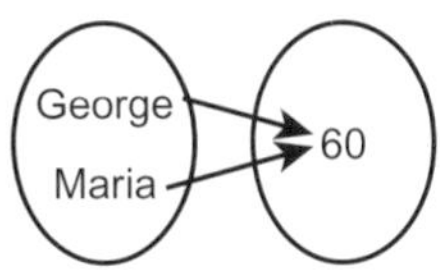

Function

Determining if a Relation Is a Function

Example 1 Determine if each relation is a function.

A. $\{(-5, 4), (-4, 0), (-2, 4), (-1, 0)\}$

Solution No element from the domain is paired with more than one element from the range. The relation is a function. ■

B.

x	2	2	2	4	5
y	−9	−7	−3	1	8

Solution The domain value of 2 is assigned to −9, −7, and −3. The relation is not a function. ■

TIP

In a table or a set of ordered pairs, if no *x*-values are repeated, the relation is a function.

Applying the Vertical Line Test

When a function is graphed in the coordinate plane, each x-value is assigned to no more than one y-value. This makes it impossible for any vertical line to intersect the graph at more than one point.

THE VERTICAL LINE TEST

For any relation, if a vertical line intersects the graph more than once, the relation is not a function.

Also, if you cannot draw a vertical line that intersects a relation more than once, the relation is a function.

TIP

Place an uncooked piece of spaghetti over the graph of a relation vertically. Slide it over the graph from left to right. If the spaghetti intersects the graph more than once at any *x*-value, then the relation is not a function.

Example 2 Determine if each relation is a function.

A.

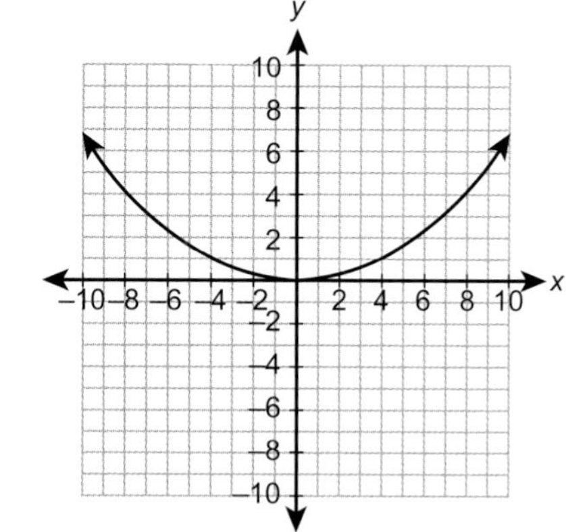

Solution No vertical line intersects the graph at more than one point. The relation is a function. ■

B.

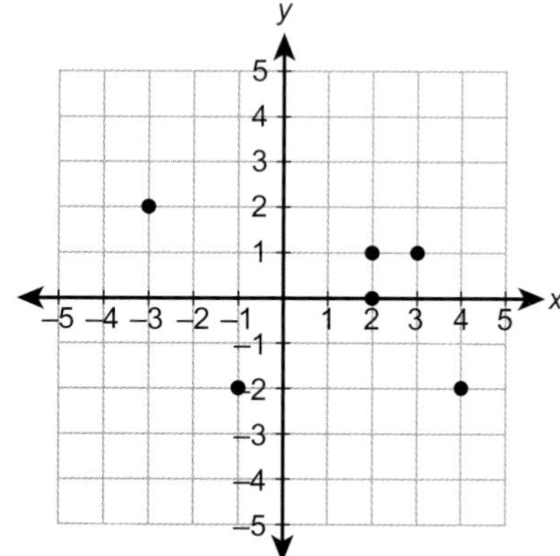

Solution A vertical line will intersect both (2, 1) and (2, 0). The relation is not a function. ■

Evaluating a Function

To evaluate a function, find the y-value that corresponds to a given x-value.

Example 3 Evaluate each function at the given point.

A. $x = 3$

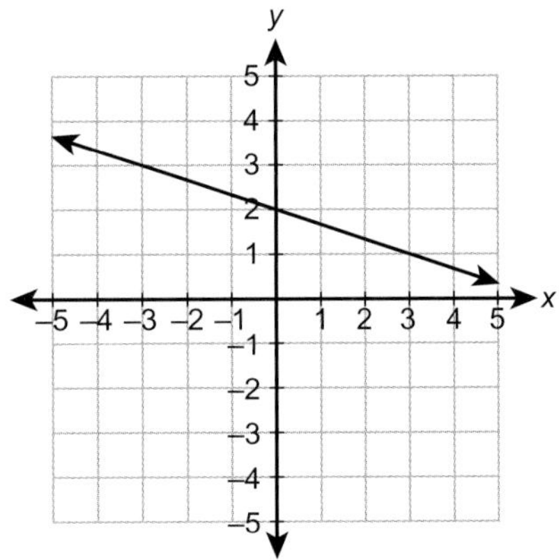

Solution Place your finger at 3 on the x-axis and slide it vertically until your finger reaches the graph. Then, move your finger horizontally to find the corresponding y-value on the y-axis. When $x = 3$, the value of the function is $y = 1$.

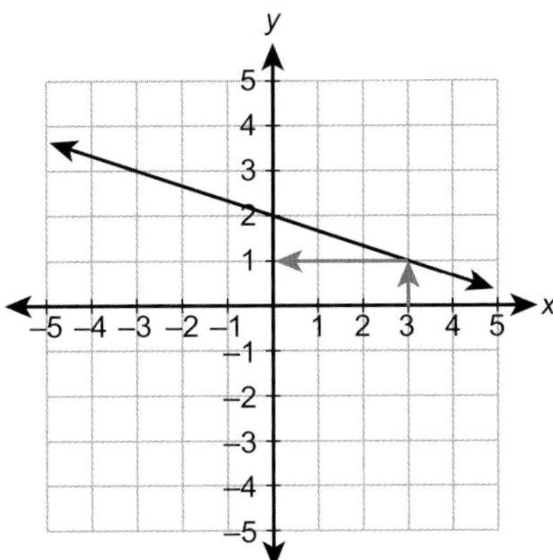

■

B. $x = -1$

x	−3	−2	−1	0	1	2
y	−5	−4	−3	−2	−1	0

Solution Locate $x = -1$ in the top row of the table, then find the corresponding y-value. The value of the function at $x = -1$ is $y = -3$. ■

Applications: Donations, Distance, and Population

When choosing a graph to represent a real-life situation, consider whether a connected graph (called a continuous graph) or a graph of individual points (called a discrete graph) is appropriate.

Example 4

A. People registered for a charity event will tell three other people about the charity and ask for donations. Which graph better represents this situation? Explain.

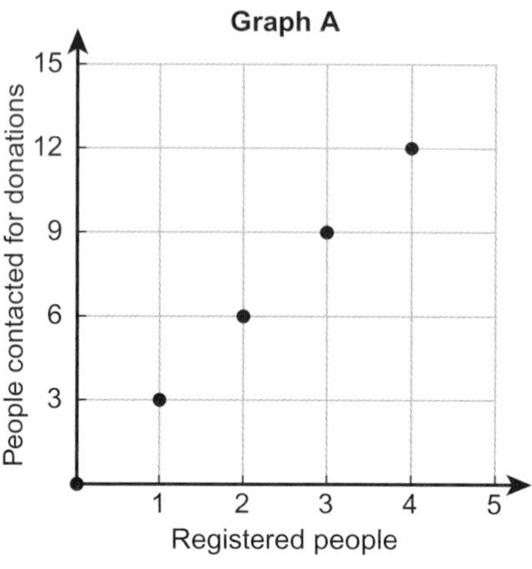

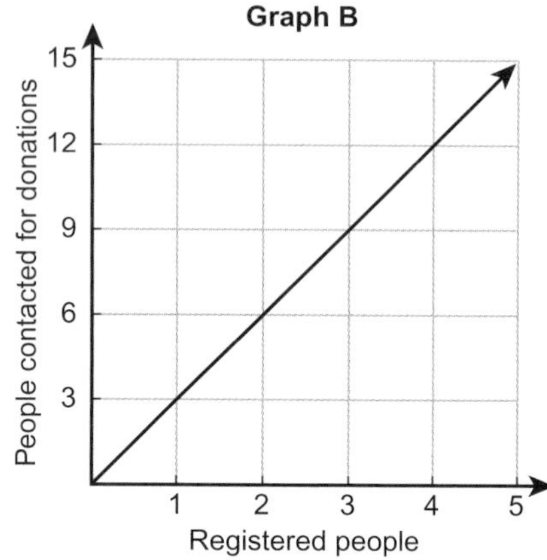

Solution There cannot be a fraction of a person, so Graph A is the better choice. ■

THINK ABOUT IT

The flat segment of Leroy's graph indicates no change in distance. Time continues to pass, yet distance does not increase. For instance, this happens when Leroy stops at a traffic light.

B. Which graph better represents the function between the time Leroy leaves home on a bicycle and the distance he travels? Explain.

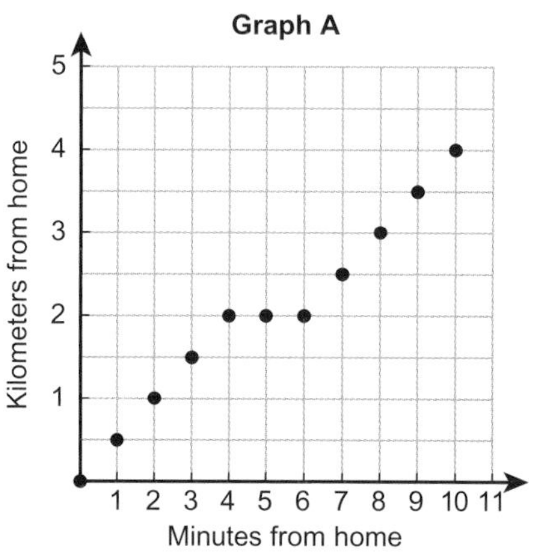

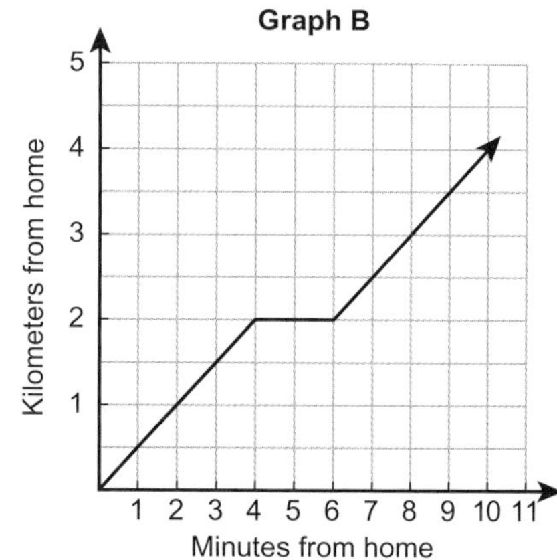

Solution Time and distance are continuous, so Graph B is the better choice. ■

Example 5 The graph shows the population of North Carolina every decade from 1940 to 2000. Use the graph to estimate the population in 1995.

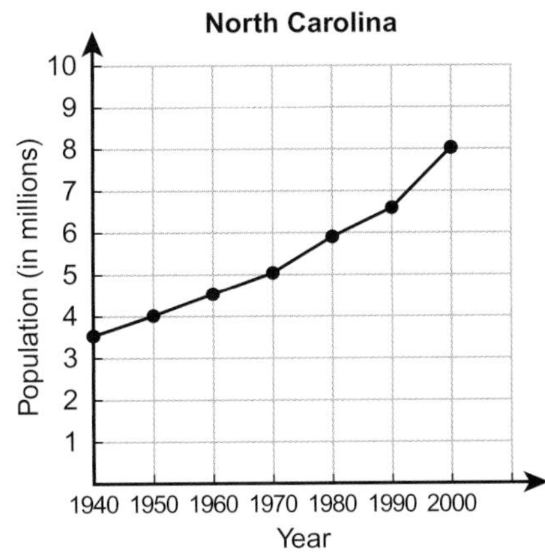

Solution Locate 1995 on the x-axis by putting your finger halfway between 1990 and 2000. Move vertically until your finger reaches the graph. Move horizontally to the y-axis to estimate the value: about 7.4 million. ■

Problem Set

For Problems 1–12: Determine if each relation is a function. Explain.

1. $\{(3, 2), (0, 1), (-2, 1), (3, -2)\}$

2. $\{(7, 2), (-3, 2), (-1, 9), (9, 2), (-4, 7)\}$

3. $\{(14, 12), (15, -2), (12, -5), (-2, 15)\}$

4. $\{(-2, 6), (4, 5), (3, -3), (6, 9), (4, -4)\}$

5.

x	−6	−4	0	2	4
y	5	5	3	3	0

6.

x	−2	2	3	3	7
y	−3	8	2	1	−5

7.

x	−8	−2	−2	6	8
y	−16	−8	0	4	12

8.

x	−2	−1	0	2	3
y	−5	−3	2	5	7

9.

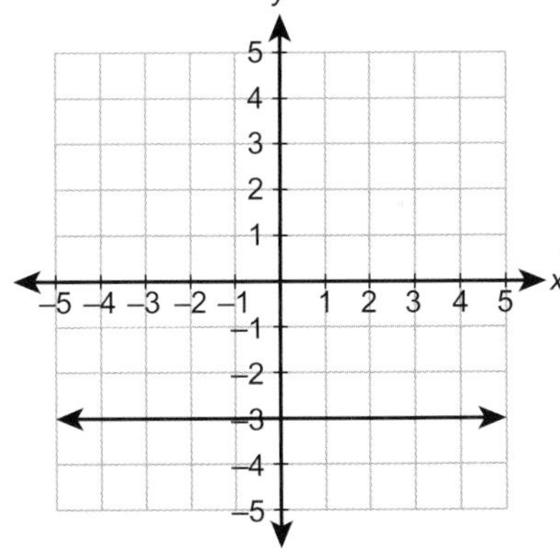

10.

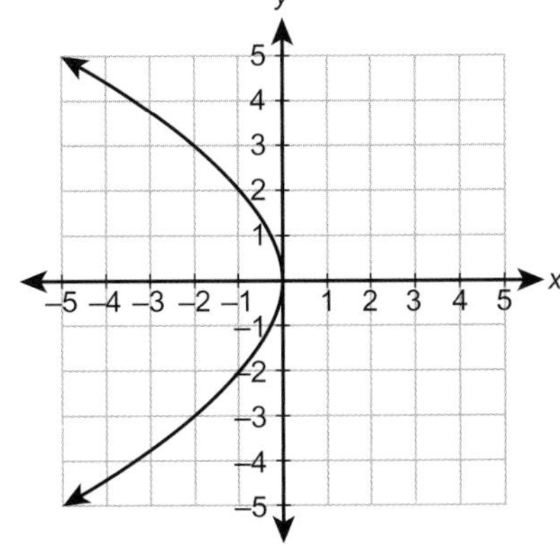

11.

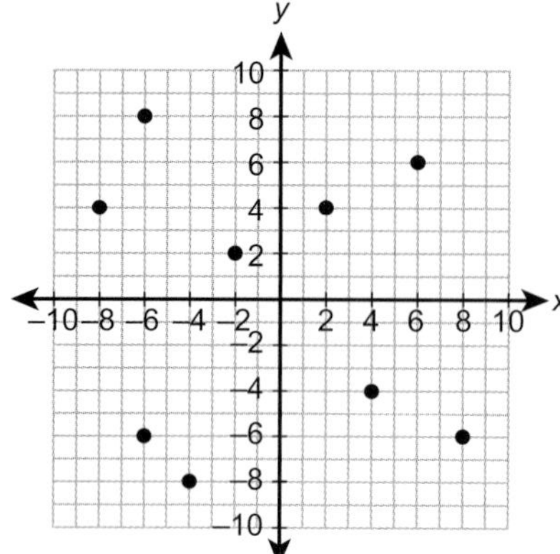

12.

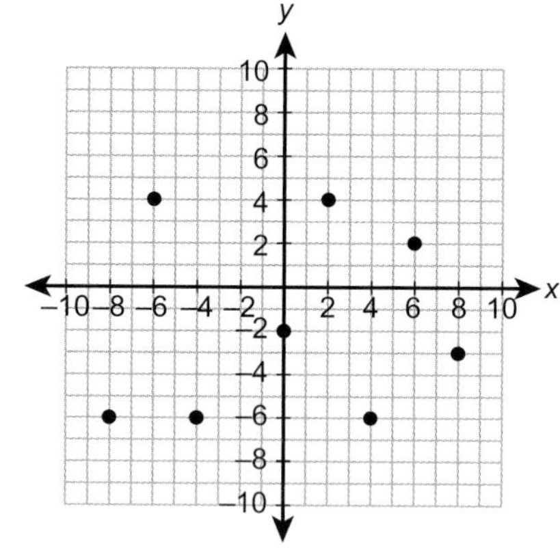

For Problems 13–20: Evaluate each function at the given point.

13. $x = 0$

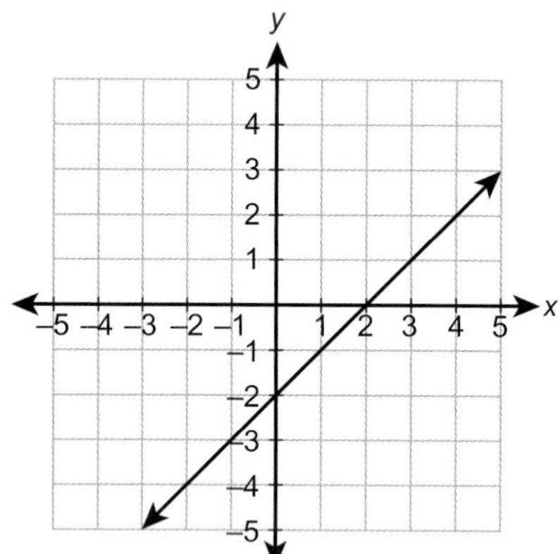

15. $x = 1$

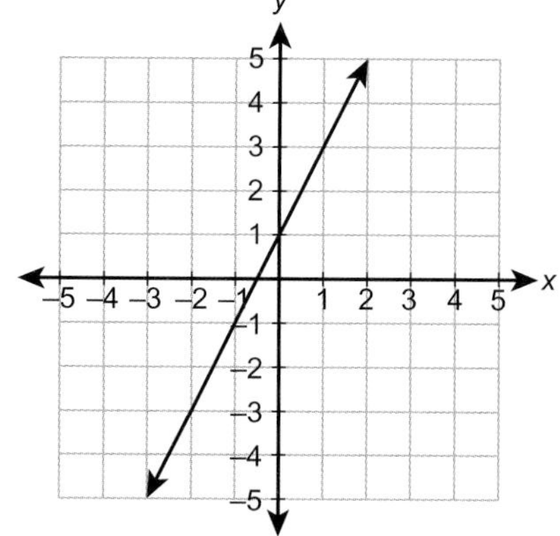

14. $x = 8$

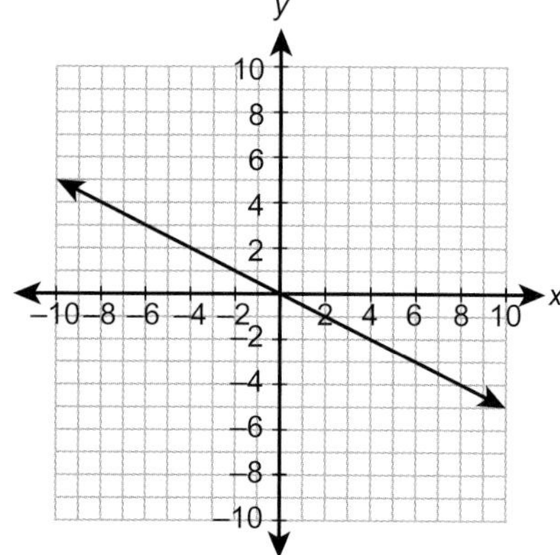

16. $x = -8$

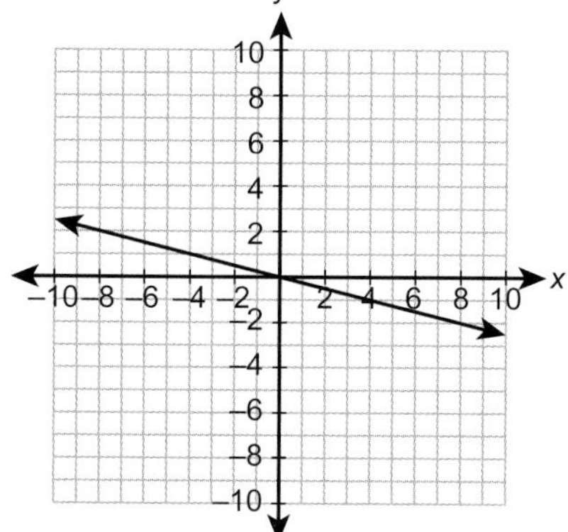

17. $x = -1$

x	−6	−5	−1	3	7	9	10
y	−19	−16	−4	8	20	26	29

18. $x = 3$

x	−2	0	1	3	6	8	12
y	−5	0	2.5	7.5	15	20	30

19. $x = -7$

x	−7	−3	−2	0	3	5	9
y	18	10	8	4	−2	−6	−14

20. $x = 4$

x	−9	−3	−1	0	4	7	15
y	−13	−4	−1	1	6.5	11	23

For Problems 21–25: Choose the graph that better represents each situation. Explain your choice.

21. A student taking a survey asked the first 10 people in line in the cafeteria how many people are in their family.

A.

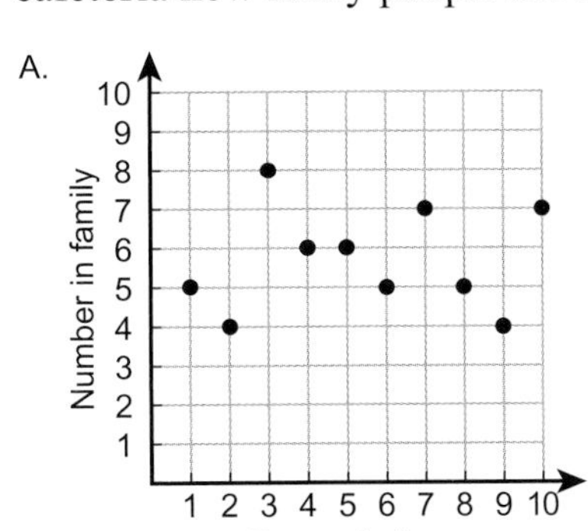

B.

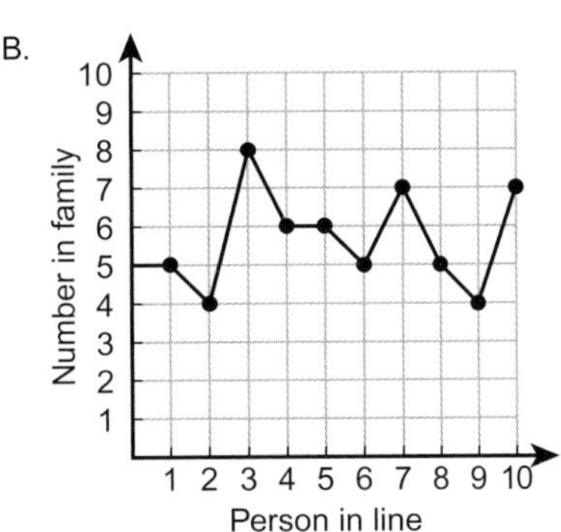

22. Bethany's track team recorded runners' times in 10 sprints. Bethany ran in 7 of the sprints and made a graph to show her times.

A.

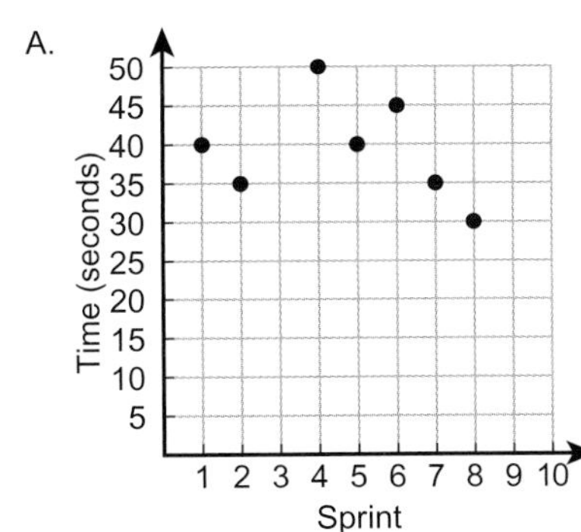

B.

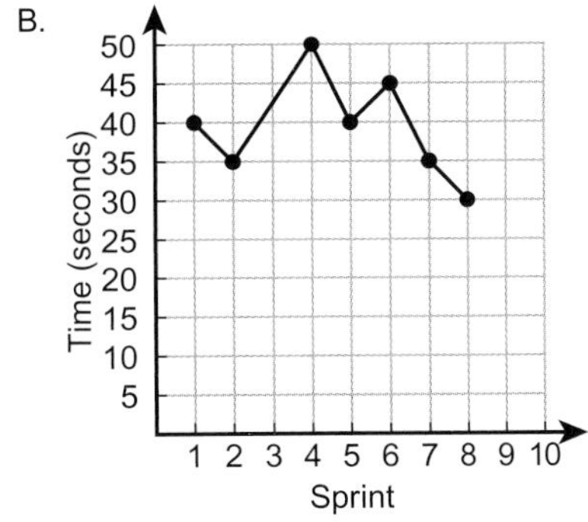

23. The graph shows the number of computers owned by U.S. residents during the earlier years of personal computer ownership.

A.

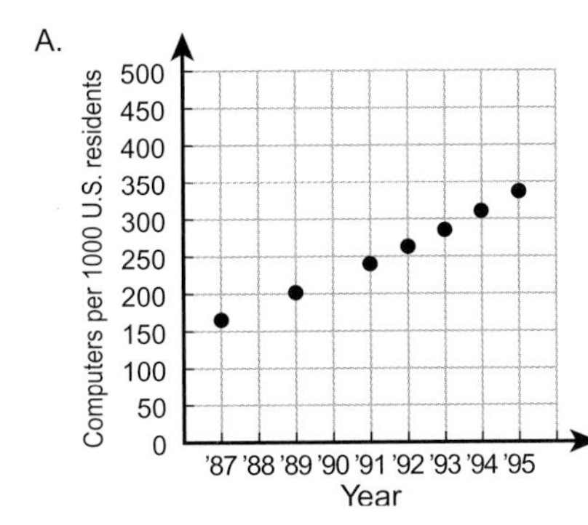

B.

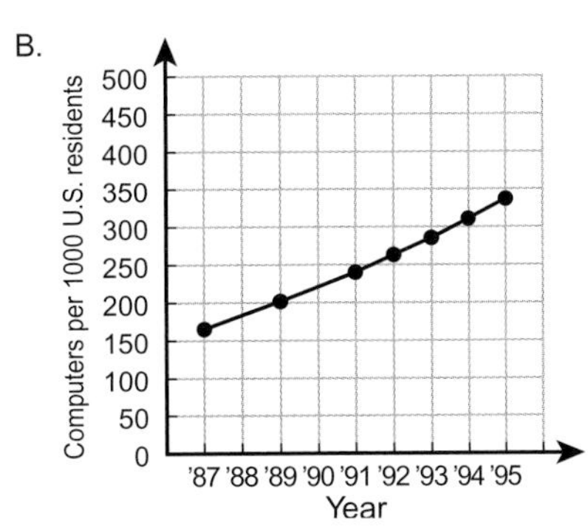

24. The graph shows the population of several U.S. states in 1990, rounded to the nearest million.

A.

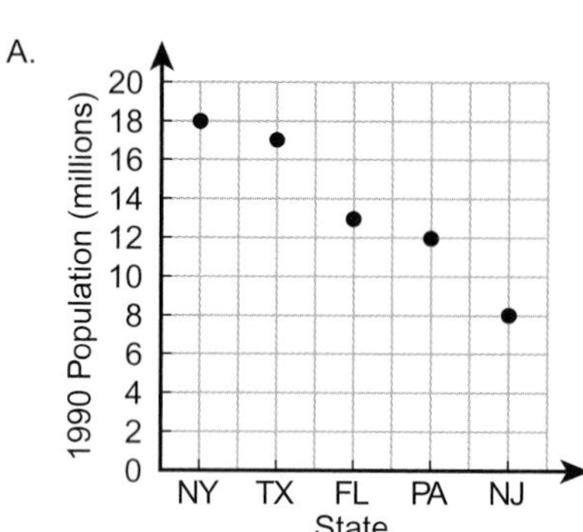

B.

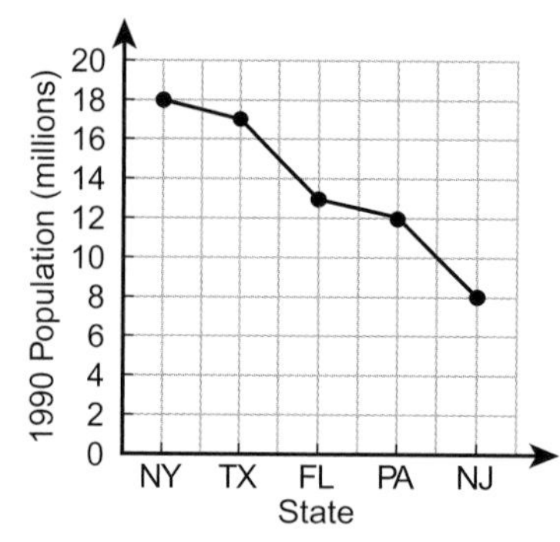

25. Rebecca read every day for 10 days to complete her history assignment. The graph shows the total number of pages she read by the end of each day.

A.

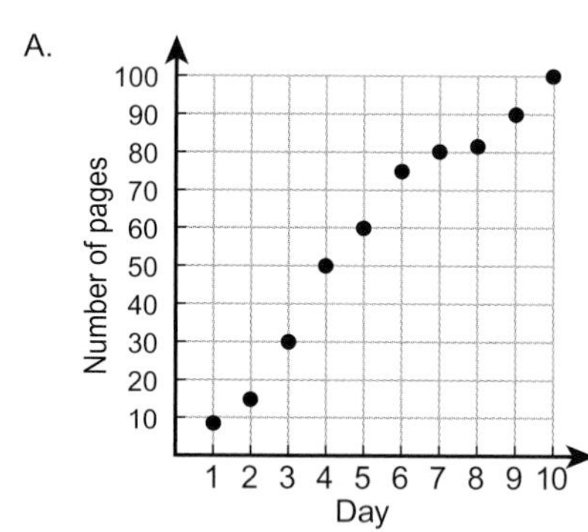

B.

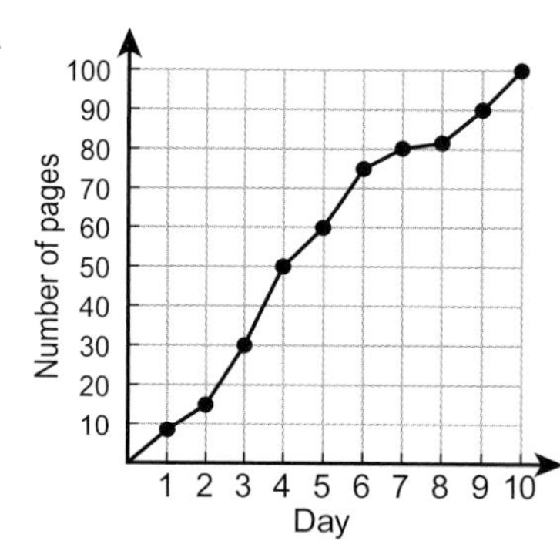

For Problems 26–30: Use the function graph to answer each question.

26. When he was 25, Mr. Morton started a retirement fund. The balance of the retirement fund is shown in the graph.

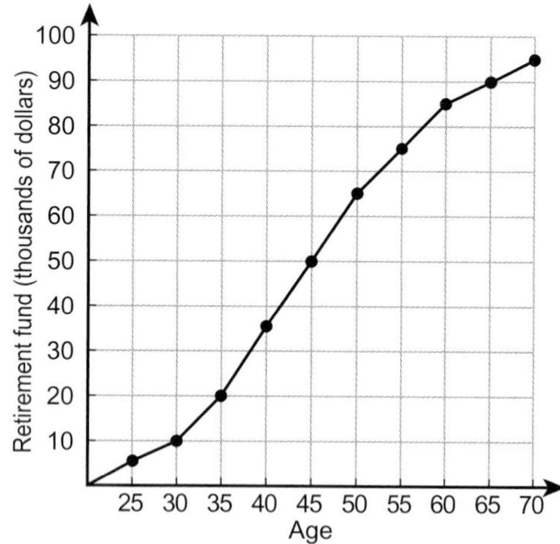

A. Use the graph to estimate how much money was in the fund when Mr. Morton was 48 years old.

B. About how old was Mr. Morton when the money in the fund reached $25,000?

27. Willard drove from Maine to Florida in two days, and wrote down how many miles he traveled during each hour of driving.

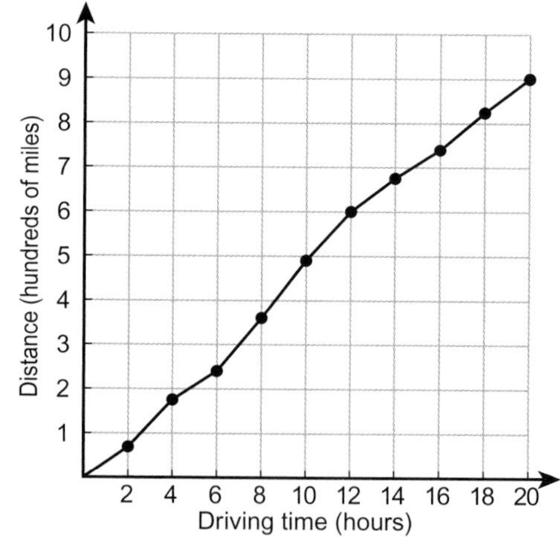

A. After 5 hours of driving, about how far had he traveled?

B. What was Willard's average speed for the 20 hours of driving?

***28. Challenge** Tia's math teacher gives quizzes several times a week. Tia's scores continued to improve all year.

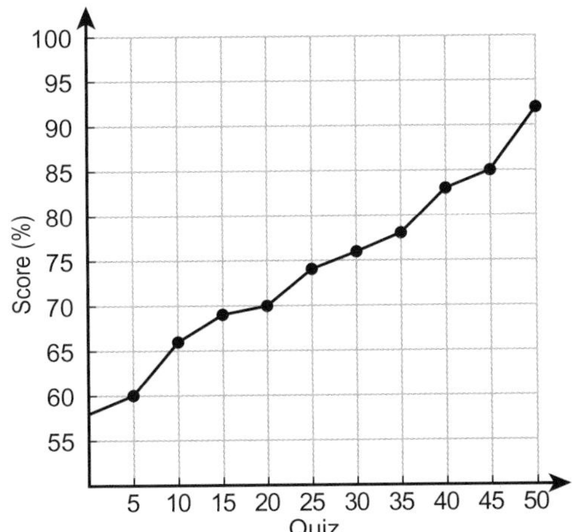

A. Use the graph to estimate Tia's score on the 27th quiz.

B. Assuming that Tia's scores continue to improve at a rate equivalent to her previous average rate of improvement, estimate how many total quizzes she is likely to take before her score reaches 100%.

***29. Challenge** The graph shows the average length of a baby in the first two years of life.

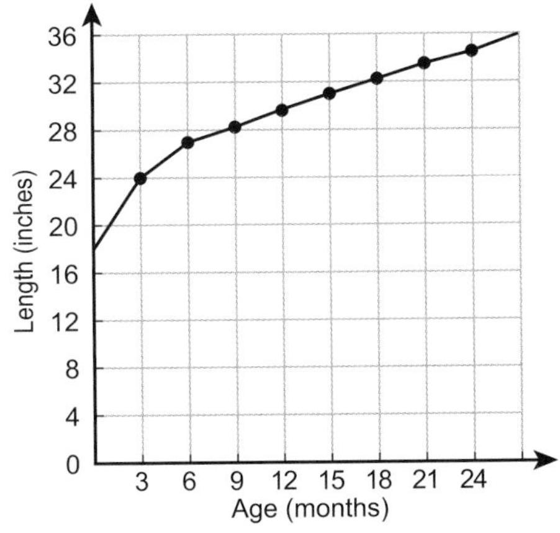

A. Use the graph to estimate the average length of a baby that is 5 months old.

B. According to the graph, how old is the average baby when it is 32 inches long?

***30. Challenge** Emilio earns a percent commission on his sales at the car dealership, plus a fixed bonus on all weekly sales totals of at least \$10,000. The graph shows possible commissions for sales totals of \$5,000 to \$50,000.

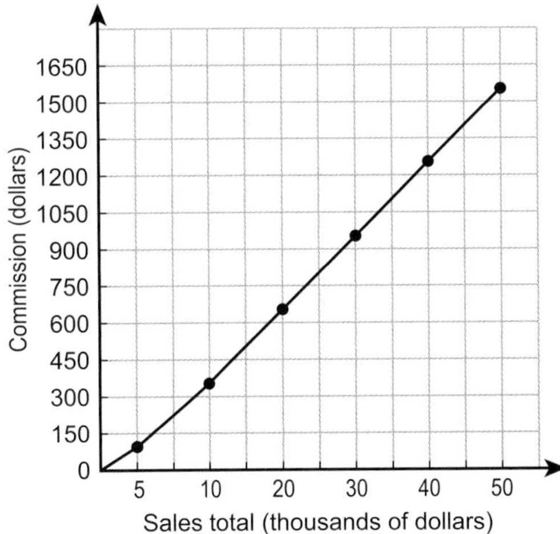

A. Use the graph to estimate Emilio's commission if his sales total is \$35,000.

B. If the fixed bonus is \$50, what percent is Emilio's commission?

Function Equations

You can use equations to represent many functions.

Suppose every y-value of a function is one greater than three times the corresponding x-value. This function can be expressed as the equation $y = 3x + 1$. In this equation, x is the **independent variable** (the input variable), and y is the **dependent variable** (the output variable).

NOTATION

The notation $f(x)$ is read as "f of x" or "f is a function of x."

You can use **function notation** to rewrite a function equation by replacing the dependent variable with $f(x)$. For example, you can write the equation $y = 3x + 1$ as $f(x) = 3x + 1$ or $f: x \to 3x + 1$.

Writing a Function Equation

REMEMBER

$f(x)$ does not mean the product of f and x.

Example 1 Write the equation of the line using function notation.

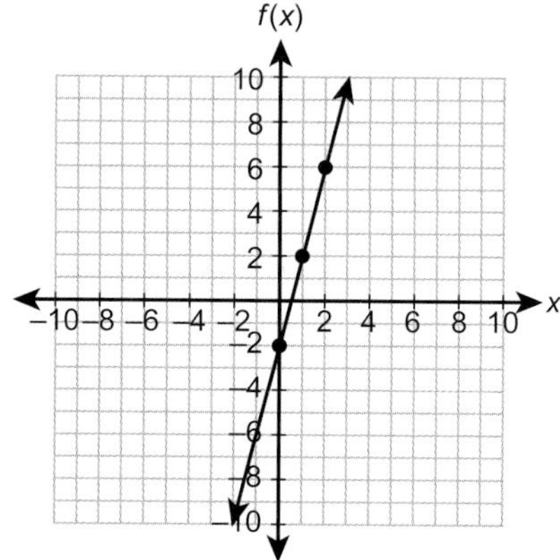

Solution The line has a slope of 4 and a y-intercept of −2. So, write the equation in slope-intercept form: $y = 4x - 2$.

Now, write the equation using function notation.

$y = 4x - 2$

$f(x) = 4x - 2$ Substitute $f(x)$ for y. ■

Evaluating Functions

To evaluate a function, substitute the given value of x into the function, then simplify the expression.

Example 2 Evaluate $f(x) = -5x + 4$ for the given value of x.

A. $f(-2)$

Solution Substitute -2 for x and simplify.

$f(-2) = -5 \cdot (-2) + 4$	Substitute -2 for x.
$= 10 + 4$	Multiply.
$= 14$	Add.

So, $f(-2) = 14$, or when $x = -2$, $f(x) = 14$. ■

B. $f(3)$

Solution Substitute 3 for x and simplify.

$f(3) = -5 \cdot 3 + 4$	Substitute 3 for x.
$= -15 + 4$	Multiply.
$= -11$	Add.

So, $f(3) = -11$, or when $x = 3$, $f(x) = -11$. ■

Example 3 Evaluate $g(x) = 5$ for the given value of x.

A. $g(2)$

Solution For every value of x, $g(x)$ will equal 5. So, $g(2) = 5$. ■

B. $g(0)$

Solution For every value of x, $g(x)$ will equal 5. So, $g(0) = 5$. ■

C. $g(-3)$

Solution For every value of x, $g(x)$ will equal 5. So, $g(-3) = 5$. ■

Example 4 If $h(x) = 3x^2 - x$, find $h\left(\frac{1}{3}\right)$.

Solution Substitute $\frac{1}{3}$ for x, then simplify.

$h\left(\frac{1}{3}\right) = 3 \cdot \left(\frac{1}{3}\right)^2 - \left(\frac{1}{3}\right)$	Substitute $\frac{1}{3}$ for x.
$= 3 \cdot \frac{1}{9} - \frac{1}{3}$	Evaluate the power.
$= \frac{1}{3} - \frac{1}{3}$	Multiply.
$= 0$	Subtract.

So, $h\left(\frac{1}{3}\right) = 0$. ■

REMEMBER

Evaluate powers before multiplying.

RECONNECT TO THE BIG IDEA

Many events in the physical world can be modeled as functions.

Application: Graph of a Real-World Function

Example 3 Ronnie went for a 20-minute jog. The graph below shows her jogging distance as a function of time.

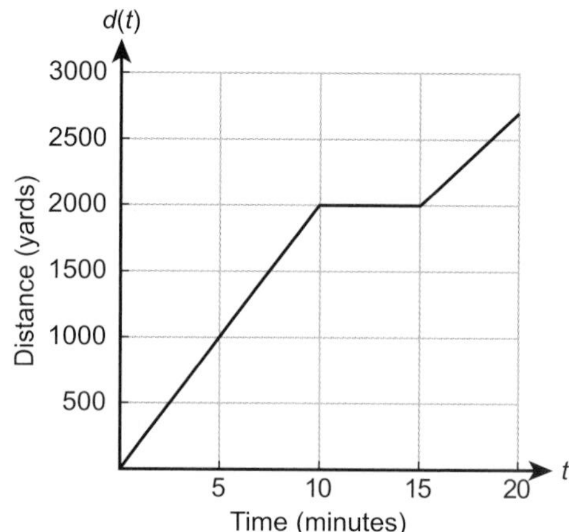

A. About how many yards did she jog after 5 minutes? 12 minutes?

Solution After 5 minutes, she jogged $d(5)$ yards. The function $d(5) = 1000$. After 12 minutes, she jogged $d(12)$ yards. The function $d(12) = 2000$. So, after 5 minutes, she jogged 1000 yards, and after 12 minutes she jogged 2000 yards. ■

B. How would you describe Ronnie's motion in the first 10 minutes, between 10 and 15 minutes, and in the last 5 minutes?

Solution In the first 10 minutes the graph goes up at a constant rate, so Ronnie was moving at a constant speed.

The graph is constant from $t = 10$ minutes to $t = 15$ minutes. This means that Ronnie covered no distance during this time. Ronnie was not moving during this time.

In the last 5 minutes, she went back to jogging at the same speed she moved in the first 10 minutes. ■

Problem Set

Use function notation to write the equation of the line.

1.

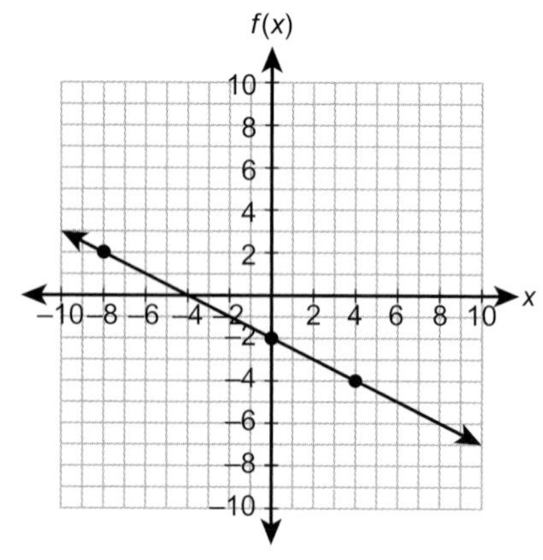

2.

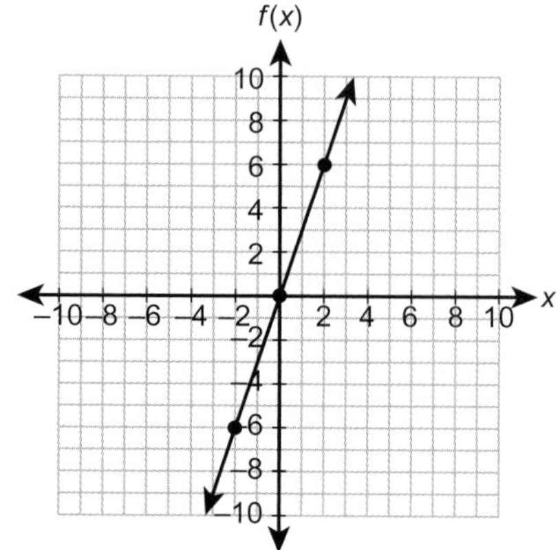

3.

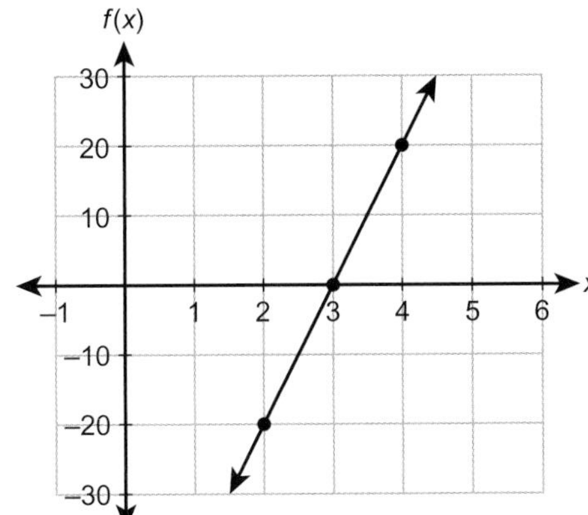

4.

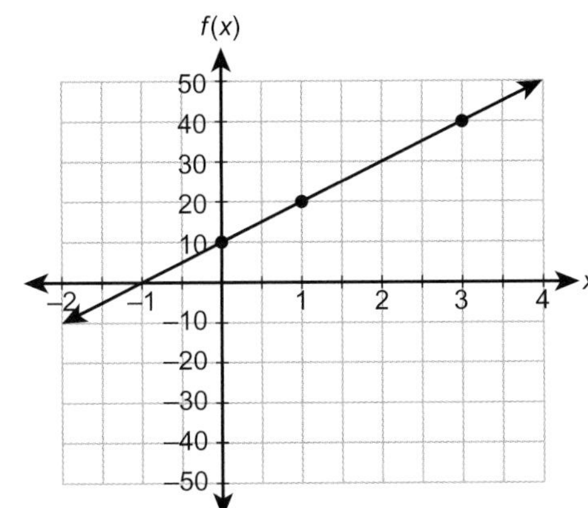

5.

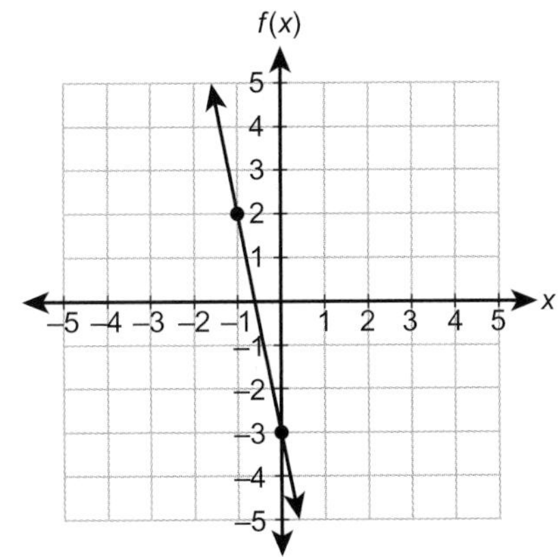

6.

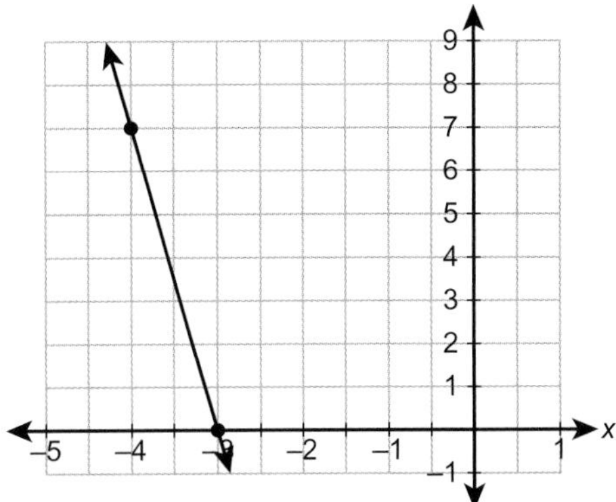

7.

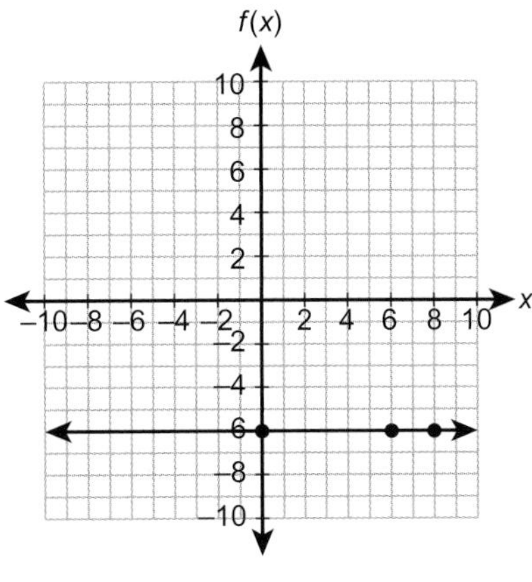

8.

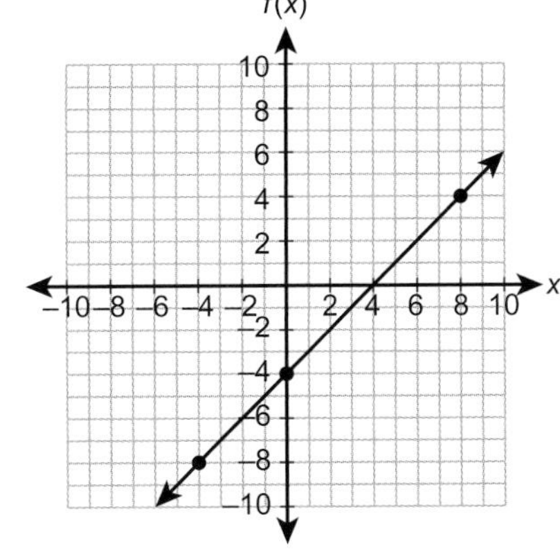

Evaluate each function for the given values.

9. $f(x) = 3x + 4$

A. $f(1)$

B. $f(-5)$

10. $T(x) = -x - 2$

A. $T(-4)$

B. $T(4)$

11. $g(x) = \frac{1}{4}x + 1$

A. $g(-16)$

B. $g(-4)$

12. $f(a) = 17 - a$

A. $f(13)$

B. $f(-2)$

13. $p(x) = 6x - 15$

A. $p(2)$

B. $p(0)$

14. $C(m) = 20 + 5m$

A. $C(6)$

B. $C(12)$

15. $v(x) = -5x + 25$

A. $v(-10)$

B. $v(15)$

16. $t(n) = 0.075n$

A. $t(20)$

B. $t(100)$

17. $f(g) = 2g - 1$

A. $f(-3)$

B. $f(2)$

18. $w(x) = 14 - 6x$

A. $w(-2)$

B. $w(-3)$

19. $h(x) = x + 11$

A. $h(-9)$

B. $h(-5)$

20. $k(x) = 1.5x - 2.5$

A. $k(-8)$

B. $k(6)$

21. $z(n) = 13n - 29$

A. $z(7)$

B. $z(5)$

22. $f(x) = 2x + 7$

A. $f(-1)$

B. $f(4)$

23. $l(x) = \frac{4}{3}x - \frac{5}{3}$

A. $l(1)$

B. $l(2)$

24. $u(n) = 5n - 18$

A. $u(3)$

B. $u(6)$

Solve. Use function notation when applicable.

25. When a spring is extended from its natural state, the spring exerts a force to return back to its natural state. The graph below shows Hooke's Law for a specific spring, or how this force (in Newtons, N) is dependent on the extension (in cm) of the spring.

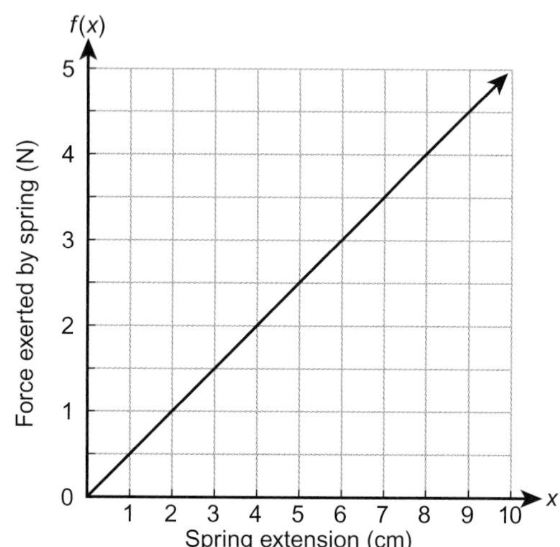

A. What force does the spring exert when it is extended 6 cm from its natural state?

B. How much more force does the spring exert when extended 9 cm than when extended 7 cm?

26. The graph below shows Leyla's driving speed over a 5-minute period.

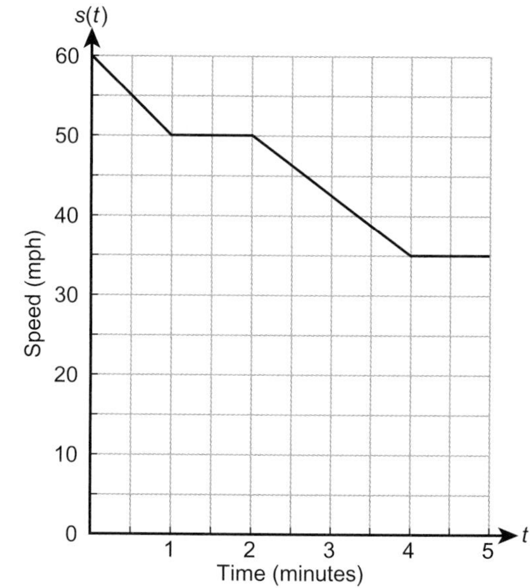

A. What was her speed after 2 minutes of driving? 3 minutes?

B. During what time period(s) was she decelerating?

27. The graph below shows a pond's depth during a 40-minute rainstorm.

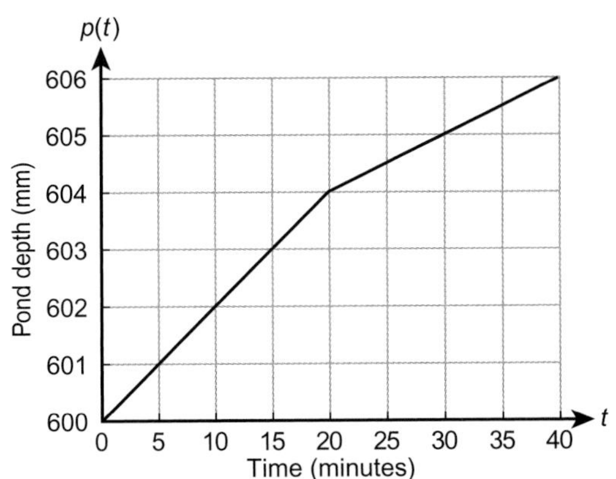

A. By how much did the pond's depth increase during the first 30 minutes of the storm?

B. During what time period did it rain harder?

*28. **Challenge** Ahmed signed a contract for cable service. The graph below shows the total cost that he paid for cable after each month of service.

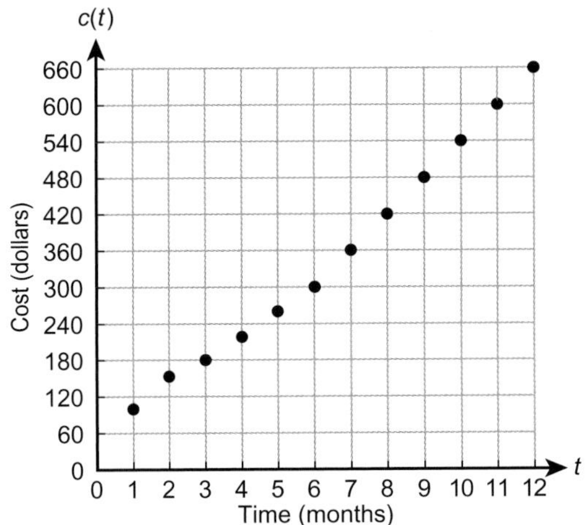

A. How much did he pay for cable after 3 months? 10 months?

B. Explain what happened at 6 months.

*29. **Challenge** On Tax-Free Day, shoppers can purchase certain taxable items without paying tax. The graph below shows the total discount at a given tax rate seen as a function of the cost of the item(s) purchased.

A. If Sam purchased items that cost \$150, what is his approximate discount?

B. Describe how to determine the tax rate.

C. Is there another way to determine the rate?

*30. **Challenge** During a men's relay race, three runners compete as a team and pass off a baton to one another. The graph below shows the speed of the three runners.

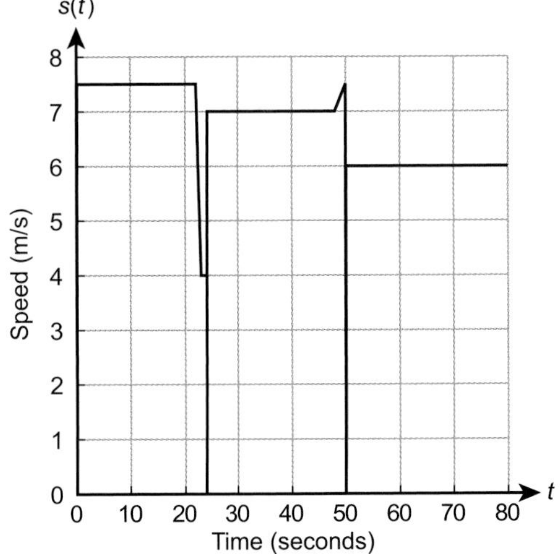

A. What was the runner's approximate speed at 20 seconds? 40 seconds?

B. Which runner might have experienced an injury toward the end of his segment? Explain.

C. If distance can be represented by speed multiplied by time, explain how you could approximate the total distance of the race using geometry and the graph.

Absolute Value Functions

An **absolute value function** is a function whose rule includes an absolute value expression.

Evaluating Absolute Value Functions

To evaluate an absolute value function, substitute the specified value of x into the function, then simplify.

Example 1 Evaluate $f(x) = |x - 4.5|$ for the specified x value.

A. $f(1.5)$

Solution $f(1.5) = |1.5 - 4.5| = |-3| = 3$ ■

B. $f(0)$

Solution $f(0) = |0 - 4.5| = |-4.5| = 4.5$ ■

Example 2 Evaluate $g(x) = -|x| + \frac{1}{2}$ for the specified x value.

A. $g\left(-\frac{3}{2}\right)$

Solution $g\left(-\frac{3}{2}\right) = -\left|-\frac{3}{2}\right| + \frac{1}{2} = -\frac{3}{2} + \frac{1}{2} = -1$ ■

B. $g\left(\frac{1}{2}\right)$

Solution $g\left(\frac{1}{2}\right) = -\left|\frac{1}{2}\right| + \frac{1}{2} = -\frac{1}{2} + \frac{1}{2} = 0$ ■

Graphs of Absolute Value Functions

The most basic absolute value function is $f(x) = |x|$. The graph of $f(x) = |x|$ has two parts: $f(x) = x$, if $x \geq 0$, and $f(x) = -x$, if $x < 0$. Since the equation of this absolute value function can be separated into two linear parts, its graph is V-shaped.

> **REMEMBER**
> The absolute value of a number x is equal to x if x is positive, 0 if x is equal to 0, and $-x$ if x is negative.

x	$f(x)$
−3	3
−2	2
−1	1
0	0
1	1
2	2
3	3

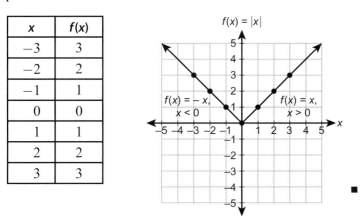

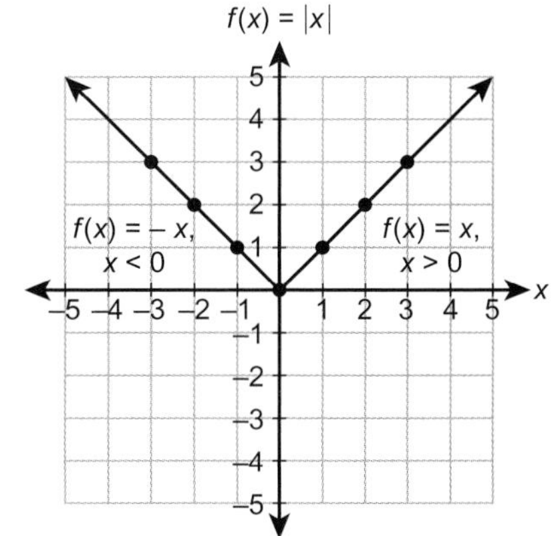

■

Example 3

A. Graph $f(x) = -|2x| + 3$.

Solution Make a table of ordered pairs. Then, plot and connect the points.

> **TIP**
> While it may take some guess and check, always locate the "point" of the V and find points on either side of it.

x	$f(x)$
−3	−3
−2	−1
−1	1
0	3
1	1
2	−1
3	−3

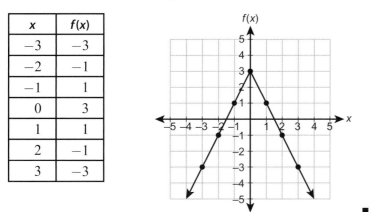

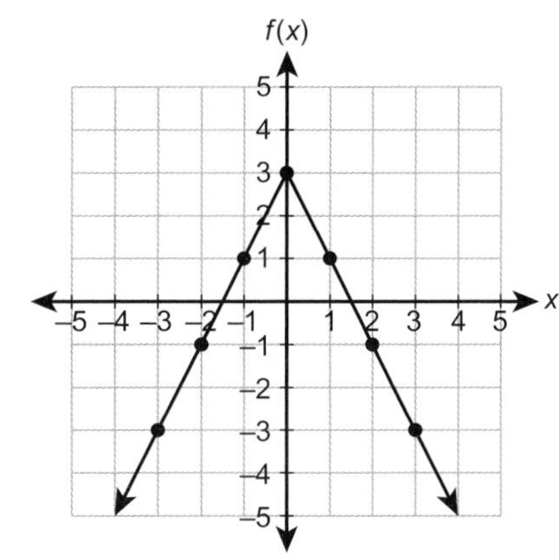

■

B. Identify the function graphed.

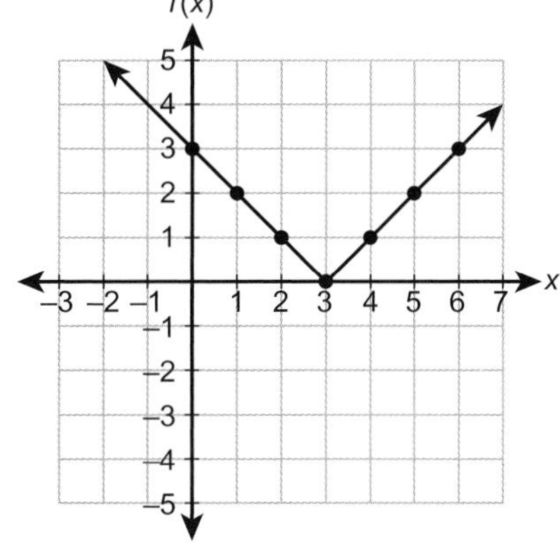

(continued)

> **THINK ABOUT IT**
> The expression $|x - 3|$ is equivalent to $|3 - x|$.

Solution Put the ordered pairs into a table. Because the graph is V-shaped, determine a rule with an absolute value expression.

x	0	1	2	3	4	5	6
$f(x)$	3	2	1	0	1	2	3

A function that works for every ordered pair is $f(x) = |x - 3|$. ■

Application: A Counting Contest

Example 4 As part of a promotion at a health club, contestants guess the number of beans in a jar. For every bean they are away from the correct number (203 beans), they must complete 2 times that many jumping jacks.

A. A contestant guesses that there are x beans in the jar. Write an absolute value function to determine the number of jumping jacks the contestant will have to do.

B. Belen guesses that there are 225 beans in the jar. Use the function to determine the number of jumping jacks she will have to do.

Solution

A. Since it does not matter if the guess is above or below the actual amount, the number of beans away from the actual amount is $|203 - x|$. The number of jumping jacks is twice that amount, so multiply the absolute value expression by 2, and use function notation: $f(x) = 2|203 - x|$, where x is the contestant's guess.

B. Evaluate $f(225)$.

$f(225) = 2 \cdot |203 - 225| = 2 \cdot |-22| = 2 \cdot 22 = 44$

Belen will have to do 44 jumping jacks. ■

Problem Set

For Problems 1–12: Evaluate each function for the given values.

1. $f(x) = |x + 1|$
   A. $f(-4)$
   B. $f(-1)$

2. $h(x) = -|2 - x|$
   A. $h(-3)$
   B. $h(4)$

3. $v(a) = 2a - |a|$
   A. $v(7)$
   B. $v(-11)$

4. $z(t) = |17 - 3t|$
   A. $z(-4)$
   B. $z(-6)$

5. $m(d) = -\left|d - \frac{1}{4}\right|$
   A. $m\left(-\frac{9}{4}\right)$
   B. $m\left(-\frac{3}{4}\right)$

6. $p(n) = 6 - 2|1 + n|$
   A. $p(-5)$
   B. $p(2)$

7. $g(c) = |-8 + c|$
   A. $g(6)$
   B. $g(10)$

8. $w(j) = |j - 24| + 19$
   A. $w(34)$
   B. $w(16)$

9. $x(y) = -3\left|\frac{y + 1}{2}\right|$
   A. $x(-5)$
   B. $x(5)$

10. $u(b) = |b + 13| - 13$

A. $u(-10)$

B. $u(-30)$

11. $q(s) = |s - 1| \cdot |1 - s|$

A. $q(-6)$

B. $q(14)$

12. $r(a) = |-6a|$

A. $r(2)$

B. $r(-7)$

Complete the table and then graph the function.

13. $f(x) = -2|3 + x|$

x	$f(x)$
−6	
−5	
−4	
−3	
−2	
−1	
0	

14. $c(n) = |0.5n - 1.5|$

n	$c(n)$
0	
1	
2	
3	
4	
5	
6	

15. $d(h) = \dfrac{|h + 200|}{3}$

h	$d(h)$
−800	
−500	
−200	
100	
400	
700	
1000	

16. $v(t) = -3|4 - t| + 2$

t	$v(t)$
0	
1	
2	
3	
4	
5	
6	

17. $g(w) = \dfrac{-|3 + 2w|}{2} + 1$

w	$g(w)$
−4	
−3	
−2	
−1	
0	
1	
2	

For Problems 18–21: Create a table of values for the points graphed and write the equation of the function.

18.

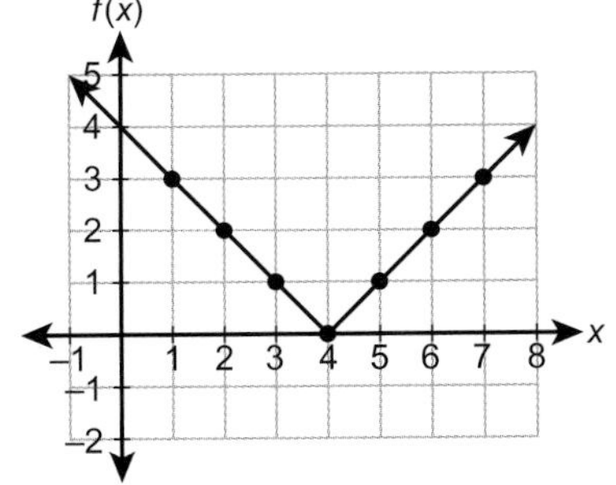

19.

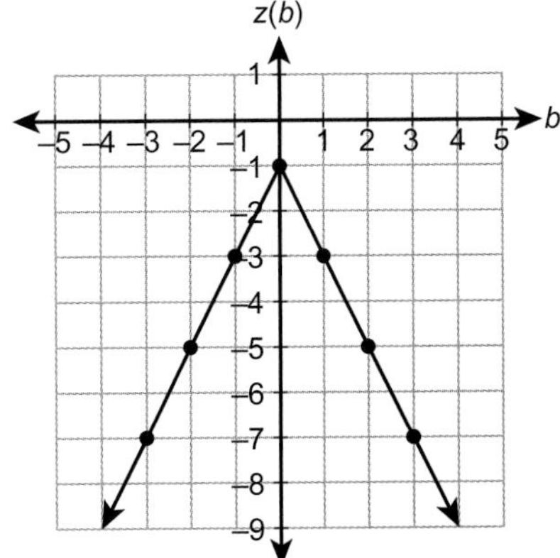

20.

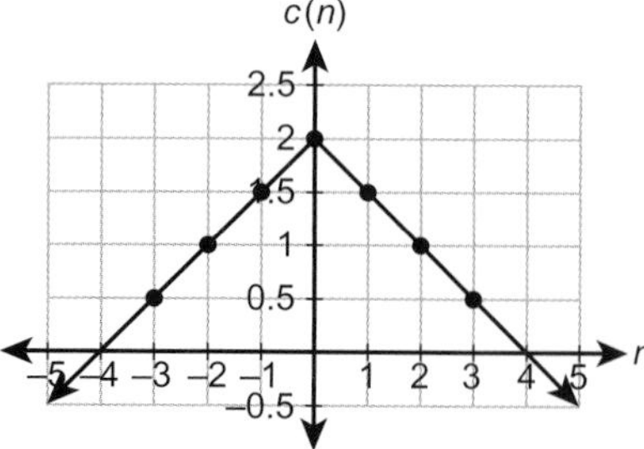

21.

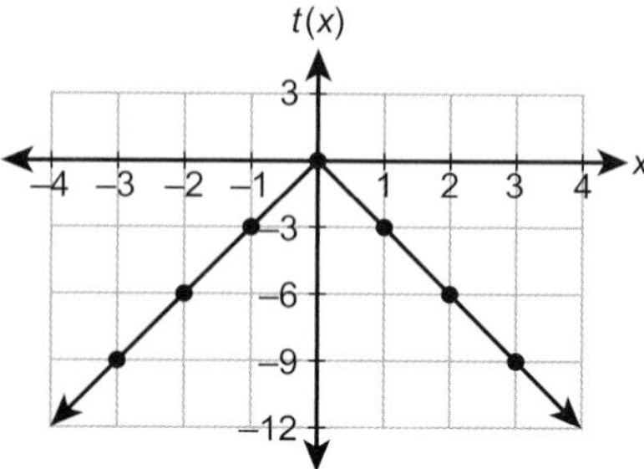

22.

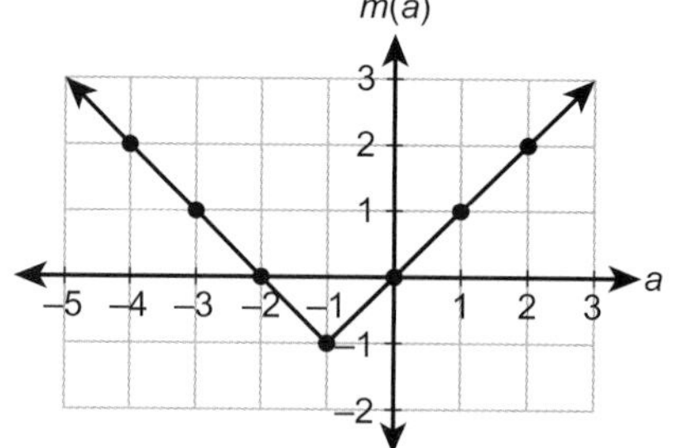

Use absolute value functions to solve.

23. A scale in the grocery store is tested for accuracy. For every ounce that the actual weight is away from 2 pounds, the scale reads an additional 0.5 ounces away.

- **A.** A customer places x actual pounds of strawberries on the scale. Write an absolute value function to determine how far off the reading on the scale is.
- **B.** Matthias places 1 actual pound of strawberries on the scale. Use the function to determine how far off the reading of the scale is.

24. On the first day of practice, a coach announces that the players must guess the day of her birthday using numbers 1–31. For each day a player's guess is away from the coach's actual birthday, that player must run one-fourth of a mile on the track. The coach's birthday is on the 17th of the month.

- **A.** Write an absolute value function to determine the number of miles a player with a guess that is d must run.
- **B.** Jaheim guesses the 4th. Use the function to determine how far Jaheim must run on the track.

25. A store owner balances the register at the end of the day and expects to have a balance of $8000.

- **A.** Write an absolute value function to determine the percent absolute deviation that the actual balance b is from the expected balance.
- **B.** The store owner calculates an actual balance of $8012. Use the function to determine the percent absolute deviation from the expected balance.

26. In a factory, rice is sorted into bags labeled with various weights. One of the factory scales is miscalibrated and miscalculates the weight required for all bags that deviate from 3 pounds. For every pound away from 3 pounds that is required for the bag, the machine adds 0.1 additional pound of rice to the bag.

- **A.** Write an absolute value function to determine the number of pounds the machine places into a bag with a labeled weight of w.
- **B.** Use the function to determine how much a bag with a labeled weight of 5 pounds actually contains.

27. Michael paints house interiors, and he estimates that 15 gallons of paint is required for the average house that he paints. He determines that too little paint will result in insufficient coverage, and too much paint is wasting his product.

A. Write an absolute value function to determine the percent absolute deviation from his estimate if he actually uses g gallons.

B. Use the function to determine the percent absolute deviation from Michael's estimate for a house on which he uses 13.5 gallons of paint.

28. A charity holds a contest for participants to guess the number of website hits last month. For every hit that they are away from the correct number (3000 hits), they agree to donate $0.05.

A. Write an absolute value function to determine the donation required for a guess of h.

B. Use the function to determine the required donation for the worst guess, which is 7500 hits.

***29.** **Challenge** Gabe wants to buy a used car and test drives six cars worth $10,300, $8500, $11,200, $9800, $6500, and $15,800.

A. Calculate the mean price of the cars that he test drove.

B. Write an absolute value function to determine the absolute deviation from the mean if he buys a car worth v.

C. He decides to narrow down his options to cars with an absolute deviation of $700 from the mean. What is his lower limit? Upper limit? How many cars are options?

***30.** **Challenge** A lab measures 10 similar samples. Their masses are 1.51 g, 1.60 g, 1.54 g, 1.49 g, 1.57 g, 1.51 g, 1.54 g, 1.56 g, 1.55 g, and 1.55 g.

A. Calculate the mean mass of the samples.

B. Write an absolute value function to determine the absolute deviation for a sample of mass m.

C. Find the average absolute deviation of the samples from the mean.

Direct Linear Variation

A *direct variation* occurs when the output of a function is a nonzero constant multiple of the input.

DEFINITION

A relationship between x and $f(x)$ is a **direct linear variation** if you can write the function describing the relationship in a form of the **general equation,** $f(x) = kx$, where k is the nonzero **constant of variation.**

Identifying Direct Variation and the Constant of Variation

Since $f(x) = kx$, $k = \frac{f(x)}{x}$. If $\frac{f(x)}{x}$ is the same value for every ordered pair in a relationship (except $x = 0$), the relationship is a direct linear variation.

Example 1 Determine if the relationship shows a direct linear variation. If so, state the constant of variation.

A.

x	2	4	6	8	10
$f(x)$	5	10	15	20	25

Solution Divide each value of $f(x)$ by its corresponding x-value.

$\frac{5}{2} = 2.5, \frac{10}{4} = 2.5, \frac{15}{6} = 2.5, \frac{20}{8} = 2.5, \frac{25}{10} = 2.5$

The relationship shows a direct linear variation with a constant of variation of 2.5. ■

B. $y - 4 = -2x$

Solution Solve for y to see if the specific equation fits the form of the general equation $f(x) = kx$.

$y - 4 = -2x$

$y = -2x + 4$ Add 4 to each side.

The equation does not fit the form of the general equation because it has a constant term 4. The relationship does not show a direct linear variation. ■

REMEMBER

Remember, $f(x) = y$, so the general equation can also be written as $y = kx$.

Writing and Using Direct Linear Variation Equations

You can write a direct linear variation equation, given certain information about the function. You can then evaluate the function for any given value of x.

Example 2 If $h(x)$ varies directly with x and $h(x) = -12$ when $x = 18$, find the value of $h(x)$ when $x = 15$.

Solution

Step 1 Find k.

$h(x) = kx$	General form of equation
$k = \frac{h(x)}{x}$	Solve the general equation for k.
$k = \frac{-12}{18}$	Substitute -12 for $h(x)$ and 18 for x.
$k = -\frac{2}{3}$	Simplify.

Step 2 Substitute the value of k found in Step 1 into the general equation.

$h(x) = kx$	General form of equation
$h(x) = -\frac{2}{3}x$	Substitute $-\frac{2}{3}$ for k to obtain the specific equation.

Step 3 Use the specific equation $h(x) = -\frac{2}{3}x$ to find $h(15)$.

$h(x) = -\frac{2}{3}x$	Specific equation
$h(15) = -\frac{2}{3} \cdot 15$	Substitute 15 for x.
$= -10$	Simplify.

So, $h(15) = -10$. ■

TIP

The general direct linear variation equation is $f(x) = kx$.

Once you find the constant of variation and substitute that value for k in the general equation, you get the specific equation for a particular problem.

Graphing Direct Linear Variation

Example 3 Suppose y varies directly with x and $y = -2$ when $x = 6$. Graph the direct linear variation equation.

Solution

Step 1 Find k.

$$k = \frac{y}{x} = \frac{-2}{6} = -\frac{1}{3}$$

Step 2 Substitute the value of k found in Step 1 into the general equation $y = kx$.

The specific equation is $y = -\frac{1}{3}x$.

THINK ABOUT IT

The slope of the graph of a direct linear variation is equal to k, and the y-intercept is zero.

(continued)

Step 3 Graph the equation.

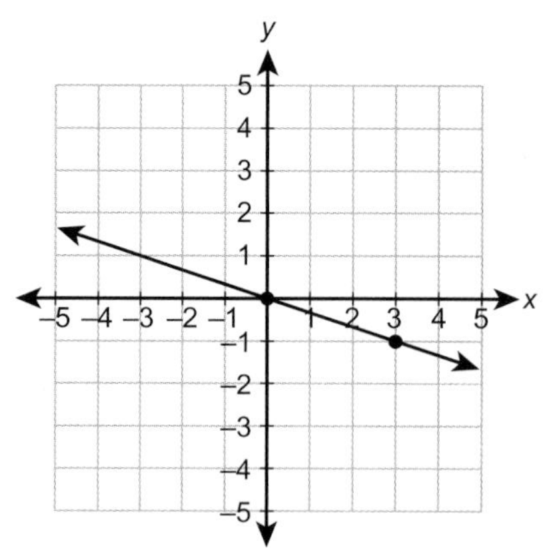

■

Application: Cost

Example 4 The cost of grapes varies directly with the weight. If 3.5 pounds of grapes cost \$4.55, write the direct linear variation equation. Then determine the number of pounds of grapes that can be purchased for \$10.14, before tax.

Solution

Step 1 Find the equation. Let w represent the weight and $c(w)$ represent the cost.

The cost varies directly with the number of pounds, so $c(3.5) = 4.55$. Find k.

$$k = \frac{c(w)}{w} = \frac{4.55}{3.5} = 1.3$$

The specific direct linear variation equation is $c(w) = 1.3w$.

Step 2 Substitute 10.14 for $c(w)$ and solve for w.

$c(w) = 1.3w$

$10.14 = 1.3w$ Substitute 10.14 for $c(w)$.

$7.8 = w$ Divide each side by 1.3.

So, 7.8 pounds of grapes can be purchased for \$10.14, before tax. ■

Problem Set

Determine if the relationship shows a direct linear variation. If so, state the constant of variation.

1.

x	3	6	9	12	15
$f(x)$	6	12	18	24	30

2.

x	1	3	5	7	9
$f(x)$	4	10	16	22	28

3. $f(x) = 10x$

4. $f(x) = x - 12$

5. $y = \frac{9}{x}$

6. $f(x) = \frac{1}{7}x$

7.

x	2	4	6	8	10
y	8	16	24	32	40

8.

x	1	2	3	4	5
y	3	5	7	9	11

Write a direct linear variation equation and evaluate the function for the given value.

9. If $f(x)$ varies directly with x and $f(x) = 6$ when $x = 9$, find the value of x when $f(x) = 7$.

10. If $f(x)$ varies directly with x and $f(x) = 20$ when $x = -4$, find the value of $f(x)$ when $x = 2$.

11. If $g(t)$ varies directly with t and $g(t) = 5$ when $t = 20$, find the value of t when $g(t) = 9$.

12. If $f(x)$ varies directly with x and $f(x) = 49$ when $x = 7$, find the value of $f(x)$ when $x = 12$.

13. If $h(d)$ varies directly with d and $h(d) = 30$ when $d = -10$, find the value of d when $h(d) = 4$.

14. If $g(a)$ varies directly with a and $g(a) = 3$ when $a = 9$, find the value of $g(a)$ when $a = 6$.

15. If $f(x)$ varies directly with x and $f(x) = 1$ when $x = -4$, find the value of $f(x)$ when $x = 10$.

16. If $h(z)$ varies directly with z and $h(z) = 6$ when $z = -20$, find the value of z when $h(z) = 11$.

Write the direct linear variation equation and graph.

17. y varies directly with x and $y = 4$ when $x = 12$

18. y varies directly with x and $y = 30$ when $x = 3$

19. b varies directly with a and $b = -5$ when $a = 2$

20. y varies directly with x and $y = 8$ when $x = -16$

21. y varies directly with x and $y = 2$ when $x = -8$

22. n varies directly with m and $n = 6$ when $m = 3$

Write the direct linear variation equation and solve.

23. The total cost of gas varies directly with the price paid per gallon. If 5 gallons of gas cost \$13.35, determine the number of gallons of gas purchased if the total cost is \$34.71.

24. The acceleration of an object varies directly with the force acting on it. If a force of 70 Newtons causes an acceleration of 6.5 m/s^2, what force will cause an acceleration of 8 m/s^2?

25. The time Oni spends running varies directly with the miles he runs. If he runs 4 miles in 1 hour at a steady pace, determine how long it will take Oni to run 5.7 miles.

26. The circumference of a circle varies directly with its radius. If the circumference of a circle with a radius of 1.5 inches is 9.42 inches, what is the circumference of a circle with a radius of 9 inches?

27. The stretch of a loaded spring varies directly with the load it supports. If a load of 7 kg stretches a certain spring 2.5 cm, what load would stretch the spring 5 cm?

28. The area of a circle varies directly with the square of the circle's radius. If the area of a circle with a radius of 2.4 inches is 18.10 in^2, what is the area of a circle with a radius of 7 inches?

*29. **Challenge** The height reached by a ball thrown vertically upward varies directly with the square of the speed with which the ball is thrown. If a ball reaches a height of 20 m when it is thrown at 18 m/s, what initial speed will cause it to reach a height of 30 m?

*30. **Challenge** The kinetic energy of a moving object varies directly with the square of its speed. How much would the speed of a car traveling at 30 mph need to increase to triple the kinetic energy?

Quadratic Variation

When the output of a function is a constant multiple of the square of the input, mathematicians call this quadratic variation.

DEFINITION

A relationship between x and y is a **quadratic variation** if you can write the function describing the relationship in a form of the general equation, $f(x) = kx^2$, where k is a nonzero constant.

Identifying Quadratic Variation and the Constant of Variation

Since $f(x) = kx^2$, $k = \frac{f(x)}{x^2}$. If $\frac{f(x)}{x^2}$ is the same value for every ordered pair in a relationship (except $x = 0$), the relationship is a quadratic variation.

REMEMBER

Remember, $f(x) = y$, so $k = \frac{f(x)}{x^2}$ can also be written as $k = \frac{y}{x^2}$, and the general equation can be written as $y = kx^2$.

Example 1 Determine if the relationship shows a quadratic variation. If so, state the constant of variation.

A.

x	1	2	3	4	5
y	3	16	45	96	175

Solution Divide each value of y by the square of its corresponding x-value.

$\frac{3}{1^2} = 3, \frac{16}{2^2} = 4, \frac{45}{3^2} = 5, \frac{96}{4^2} = 6, \frac{175}{5^2} = 7$

These ratios are not constant. This relationship does not show a quadratic variation. ■

B.

x	1	2	3	4	5
$f(x)$	4	16	36	64	100

Solution Divide each value of $f(x)$ by the square of its corresponding x-value.

$\frac{4}{1^2} = 4, \frac{16}{2^2} = 4, \frac{36}{3^2} = 4, \frac{64}{4^2} = 4, \frac{100}{5^2} = 4$

These ratios are constant. So, this relationship does show a quadratic variation. ■

C. $4y = 3x^2$

Solution Solve for y to see if the function fits the form of the general equation.

$4y = 3x^2$

$y = \frac{3}{4}x^2$ Divide each side by 4.

The relationship shows a quadratic variation with $k = \frac{3}{4}$. ■

Writing and Using Quadratic Variation Equations

Example 2 If $f(x)$ varies directly with x^2, and $f(x) = 18$ when $x = 6$, find the value of $f(8)$.

Solution

Step 1 Find k.

$f(x) = kx^2$ General form of equation

$k = \frac{f(x)}{x^2}$ Solve the general equation for k.

$k = \frac{18}{6^2}$ Substitute 18 for $f(x)$ and 6 for x.

$k = \frac{1}{2}$ Simplify.

Step 2 Substitute the value of k found in Step 1 into the general equation.

$f(x) = kx^2$ General form of equation

$f(x) = \frac{1}{2}x^2$ Substitute $\frac{1}{2}$ for k to obtain the specific equation.

Step 3 Use the specific equation $f(x) = \frac{1}{2}x^2$ to find $f(8)$.

$f(x) = \frac{1}{2}x^2$ Specific equation

$f(8) = \frac{1}{2} \cdot 8^2$ Substitute 8 for x.

$= \frac{1}{2} \cdot 64$ Simplify.

$= 32$ Simplify.

So, $f(8) = 32$, or when $x = 8$, $f(x) = 32$. ■

Graphing Quadratic Variation

The graph of a quadratic variation function is a U-shaped curve called a parabola that passes through the origin. The width and direction of the curve depend on the value of the constant of variation.

Example 3 Suppose y varies directly with x^2 and $y = 8$ when $x = 2$. Graph the quadratic variation equation.

Solution

Step 1 Find k.

$$k = \frac{y}{x^2} = \frac{8}{4} = 2$$

Step 2 Substitute the value of k found in Step 1 into the general equation $y = kx^2$.

The equation is $y = 2x^2$.

TIP

Use positive and negative values of *x*.

Step 3 Make a table of ordered pairs and connect the points with a smooth curve.

x	−3	−2	−1	0	1	2	3
y	18	8	2	0	2	8	18

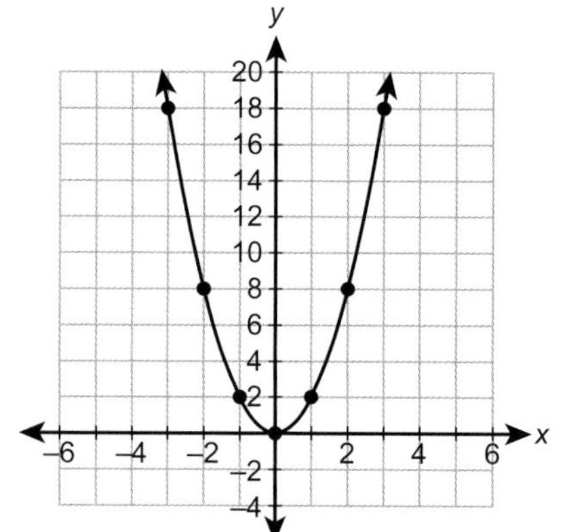

■

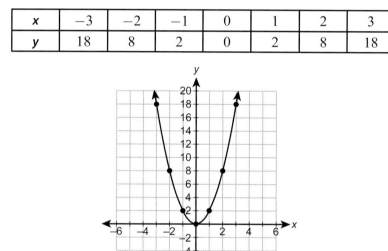

Application: Physics

The amount of kinetic energy (E) that an object has varies directly with the square of its velocity v. It is given by the quadratic variation equation $E = 0.5mv^2$, where m is the mass of the object.

Example 4 Write the specific equation for the kinetic energy E (measured in Joules) of an 1100-kg car. Use this equation to compare the kinetic energy of an 1100-kg car moving at a velocity of 10 meters per second to the kinetic energy of the same car moving at 3 times the velocity.

Solution First, use the general equation $E = 0.5mv^2$ to calculate the specific equation.

$E = 0.5mv^2$ Write the general equation for kinetic energy.

$= 0.5 \cdot 1100 \cdot v^2$ Substitute 1100 for m.

$= 550v^2$ Multiply.

Now use the specific equation to find the kinetic energy of the car moving at the two speeds.

Moving at 10 m/s:

$E = 550v^2$ Specific equation

$= 550 \cdot 10^2$ Substitute 10 for v.

$= 550 \cdot 100$ Evaluate the power.

$= 55{,}000$ Multiply.

Moving at 30 m/s:

$E = 550v^2$ Specific equation

$= 550 \cdot 30^2$ Substitute 30 for v.

$= 550 \cdot 900$ Evaluate the power.

$= 495{,}000$ Multiply.

The kinetic energy of a 1100-kg car is 55,000 Joules moving at a velocity of 10 meters per second and 495,000 Joules moving at a velocity of 30 meters per second. You can compare by dividing the kinetic energies: $\frac{495{,}000}{55{,}000} = 9$.

When the speed triples, the kinetic energy increases by a factor of 9. ■

Problem Set

Determine if the relationship shows a quadratic variation. If so, state the constant of variation.

1.

x	2	4	6	8	10
f(x)	32	128	288	512	800

2. $5y^2 = 2x^2$

3. $10y = 5x^2$

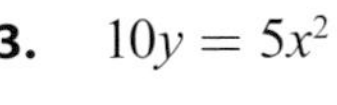

4.

x	1	2	3	4	5
f(x)	4	10	16	22	28

5. $f(x) = \frac{1}{8}x^2$

6. $6y = 12x^2$

7.

x	1	3	5	7	9
f(x)	2	18	50	98	162

8.

x	2	4	6	8	10
f(x)	5	10	15	20	25

Write a quadratic variation equation and evaluate the function for the given value.

9. If $g(x)$ varies directly with x^2 and $g(x) = 18$ when $x = 3$, find the value of $g(x)$ when $x = 1$.

10. If $f(x)$ varies directly with x^2 and $f(x) = 10$ when $x = -4$, find the value of $f(x)$ when $x = 3$.

11. If $f(x)$ varies directly with x^2 and $f(x) = 4$ when $x = 2$, find the value of $f(x)$ when $x = 9$.

12. If $g(c)$ varies directly with c^2 and $g(c) = 2$ when $c = 7$, find the value of $g(c)$ when $c = 12$.

13. If $f(x)$ varies directly with x^2 and $f(x) = 30$ when $x = -10$, find the value of $f(x)$ when $x = 2$.

14. If $f(x)$ varies directly with x^2 and $f(x) = 3$ when $x = 9$, find the value of $f(x)$ when $x = -2$.

15. If $h(w)$ varies directly with w^2 and $h(w) = 1$ when $w = -2$, find the value of $h(w)$ when $w = 4$.

16. If $f(x)$ varies directly with x^2 and $f(x) = 8$ when $x = 4$, find the value of $f(x)$ when $x = 10$.

Write the quadratic variation equation and graph.

17. y varies directly with x^2 and $y = 10$ when $x = 2$

18. y varies directly with x^2 and $y = 15$ when $x = 3$

19. k varies directly with g^2 and $k = 20$ when $g = 2$

20. y varies directly with x^2 and $y = 4$ when $x = 2$

21. y varies directly with x^2 and $y = 4$ when $x = -8$

22. n varies directly with m^2 and $n = 6$ when $m = 1$

Write the quadratic variation equation and solve.

23. The area of a square varies directly with the square's side length. If the area of a square with a side length of 5.5 inches is 30.25 in^2, what is the area of a square with a side length of 3 inches?

24. The kinetic energy of a moving object varies directly with the square of its speed. How much would a car traveling at 40 mph need to increase its speed to double its kinetic energy?

25. The height reached by a ball thrown vertically upward varies directly with the square of the speed with which the ball is thrown. If a ball reaches a height of 50 m when it is thrown at 12 m/s, what initial speed will allow it to travel 60 m high?

26. The length of a pendulum varies directly with the period of the pendulum. If a pendulum 2 m long has a period of 4 seconds, what is the length of a pendulum with a period of 10 seconds?

27. The wind force on a surface perpendicular to the wind direction varies directly with the square of the wind speed. If the force on a skydiver is 90 Newtons when the wind is blowing at 30 km/h, what is the force on the skydiver when the wind speed is 60 km/h?

28. The area of a circle varies directly with the square of the circle's radius. If the area of a circle with a radius of 6 inches is 113.10 in^2, what is the area of a circle with a radius of 9 inches?

*29. **Challenge** The volume of a cylinder varies directly with the product of the height and square of the radius. If the volume of a cylinder is 113.10 cubic inches when the height is 9 inches and the radius is 2 inches, what is the radius of a cylinder with a volume of 226.19 cubic inches and a height of 3 inches?

*30. **Challenge** The surface area of a sphere varies directly with the square of the radius. If the surface area of a sphere is 314.16 square inches when the radius is 5 inches, what is the surface area of a sphere with a radius of 10 inches? Examine the coefficient of the radius in the quadratic variation equation. What multiplied by 3.14 will give this value?

Inverse Variation

When the output of a function is equal to a constant multiplied by the reciprocal of the input, mathematicians call this inverse variation.

DEFINITION

A relationship between x and $f(x)$ is an **inverse variation** if you can write the function describing the relationship in a form of the general equation, $f(x) = \frac{k}{x}$, where k is constant.

Identifying Inverse Variation and the Constant of Variation

Since $y = \frac{k}{x}$, $k = xy$. If xy is the same value for every ordered pair in a relationship, the relationship is an inverse variation.

Example 1 Determine if the relationship shows an inverse variation. If so, state the constant of variation.

A.

x	1	2	4	5	10
y	20	10	5	4	2

Solution Multiply the corresponding x- and y-values.

$1 \cdot 20 = 20, 2 \cdot 10 = 20, 4 \cdot 5 = 20, 5 \cdot 4 = 20, 10 \cdot 2 = 20$

The relationship shows an inverse variation with $k = 20$. ■

B.

x	1	2	3	4	5
y	0.1	0.2	0.3	0.4	0.5

Solution Multiply the corresponding x- and y-values.

$1 \cdot 0.1 = 0.1, 2 \cdot 0.2 = 0.4, 3 \cdot 0.3 = 0.9, 4 \cdot 0.4 = 1.6, 5 \cdot 0.5 = 2.5$

Since xy is not the same value for every pair, the relationship does not show an inverse variation. ■

(continued)

C. $x = 3y$

Solution Dividing by 3 gives the equation $y = \frac{x}{3}$, which is a direct linear variation with $k = \frac{1}{3}$. So, the equation does not represent an inverse variation. ■

D. $xy = -1$

Solution Solve for y to see if the function fits the form of the general equation.

$xy = -1$

$y = \frac{-1}{x}$ Divide each side by x.

The relationship shows an inverse variation with $k = -1$. ■

Writing and Using Inverse Variation Equations

TIP

The phrase "*y* varies inversely with *x*" means the same as "*x* and *y* are inversely proportional."

Example 2 If y varies inversely with x and $y = 1$ when $x = -4$, find y when $x = 0.8$.

Solution

Step 1 Find k.

$y = \frac{k}{x}$ General form of equation

$k = xy$ Solve the general equation for k.

$k = -4 \cdot 1$ Substitute -4 for x and 1 for y.

$k = -4$ Simplify.

Step 2 Substitute the value of k found in Step 1 into the general equation.

$y = \frac{k}{x}$ General form of equation

$y = \frac{-4}{x}$ Substitute -4 for k to obtain the specific equation.

Step 3 Use the specific equation $y = \frac{-4}{x}$ to find y when $x = 0.8$.

$y = \frac{-4}{x}$

$y = \frac{-4}{0.8}$ Substitute 0.8 for x.

$= -5$ Divide.

So, when $x = 0.8$, $y = -5$. ■

Graphing Inverse Variation Functions

The graph of an inverse variation function is a two-part graph called a hyperbola. Each part is a curve and neither part intersects the y-axis. The quadrants in which the hyperbola exists depend on the value of k.

REMEMBER

A quadrant is one of the four regions on a coordinate plane.

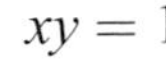

$xy = 1$

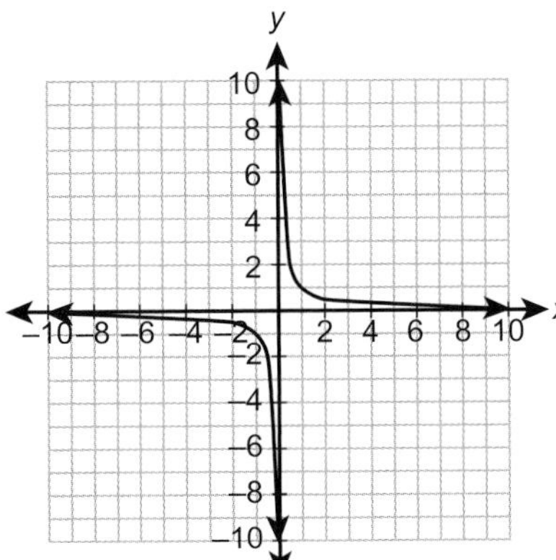

When the value of k is positive, the hyperbola is in quadrants I and III.

$xy = -1$

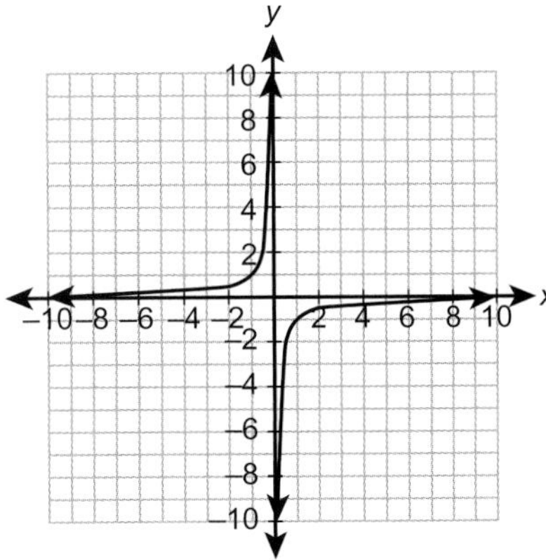

When the value of k is negative, the hyperbola is in quadrants II and IV.

Example 3 Suppose y varies inversely with x and $y = 3$ when $x = 2$. Graph the inverse variation equation.

Solution

Step 1 Find k.

$k = xy = 2 \cdot 3 = 6$

Step 2 Substitute the value of k found in Step 1 into the general equation.

$y = \frac{k}{x}$

The specific equation is $y = \frac{6}{x}$.

TIP

If possible, choose values of x that are factors of the numerator.

Step 3 Make a table of ordered pairs and connect the points with a smooth curve.

x	−6	−3	−2	−1	1	2	3	6
y	−1	−2	−3	−6	6	3	2	1

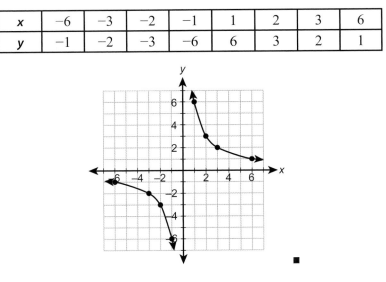

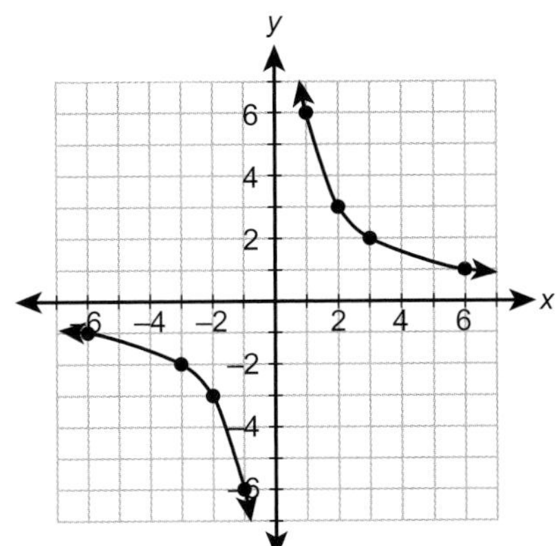

■

Application: Gears

When gears are interlocked and turning, the angular speed of a gear varies inversely with the number of teeth on the gear.

Example 4 When attached to an engine, the gear with 20 teeth has an angular speed of 30 revolutions per minute. Determine the angular speed of the interlocking gear with 15 teeth.

Solution Let y represent the angular speed, and let x represent the number of teeth. This means that $y = 30$ when $x = 20$. Now, find k.

$k = xy = 20 \cdot 30 = 600$

The specific inverse variation equation is $y = \frac{600}{x}$.

To find the speed of a gear with 15 teeth, substitute 15 for x and solve for y: $y = \frac{600}{15} = 40$. The speed of a gear with 15 teeth is 40 revolutions per minute. ■

Problem Set

Determine if each relationship shows an inverse variation. If so, state the constant of variation.

1.

x	3	4	6	9
y	12	9	6	4

2.

x	2	4	6	8
y	4	6	8	10

3. $\frac{2}{x} = y$

4. $\frac{y}{6} = x$

5.

x	1	2	3	4
y	3	12	27	48

6.

x	1	5	10	15
y	30	6	3	2

7. $xy = -6$

8. $\frac{7}{y} = x$

Write an inverse variation equation and evaluate the function for the given value.

9. If y varies inversely with x and $y = -8$ when $x = 4$, find y when $x = 10$.

10. If y varies inversely with x and $y = 5$ when $x = 2.5$, find y when $x = 20$.

11. If w varies inversely with z and $w = 4.8$ when $z = 2$, find w when $z = 8$.

12. If d varies inversely with c and $d = 105$ when $c = 3$, find d when $c = 15$.

13. If y varies inversely with x and $y = -72$ when $x = 12$, find y when $x = 9$.

14. If y varies inversely with x and $y = 220$ when $x = 11$, find y when $x = 5$.

15. If y varies inversely with x and $y = 30$ when $x = 3$, find y when $x = 8$.

16. If q varies inversely with p and $q = 66$ when $p = 33$, find q when $p = 3$.

Write the inverse variation equation and graph.

17. v varies inversely with t and $v = 6$ when $t = -9$

18. y varies inversely with x and $y = -5$ when $x = 3$

19. y varies inversely with x and $y = 4$ when $x = -12$

20. y varies inversely with x and $y = 8$ when $x = -2$

21. s varies inversely with r and $s = 3$ when $r = -4$

22. y varies inversely with x and $y = 3$ when $x = 12$

Write the inverse variation equation and solve.

23. Tire pressure varies inversely with the volume of the air inside the tire.

    A. If the pressure is 40 psi when the volume is 105 cubic inches, find the pressure when the volume is 120 cubic inches.

    B. If the pressure is 30 psi when the volume is 140 cubic inches, find the pressure when the volume is 100 cubic inches.

24. The current I in a circuit varies inversely with the resistance, R.

    A. If the resistance is 12 when the current is 3, find the resistance when the current is 6.

    B. If the resistance is 3 when the current is 2, find the resistance when the current is 5.

25. The time t it takes to fill a water tank varies inversely with the rate r the tank is being filled.

    A. If it takes 39 seconds to fill a tank at the rate of 3 gallons per second, find the time it takes to fill the tank at 2 gallons per second.

    B. If it takes 90 minutes to fill a tank at the rate of 10 liters per minute, find the time it takes to fill the tank at 4 liters per minute.

26. The speed it takes to travel a given distance varies inversely with time.

    A. If a trip takes 12 hours traveling at 60 miles per hour, how many hours would the same trip take at a speed of 80 miles per hour?

    B. If a trip takes 3 hours traveling at 75 miles per hour, how many hours would the same trip take at a speed of 45 miles per hour?

Translating Functions

A transformation is a one-to-one mapping between two sets of points.

A *translation* is a type of transformation that moves a figure to a new location, but does not change the size, shape, or orientation of the original figure.

DEFINITION

A **translation** is the sliding of a figure in a straight path.

Figure 1 below shows the red graph translated horizontally by moving every point on the original figure (in red) 4 units to the right. Figure 2 shows the red graph translated vertically by moving every point on the original figure (in red) 4 units up.

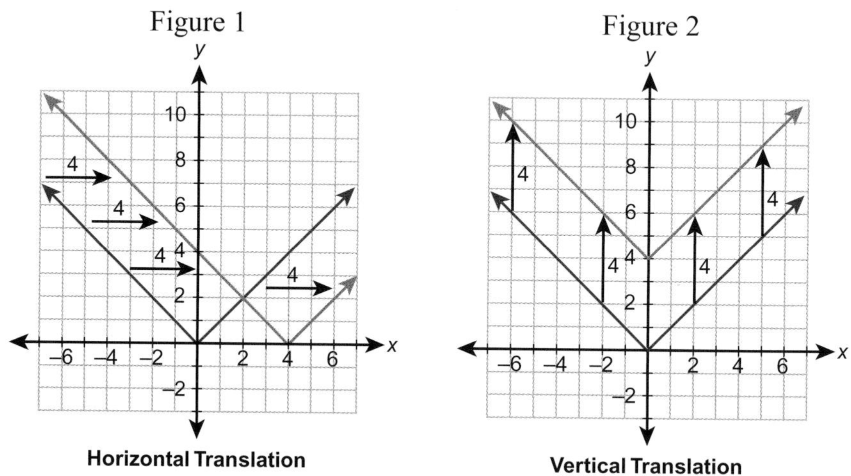

Horizontal Translation

Vertical Translation

The table shows how the coordinates of three selected points from each graph changed. Read the arrow symbol as "maps to," or "is mapped to."

TIP

The arrow symbol is used to denote a transformation.

Translations	
Horizontal	**Vertical**
$(-6, 6) \rightarrow (-2, 6)$	$(-5, 5) \rightarrow (-5, 9)$
$(0, 0) \rightarrow (4, 0)$	$(0, 0) \rightarrow (0, 4)$
$(5, 5) \rightarrow (9, 5)$	$(4, 4) \rightarrow (4, 8)$

Notice that in the horizontal translation, the x-coordinates change and the y-coordinates stay the same. In the vertical translation, the y-coordinates change and the x-coordinates stay the same.

Translating a Graph

Use the following coordinate rules to translate graphs in the coordinate plane.

PROPERTIES

Finding the Rule for a Translation

If (x, y) is translated h units to the right, then $(x, y) \to (x + h, y)$.
If (x, y) is translated h units to the left, then $(x, y) \to (x - h, y)$.
If (x, y) is translated k units up, then $(x, y) \to (x, y + k)$.
If (x, y) is translated k units down, then $(x, y) \to (x, y - k)$.

Example 1 Translate the graph using the rule $(x, y) \to (x - 3, y)$. Then, describe the translation.

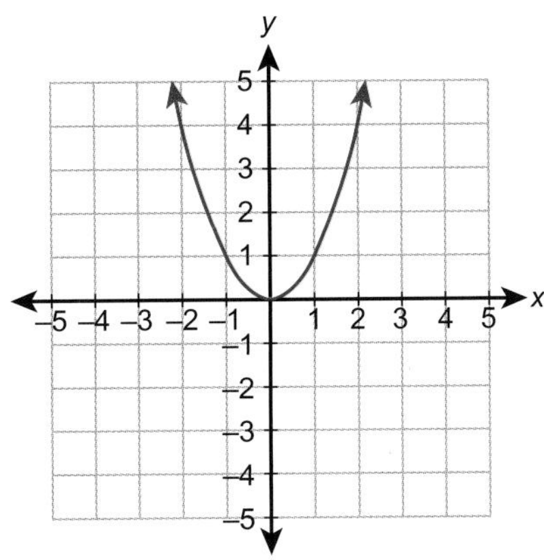

Solution Apply the rule to selected points on the graph.

$(-2, 4) \to (-2 - 3, 4) = (-5, 4)$

$(-1, 1) \to (-1 - 3, 1) = (-4, 1)$

$(0, 0) \to (0 - 3, 0) = (-3, 0)$

$(1, 1) \to (1 - 3, 1) = (-2, 1)$

$(2, 4) \to (2 - 3, 4) = (-1, 4)$

The graph is translated 3 units to the left. ■

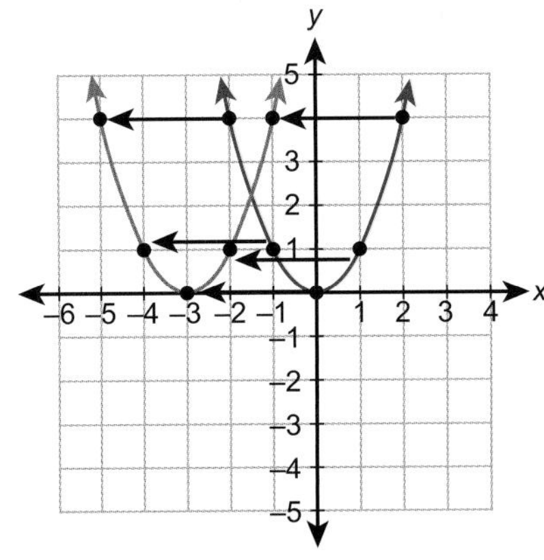

Writing a Coordinate Rule

Example 2 Write a coordinate rule for the translation of $f(x)$ to $g(x)$.

TIP

When figuring out the translation, look at turning points. For instance, the point $(-1, 3)$ on $f(x)$ maps to the point $(4, 2)$ on $g(x)$.

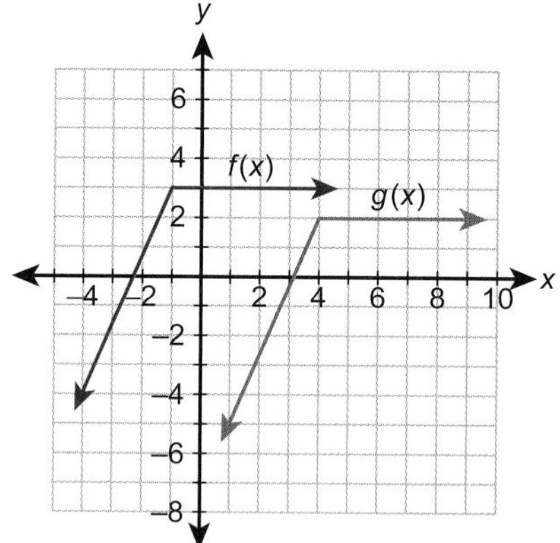

Solution Notice how each point on $f(x)$ is translated 5 units to the right and 1 unit down to obtain $g(x)$. So, the coordinate rule is $(x, y) \rightarrow (x + 5, y - 1)$. ■

Application: Business

Example 3 Describe the translation from the regular price to the sale price, then write a coordinate rule.

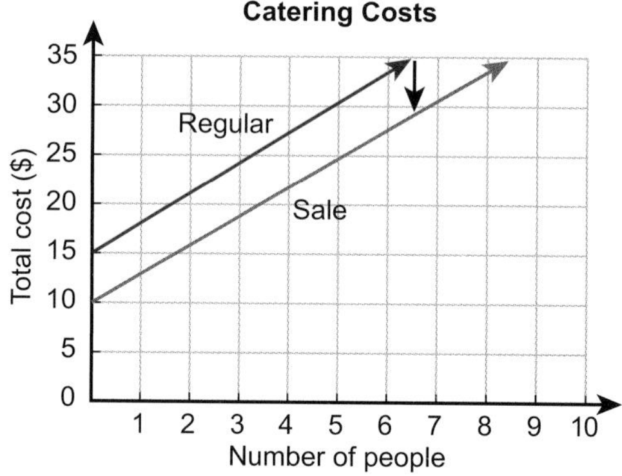

Solution The graph shows that the sale price is $5 less than the regular price. So, the coordinate rule is $(x, y) \rightarrow (x, y - 5)$. ■

Problem Set

Use the given rule to translate each graph. Then, describe the translation.

1. $(x, y) \rightarrow (x - 2, y)$

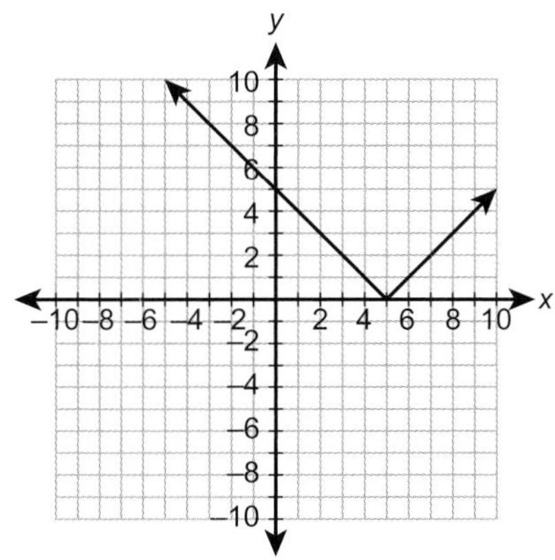

2. $(x, y) \rightarrow (x, y + 1)$

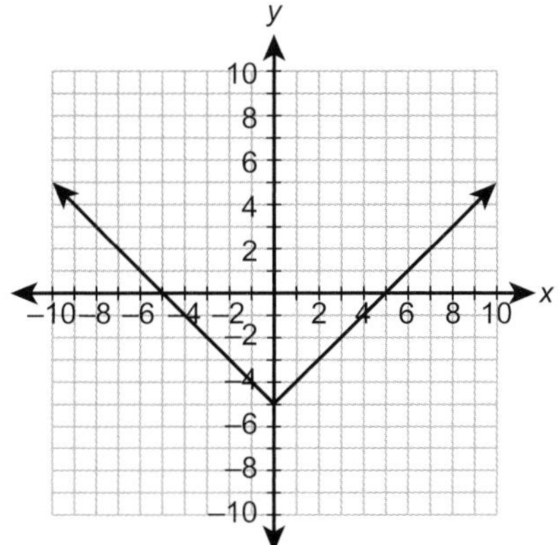

3. $(x, y) \rightarrow (x, y + 6)$

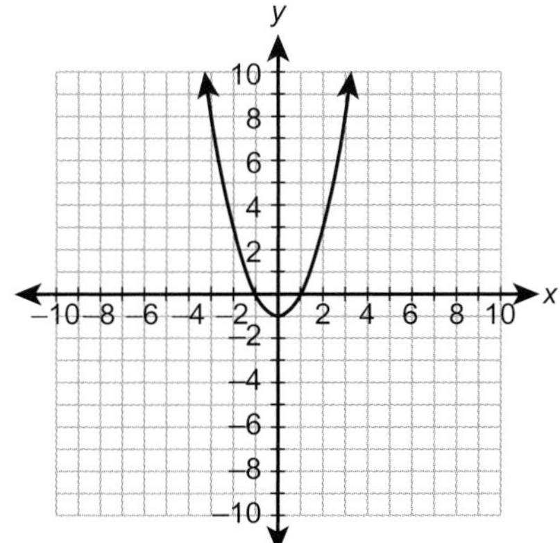

4. $(x, y) \rightarrow (x, y - 2)$

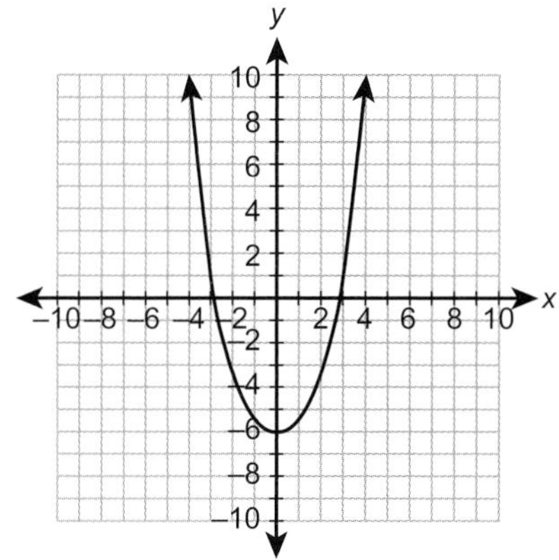

5. $(x, y) \rightarrow (x - 5, y)$

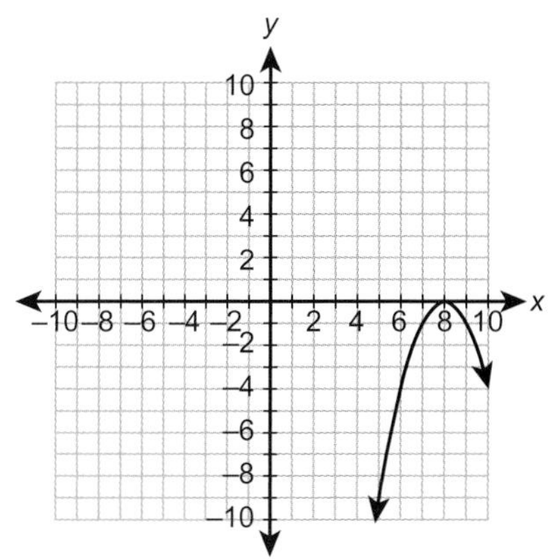

6. $(x, y) \rightarrow (x, y + 9)$

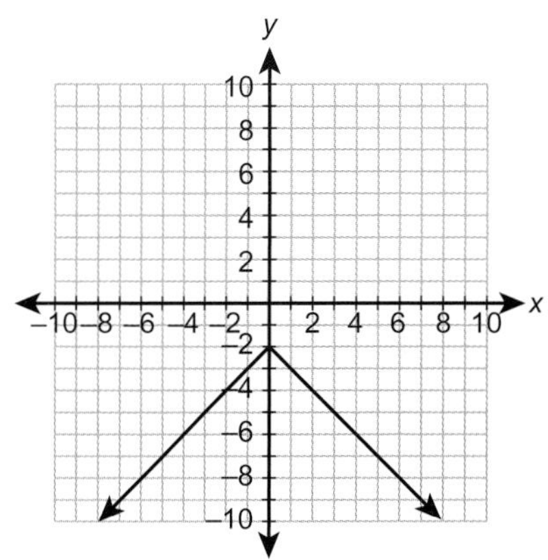

7. $(x, y) \rightarrow (x - 6, y)$

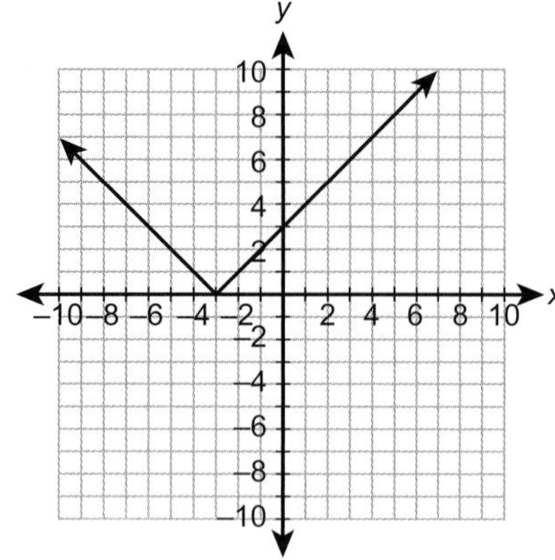

8. $(x, y) \rightarrow (x, y + 3)$

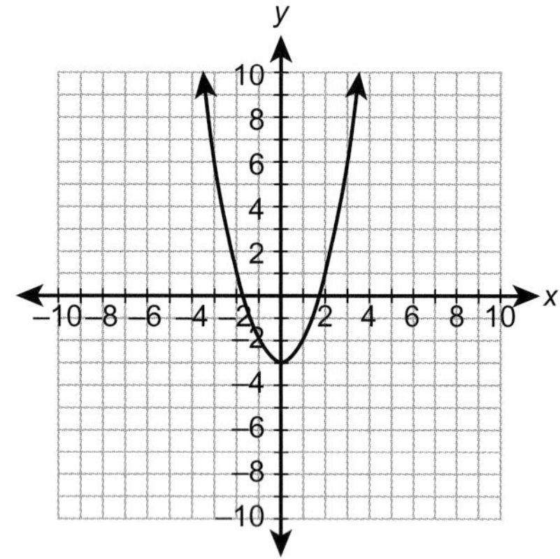

9. $(x, y) \rightarrow (x - 12, y)$

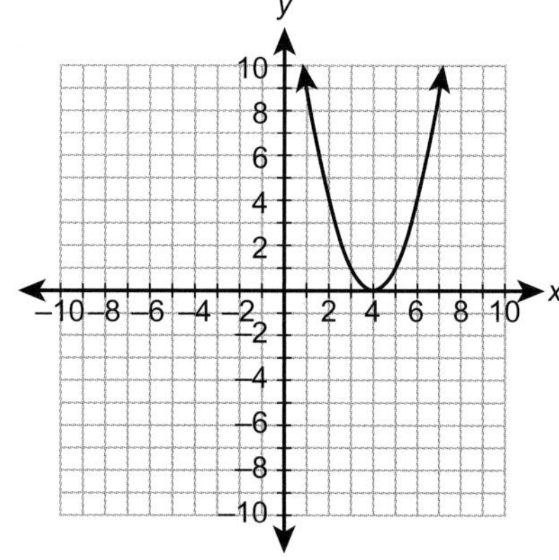

10. $(x, y) \rightarrow (x, y + 14)$

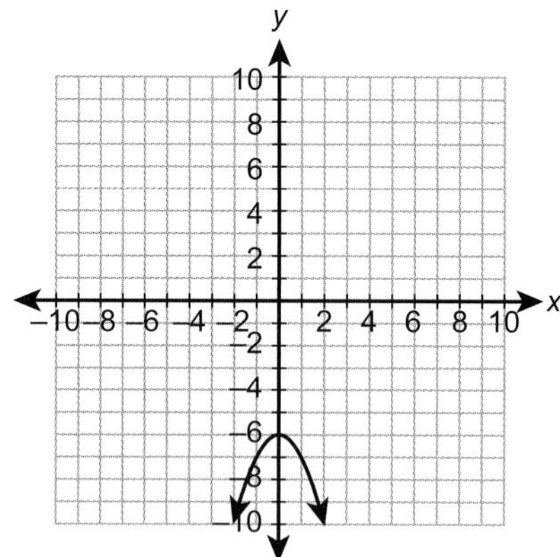

11. $(x, y) \rightarrow (x + 5, y)$

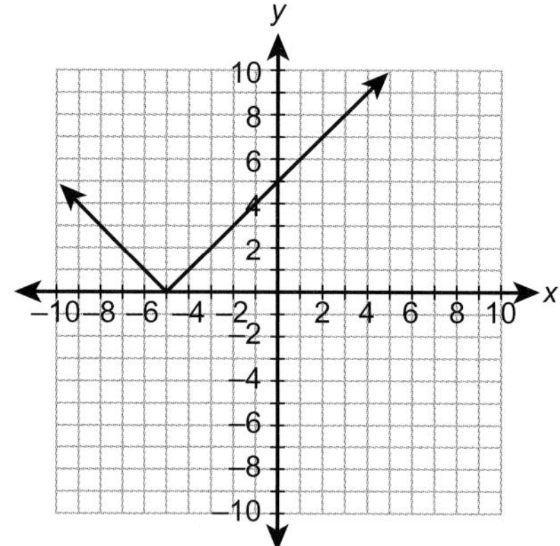

12. $(x, y) \rightarrow (x, y - 10)$

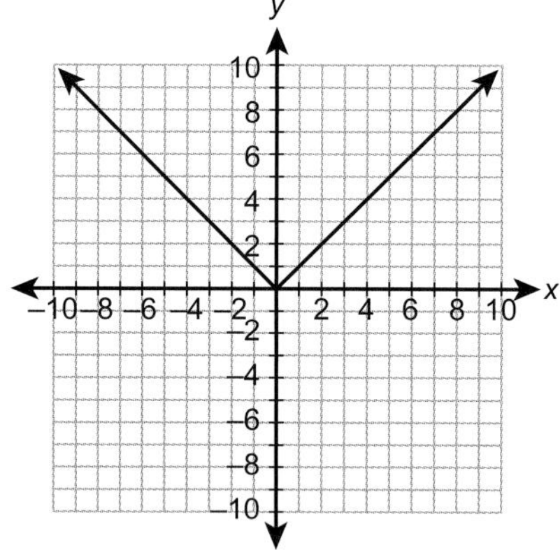

Write a coordinate rule for the translation of $f(x)$ to $g(x)$.

13.

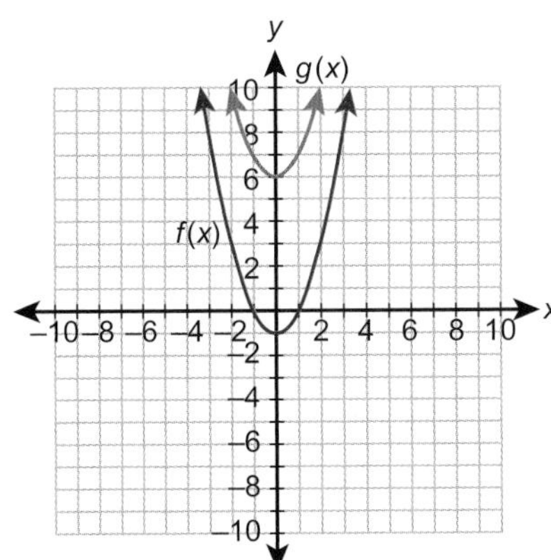

14.

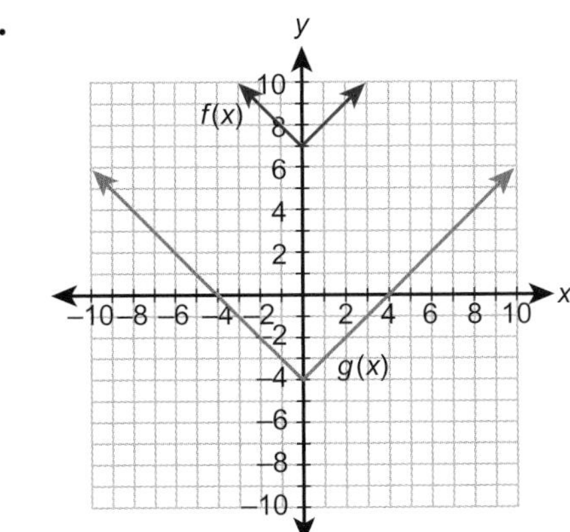

15.

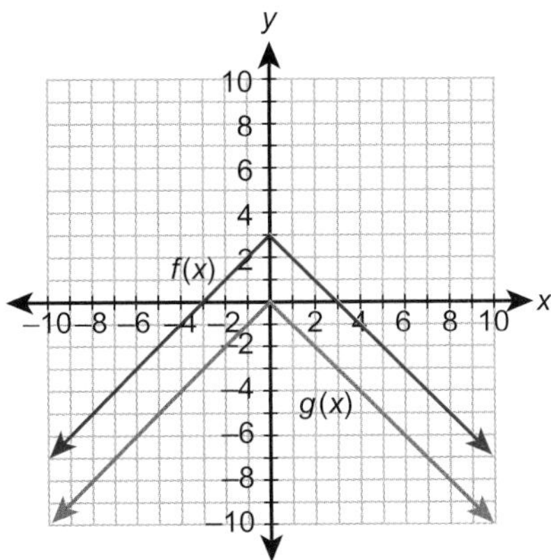

16.

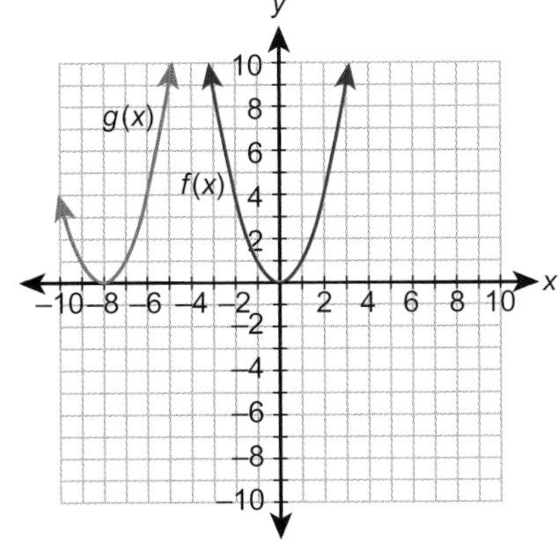

17.

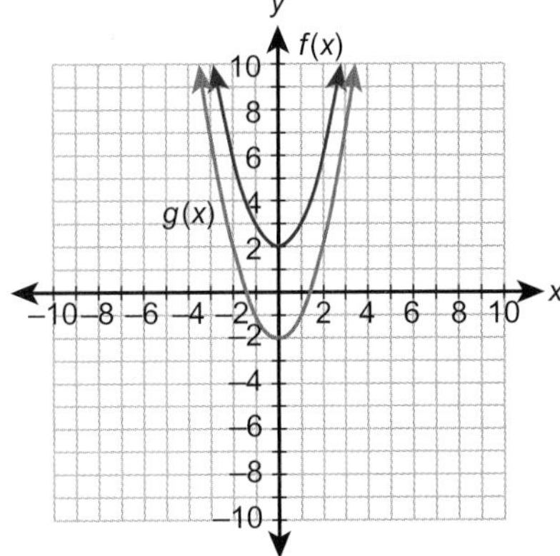

18.

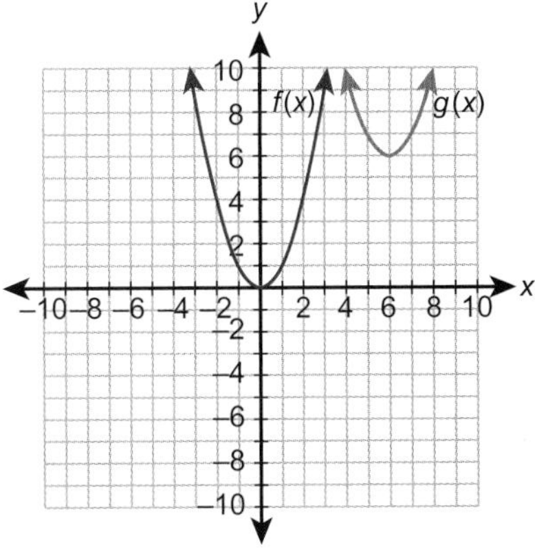

19.

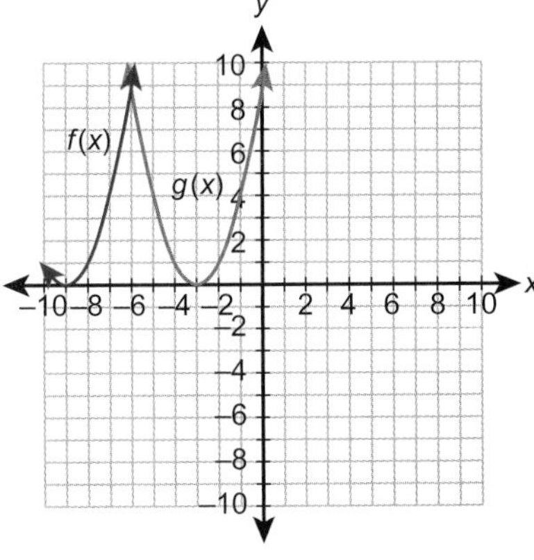

20.

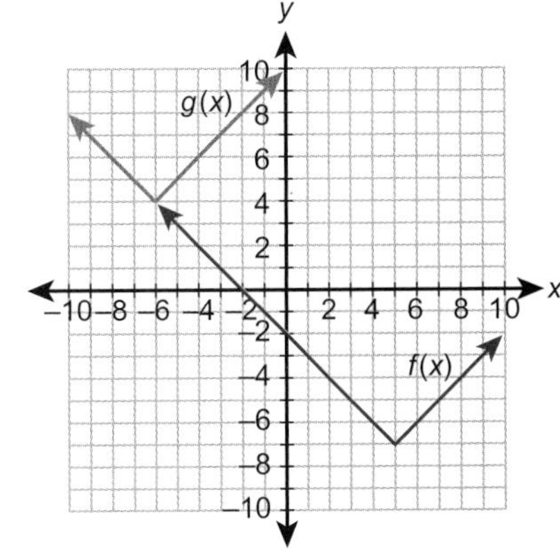

21.

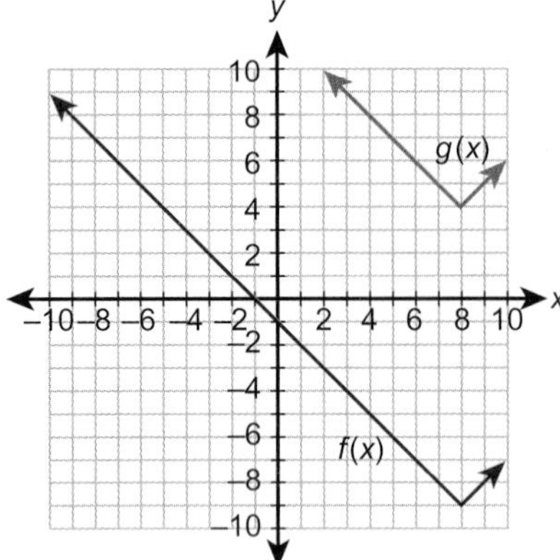

22.

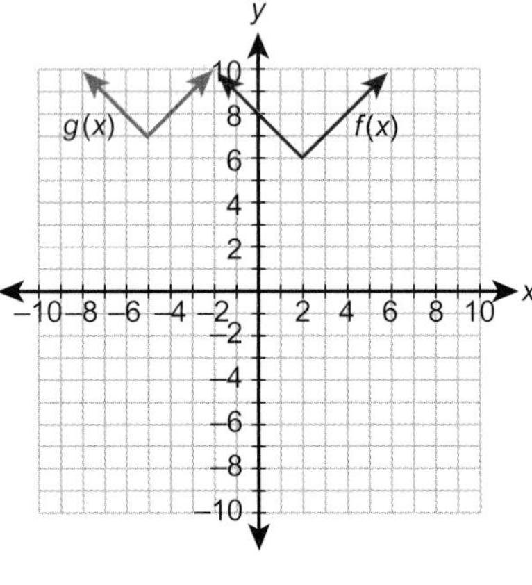

23.

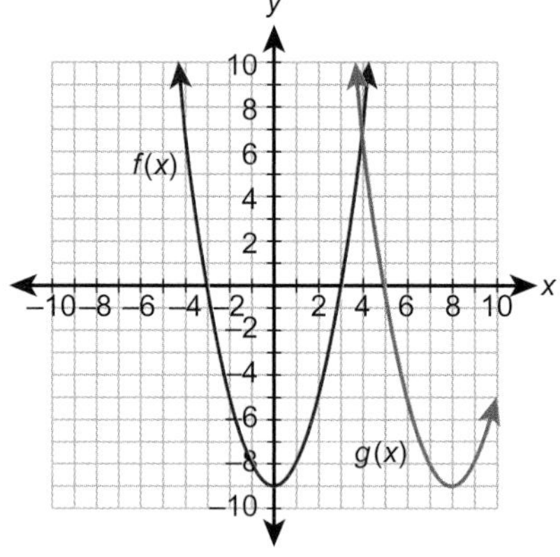

24.

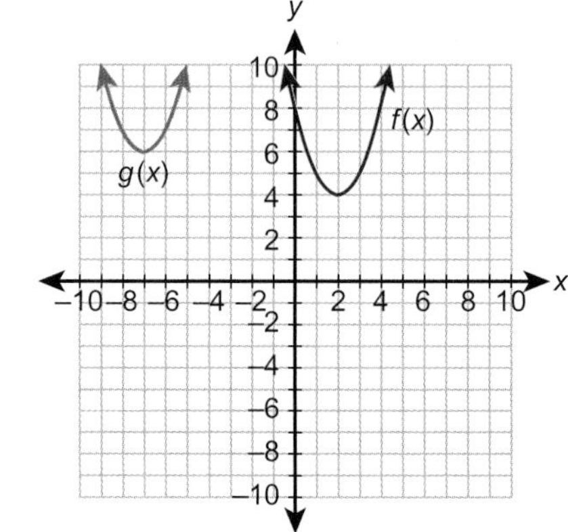

Solve.

25. Describe the translation from Diver A's starting height to Diver B's starting height, and then write a coordinate rule.

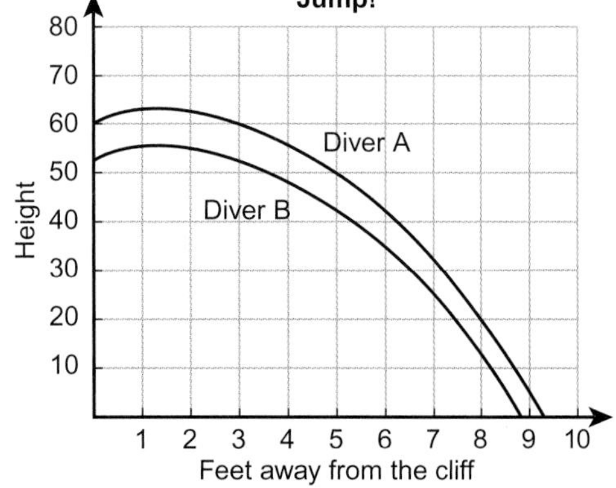

26. Describe the translation from Plane B's height to Plane A's height, and then write a coordinate rule.

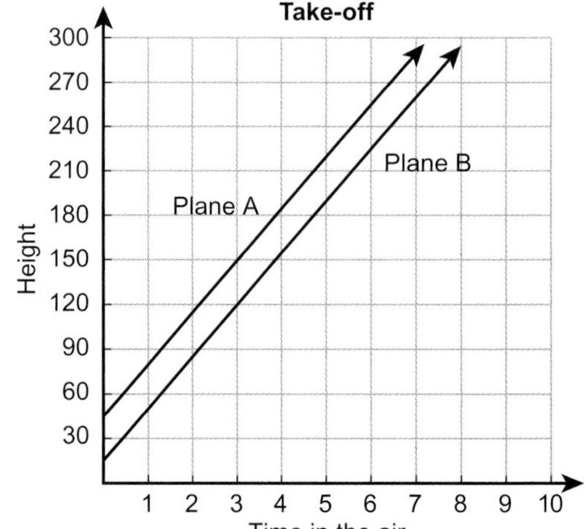

27. Describe the translation from the score before test prep to the scores after test prep, and then write a coordinate rule.

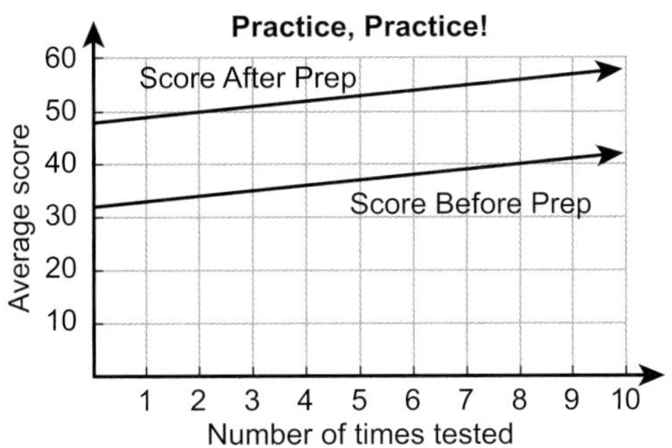

28. Describe the translation from the original price of shoes to the sale price, and then write a coordinate rule.

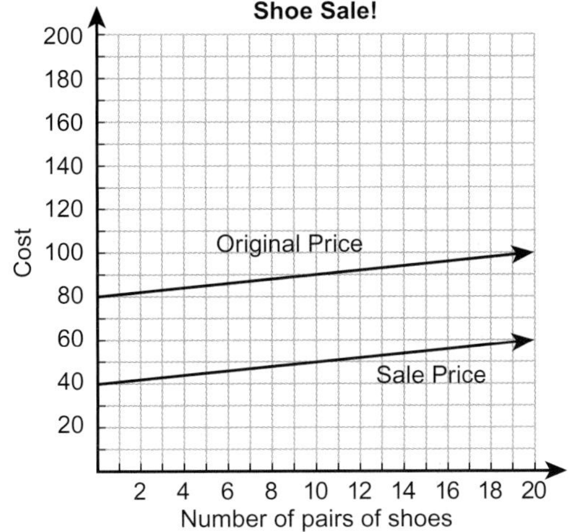

***29.** **Challenge** Describe the translation from the cost of the senior trip for the class of '06 to the cost of the senior trip for the class of '07, and then write a coordinate rule.

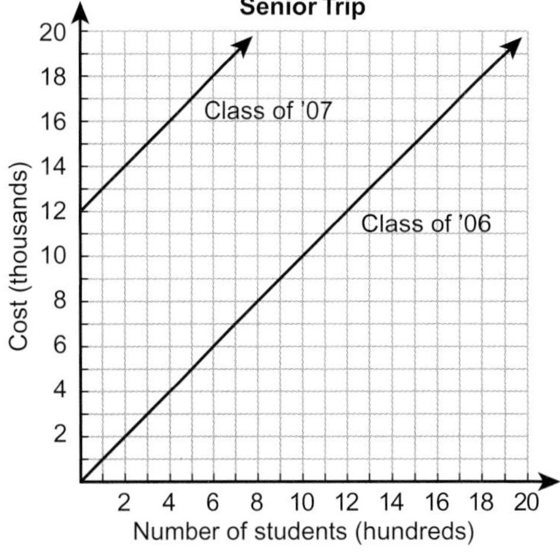

***30.** **Challenge** Describe the translation from the profit in 2005 to the profit in 2006, and then write a coordinate rule.

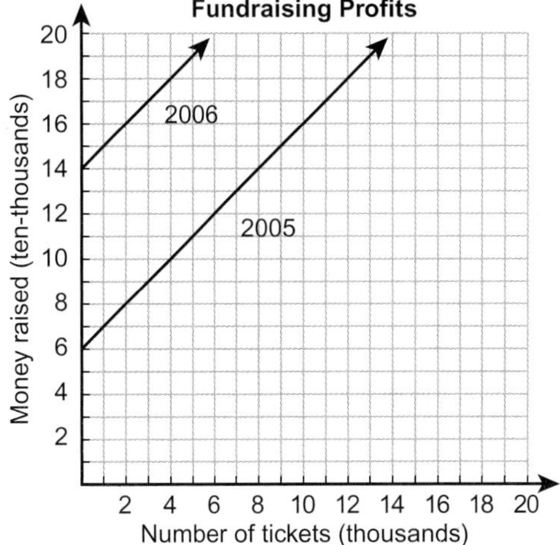

UNIT 9 Rationals, Irrationals, and Radicals

People of ancient times used a rope with knots for measuring right triangles.

Are rational numbers very levelheaded? Are irrational numbers hard to reason with? Not really, but rational and irrational numbers have things in common and things that make them different.

Big Ideas

- A number is any entity that obeys the laws of arithmetic; all numbers obey the laws of arithmetic. The laws of arithmetic can be used to simplify algebraic expressions.
- If you can create a mathematical model for a situation, you can use the model to solve other problems that you might not be able to solve otherwise. Algebraic equations can capture key relationships among quantities in the world.

Unit Topics

- Rational Numbers
- Terminating and Repeating Decimals
- Square Roots
- Irrational Numbers
- Estimating Square Roots
- Radicals with Variables
- Using Square Roots to Solve Equations
- The Pythagorean Theorem
- Higher Roots

Rational Numbers

The rational numbers are a subset of the real numbers. Examples of rational numbers are $\frac{1}{2}$, 5, −3, 0.25, $10\frac{3}{4}$, and $23.7\overline{8}$.

DEFINITION

A **rational number** is any number that can be expressed as a ratio $\left(\frac{a}{b}\right)$, where a and b are integers and $b \neq 0$.

NOTATION

The letter $\mathbb{Q}$ denotes the set of rational numbers.

The letter $\mathbb{Q}$ represents the set of rational numbers. Integers are rational numbers because you can write them as a fraction (a ratio) with a denominator of 1. For example, $-6 = \frac{-6}{1}$.

A **proper fraction** is a fraction where the numerator is less than the denominator. An **improper fraction** is a fraction where the numerator is greater than or equal to the denominator. Improper fractions have values greater than or equal to 1 and can be written as *mixed numbers*. A **mixed number** is a number consisting of both a whole number and a fraction or the opposite of such a number.

Proper Fractions	Improper Fractions	Mixed Numbers
$-\frac{7}{8}, \frac{1}{3}, \frac{1}{2}, \frac{3}{4}$	$-\frac{26}{5}, \frac{4}{4}, \frac{16}{8}, \frac{12}{5}$	$-3\frac{2}{3}, 1\frac{1}{4}, 5\frac{7}{8}$

Writing Rational Numbers

Example 1

A. Write $-\frac{25}{8}$ as a mixed number.

Solution Write the improper fraction as a mixed number by dividing the numerator by the denominator. Because a mixed number has a whole number part, and whole numbers are not negative, consider $-\frac{25}{8}$ as the opposite of $\frac{25}{8}$.

(continued)

$-\left(\frac{25}{8}\right) = -\left(3\frac{1}{8}\right)$ Divide.

$= -3\frac{1}{8}$ Simplify. ■

B. Write 4.25 as a percent, a mixed number, and an improper fraction.

REMEMBER

To write a decimal as a percent, move the decimal point to the right two places and add zeros if necessary.

Solution Write 4.25 as a percent. $4.25 = 425\%$

Write 4.25 as a mixed number.

$4.25 = 4\frac{25}{100}$ Write 0.25 as a fraction.

$= 4\frac{1}{4}$ Simplify.

Write 4.25 as an improper fraction.

$4.25 = 4\frac{1}{4}$ Write the decimal as a mixed number.

$= \frac{4 \cdot 4 + 1}{4}$ Multiply the whole number by the denominator and add it to the numerator.

$= \frac{16 + 1}{4}$ Multiply.

$= \frac{17}{4}$ Add. ■

Comparing Rational Numbers

Two rational numbers are either equal or not equal to each other. If they are not equal, then one of the numbers is greater than the other number.

COMPARISON PROPERTY OF RATIONAL NUMBERS

For positive integers a and c and nonzero integers b and d,

$\frac{a}{b} > \frac{c}{d}$ if and only if $ad > bc$.

$\frac{a}{b} < \frac{c}{d}$ if and only if $ad < bc$.

$\frac{a}{b} = \frac{c}{d}$ if and only if $ad = bc$.

Example 2 Write <, =, or > to make a true statement.

A. $\frac{3}{4}$ ▢ $\frac{7}{9}$

Solution Compare the rational numbers $\frac{3}{4}$ and $\frac{7}{9}$. Use the comparison property of rational numbers, with $\frac{a}{b} = \frac{3}{4}$ and $\frac{c}{d} = \frac{7}{9}$.

$ad = 3 \cdot 9 = 27$ and $bc = 4 \cdot 7 = 28$

Since $27 < 28$, $\frac{3}{4} < \frac{7}{9}$. ■

B. $-\frac{23}{9}$ ▢ $-\frac{18}{7}$

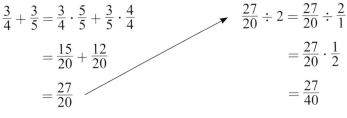

Solution Write each fraction as a mixed number.

$-\left(\frac{23}{9}\right) = -\left(2\frac{5}{9}\right) = -2\frac{5}{9}$ and $-\left(\frac{18}{7}\right) = -\left(2\frac{4}{7}\right) = -2\frac{4}{7}$

Compare $\frac{5}{9}$ and $\frac{4}{7}$. Multiply so you can use the comparison property of rational numbers, $ad = 5 \cdot 7 = 35$ and $bc = 9 \cdot 4 = 36$. Since $35 < 36$, $\frac{5}{9} < \frac{4}{7}$. That means $-2\frac{5}{9}$ is closer to 0 on the number line than $-2\frac{4}{7}$ and $-2\frac{5}{9} > -2\frac{4}{7}$. Therefore, $-\frac{23}{9} > -\frac{18}{7}$. ■

THINK ABOUT IT

On a number line, a number to the right of another number is the greater of the two numbers.

Finding a Rational Number Between Two Rational Numbers

The density property of rational numbers states that there are infinitely many numbers between any two rational numbers.

Example 3 Find a rational number between $\frac{3}{4}$ and $\frac{3}{5}$.

Solution One solution is to find the number halfway between the two numbers. Find the average of the two numbers by finding their sum and dividing by 2.

Step 1 Add the numbers.

$$\frac{3}{4} + \frac{3}{5} = \frac{3}{4} \cdot \frac{5}{5} + \frac{3}{5} \cdot \frac{4}{4}$$
$$= \frac{15}{20} + \frac{12}{20}$$
$$= \frac{27}{20}$$

Step 2 Divide the sum by 2.

$$\frac{27}{20} \div 2 = \frac{27}{20} \div \frac{2}{1}$$
$$= \frac{27}{20} \cdot \frac{1}{2}$$
$$= \frac{27}{40}$$

The rational number $\frac{27}{40}$ is between $\frac{3}{4}$ and $\frac{3}{5}$. ■

TIP

Check the answer to Example 3 by writing each fraction as a decimal.

$\frac{3}{4} = 0.75$, $\frac{27}{40} = 0.675$, and $\frac{3}{5} = 0.6$

Proving that the Rational Numbers Are Closed Under a Given Operation

Recall that a set of numbers is closed under an operation if the result of the operation with two numbers in the set is also a member of that set. The rational numbers are closed under addition, subtraction, multiplication, and division.

Example 4 Prove that the rational numbers are closed under multiplication.

Solution For all integers a and c and nonzero integers b and d, $\frac{a}{b} \cdot \frac{c}{d} = \frac{ac}{bd}$. The number $\frac{ac}{bd}$ is a rational number because the set of integers is closed under multiplication. The denominator cannot be zero because neither b nor d is zero. ■

Problem Set

Write each number as a mixed number, proper or improper fraction, decimal, and percent, if possible.

1. $\frac{7}{20}$
2. 2.8
3. 0.3125
4. $\frac{15}{2}$
5. $11\frac{1}{8}$
6. $\frac{13}{5}$

Write <, =, or > to make a true statement.

7. $-\frac{5}{6} \square -\frac{6}{7}$
8. $\frac{8}{13} \square \frac{11}{16}$
9. $12\frac{1}{3} \square \frac{37}{3}$
10. $\frac{36}{15} \square \frac{29}{8}$
11. $7\frac{5}{8} \square \frac{31}{4}$
12. $-0.71 \square -\frac{7}{9}$
13. $-\frac{25}{19} \square -1\frac{4}{17}$
14. $\frac{13}{14} \square \frac{169}{182}$

Arrange each list of numbers in increasing order.

15. $\frac{7}{8}, \frac{8}{10}, \frac{11}{13}$
16. $-3\frac{2}{3}, -\frac{9}{2}, -\frac{13}{3}$
17. $\frac{1}{3}, \frac{3}{5}, \frac{5}{7}, \frac{7}{9}$
18. $-\frac{7}{13}, -\frac{3}{5}, -\frac{5}{8}$
19. $2.58, \frac{64}{25}, \frac{27}{10}$
20. $-\frac{130}{63}, -\frac{140}{46}, -\frac{45}{6}, -\frac{52}{9}$
21. $\frac{64}{9}, \frac{69}{10}, 6.4$
22. $\frac{53}{68}, \frac{99}{104}, \frac{79}{85}$

Find a rational number between the two given numbers.

23. $\frac{5}{6}, \frac{5}{9}$
24. $-\frac{14}{31}, -\frac{17}{33}$
25. $9\frac{2}{3}, \frac{47}{8}$
26. $-3\frac{4}{5}, -\frac{39}{11}$
27. $1, \frac{2}{3}$

Solve.

28. Prove that the rational numbers are closed under:
    - **A.** addition
    - **B.** subtraction
    - **C.** division

***29.** **Challenge**

- **A.** Find a rational number between $\frac{3}{5}$ and $\frac{10}{13}$.
- **B.** Determine if your answer is greater than 0.7. If not, find a rational number between $\frac{3}{5}$ and $\frac{10}{13}$ that is greater than 0.7.

***30.** **Challenge**

- **A.** Find a rational number between $-\frac{7}{8}$ and $-\frac{2}{3}$.
- **B.** Determine if your answer is less than -0.7. If not, find a rational number between $-\frac{7}{8}$ and $-\frac{2}{3}$ that is less than -0.7.

Terminating and Repeating Decimals

There are different types of decimals.

DEFINITIONS

Terminating decimals are decimals that have a finite number of nonzero digits. **Nonterminating decimals** are decimals that do not terminate, or end.

TIP

The word *terminate* means stop. Terminating decimals stop; nonterminating decimals do not stop.

There are two types of nonterminating decimals: repeating and nonrepeating decimals. **Repeating decimals** have a repeating pattern of digits, while **nonrepeating decimals** do not. Place a bar over the block of digits that repeat in a repeating decimal.

Terminating Decimals	Nonterminating Decimals	
	Repeating	Nonrepeating
0.25, 6, −1.5836	$0.\overline{4} = 0.44444\ldots$ $3.\overline{256} = 3.256256\ldots$ $20.76\overline{3} = 20.76333\ldots$	0.356987412569112... 3.1415926535...

NOTATION

$\overline{}$ A bar placed over digits in a decimal shows the digits repeat.

Converting Fractions to Decimals

Example 1 Express each fraction as a decimal. Determine if the decimal repeats or terminates.

A. $\frac{7}{25}$

Solution Divide 7 by 25: $7 \div 25 = 0.28$. The decimal is a terminating decimal. ■

B. $\frac{7}{9}$

Solution Divide 7 by 9: $7 \div 9 = 0.777777\ldots = 0.\overline{7}$. The decimal is a repeating decimal. ■

C. $\frac{5}{12}$

Solution Divide 5 by 12: $5 \div 12 = 0.41666666\ldots = 0.41\overline{6}$. The decimal is a repeating decimal. ■

TIP

On a calculator, the last digit displayed may be rounded up, even when the digits continue to repeat.

REMEMBER

Place the bar over the repeating part of the decimal only.

Expressing Terminating and Repeating Decimals as Fractions

A number is rational if and only if you can write it as a terminating or repeating decimal. Both terminating and repeating decimals can be written as the quotient of two integers.

Example 2 Write each decimal as a quotient of two integers.

A. 4.25

Solution Since the last digit in the decimal part is in the hundredths place, write 0.25 as a fraction with a demonimator of 100.

$$4.25 = 4 + 0.25 = 4 + \frac{25}{100} = 4 + \frac{1}{4} = 4\frac{1}{4} = \frac{17}{4} \blacksquare$$

B. $4.\overline{25}$

Solution Write the number as an equation. Multiply each side of the equation by the power of 10 that has as many zeros as there are digits in the repeating block.

$$x = 4.\overline{25}$$

$$100x = 425.\overline{25}$$

Subtract the first equation from the second. This will eliminate the repeating part. Then isolate the variable and simplify the fraction if possible.

$$\begin{array}{rl} 100x = & 425.\overline{25} \\ - \quad x = & 4.\overline{25} \\ \hline 99x = & 421 \end{array}$$

$$\frac{99x}{99} = \frac{421}{99}$$

$$x = \frac{421}{99}$$

TIP

When multiplying both sides of the equation by a power of 10, it helps to write the repeating decimal without the bar and display the digits in the repeating block a couple of times.

Check $421 \div 99 = 4.\overline{25}$ ✓ ■

C. $2.02\overline{342}$

Solution Multiply each side of the equation by 1000.

$$x = 2.02\overline{342}$$

$$1000x = 2023.42\overline{342}$$

Subtract the first equation from the second.

$$\begin{array}{rl} 1000x = & 2023.42\overline{342} \\ - \quad x = & 2.02\overline{342} \\ \hline 999x = & 2021.4 \end{array}$$

Multiply each side by 10 to eliminate the decimal. Then isolate the variable and simplify.

$$9990x = 20{,}214$$

$$\frac{9990x}{9990} = \frac{20{,}214}{9990}$$

$$x = \frac{1123}{555} \blacksquare$$

Finding a Rational Number between a Fraction and a Repeating Decimal

Example 3 Find a rational number between $\frac{8}{11}$ and $0.\overline{81}$.

Solution

Step 1 Write the repeating decimal as a fraction.

$$\begin{aligned} 100x &= 81.\overline{81} \\ - \quad x &= 0.\overline{81} \\ \hline 99x &= 81 \\ x &= \frac{81}{99} = \frac{9}{11} \end{aligned}$$

Step 2 Find the average of the two fractions.

Add the numbers. $\frac{8}{11} + \frac{9}{11} = \frac{17}{11}$

Divide the sum by 2. $\frac{17}{11} \div 2 = \frac{17}{11} \cdot \frac{1}{2} = \frac{17}{22}$

The number $\frac{17}{22}$ is between $\frac{8}{11}$ and $0.\overline{81}$.

Step 3 Check. Write $\frac{8}{11}$ and $\frac{17}{22}$ as decimals.

$\frac{8}{11} = 0.\overline{727}$ and $\frac{17}{22} = 0.7\overline{727}$

$0.\overline{727} < 0.7\overline{727} < 0.\overline{81}$ ■

Application: Proof with Repeating Decimals

Example 4 Prove that $0.\overline{9} = 1$.

Solution Write $0.\overline{9}$ as a fraction.

Let $x = 0.\overline{9}$.

$$\begin{aligned} 10x &= 9.\overline{9} \\ - \quad x &= 0.\overline{9} \\ \hline 9x &= 9 \\ x &= \frac{9}{9} = 1 \end{aligned}$$

Since $x = 0.\overline{9}$ from the first assumption, and $x = 1$ from the algebra, $0.\overline{9} = 1$ by the substitution property of equality. ■

Problem Set

Express each fraction as a decimal. Determine if the decimal repeats or terminates.

1. $\frac{3}{4}$

2. $\frac{2}{13}$

3. $\frac{1}{9}$

4. $\frac{9}{5}$

5. $\frac{4}{15}$

6. $\frac{7}{2}$

7. $\frac{23}{6}$

8. $\frac{10}{27}$

Write each decimal as a quotient of two integers.

9. 7.2

10. $5.1\overline{3}$

11. 0.125

12. 270.35

13. $0.\overline{074}$

14. $1.\overline{72}$

15. 2.54

16. $3.\overline{2}$

17. $4.0\overline{7}$

Find a rational number between the two given numbers.

18. $\frac{3}{10}$ and $0.4\overline{5}$

19. $\frac{3}{2}$ and $1.\overline{8}$

20. $0.6\overline{81}$ and $\frac{10}{11}$

21. $0.1\overline{6}$ and $\frac{1}{3}$

22. $0.1\overline{36}$ and $\frac{5}{6}$

23. $-\frac{11}{6}$ and $-1.3\overline{18}$

24. $0.08\overline{3}$ and $\frac{1}{13}$

25. $\frac{32}{15}$ and $2.\overline{4}$

26. $-3.\overline{5}$ and $-\frac{11}{3}$

27. $-\frac{7}{24}$ and $-0.22\overline{72}$

Prove each statement.

28. $2.\overline{9} = 3$

29. $19.\overline{9} = 20$

30. $1999.\overline{9} = 2000$

Solve and show your work.

***31. Challenge**

A. Write $\frac{13}{50}$ and $\frac{1}{4}$ as decimals.

B. Find a repeating decimal between these two numbers.

C. Write your answer for Part B as a fraction.

***32. Challenge**

A. Write $\frac{7}{11}$ and $\frac{8}{11}$ as decimals.

B. Find a repeating decimal between these two numbers.

C. Write your answer for Part B as a fraction.

Square Roots

The result of multiplying a number by itself is the square of the number.

DEFINITION

A **square root** is the factor of a number that when multiplied by itself results in the number.

Every positive real number has two square roots, one positive and one negative. If $x^2 = a$, then $x \cdot x = a$ and $(-x) \cdot (-x) = a$. For example, 9 is the square of 3 because $3 \cdot 3 = 9$. Notice also that $(-3) \cdot (-3) = 9$. Since both 3^2 and $(-3)^2$ equal 9, both 3 and -3 are square roots of 9.

When the radical sign $\sqrt{}$ is used, only the positive square root is being asked for. So, $\sqrt{9} = 3$. The positive square root is also called the principal, or nonnegative, square root.

NOTATION

The radical sign $\sqrt{}$ indicates the principal square root.

Finding Square Roots

Example 1 Evaluate.

A. The square root of 100.

Solution The square roots of 100 are -10 and 10 because $(-10)^2 = 100$ and $10^2 = 100$. ■

B. $\sqrt{49}$

Solution The square roots of 49 are 7 and -7, but since the radical sign is used, give only the principal square root: $\sqrt{49} = 7$. ■

C. $\sqrt{\frac{4}{9}}$

Solution Use the principal square root. Since $\frac{2}{3} \cdot \frac{2}{3} = \frac{4}{9}$, $\sqrt{\frac{4}{9}} = \frac{2}{3}$. ■

D. $-\sqrt{1.44}$

Solution Find the opposite of the principal square root. The principal square root is 1.2. The opposite of 1.2 is -1.2. So, $-\sqrt{1.44} = -1.2$. ■

THINK ABOUT IT

The radical sign $\sqrt{}$ can also be written as $\sqrt[2]{}$ to indicate the second, or square, root. Most books omit the 2.

Like Radicals

In the square root expression $3\sqrt{7}$, 3 is the coefficient and 7 is the **radicand**. When two or more square root expressions have the same radicand, the expressions are **like radicals** and can be combined by adding or subtracting the coefficients.

THINK ABOUT IT

Combining like radicals is similar to combining like terms.

Like Terms	Like Radicals
$3x + 5x = 8x$	$3\sqrt{7} + 5\sqrt{7} = 8\sqrt{7}$
$3y - y = 2y$	$3\sqrt{14} - \sqrt{14} = 2\sqrt{14}$

Example 2 Simplify.

A. $4\sqrt{2} + 9\sqrt{2} + 9\sqrt{3}$

Solution Identify the like radicals: $4\sqrt{2}$ and $9\sqrt{2}$. Add their coefficients.

$4\sqrt{2} + 9\sqrt{2} + 9\sqrt{3}$

$= 13\sqrt{2} + 9\sqrt{3}$

The sum is $13\sqrt{2} + 9\sqrt{3}$. These two expressions cannot be combined because their radicands are different. ■

B. $-9\sqrt{5} - 2\sqrt{5}$

Solution The radicals are like radicals. Subtract the coefficients.

$-9\sqrt{5} - 2\sqrt{5}$

$= -11\sqrt{5}$ ■

Computing Products of Square Roots

The product of two square root expressions is the square root of the product of the radicands: $\sqrt{a} \cdot \sqrt{b} = \sqrt{ab}$.

Example 3 Multiply $\sqrt{5} \cdot \sqrt{2}$.

Solution Multiply the radicands: $\sqrt{5} \cdot \sqrt{2} = \sqrt{5 \cdot 2} = \sqrt{10}$. ■

Application: Verifying and Justifying Facts About Square Roots

Example 4

A. Verify that $\sqrt{a} + \sqrt{b} \neq \sqrt{a + b}$.

Solution Substitute nonzero numbers for a and b. Let $a = 16$ and $b = 25$.

$\sqrt{16} + \sqrt{25}$	$\sqrt{16 + 25}$
$4 + 5$	$\sqrt{41}$
9	≈ 6.4

$9 \neq 6.4$, so $\sqrt{a} + \sqrt{b} \neq \sqrt{a + b}$ ■

B. Explain why a negative number cannot have a real square root.

Solution A square root of a number is a number that, when multiplied by itself, equals the original number. Any number times itself cannot be a negative number because the product of two positive numbers is positive and the product of two negative numbers is positive. ■

Problem Set

Evaluate.

1. $\sqrt{81}$
2. $-\sqrt{9}$
3. $\sqrt{\frac{1}{36}}$
4. $-\sqrt{0.04}$
5. $\sqrt{\frac{121}{169}}$

Find the square roots of each number.

6. $\frac{144}{49}$
7. 1600
8. 0.25

Simplify.

9. $\sqrt{7} + 7\sqrt{7}$
10. $9\sqrt{2} - 3\sqrt{2}$
11. $\sqrt{3} \cdot \sqrt{5}$
12. $\sqrt{2} \cdot \sqrt{1.1}$
13. $2\sqrt{7} + 3\sqrt{6} + 4\sqrt{7} + 2\sqrt{6}$
14. $\sqrt{\frac{5}{7}} \cdot \sqrt{\frac{2}{6}} + \sqrt{\frac{1}{14}} \cdot \sqrt{\frac{10}{3}}$
15. $\sqrt{5} \cdot \sqrt{2} + \sqrt{3} \cdot \sqrt{10}$
16. $-3\sqrt{26} + 3\sqrt{13} + 10\sqrt{26} - 3\sqrt{13}$
17. $\sqrt{2} \cdot \sqrt{0.33} + \sqrt{0.06} \cdot \sqrt{11}$
18. $15\sqrt{17} + 25\sqrt{34} - 10\sqrt{17}$
19. $\sqrt{\frac{71}{91}} + \sqrt{\frac{38}{91}}$
20. $-4\sqrt{2} - 4\sqrt{2}$
21. $\sqrt{5} \cdot \sqrt{3} \cdot \sqrt{6} \cdot \sqrt{10}$
22. $8\sqrt{82} + 2\sqrt{82}$
23. $(3\sqrt{2} + 2\sqrt{2} - 4\sqrt{2}) \cdot \sqrt{2}$
24. $\sqrt{1.5} \cdot \sqrt{150}$
25. $\sqrt{\frac{1}{30}} \cdot \sqrt{\frac{1}{42}} \cdot \sqrt{\frac{1}{35}}$

Solve.

26. A square has an area of $\frac{64}{169}$ in^2. Find the side length.
27. A rectangle has a length of $\sqrt{43}$ meters and a width of $\sqrt{21}$ meters. Find the area of the rectangle.
28. A circle has an area of 256π square units. Find the radius.

***29. Challenge** Verify that the set of irrational numbers is not closed under multiplication.

***30. Challenge**

A. Prove that $\sqrt{8} = 2\sqrt{2}$.

B. Find $\sqrt{3} \cdot \sqrt{6}$ and simplify.

Irrational Numbers

Real numbers that are not rational numbers are irrational numbers.

NOTATION

The letter $\mathbb{I}$ denotes the set of irrational numbers.

Unlike a rational number, an **irrational number** is a real number that can*not* be written in the form $\frac{a}{b}$, for any integers a and b. The set of rational numbers $\mathbb{Q}$ and the set of irrational numbers $\mathbb{I}$ make up the set of real numbers.

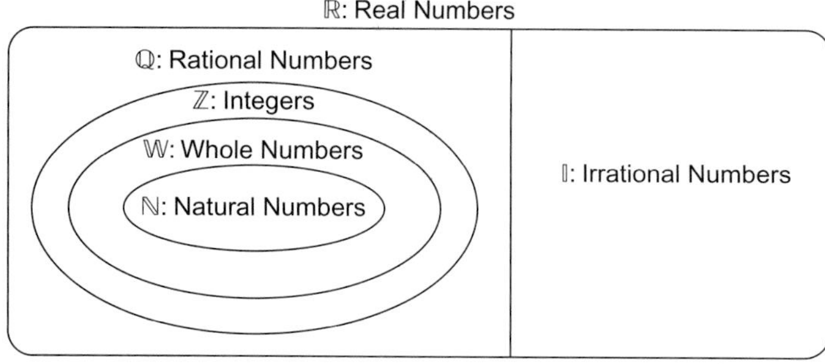

Determining if a Number Is Rational or Irrational

REMEMBER

$\pi = 3.14159...$

Any decimal that is nonterminating and nonrepeating is an irrational number. The number π is an example of an irrational number. There is no way to convert the decimal into a fraction of integers because there is no repeating block of digits.

A **perfect square** is a rational number whose square root is also rational. Examples of perfect squares are 9, 25, and $\frac{4}{9}$. The square root of any number that is not a perfect square is an irrational number, such as $\sqrt{2}$ and $\sqrt{14}$.

THINK ABOUT IT

A decimal cannot accurately represent an irrational number, but a decimal can approximate its value. $\sqrt{2}$ is an exact value; 1.414 approximates $\sqrt{2}$.

Rational Numbers	Irrational Numbers
$\sqrt{9} = 3$, $\sqrt{25} = 5$, $\sqrt{36} = 6$	$\sqrt{2} = 1.414213562...$ $\sqrt{14} = 3.741657387...$

Example 1 Determine if each number is rational or irrational.

A. $\sqrt{90}$

Solution Because 90 is not a perfect square, $\sqrt{90}$ is irrational. ■

B. $\sqrt{256}$

Solution 256 is a perfect square because $16 \cdot 16 = 256$. $\sqrt{256}$ is rational. ■

C. $-\sqrt{121}$

Solution The square root of 121 is 11. The opposite of 11 is -11, which is rational. $-\sqrt{121}$ is rational. ■

D. $\sqrt{\frac{1}{5}}$

Solution Because no number times itself equals 5, there is no number that can be multiplied by itself to equal $\frac{1}{5}$. $\sqrt{\frac{1}{5}}$ is irrational. ■

E. $\sqrt{\frac{64}{49}}$

Solution Both 64 and 49 are perfect squares. Since $\sqrt{\frac{64}{49}} = \frac{8}{7} = 1.\overline{142857}$, $\sqrt{\frac{64}{49}}$ is rational. ■

Simplifying Radicals

To simplify radicals, use $\sqrt{ab} = \sqrt{a} \cdot \sqrt{b}$. When a radical expression contains no radicands with factors that are perfect squares other than 1, the expression is in **simplified radical form**.

Example 2 Simplify.

A. $\sqrt{40}$

Solution Choose two factors of 40 so that one of them is a perfect square.

$$\begin{aligned}\sqrt{40} &= \sqrt{4 \cdot 10}\\ &= \sqrt{4} \cdot \sqrt{10}\\ &= 2\sqrt{10}\end{aligned}$$

Ten is not a perfect square and there are no factors of 10 that are perfect squares other than 1, so $\sqrt{40}$ simplifies to $2\sqrt{10}$. ■

B. $\sqrt{108}$

Solution Choose two factors of 108 so that one of them is a perfect square.

$$\begin{aligned}\sqrt{108} &= \sqrt{36 \cdot 3}\\ &= \sqrt{36} \cdot \sqrt{3}\\ &= 6\sqrt{3}\end{aligned}$$

$\sqrt{108}$ simplifies to $6\sqrt{3}$

It is possible to choose a perfect square factor that is not the greatest perfect square factor. Suppose you chose 4 and 27.

$$\begin{aligned}\sqrt{108} &= \sqrt{4 \cdot 27}\\ &= \sqrt{4} \cdot \sqrt{27}\\ &= 2 \cdot \sqrt{27}\\ &= 2 \cdot \sqrt{9} \cdot \sqrt{3}\\ &= 2 \cdot 3 \cdot \sqrt{3} = 6\sqrt{3}\end{aligned}$$ ■

TIP

Make a list of the first 15 perfect squares to refer to while simplifying radicals.

Verifying the Closure Properties for Irrational Numbers

The irrational numbers are closed under addition and subtraction.

Example 3 Determine if the set of irrational numbers is closed under multiplication.

Solution The product of two irrational numbers is not always an irrational number. Here is an example.

$\sqrt{3} \cdot \sqrt{3} = \sqrt{9} = 3$

The set of irrational numbers is not closed under multiplication. ■

Application: Proving That a Square Root Is Irrational

The square of an even number is always an even number and the square of an odd number is always an odd number. Use these facts in the following example.

THINK ABOUT IT

If $\frac{a}{b}$ is not a simplified fraction, then common factors can be divided out until it is, resulting in an equivalent fraction.

Example 4 Prove that $\sqrt{2}$ is irrational.

Solution Assume that $\sqrt{2}$ is rational. Then it would be possible to represent the value as a simplified fraction $\frac{a}{b}$, where a and b are integers and b is not zero. Because the fraction is simplified, a and b have no common factors other than 1.

$\sqrt{2} = \frac{a}{b}$

$(\sqrt{2})^2 = \left(\frac{a}{b}\right)^2$ Square both sides of the equation.

$2 = \frac{a^2}{b^2}$ $\sqrt{2} \cdot \sqrt{2} = \sqrt{4} = 2$ and $\frac{a}{b} \cdot \frac{a}{b} = \frac{a^2}{b^2}$

$2b^2 = a^2$ Means-Extremes Product Property

Since a number with a factor of 2 is an even number, $2b^2$ is an even number. That means a^2 is an even number, and since only an even number squared can result in an even number, a must also be even.

Since a is an even number, it can be written as a product with a factor of 2. Let $a = 2c$, where c is an integer.

$2b^2 = a^2$ Last line from above

$2b^2 = (2c)^2$ Substitution Property of Equality

$2b^2 = 4c^2$ $2c \cdot 2c = 4c^2$

$b^2 = 2c^2$ Divide each side by 2.

TIP

When an assumption leads to a contradiction (two statements with opposite ideas), the assumption is false.

Now b^2 is shown to be an even number because it is equal to a product with a factor of 2. Since b^2 is even, b is even.

Both a and b have been shown to be even, which means they both have a common factor of 2. However, it was stated in the beginning of the proof that a and b have no common factors other than 1. This is a contradiction. Therefore, the assumption that $\sqrt{2}$ is rational must be incorrect. A number is either rational or irrational, so $\sqrt{2}$ is irrational. ■

Problem Set

Determine if each number is rational or irrational. Explain.

1. $\sqrt{75}$
2. $\sqrt{100}$
3. $\sqrt{\frac{3}{7}}$
4. $-\sqrt{49}$
5. $\sqrt{144}$
6. π
7. $-\sqrt{170}$
8. $\sqrt{\frac{16}{25}}$

Simplify.

9. $\sqrt{72}$
10. $\sqrt{\frac{4}{9}}$
11. $\sqrt{100}$
12. $\sqrt{125}$
13. $-\sqrt{12}$
14. $\sqrt{45}$
15. $\sqrt{9}$
16. $\sqrt{\frac{36}{81}}$
17. $\sqrt{196}$
18. $-\sqrt{162}$
19. $\sqrt{300}$
20. $\sqrt{121}$
21. $-\sqrt{288}$
22. $\sqrt{\frac{1}{4}}$
23. $\sqrt{169}$
24. $\sqrt{27}$
25. $5\sqrt{8}$

Solve.

26. Show that the set of irrational numbers is not closed under division. That is, show that there are two irrational numbers with a quotient that is not an irrational number.

*27. **Challenge** The unit square diagrams show that every perfect square can be written as a sum of the form $1 + 3 + 5 + 7 + \ldots$

1

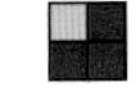

$4 = 1 + 3$

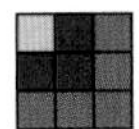

$9 = 1 + 3 + 5$

A. Complete the list below:

$1 = 1$
$4 = 1 + 3$
$9 = 1 + 3 + 5$
$16 =$
$25 =$
$36 =$

B. Predict the number of addends in the expansion for 144 and 1024.

*28. **Challenge** Write an example to illustrate the process of finding the greatest perfect square divisor of x. Choose a value a and test to see if $\frac{x}{a^2}$ is an integer. If $\frac{x}{a^2}$ is an integer, a is the greatest perfect square divisor of x. Begin with the least value of a that is greater than $\sqrt{x}$ and work backwards.

Estimating Square Roots

REMEMBER

Irrational numbers are nonterminating, nonrepeating decimals.

Because the square root of a number that is not a perfect square is an irrational number, its decimal value can only be estimated.

PROPERTY

For nonnegative values of m, n, and p,

if $m < n < p$, then $\sqrt{m} < \sqrt{n} < \sqrt{p}$.

If a number is between two other numbers, then its square root is between the square roots of the other numbers. To illustrate, $3 < 4 < 5$ and $\sqrt{3} < \sqrt{4} < \sqrt{5}$.

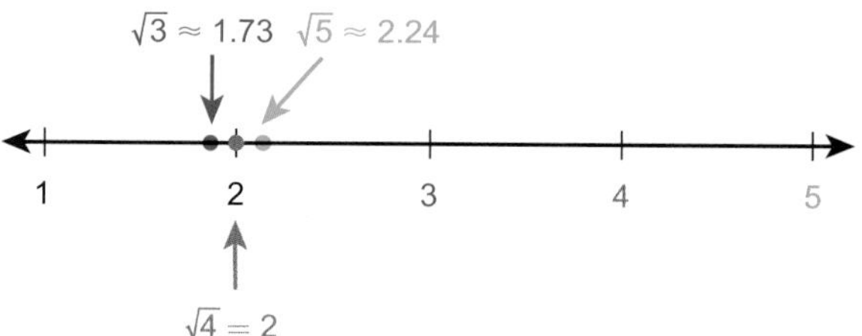

Determining the Location of the Square Root of a Non-Perfect Square

Example 1 Determine between which two consecutive integers each square root lies.

A. $\sqrt{52}$

Solution Think of the perfect squares: 1, 4, 9, 16, 25, 36, 49, 64, 81, 100, ... Choose the nearest perfect squares less than and greater than 52. They are 49 and 64. Because $\sqrt{49} = 7$ and $\sqrt{64} = 8$, $\sqrt{52}$ lies between 7 and 8. ■

B. $\sqrt{125}$

Solution Since 125 lies between the perfect squares 121 (11^2) and 144 (12^2), $\sqrt{125}$ lies between 11 and 12. ■

Estimating Square Roots of Non-Perfect Squares

To estimate the square root of a number, first determine between which two consecutive integers the square root lies. Adjust the estimate based on which perfect square the number is closer to and by how much.

Example 2 Estimate $\sqrt{23}$ to the nearest tenth.

Solution Twenty-three lies between 16 and 25, so $\sqrt{23}$ lies between 4 and 5. Since 23 is about three-quarters of the way between 16 and 25, $\sqrt{23}$ should be about three-quarters of the way between 4 and 5, or at about 4.75. Test values around 4.75.

$4.7^2 = 22.09$ and $4.8^2 = 23.04$

So, $\sqrt{23} \approx 4.8$. ■

Using the Babylonian Method to Estimate a Square Root

Another method to use when estimating the square root of a number is the Babylonian method.

USING THE BABYLONIAN METHOD TO FIND THE SQUARE ROOT OF *x*

Step 1 Start with any guess r_1 of the square root.

Step 2 Find the average of r_1 and $\frac{x}{r_1}$ to compute a new guess r_2.

Step 3 Repeat Step 2 using r_2. Continue this process until r_n and $\frac{x}{r_n}$ are as close as desired.

THINK ABOUT IT

The first guess is r_1, the second guess is r_2, and the *n*th guess is r_n.

Example 3 Use the Babylonian method to estimate $\sqrt{7}$ to the nearest hundredth.

Solution

Step 1 Guess 2.5 because $2 \cdot 2 = 4$ and $3 \cdot 3 = 9$.

Step 2 $$\frac{r_1 + \frac{x}{r_1}}{2} = \frac{2.5 + \frac{7}{2.5}}{2} = \frac{2.5 + 2.8}{2} = \frac{5.3}{2} = 2.65$$

Step 3 $$\frac{r_2 + \frac{x}{r_2}}{2} = \frac{2.65 + \frac{7}{2.65}}{2} \approx \frac{2.65 + 2.64}{2} \approx \frac{5.29}{2} \approx 2.645 \approx 2.65$$

The estimates after Step 2 and Step 3 are so close that the hundredths place doesn't change, so this is a good stopping point. So, $\sqrt{7} \approx 2.65$. ■

Application: Geometry

Example 4 Find the perimeter of a square whose area is 450 square meters. Round your answer to the nearest tenth of a meter.

Solution The side length of a square is the square root of the area. Perimeter is four times the length of one side, so the expression $4\sqrt{450}$ represents the perimeter of the square.

$4\sqrt{450} \approx 84.9$

The perimeter is about 84.9 meters.

Check $\left(\frac{84.9}{4}\right)^2 = 450.500625 \approx 450$ ✓ ■

Problem Set

Determine between which two consecutive integers each square root lies.

1. $\sqrt{19}$
2. $\sqrt{28}$
3. $\sqrt{12}$
4. $\sqrt{240}$
5. $\sqrt{70}$
6. $\sqrt{92}$
7. $\sqrt{40}$
8. $\sqrt{61}$
9. $\sqrt{136}$

Estimate the given square root to the nearest tenth.

10. $\sqrt{17}$
11. $\sqrt{78}$
12. $\sqrt{45}$
13. $\sqrt{85}$
14. $\sqrt{5}$
15. $\sqrt{150}$
16. $\sqrt{20}$
17. $\sqrt{55}$
18. $\sqrt{23}$
19. $\sqrt{3}$
20. $\sqrt{60}$

Use the Babylonian method to estimate the given square root to the nearest tenth.

21. $\sqrt{30}$
22. $\sqrt{200}$
23. $\sqrt{165}$
24. $\sqrt{99}$

Solve. When estimating, round to the nearest tenth.

25. Complete the missing information in the problem to find $\sqrt{300}$ using the Babylonian method.

    First Guess: 17

    $$\frac{17 + \frac{300}{\square}}{2} = \frac{\frac{\square + 300}{17}}{2} = \frac{\frac{589}{17}}{\square} \approx \square.3235;$$

    $$\frac{\square + \frac{\square}{17.3235}}{2} = \frac{\frac{300.1036523 + 300}{17.3235}}{2} =$$

    $$\frac{\frac{\square}{17.3235}}{2} \approx 17.32 \approx 17.3$$

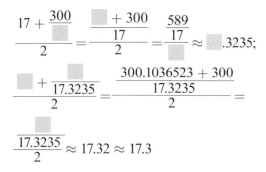

26. The area of a square is 45 square units. Estimate the side length.
27. Five times the square of a number is 165. Estimate the number.
28. The quotient of the square of a number and 2 is 0.6. Estimate the number.
29. The area of a circle is 20π m^2. Find the approximate radius of the circle.

*30. **Challenge** Square a number, divide the result by 10 and multiply that result by 2 to obtain 57.8. What is the number?

Radicals with Variables

Radical expressions may contain variables.

The square root of a nonnegative number that is squared is the original number. For example, $\sqrt{3^2} = 3$ because $\sqrt{3^2} = \sqrt{3 \cdot 3} = \sqrt{9} = 3$.

Suppose the base of the power is a variable: $\sqrt{a^2}$. Since the radical sign indicates the principal square root, $\sqrt{a^2} = a$.

Evaluating a Variable Square-Root Expression

When evaluating a variable square-root expression, treat the radical sign as a grouping symbol.

Example 1 Evaluate. If necessary, round your answer to the nearest hundredth.

A. $\sqrt{11 - a}$, when $a = 2$ and when $a = -3$

Solution

$\sqrt{11 - 2} = \sqrt{9} = 3$

$\sqrt{11 - (-3)} = \sqrt{14} \approx 3.74$ ■

B. $10 - \sqrt{2d} + 2\sqrt{d + 15}$, when $d = 15$

Solution

$10 - \sqrt{2 \cdot 15} + 2\sqrt{15 + 15}$

$10 - \sqrt{30} + 2\sqrt{30}$ Simplify under the radical signs.

$10 + \sqrt{30}$ Add like radicals.

≈ 15.48 Find the sum. Then round. ■

C. $4\sqrt{(b + c)^2 + (b - 5)^2}$, when $b = 7$ and $c = 6$

Solution

$4\sqrt{(7 + 6)^2 + (7 - 5)^2}$

$4\sqrt{13^2 + 2^2}$ Simplify inside the parentheses.

$4\sqrt{169 + 4}$ Evaluate the powers.

$4\sqrt{173}$ Add.

≈ 52.61 Find the product. Then round. ■

TIP

Rounding should always be the last step in evaluating a square-root expression.

Simplifying Square Roots of Powers with Variable Bases

Example 2 Simplify each expression. Assume all variables are nonnegative.

A. $\sqrt{x^6y^2}$

Solution $\sqrt{x^6y^2} = \sqrt{(x^3)^2y^2} = x^3y$ ■

B. $\sqrt{16a^5}$

Solution $\sqrt{16a^5} = \sqrt{16a^4a} = \sqrt{4^2(a^2)^2a} = 4a^2\sqrt{a}$ ■

C. $2\sqrt{150p^{18}q^3}$

Solution

$$\begin{aligned} 2\sqrt{150p^{18}q^3} &= 2\sqrt{5^2 \cdot 6(p^9)^2q^2q} \\ &= 2 \cdot 5p^9q\sqrt{6q} \\ &= 10p^9q\sqrt{6q} \end{aligned}$$ ■

TIP

The square root of a power with an exponent that is an even number is a perfect square.

Simplifying Radical Expressions with Quotients

Just as the product of two square roots is the square root of the product, a quotient of two square roots is the square root of the quotient.

PROPERTY

For nonnegative values a and b, where $b \neq 0$,

$$\frac{\sqrt{a}}{\sqrt{b}} = \sqrt{\frac{a}{b}}$$

Example 3 Simplify each expression.

A. $\sqrt{\frac{x}{9}}$

Solution Rewrite the expression as a quotient of two radicals. Then simplify.

$$\sqrt{\frac{x}{9}} = \frac{\sqrt{x}}{\sqrt{9}} = \frac{\sqrt{x}}{3}$$ ■

THINK ABOUT IT

The expression $\frac{\sqrt{x}}{3}$ is simplified because the radicand $\sqrt{x}$ does not contain a quotient.

B. $\frac{\sqrt{72}}{\sqrt{2}}$

Solution Rewrite the expression as the square root of the quotient of the radicands.

$$\frac{\sqrt{72}}{\sqrt{2}} = \sqrt{\frac{72}{2}} = \sqrt{36} = 6$$ ■

Rationalizing the Denominator

A radical expression is not considered simplified if a radical appears in a denominator. To clear a radical from a denominator, you can **rationalize the denominator**. To rationalize a denominator, multiply the numerator and denominator of the expression by the radical in the denominator of the expression.

Example 4 Simplify each expression.

A. $\sqrt{\frac{x}{7}}$

Solution

$$\sqrt{\frac{x}{7}} = \frac{\sqrt{x}}{\sqrt{7}}$$

$$= \frac{\sqrt{x}}{\sqrt{7}} \cdot \frac{\sqrt{7}}{\sqrt{7}} = \frac{\sqrt{7}\sqrt{x}}{\sqrt{49}} = \frac{\sqrt{7x}}{7} \quad \blacksquare$$

B. $\frac{-4y}{\sqrt{8}}$

Solution

$$\frac{-4y}{\sqrt{8}} = \frac{-4y}{\sqrt{4}\sqrt{2}} = \frac{-4y}{2\sqrt{2}} = \frac{-2y}{\sqrt{2}}$$

$$= \frac{-2y}{\sqrt{2}} \cdot \frac{\sqrt{2}}{\sqrt{2}} = \frac{-2\sqrt{2}y}{2} = -\sqrt{2}y \quad \blacksquare$$

THINK ABOUT IT

The expression $\frac{\sqrt{7}}{\sqrt{7}}$ is equivalent to 1, so multiplying an expression by it does not change the value of the expression.

TIP

Simplifying the radical in the denominator first will minimize reducing later in the problem.

Application: Analyzing a Bogus Proof

Example 5 The statement $\left(1 - \frac{3}{2}\right)^2 = \left(2 - \frac{3}{2}\right)^2$ is true.

Find the error in the following proof that $1 \neq 2$.

Step 1 $\left(1 - \frac{3}{2}\right)^2 = \left(2 - \frac{3}{2}\right)^2$ Given

Step 2 $\sqrt{\left(1 - \frac{3}{2}\right)^2} = \sqrt{\left(2 - \frac{3}{2}\right)^2}$ Take the square root of each side.

Step 3 $1 - \frac{3}{2} = 2 - \frac{3}{2}$

Step 4 $1 = 2$ ✗ Add $\frac{3}{2}$ to each side and simplify.

Therefore, $1 \neq 2$.

Solution Simplify $1 - \frac{3}{2}$ and $2 - \frac{3}{2}$.

$1 - \frac{3}{2} = -\frac{1}{2}$ and $2 - \frac{3}{2} = \frac{1}{2}$

This means that in Step 2, when the square root of each side is taken, the square root of a negative number was taken on the left side. This step is not allowed. ■

Problem Set

Simplify. Assume all variables are nonnegative.

1. $\sqrt{x^4y^{10}}$
2. $\sqrt{25x^9}$
3. $3\sqrt{90a^{12}b^{15}}$
4. $\sqrt{x^7y^8}$
5. $\sqrt{72x^3}$
6. $\sqrt{64x^{13}}$
7. $4\sqrt{50x^{14}y^{11}z^2}$
8. $\sqrt{\frac{x}{4}}$
9. $\frac{\sqrt{36}}{\sqrt{4}}$
10. $\frac{\sqrt{128}}{\sqrt{2}}$
11. $\sqrt{\frac{x}{25}}$
12. $\frac{\sqrt{700}}{\sqrt{7}}$
13. $\sqrt{\frac{a}{121}}$
14. $\frac{\sqrt{80}}{\sqrt{5}}$
15. $\sqrt{\frac{x}{11}}$
16. $\frac{2x}{\sqrt{18}}$
17. $-\frac{3x}{\sqrt{27}}$
18. $\sqrt{\frac{x}{13}}$
19. $-\frac{4x}{\sqrt{108}}$
20. $\sqrt{\frac{x}{10}}$
21. $\frac{5a}{\sqrt{84}}$

Evaluate each expression for the given values. Provide answers in simplified radical form and approximate irrational answers to the nearest hundredth.

22. $\sqrt{x+7}$
    A. $x = 10$
    B. $x = -2$
23. $15 + 2\sqrt{a+8} - \sqrt{3a}$, when $a = 4$
24. $2\sqrt{(x+y) - (x-y)^2}$, when $x = 8$ and $y = 5$
25. $20 + \sqrt{4-x} - 3\sqrt{x}$, when $x = 2$
26. $\sqrt{2x-1}$
    A. $x = 1$
    B. $x = 3$
27. $3\sqrt{(ab)^2 + (2a+b)^3}$, when $a = 1$ and $b = 4$
28. $\sqrt{2x+3} - 10\sqrt{x+1} - 5$, when $x = -1$

Solve.

*29. **Challenge** The statement $\left(1 + \frac{1}{2}\right)^2 = \left(\frac{1}{2} - 2\right)^2$ is true. Find and explain the error in the following proof.

$$\left(1 + \frac{1}{2}\right)^2 = \left(\frac{1}{2} - 2\right)^2$$

$$\sqrt{\left(1 + \frac{1}{2}\right)^2} = \sqrt{\left(\frac{1}{2} - 2\right)^2}$$

$$1 + \frac{1}{2} = \frac{1}{2} - 2$$

$$1 = -2 \ \chi$$

*30. **Challenge** The statement $(1-4)^2 = (1+2)^2$ is true. Find and explain the error in the following proof.

$$(1-4)^2 = (1+2)^2$$

$$\sqrt{(1-4)^2} = \sqrt{(1+2)^2}$$

$$1 - 4 = 1 + 2$$

$$-4 = 2 \ \chi$$

Using Square Roots to Solve Equations

An equation can have zero, one, two, or even an infinite number of solutions.

When a solution of an equation is substituted for the variable, the statement is a true statement.

Using Square Roots to Solve Equations

Consider the equation $x^2 = 9$. This equation has two solutions because both 3 and -3, which are the square roots of 9, make the equation true. To solve an equation in which the variable is squared, take the square root of each side of the equation. Because $\sqrt{x^2} = |x|$, and both the positive and negative square roots are solutions, write $x = \pm\sqrt{9}$.

NOTATION

The symbol $\pm$ is read as "plus or minus." The expression $\pm\sqrt{9}$ is an abbreviated way of writing "$\sqrt{9}$ and $-\sqrt{9}$."

PROPERTY

For nonnegative values of a, if $x^2 = a$, then $x = \pm\sqrt{a}$.

Example 1 Solve the equation. If necessary, round your answer to the nearest tenth.

A. $n^2 = 25$

Solution

$n^2 = 25$

$n = \pm\sqrt{25}$ Take the square root of each side.

$n = \pm 5$ Simplify $\sqrt{25}$.

The solutions are 5 and -5. ■

B. $5t^2 = 31$

Solution Isolate the variable and take the square root of each side.

$5t^2 = 31$

$t^2 = \frac{31}{5}$ Divide each side by 5.

$t = \pm\sqrt{\frac{31}{5}}$ Take the square root of each side.

$t = \pm\sqrt{6.2}$ Simplify the radicand.

$t \approx \pm 2.5$ Estimate $\sqrt{6.2}$ with a calculator.

The solutions are exactly $\sqrt{6.2}$ and $-\sqrt{6.2}$ or about 2.5 and -2.5. ■

(continued)

C. $9x^2 - 64 = 0$

Solution Use inverse operations to isolate the variable.

$9x^2 - 64 = 0$

$9x^2 = 64$	Add 64 to each side.
$x^2 = \frac{64}{9}$	Divide each side by 9.
$x = \pm\sqrt{\frac{64}{9}}$	Take the square root of each side.
$x = \pm\frac{\sqrt{64}}{\sqrt{9}}$	Write the square root as a quotient.
$x = \pm\frac{8}{3}$	Simplify $\sqrt{64}$ and $\sqrt{9}$.

The solutions are $\frac{8}{3}$ and $-\frac{8}{3}$. ■

Applications: Geometry and Physics

Example 2 The area of a circle is 40 square centimeters. Estimate the radius to the nearest tenth of a centimeter.

Solution Solve the area formula $A = \pi r^2$ for r.

$40 = \pi r^2$	Substitute 40 for A.
$\frac{40}{\pi} = r^2$	Divide each side by π.
$\pm\sqrt{\frac{40}{\pi}} = r$	Take the square root of each side.
$\pm 3.6 \approx r$	Use a calculator to estimate.

Because length cannot be negative, disregard the negative answer. The radius is about 3.6 centimeters. ■

Example 3 Solve $-16t^2 + 80 = 0$ to estimate the number of seconds t it takes for an object dropped from 80 feet above the ground to hit the ground.

Solution

$-16t^2 + 80 = 0$

$-16t^2 = -80$	Subtract 80 from each side.
$t^2 = 5$	Divide each side by -16.
$t = \pm\sqrt{5} \approx \pm 2.236$	Take the square root of each side.

Since time cannot be negative, disregard the negative answer. The time is about 2.24 seconds. ■

Problem Set

Solve each equation. If necessary, round your answers to the nearest tenth.

1. $x^2 = 64$
2. $y^2 = 121$
3. $n^2 = 625$
4. $t^2 = 12$
5. $x^2 = 96$
6. $y^2 = 196$
7. $16x^2 = 81$
8. $25t^2 = 144$
9. $4x^2 - 49 = 0$
10. $3y^2 - 27 = 0$
11. $5m^2 - 140 = 40$
12. $9x^2 + 50 = 219$
13. $6z^2 - 183 = 111$
14. $3x^2 = 48$
15. $4y^2 = 14$
16. $5z^2 = 56$
17. $4x^2 + 37 = 127$
18. $2(6n^2 - 17) = 19$

Challenge

*19. $\frac{2(4x^2 + 7)}{7} = x^2 + 3$

*20. $\frac{15m^2}{4} - 6 = 28.5$

*21. $x^2 = 36y$

Solve.

22. Estimate to the nearest hundredth of a second the time it would take a car to travel 50 feet from a stop, at a constant acceleration of 3.2 ft/s^2. Use $d = \frac{1}{2}at^2$, where d represents distance, a represents acceleration, and t represents time in seconds.

23. The area of a circle is 20 square inches. Estimate the radius to the nearest tenth of an inch.

24. The surface area of a cube is 100 square centimeters. Estimate to the nearest tenth of a centimeter the side length of the cube using the formula $S = 6s^2$, where S represents surface area and s represents side length.

25. The kinetic energy of an object in motion can be modeled by the equation $E = \frac{1}{2}mv^2$, where E represents the kinetic energy, m represents the mass, and v represents velocity. What is the velocity (in meters per second) of an object with a mass of 20 kilograms and kinetic energy of 33,640 Joules?

26. The height of a dropped object can by modeled by the formula $h(t) = -\frac{1}{2}gt^2 + h_0$ where h represents the height after time t (in seconds), h_0 represents the initial height, and g represents the acceleration due to gravity.

    A. Estimate to the nearest hundredth of a second the time it takes an object dropped from an initial height of 63 meters to reach the ground on earth ($g = 9.8$ meters per square second).

    B. Estimate to the nearest hundredth of a second the time it takes an object dropped from an initial height of 63 meters to reach the moon ($g = 1.62$ meters per square second).

The Pythagorean Theorem

Squaring and taking square roots of numbers can help you solve many geometric problems, such as those involving triangles.

REMEMBER

A right angle measures 90° and is indicated by a square □.

DEFINITIONS

A triangle with a right angle is a **right triangle**. The two sides of the triangle that form the right angle are the **legs**. The side opposite the right angle is the **hypotenuse**.

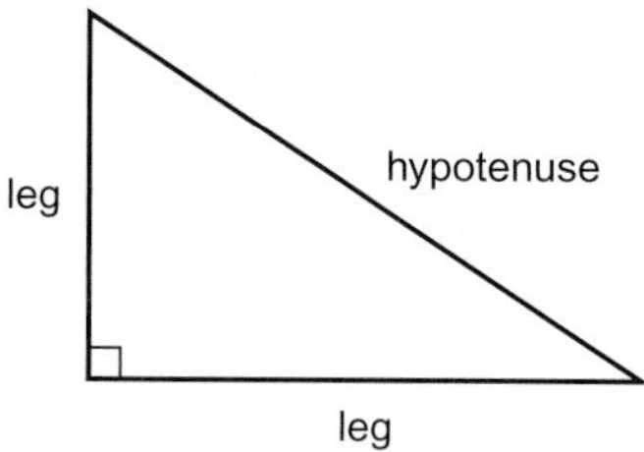

Using the Pythagorean Theorem

The Pythagorean theorem states the relationship between the lengths of the sides of a right triangle.

PROPERTY: THE PYTHAGOREAN THEOREM

In a right triangle, the sum of the squares of the lengths of the legs equals the square of the length of the hypotenuse.

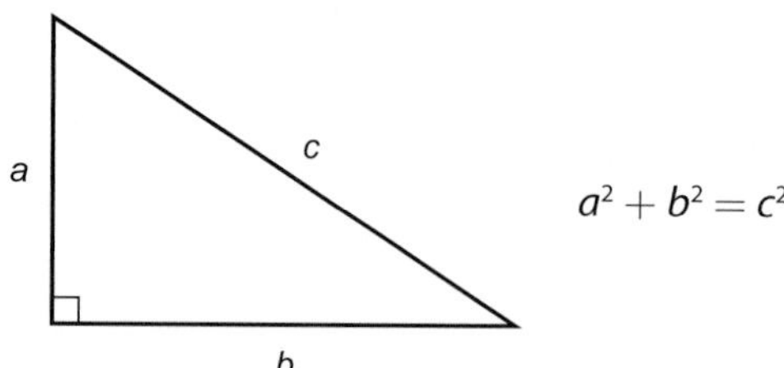

Example 1 Find the value of x.

A.

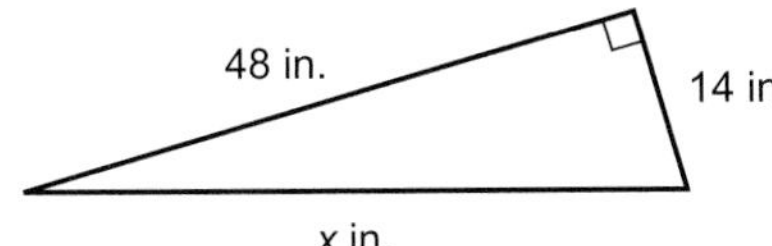

Solution The unknown side is the hypotenuse c.

$a^2 + b^2 = c^2$	
$14^2 + 48^2 = x^2$	Substitute 14 and 48 for a and b, and x for c.
$196 + 2304 = x^2$	Simplify the left side.
$2500 = x^2$	
$\pm\sqrt{2500} = x$	Take the square root of each side.
$\pm 50 = x$	

Disregard the negative answer because lengths must be nonnegative. The value of x is 50. ■

B.

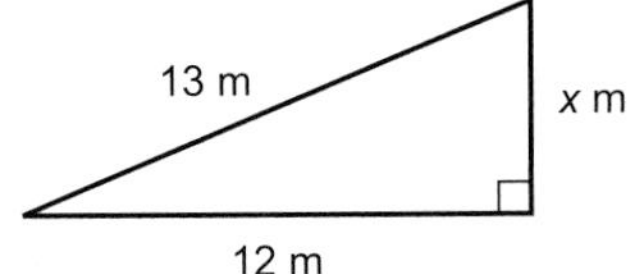

Solution The unknown side is a leg.

$a^2 + b^2 = c^2$	
$x^2 + 12^2 = 13^2$	Substitute x for a, 12 for b, and 13 for c.
$x^2 + 144 = 169$	Evaluate powers.
$x^2 = 25$	Subtract 144 from each side.
$x = \pm\sqrt{25}$	Take the square root of each side.
$x = \pm 5$	

Disregard the negative answer. The value of x is 5. ■

THINK ABOUT IT

You would get the same answer by substituting 48 for *a* and 14 for *b*.

TIP

The hypotenuse is always the longest side of a right triangle. You know you have made an error if the length of a leg is greater than the length of the hypotenuse.

Using the Converse of the Pythagorean Theorem

The Pythagorean theorem tells you how to find the length of a side of a triangle given the triangle is a right triangle. The converse of the Pythagorean theorem tells you how to determine if a triangle is a right triangle given the lengths of all three sides.

THE CONVERSE OF THE PYTHAGOREAN THEOREM

If the sum of the squares of the lengths of the shorter sides of a triangle equals the square of the length of the longest side, then the triangle is a right triangle.

(continued)

Example 2 Determine if a triangle with the given side lengths is a right triangle.

A. 15 ft, 32 ft, and 36 ft

Solution Substitute 15 for a, 32 for b, 36 for c, and simplify.

$$a^2 + b^2 = c^2$$

$$15^2 + 32^2 \stackrel{?}{=} 36^2$$

$$225 + 1024 \stackrel{?}{=} 1296$$

$$1249 \neq 1296$$

The two sides of the equation are not equal, so the side lengths do not form a right triangle. ■

B. 20 ft, 16 ft, and 12 ft

Solution Substitute 20 for c, 16 for a, 12 for b, and simplify.

$$a^2 + b^2 = c^2$$

$$16^2 + 12^2 \stackrel{?}{=} 20^2$$

$$256 + 144 \stackrel{?}{=} 400$$

$$400 = 400 \checkmark$$

The two sides of the equation are equal. The side lengths form a right triangle. ■

Determining the Relative Measure of the Greatest Angle

The greatest angle in a triangle is opposite the longest side c.

TIP

The inequalities $c > a$ and $c > b$ mean that c is the longest side in the triangle.

PROPERTY

For a triangle with side lengths of a, b, and c, where $c > a$ and $c > b$,

- if $c^2 > a^2 + b^2$, then the angle opposite side c has a measure greater than 90°.
- if $c^2 < a^2 + b^2$, then the angle opposite side c has a measure less than 90°.

Example 3 The side lengths of a triangle are 9 m, 12 m, and 14 m. Does the greatest angle in the triangle measure 90°, more than 90°, or less than 90°?

Solution Determine if c^2 is less than, greater than, or equal to $a^2 + b^2$.

$$c^2 \; \square \; a^2 + b^2$$

$$14^2 \; \square \; 9^2 + 12^2$$

$$196 \; \square \; 81 + 144$$

$$196 < 225$$

Because $c^2 < a^2 + b^2$, the angle opposite side c, which is the greatest angle, has a measure that is less than 90°. ■

Application: Boating and Kites

Example 4 A boat leaves a dock and travels 3.5 miles due north and 6 miles due west. How far is the boat from the dock? Round your answer to the nearest tenth of a mile.

Solution Draw a diagram.

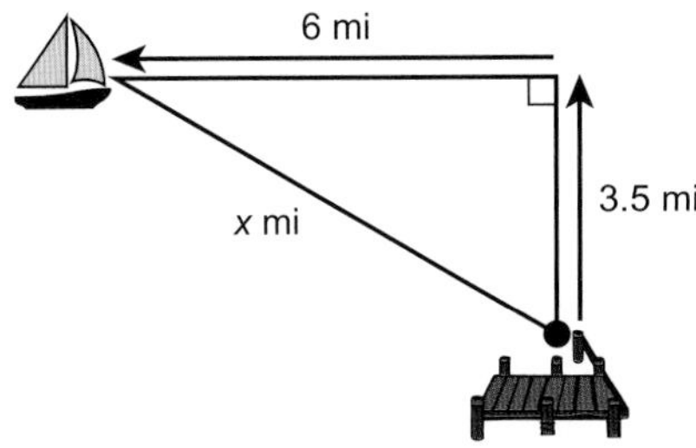

The unknown distance x is the length of the hypotenuse of a right triangle. Use the Pythagorean theorem.

$$a^2 + b^2 = c^2$$
$$3.5^2 + 6^2 = x^2$$
$$12.25 + 36 = x^2$$
$$48.25 = x^2$$
$$\pm\sqrt{48.25} = x$$
$$\pm 6.946 \approx x$$

Disregard the negative answer. The boat is about 6.9 miles from the dock. ■

Example 5 Eduardo is flying a kite on a string that is 75 meters long. The kite is 62 meters above the ground. Estimate the distance between Eduardo and the spot on the ground directly beneath the kite.

Solution Draw a diagram.

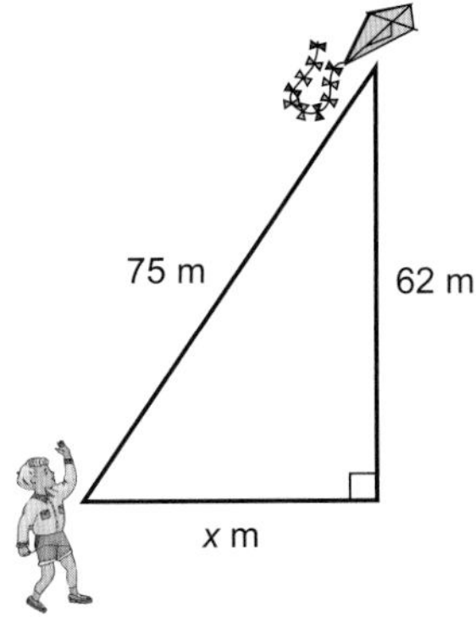

The unknown distance x is the length of a leg of a right triangle. Use the Pythagorean theorem.

$$a^2 + b^2 = c^2$$
$$x^2 + 62^2 = 75^2$$
$$x^2 + 3844 = 5625$$
$$x^2 = 1781$$
$$x = \pm\sqrt{1781} \approx \pm 42.2$$

Disregard the negative answer. Eduardo is about 42.2 meters from the spot beneath the kite. ■

REMEMBER

The shortest distance between two points is a straight line.

TIP

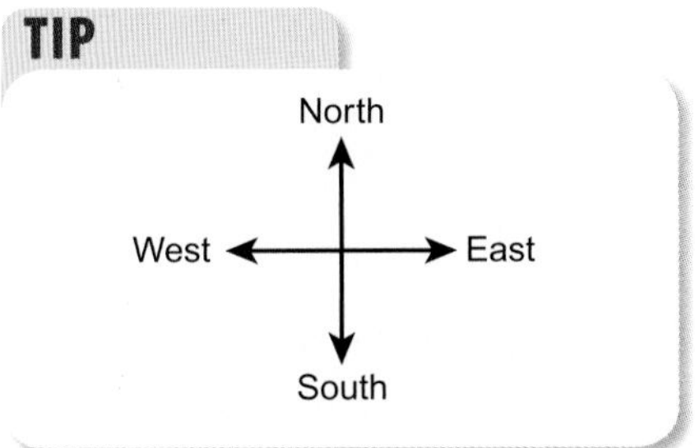

Problem Set

Find the value of x. If necessary, round your answer to the nearest hundredth.

1.

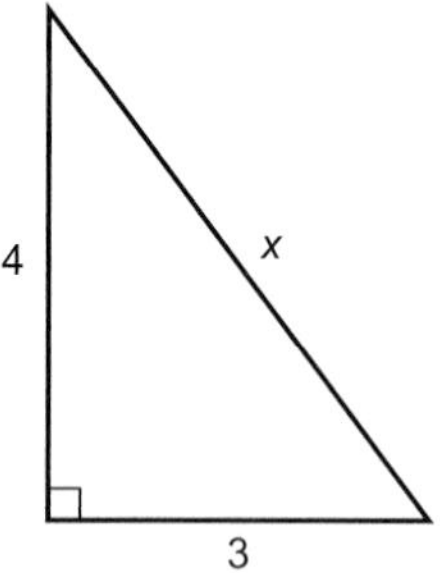

2.

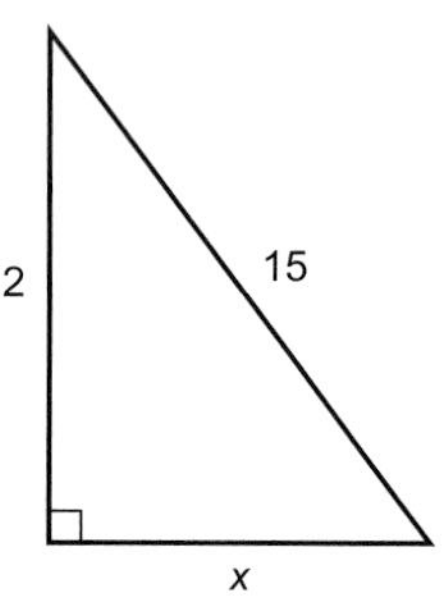

3.

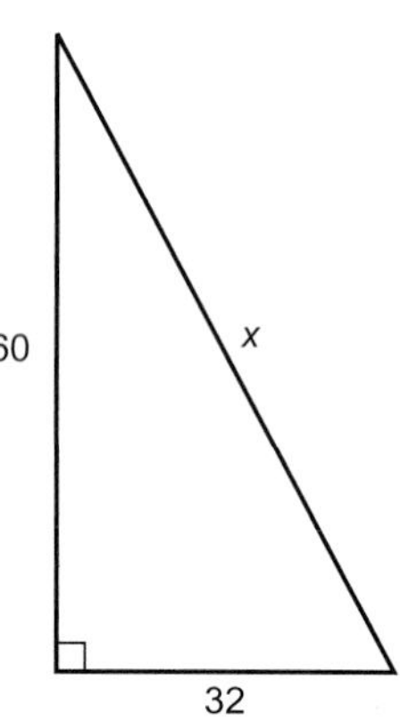

4.

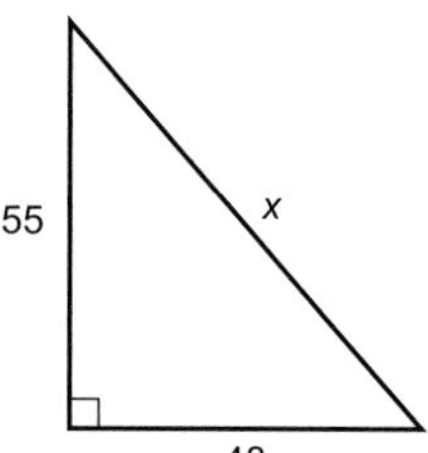

5.

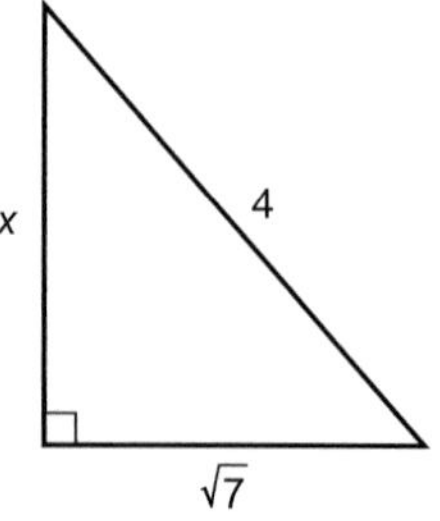

6.

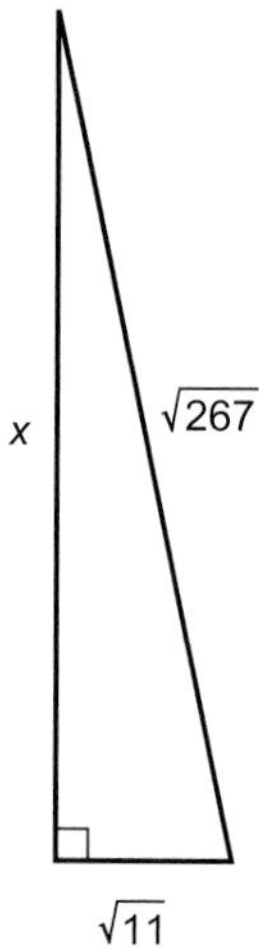

7.

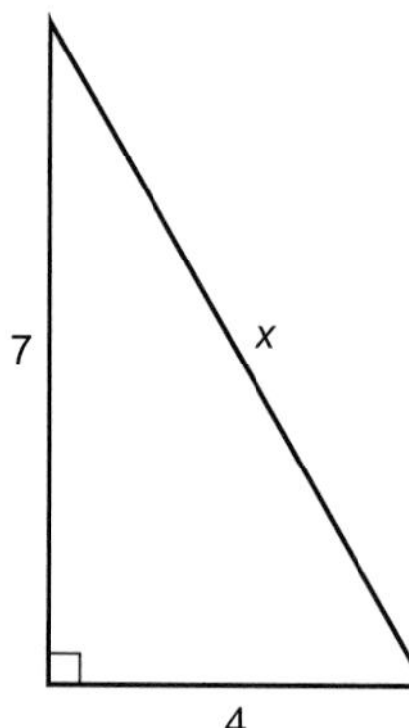

8.

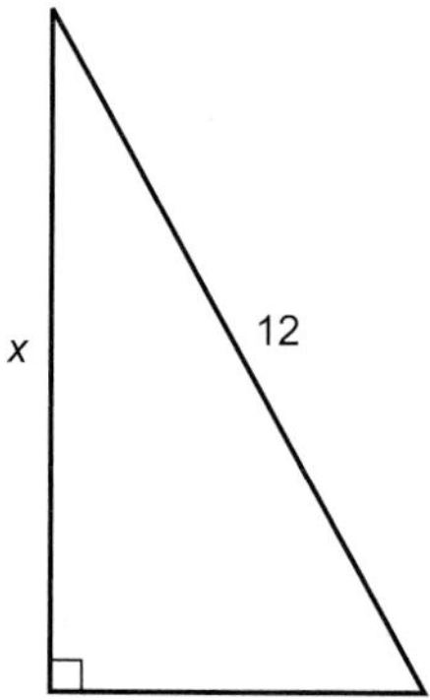

Determine if a triangle with the given side lengths is a right triangle.

9. 10 in., 24 in., and 26 in.

10. 18 cm, 24 cm, and 30 cm

11. 12 ft, 20 ft, and 24 ft

12. 20 mm, 24 mm, and 36 mm

13. 11 in., 60 in., and 61 in.

14. 51 m, 68 m, and 85 m

15. 40 yd, 56 yd, and 70 yd

For a triangle with the given side lengths, determine if the measure of its largest angle is greater than, less than, or equal to 90°.

16. 2 yd, 3 yd, and 4 yd

17. 40 cm, 42 cm, and 58 cm

18. 21 m, 23 m, and 25 m

19. 5 mi, 18 mi, and 20 mi

20. 65 km, 72 km, and 97 km

21. 96 ft, 140 ft, and 165 ft

For each problem, make a sketch and solve.

22. Southville is 57 miles due south of Portland.

A. Westfield is 76 miles due west of Portland. How far apart are Southville and Westfield?

B. Eastborough is 27 miles due east of Southville. About how far is Eastborough from Portland? Round to the nearest mile.

23. Kenji and Isabel are standing exactly opposite one another on either side of the bank of a 40-meter-wide river.

A. Kenji turns and walks 9 meters along the river. If Isabel is still standing in her original position, how far apart are Kenji and Isabel now?

B. Isabel turns and walks 13 meters in the opposite direction, also along the river. About how far apart is Isabel from Kenji's original position? Round to the nearest meter.

24. Min is building a ramp from the ground to her front doorstep. The top of the doorstep is 3.5 feet above the ground, and the ramp is 9.5 feet long. How far will it extend from the house? Round to the nearest tenth of a foot.

25. Hans leaned a 17-foot ladder against his house. He placed the base of the ladder 8 feet from his house, and the top of the ladder reached the base of his window. How high is the base of his window from the ground?

26. Mr. Edwards has placed a 20-foot flagpole in his front yard. To help secure the pole, he has strung wires from 2 feet below the top of the flagpole to the ground. The wires are 19 feet long. About how far from the bottom of the flagpole do they reach the ground? Round to the nearest foot.

27. Taro's garden is in the shape of a square with an area of $72\frac{1}{4}$ square yards. She has made a walkway in a straight line from one corner to the opposite corner. About how long is the walkway? Round to the nearest yard.

28. Jessamyn is in a hot air balloon 63 meters from the ground. A telephone pole is directly below her. An oak tree stands 60 meters from the telephone pole. How far apart are the hot air balloon and the top of the oak tree?

***29.** **Challenge** A boat is out to sea due east of a marina on the shore. The marina stands exactly halfway between two houses to the north and south, which are 72 miles apart. The boat is 39 miles from each house. How far is the boat from the marina?

***30.** **Challenge** Ashley rode her bike 6 kilometers due south, turned and rode 4 kilometers due east, and then turned again and rode 8 kilometers due south. To the nearest hundredth of a kilometer, how far is she from her starting point?

Higher Roots

The opposite of squaring is taking a square root. Similarly, the opposite of raising to any power n is taking the nth root.

DEFINITION

For all a and b, if $a^n = b$, and n is an integer greater than 1, a is the ***n*th root** of b.

NOTATION

The expression $\sqrt[n]{b}$ indicates the principal *n*th root of *b* when *n* is an even number.

PROPERTIES OF EVEN AND ODD ROOTS

Even roots have two real answers. If n is even and b is nonnegative, $\sqrt[n]{b}$ indicates the principal, or positive, root and $-\sqrt[n]{b}$ indicates the negative root.

Odd roots have one real answer. If n is odd and b is positive or negative, $\sqrt[n]{b}$ indicates the only root, which may be positive or negative.

For instance, 3 is the third root, or cube root, of 27 because $3 \cdot 3 \cdot 3 = 3^3 = 27$. Just as 9 is a perfect square, 27 is a **perfect cube**.

Although you cannot take the square root of a negative number, you can take an odd root of a negative number. The cube root of -27 is -3 because $(-3)^3 = -27$. This can be written as $\sqrt[3]{-27} = -3$.

Evaluating *n*th Roots

Example 1 Evaluate each radical expression.

A. $\sqrt[4]{81}$

Solution Both 3^4 and $(-3)^4$ equal 81, but the principal fourth root is 3, so $\sqrt[4]{81} = 3$. ■

B. $\sqrt[6]{-1}$

Solution A negative number does not have any even roots. ■

C. $\sqrt[5]{100{,}000}$

Solution $\sqrt[5]{100{,}000} = 10$ because $10^5 = 100{,}000$. ■

D. $\sqrt[3]{-125}$

Solution $\sqrt[3]{-125} = -5$ because $(-5)^3 = -125$. ■

Simplifying *n*th Roots

PROPERTIES

If b is a perfect nth power, then b can be factored so that the exponent on each factor is n.

If b is not a perfect nth power, then the nth root of b is irrational.

Variable expressions can also be perfect nth powers. Assume all variables are nonnegative.

PROPERTY

For all a and b when n is odd, and for all nonnegative a and b when n is even, $\sqrt[n]{a} \cdot \sqrt[n]{b} = \sqrt[n]{ab}$ when n is an integer greater than 1.

REMEMBER

Assuming a is positive when n is even, $\sqrt[n]{a^n} = a$.

Example 2 Simplify each expression. Assume all variables are nonnegative.

A. $\sqrt[3]{54}$

Solution

$$\begin{aligned}\sqrt[3]{54} &= \sqrt[3]{27 \cdot 2}\\ &= \sqrt[3]{27} \cdot \sqrt[3]{2}\\ &= \sqrt[3]{3^3} \cdot \sqrt[3]{2}\\ &= 3\sqrt[3]{2} \ \blacksquare\end{aligned}$$

B. $\sqrt[3]{5y^2} \cdot \sqrt[3]{25y^4}$

Solution

$$\begin{aligned}\sqrt[3]{5y^2} \cdot \sqrt[3]{25y^4} &= \sqrt[3]{125y^6}\\ &= \sqrt[3]{125} \cdot \sqrt[3]{y^6}\\ &= \sqrt[3]{5^3} \cdot \sqrt[3]{(y^2)^3}\\ &= 5y^2 \ \blacksquare\end{aligned}$$

Simplifying Expressions with Fractional Exponents

An exponent does not have to be an integer.

PROPERTY

For all a when n is odd, and for all nonnegative a when n is even, $a^{\frac{1}{n}} = \sqrt[n]{a}$ and $a^{\frac{m}{n}} = \sqrt[n]{a^m} = \left(\sqrt[n]{a}\right)^m$ when n and m are integers greater than or equal to 1.

(continued)

Example 3 Simplify each expression.

A. $4^{\frac{1}{2}}$

Solution $4^{\frac{1}{2}} = \sqrt[2]{4} = 2$ ■

B. $(-27)^{\frac{2}{3}}$

Solution $(-27)^{\frac{2}{3}} = \left(\sqrt[3]{-27}\right)^2 = (-3)^2 = 9$ ■

C. $-625^{\frac{1}{4}}$

Solution $-625^{\frac{1}{4}} = -\left(\sqrt[4]{625}\right) = -(5) = -5$ ■

D. $\sqrt[4]{x^{14}}$

Solution

$$\begin{aligned}\sqrt[4]{x^{14}} &= \sqrt[4]{x^{12}x^2}\\ &= \sqrt[4]{(x^3)^4} \cdot \sqrt[4]{x^2}\\ &= x^3\sqrt[4]{x^2}\\ &= x^3x^{\frac{2}{4}}\\ &= x^3x^{\frac{1}{2}}\\ &= x^3\sqrt{x}\end{aligned}$$ ■

Rationalizing Denominators with *n*th Roots

When rationalizing a denominator with an *n*th root, be sure to multiply both the numerator and denominator by the radical expression that will make the radicand a perfect *n*th power.

REMEMBER

An expression with a radical in the denominator is not simplified.

Example 4 Simplify.

A. $\frac{3}{\sqrt[3]{9}}$

Solution

$$\begin{aligned}\frac{3}{\sqrt[3]{9}} &= \frac{3}{\sqrt[3]{9}} \cdot \frac{\sqrt[3]{3}}{\sqrt[3]{3}}\\ &= \frac{3\sqrt[3]{3}}{\sqrt[3]{27}}\\ &= \frac{3\sqrt[3]{3}}{3}\\ &= \sqrt[3]{3}\end{aligned}$$ ■

B. $\frac{1}{\sqrt[5]{16}}$

Solution

$$\begin{aligned}\frac{1}{\sqrt[5]{16}} &= \frac{1}{\sqrt[5]{16}} \cdot \frac{\sqrt[5]{2}}{\sqrt[5]{2}}\\ &= \frac{\sqrt[5]{2}}{\sqrt[5]{32}}\\ &= \frac{\sqrt[5]{2}}{2}\end{aligned}$$ ■

Problem Set

Simplify.

1. $\sqrt[3]{64}$
2. $\sqrt[5]{-32}$
3. $\frac{4}{\sqrt[4]{8}}$
4. $\frac{5}{\sqrt[3]{16}}$
5. $(-512)^{\frac{1}{3}}$
6. $\frac{10}{\sqrt[4]{125}}$
7. $\sqrt[3]{-125}$
8. $\sqrt[5]{243}$
9. $\sqrt[6]{-64}$
10. $8^{\frac{1}{3}}$
11. $16^{\frac{1}{2}}$
12. $\sqrt[4]{10{,}000}$
13. $\sqrt[4]{-81}$
14. $(-27)^{\frac{1}{3}}$
15. $64^{\frac{2}{3}}$
16. $-216^{\frac{1}{3}}$
17. $256^{\frac{1}{2}}$
18. $\frac{6}{\sqrt[5]{16}}$
19. $\frac{7}{\sqrt{3}}$
20. $\frac{3}{\sqrt[3]{49}}$
21. $\frac{18}{\sqrt[5]{10{,}000}}$
22. $\sqrt[3]{16}$
23. $\sqrt[5]{486}$

Simplify. Assume all variables are nonnegative.

24. $\sqrt[5]{x^{12}}$
25. $\sqrt[3]{24x^{10}}$
26. $\sqrt[7]{x^{32}}$
27. $\sqrt[3]{192x^{11}}$
28. $\sqrt[5]{25x^2} \cdot \sqrt[5]{250x^{17}}$

Solve.

29. The area of a square-shaped garden is 98 ft^2. Find the length of each side of the garden. Express your answer in simplest radical form. The formula for the area of a square is $A = s^2$.

*30. **Challenge** The volume of a cube-shaped hat box is 24 in^3. Find the length of each side of the hat box. Express your answer in simplest radical form. The formula for the volume of a cube is $V = s^3$.

UNIT 10 Working with Polynomials

The railcars are linked together.

Just as a train is built from linking railcars together, a polynomial is built by bringing terms together and linking them with plus or minus signs. You can perform basic operations on polynomials in the same way that you add, subtract, multiply, and divide numbers.

Big Ideas

- A number is any entity that obeys the laws of arithmetic; all numbers obey the laws of arithmetic. The laws of arithmetic can be used to simplify algebraic expressions.
- Expressions, equations, and inequalities express relationships between different entities.

Unit Topics

- Working with Monomials and Polynomials
- Adding and Subtracting Polynomials
- Multiplying Monomials
- Multiplying Polynomials by Monomials
- Multiplying Polynomials
- The FOIL Method

Working with Monomials and Polynomials

Some expressions are monomials or polynomials.

Classifying Monomials

DEFINITION

A **monomial** is a number, a variable, or the product of a number and one or more variables.

The exponents of the variables of monomials *must be whole numbers.* The **degree of a monomial** is the sum of the exponents of its variables. Some monomials, called constants, have no variable parts. The degree of a constant term c is equal to zero since c can be written as cx^0.

REMEMBER

A value raised to the 0 power is equal to 1.

Example 1 Determine whether each expression is a monomial. If it is not, explain why. If it is a monomial, determine its degree.

	Expression	Monomial?	Degree
A.	-25	Yes.	0
B.	$5x^{\frac{1}{2}}$	No. The variable has an exponent that is not a whole number.	—
C.	$3x$	Yes.	1
D.	$\frac{3}{y^2}$	No. The variable is in the denominator, so $\frac{3}{y^2}$ can be rewritten as $3y^{-2}$, and -2 is not a whole number.	—
E.	$3x^2$	Yes.	2
F.	$-mn^2p^3$	Yes.	6

■

REMEMBER

A term is part of an expression that is added or subtracted. A term can be a number, a variable, or a combination of numbers and variables.

Classifying Polynomials by the Number of Terms

DEFINITION

A **polynomial** is a monomial or the sum or difference of two or more monomials.

(continued)

Each monomial is a term of the polynomial. A polynomial with two terms is a **binomial.** A polynomial with three terms is a **trinomial.**

The **degree of a polynomial** is equal to the degree of the monomial with the greatest degree.

Example 2 Determine whether each expression is a polynomial. If it is not, explain why. If it is a polynomial, determine its degree.

	Expression	Polynomial?	Degree
A.	$7x$	Yes.	1
B.	$-9x^3yz + 3x^3 + \frac{1}{2}$	Yes.	5
C.	$2x - x^{-2}$	No. The term $-x^{-2}$ has an exponent that is not a whole number.	—
D.	$\frac{2}{a} + 3a^2 + a$	No. The term $\frac{2}{a}$ is not a monomial since it has a variable in the denominator.	—
E.	4	Yes.	0

■

Writing a Polynomial in Standard Form

A polynomial is in **standard form** when every term is simplified and its terms are listed by decreasing degree.

Example 3 Write $21y - 3y^2 + 4 + y^3$ in standard form.

Solution Determine the degree of each term and then list the terms by decreasing degree.

$21y$	$-3y^2$	$+4$	$+y^3$
degree 1	degree 2	degree 0	degree 3

The polynomial written in standard form is $y^3 - 3y^2 + 21y + 4$. ■

Classifying Polynomials

You can classify a polynomial by the number of terms it has or by its degree. Polynomials of certain degrees have special names.

CLASSIFYING POLYNOMIALS BY THE DEGREE

Name	Degree	Example (in simplified form)
Constant	0	10
Linear	1	$3x - 2$
Quadratic	2	$x^2 + 4x + 4$
Cubic	3	$-2x^3 + x^2 + 5$
Quartic	4	$5x^4 + 7x$
Quintic	5	$-8x^5 + 6x^4 + 2x^3 + 8x^2 + 3x - 11$

A polynomial of nth degree can be written in the form

$$a_n x^n + a_{n-1} x^{n-1} + \ldots + a_1 x + a_0,$$

where a_n denotes the coefficient of the term with a power of n, a_{n-1} denotes the coefficient of the next term of the polynomial with a power of $n - 1$, and so on. For example, the polynomial $6x^5 + 3x^4 - 2x^3 + 6x^2 + 3$ has the following coefficients.

a_n	a_{n-1}	a_{n-2}	a_{n-3}	a_{n-4}	a_{n-5}
a_5	a_4	a_3	a_2	a_1	a_0
6	3	−2	6	0	3

Notice that the coefficient of a term may be the same as another term or may equal zero.

Example 4

A. Classify the polynomial $3c + 1$ by its degree and number of terms.

Solution The polynomial $3c + 1$ has two terms, and the greatest degree of its terms is 1. It is a linear binomial. ■

B. Classify the polynomial $8b^3 + 2b^2 - 5b + 6$ by its degree.

Solution The degree of the term with the greatest degree is 3, so the polynomial is cubic. ■

Application: Geometry

Example 5 The height of a ball thrown into the air can be modeled by the polynomial $-16t^2 + v_0 t + h_0$. Classify the polynomial in the variable t by its number of terms and by its degree.

Solution The polynomial $-16t^2 + v_0 t + h_0$ has three terms, so it is a trinomial. The degree of the term with the greatest degree is 2, so the polynomial is a quadratic trinomial. ■

Problem Set

If the expression is a polynomial, write *monomial, binomial,* or *trinomial* to describe it by its number of terms. If the expression is not a polynomial, write *not a polynomial.*

1. $6x^2 - 5x$

2. $\frac{12}{a} + 2a - 8$

3. y^3

4. $5z^2 - 12z + 16$

5. $\frac{9}{2}x - \sqrt{x}$

6. $2x^4y + 4x^2y^2$

State the degree of the polynomial. If the expression is not a polynomial, write *not a polynomial.*

7. $8c^3$
8. $3x^2 - 7x + 10$
9. $8d - 3$
10. $7p^4 - 2p + 6$
11. 11
12. $8x - 6y^3$
13. $-y^4 + x$
14. $5m^6n^3 - 3m^4n^2$
15. $9b^4c^3 - 6b^3c^4$
16. $14x - x^{\frac{1}{4}}$
17. $7xy - \dfrac{4x}{y}$

Write the polynomial in standard form.

18. $2 + 3m$
19. $11x + 8x^4 - 12x^2$
20. $6y^2 + 3y^5 - 10y$
21. $9z^2 + 4z^4 - z^3 + 2z$
22. $-\frac{1}{2}f^3 + 2f - 8f^2 + 12f^4$
23. $5xy^2 + 2x^2y^5 - 11x^4y + 4x^3y^3$
24. $-9w^3z^2 + wz^4 - 5w^5z^3 + 8w^2z$
25. $-3x^2y^2z^3 + 7x^4yz^5 - 3xy^4z^2 + 8x^6y^2z$
26. $-6a^2b^4c^5 + abc + 3a^3b^3c^3 + 2a^5b^2c^2 - 8a^4b^2c^3$

Solve.

27. What is the degree of the expression that represents the perimeter of this triangle?

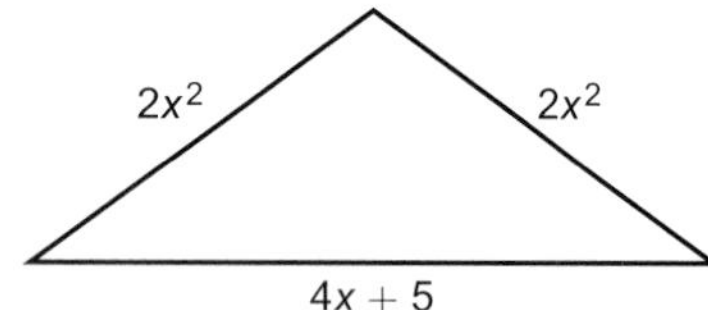

28. What is the classification and degree of the expression that represents the perimeter of this rectangle?

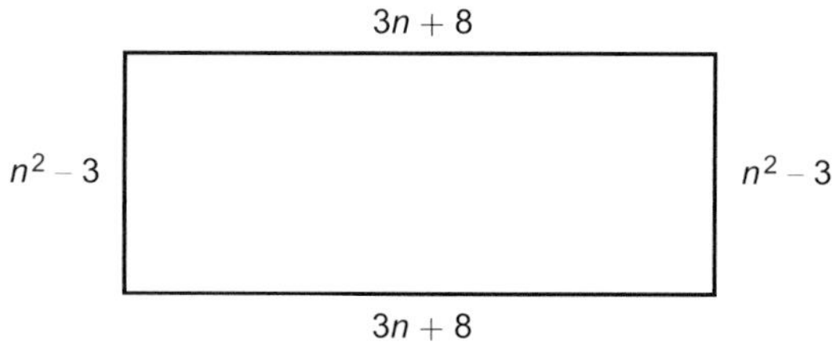

*29. **Challenge** What is the classification and degree of the expression that represents the difference in perimeter from the large square to the small square?

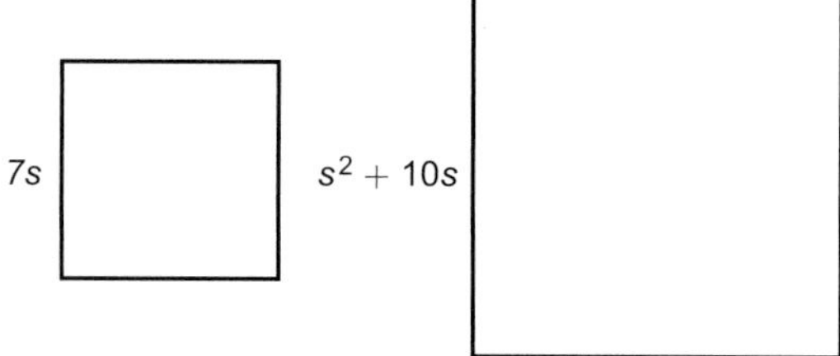

*30. **Challenge** What is the classification and degree of the expression that represents the sum of the perimeters of the rectangle and triangle?

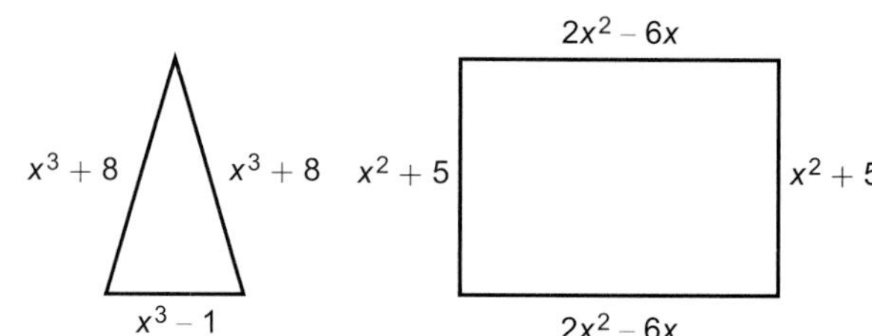

Adding and Subtracting Polynomials

You can add and subtract polynomials with like terms.

Adding Polynomials

Combine like terms to add polynomials.

REMEMBER

Like terms have the same variables raised to the same powers.

Example 1 Add.

A. $(2a^2 + a + 1) + (3a - 6)$

Solution You can add polynomials vertically or horizontally.

Vertically: Align like terms in the same column and add the coefficients of the variables.

$$\begin{array}{r} 2a^2 + a + 1 \\ + 3a - 6 \\ \hline 2a^2 + 4a - 5 \end{array}$$

REMEMBER

To combine like terms, add or subtract the coefficients and keep the variable part the same.

Horizontally: Use the commutative and associative properties to rewrite the sum with like terms grouped together. Then simplify by combining like terms.

$$\begin{aligned} (2a^2 + a + 1) + (3a - 6) &= 2a^2 + a + 1 + 3a - 6 && \text{Associative Property} \\ &= 2a^2 + (a + 3a) + (1 - 6) && \text{Commutative and Associative Properties of Addition} \\ &= 2a^2 + 4a + (-5) && \text{Combine like terms.} \\ &= 2a^2 + 4a - 5 && \text{Simplify.} \ \blacksquare \end{aligned}$$

B. $(4x^4 + 2x^3 - x^2 + 7) + (10x^4 + 8x^2 - 3)$

Solution Combine the like terms.

$$\begin{aligned} (4x^4 + 2x^3 - x^2 + 7) + (10x^4 + 8x^2 - 3) &= 4x^4 + 2x^3 - x^2 + 7 + 10x^4 + 8x^2 - 3 \\ &= (4x^4 + 10x^4) + 2x^3 + (-x^2 + 8x^2) + (7 - 3) \\ &= 14x^4 + 2x^3 + 7x^2 + 4 \ \blacksquare \end{aligned}$$

Subtracting Polynomials

Subtraction and addition are inverse operations. To subtract polynomials, you can rewrite the problem as an addition problem. You could also use the distributive property to subtract polynomials.

Example 2 Subtract.

A. $(5x + 6) - (x + 2)$

Solution You can subtract polynomials vertically or horizontally.

Vertically: Align like terms in the same column, and rewrite the problem as an addition problem.

> **TIP**
>
> Remember to distribute −1 to each term when changing to an addition problem.

Subtraction		**Addition**
$5x + 6$		$5x + 6$
$-\ (x + 2)$	→	$+(-x - 2)$
		$4x + 4$

Horizontally: Use the distributive property to remove the parentheses. Then group like terms together and simplify by combining like terms.

$(5x + 6) - (x + 2) = 5x + 6 - x - 2$ Distributive Property

$= (5x - x) + (6 - 2)$ Commutative and Associative Properties of Addition

$= 4x + 4$ Combine like terms. ■

B. $(12a^2 + 3ab - 4b^2) - (8a^2 - ab - 5b^2)$

Solution

$$\begin{aligned}(12a^2 + 3ab - 4b^2) - (8a^2 - ab - 5b^2) &= 12a^2 + 3ab - 4b^2 - 8a^2 + ab + 5b^2 \\ &= (12a^2 - 8a^2) + (3ab + ab) + (-4b^2 + 5b^2) \\ &= 4a^2 + 4ab + b^2\end{aligned}$$ ■

Application: Geometry

Example 3 Use the following triangle to answer the questions.

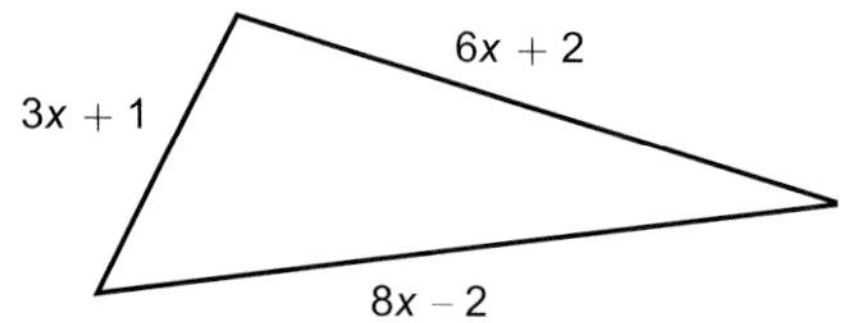

A. Express the perimeter of the triangle as a polynomial.

B. Find the perimeter of the triangle when $x = 1, 2,$ and 3.4.

Solution

A. The perimeter of a triangle is the sum of the lengths of its sides.

$P = (3x + 1) + (6x + 2) + (8x - 2)$	Write the perimeter as the sum of the side lengths.
$= 3x + 1 + 6x + 2 + 8x - 2$	Associative Property
$= (3x + 6x + 8x) + (1 + 2 - 2)$	Commutative and Associative Properties of Addition
$= 17x + 1$	Combine like terms.

The perimeter of the triangle is $17x + 1$ units.

B. Substitute each value of x into the polynomial $17x + 1$.

$x = 1$	$x = 2$	$x = 3.4$
$17x + 1 = 17 \cdot 1 + 1$	$17x + 1 = 17 \cdot 2 + 1$	$17x + 1 = 17 \cdot 3.4 + 1$
$= 17 + 1$	$= 34 + 1$	$= 57.8 + 1$
$= 18$	$= 35$	$= 58.8$
When $x = 1$, the perimeter of the triangle is 18 units.	When $x = 2$, the perimeter of the triangle is 35 units.	When $x = 3.4$, the perimeter of the triangle is 58.8 units. ■

Problem Set

Add or subtract. Simplify.

1. $(3x^2 + 7) + (x^2 - 6x + 4)$
2. $(5b^2 - 3b + 2) + (2b - 4)$
3. $(2a^2 - a + 5) + (a^2 + 4a - 1)$
4. $(6y^3 - 4y^2 + 7) + (3y^3 + y^2 - 2y - 5)$
5. $(3x^4 - 2x^3 + 4x - 2) + (3x^3 - 2x^2 - x + 4)$
6. $(2a^5 + 3a^2 - a) + (3a^5 - a^4 - 2a^2 + 3a - 4)$
7. $(3y + 2) - (y + 5)$
8. $(6x - 3) - (2x - 2)$
9. $(7b + 1) - (3b - 1)$
10. $(2a^2 - 3ab + 5b^2) - (a^2 - 2ab + 3b^2)$
11. $(3a^2 + 7ab - 4b^2) - (-5a^2 - 4ab + b^2)$
12. $(6x^2 + xy - 12y^2) - (10x^2 + xy - 2y^2)$
13. $(3x^2 - 2xy + 2y^2) + (-2x^2 + 5xy - y^2)$
14. $(15x^4 - 3x^2 + 7) - (8x^4 - 5x^3 - 2x^2 + 4)$
15. $2m(2m - 5) - 3m(m - 4)$
16. $3x(x - 2y + 1) + 2x(4x + y - 2)$
17. $(5x^3 - 3x^2 + 2x - 9) - (2x^3 - 4x^2 + 3x - 4)$
18. $(3m^2 - 2mn + 4n^2) + (-2m^2 + 5mn - 6n^2)$
19. $3p(2p^2 - p + 3n - 1) - 2p(3p - 5n + 5)$
20. $(6a^2 - 3ab + 2a - 4b) - (-2a^2 + 5ab - 5a - b)$

Challenge

*21. $\frac{1}{2}(x - y^2) - \frac{2}{3}x(x - 4) - 2y(3y - 2)$

*22. $\frac{4a(a + 6)}{a} + \frac{3a(2a - 5)}{a}$

Solve.

23. Express the perimeter of the triangle as a polynomial.

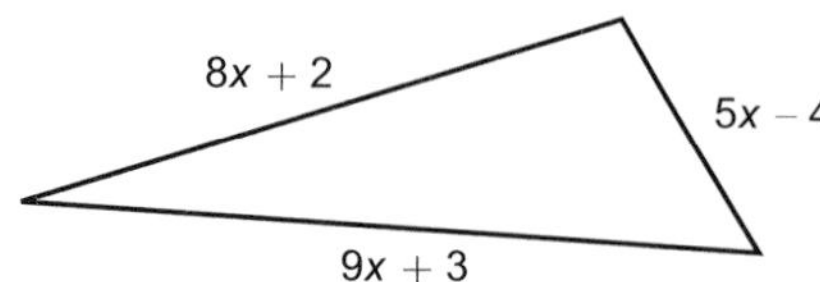

24. Express the perimeter of the rectangle as a polynomial.

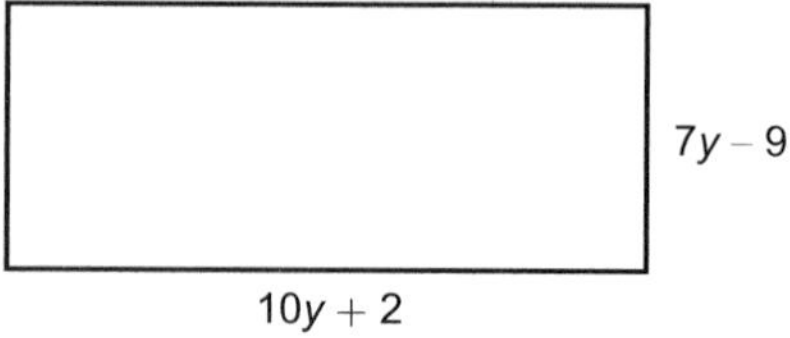

25. The height of Jake's window is $5x - 3$ inches and the width is $3x + 2$ inches. What is the perimeter of Jake's window?

26. Belinda placed stepping stones in the shape of the irregular polygon shown. She will plant thyme around the edge of each stepping stone. What is the total length of planting around each stepping stone?

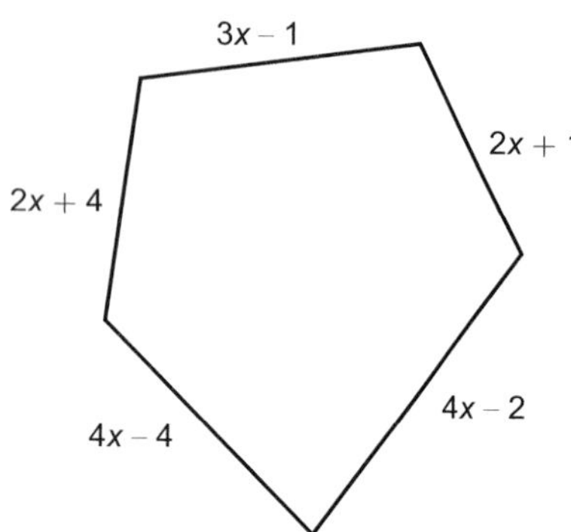

27. Craig measured these three rectangles.

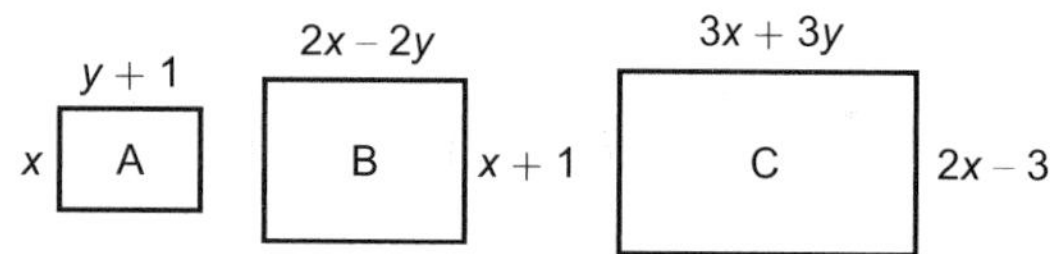

A. Express the perimeter of each rectangle as a polynomial.

B. Express the combined perimeters of the three rectangles as a polynomial.

28. Mica is using this set of figures to make a design. What is the combined perimeter of the figures?

Note: All measurements are in millimeters.

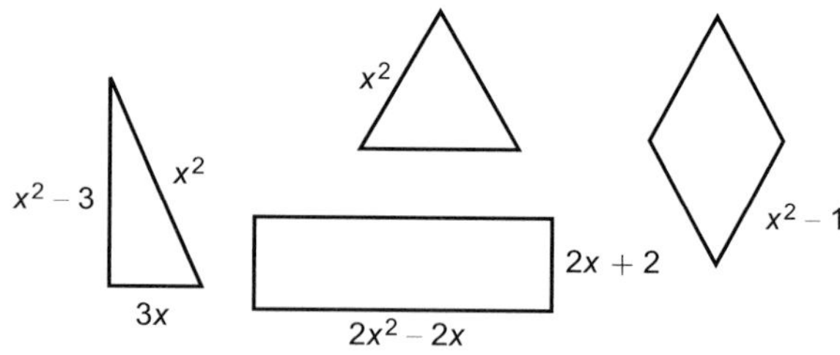

29. Arielle drew an equilateral triangle and a square. She made the sides of the square 2 centimeters less than twice the length of the side of the triangle. Express the combined perimeters of the triangle and square as a polynomial.

***30. Challenge** Benito's apartment is shown in the floor plan. He plans to put decorative baseboard along the perimeters of the living room, dining room, and bedroom, not including the doorways.

Note: All measurements are in feet.

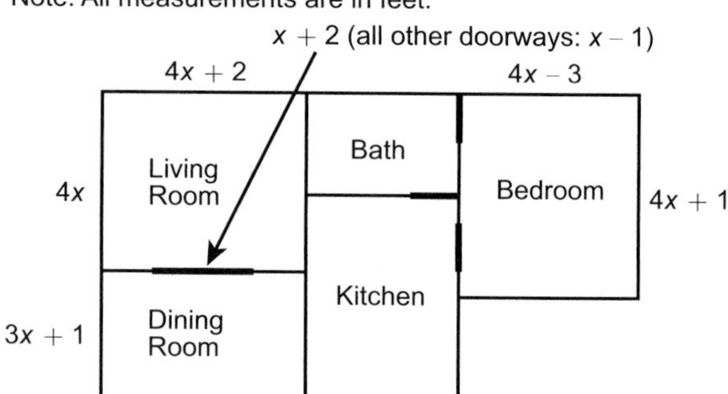

A. Express the perimeter of each of the three rooms as a polynomial.

B. How many feet of baseboard does Benito need? (Remember to subtract the doorways.)

Multiplying Monomials

Every monomial has a coefficient and most have factors that are powers of variables. Multiplying two monomials means multiplying the coefficients and multiplying the variable powers.

When you multiply two powers with the same base, you can use the product of powers property to simplify the product.

PRODUCT OF POWERS PROPERTY

If a is a real number and m and n are integers, then

$$a^m \cdot a^n = a^{m+n}.$$

Simplifying the Product of Powers

Example 1 Use the product of powers property to simplify each product.

A. $4^2 \cdot 4^5$

Solution

$4^2 \cdot 4^5 = 4^{2+5}$	Product of Powers Property
$= 4^7$	Simplify.

Check

$4^2 \cdot 4^5 \stackrel{?}{=} 4^7$

$16 \cdot 1024 \stackrel{?}{=} 16{,}384$

$16{,}384 = 16{,}384$ ✓ ■

B. $x^3 \cdot x \cdot x^4$

Solution

$x^3 \cdot x \cdot x^4 = (x^3 \cdot x^1) \cdot x^4$	Associative Property of Multiplication
$= x^{3+1} \cdot x^4$	Product of Powers Property
$= x^4 \cdot x^4$	Simplify.
$= x^{4+4}$	Product of Powers Property
$= x^8$	Simplify. ■

Multiplying Monomials

To multiply two monomials, use the commutative and associative properties of multiplication to get the constant factors together and each variable power together. Once you have all the like variables together, just use the product of powers property to simplify.

Example 2 Find each product.

A. $3x^3 \cdot 2x^5$

Solution

$3x^3 \cdot 2x^5 = (3 \cdot 2)(x^3x^5)$	Commutative and Associative Properties of Multiplication
$= 6(x^3x^5)$	Multiply.
$= 6x^{3+5}$	Product of Powers Property
$= 6x^8$	Simplify. ■

B. $-5ab^4 \cdot ab$

Solution

$-5ab^4 \cdot ab = -5(a^1a^1)(b^4b^1)$	Commutative and Associative Properties of Multiplication
$= -5a^{1+1}b^{4+1}$	Product of Powers Property
$= -5a^2b^5$	Simplify. ■

C. $\frac{1}{2}x^3y^2z \cdot 2x^5y$

Solution

$\frac{1}{2}x^3y^2z \cdot 2x^5y = \left(\frac{1}{2} \cdot 2\right)(x^3x^5)(y^2y^1)z$	Commutative and Associative Properties of Multiplication
$= 1x^{3+5}y^{2+1}z$	Product of Powers Property
$= x^8y^3z$	Simplify. ■

Application: Geometry

Example 3 Use the following figure to answer the questions.

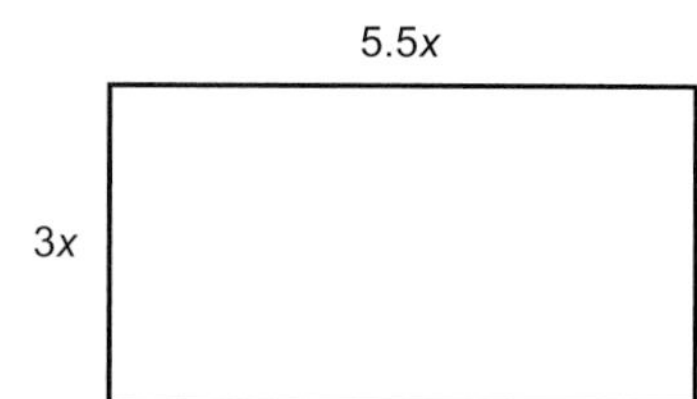

A. Express the area of the rectangle as a monomial.

B. Find the area when x is 3 in., 5 km, and 7.9 cm.

Solution

A. The area of a rectangle is the product of its length and width.

$A = lw$	
$= 5.5x \cdot 3x$	Substitute $5.5x$ for l and $3x$ for w.
$= (5.5 \cdot 3)(x^1x^1)$	Commutative and Associative Properties of Multiplication
$= 16.5(x^1x^1)$	Multiply.
$= 16.5(x^{1+1})$	Product of Powers Property
$= 16.5x^2$	Simplify.

The area of the rectangle is $16.5x^2$ square units.

B. Substitute the given values for x into the monomial $16.5x^2$.

$x = 3$ in.

$16.5x^2 = 16.5 \cdot (3 \text{ in.})^2$
$= 16.5 \cdot 9 \text{ in}^2$
$= 148.5 \text{ in}^2$

When x is 3 inches, the area of the rectangle is 148.5 square inches.

$x = 5$ km

$16.5x^2 = 16.5 \cdot (5 \text{ km})^2$
$= 16.5 \cdot 25 \text{ km}^2$
$= 412.5 \text{ km}^2$

When x is 5 kilometers, the area of the rectangle is 412.5 square kilometers.

$x = 7.9$ cm

$16.5x^2 = 16.5 \cdot (7.9 \text{ cm})^2$
$= 16.5 \cdot 62.41 \text{ cm}^2$
$= 1029.765 \text{ cm}^2$

When x is 7.9 centimeters, the area of the rectangle is 1029.765 square centimeters. ■

Problem Set

Multiply and simplify.

1. $3^3 \cdot 3^8$
2. $a^2 \cdot a^6$
3. $x^2 \cdot x \cdot x^5$
4. $2^9 \cdot 2^2 \cdot 2^4$
5. $a^2 \cdot a^4 \cdot a \cdot a^6$
6. $4y^2 \cdot 6y^3$
7. $3xy^2 \cdot x^3y$
8. $-4b^3c^2 \cdot 7bc^2$
9. $2b^8 \cdot (-6b^{12})$
10. $5abc^5 \cdot 3a^2b^3$
11. $3s \cdot s^2t^6$
12. $\frac{1}{3}m^3np^4 \cdot 18mn^7p^3$
13. $6z \cdot 3w^2 \cdot \left(-\frac{1}{9}z^3w^5\right)$
14. $-3a^2 \cdot (-b^3c) \cdot a^5bc^2$
15. $2x^3yz^6 \cdot (-4x^4y^7)$
16. $3m \cdot 0.4n^2 \cdot (-m^5n^3)$
17. $-\frac{2}{3}d \cdot c^4 \cdot 3cd^2$
18. $\frac{5}{6}y \cdot x^3y \cdot 2x^4$
19. $-2x^3y^7z \cdot \frac{1}{3}xyz^5 \cdot \left(-\frac{1}{2}x^2z^2\right)$

Challenge

*20. $\dfrac{\frac{1}{2}xy^2z^3 \cdot 9x^5y^6}{3}$

*21. $6a^2b^3 \cdot (-a^3c) \cdot (-3b^4c^2) + \left(-\frac{1}{2}a^5b\right) \cdot 8b^6c^3$

*22. $3x \cdot 2y^x \cdot x^3y^{x-4}$

Solve.

23. Express the area of the rectangle as a monomial.

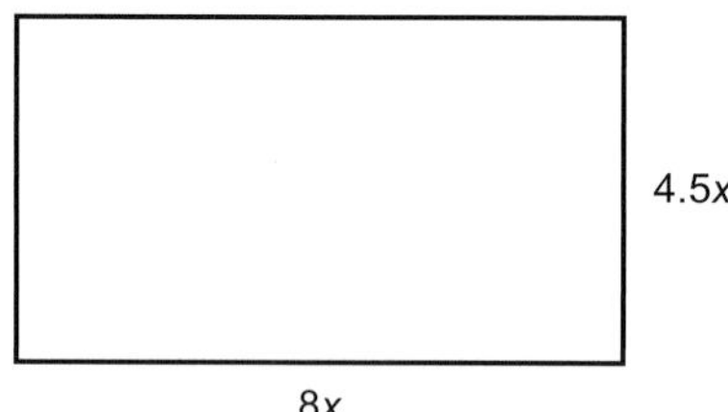

24. Express the area of the triangle as a monomial.

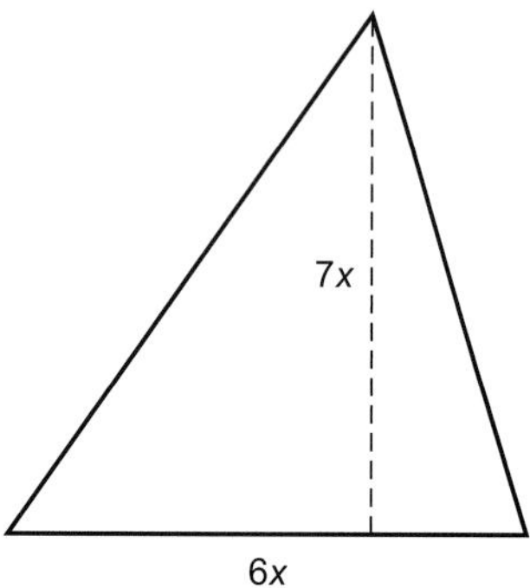

25. Mei drew a triangle with a base of $3.7y$ and a height of $5.2y$.

A. Express the area of the triangle as a monomial.

B. Find the area of the triangle if $y = 5$ centimeters.

26. Fernando's rectangular dining room table measures $2.4x$ meters by $1.6x$ meters. Express the area of the table as a monomial.

27. A cube has side length $6x$.

A. Express the volume of the cube as a monomial.

B. Find the volume of the cube if $x = 2$ inches.

28. The width of a certain rectangle is equal to 9 times the side length s of a certain cube. The length of the rectangle is equal to the volume of the cube. Express the area of the rectangle as a monomial.

***29. Challenge** Alex has two apartments for rent, as shown in the outlines below.

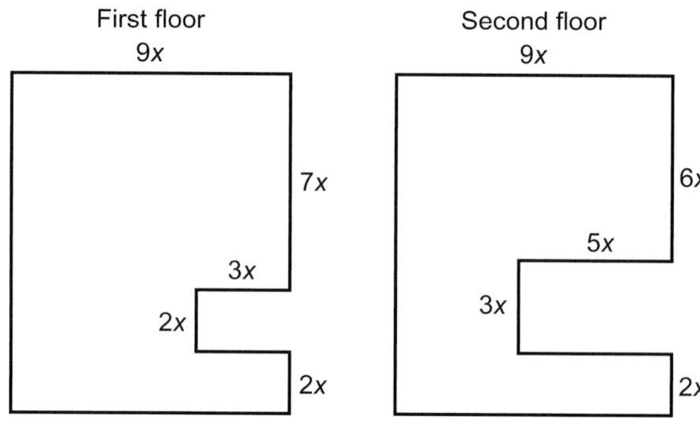

A. Express the total area of each apartment as a monomial.

B. By how many square feet is the area of the first floor apartment greater than the second floor apartment if $x = 2$?

***30. Challenge** Mrs. King has a coffee table in the shape of the hexagon shown. What is the area of the table? (Hint: divide the hexagon into triangles.)

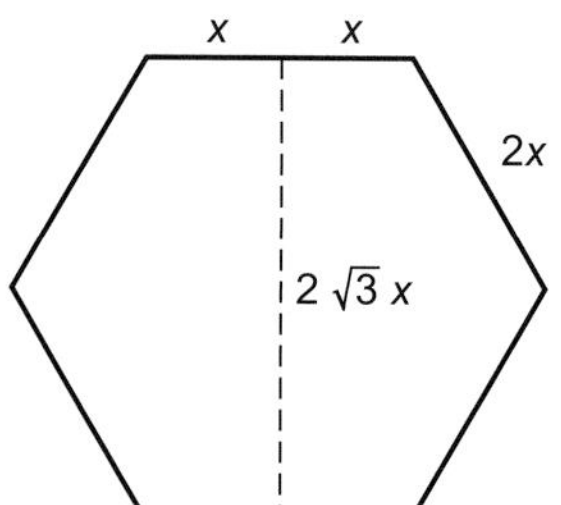

Multiplying Polynomials by Monomials

Use the distributive property to multiply a polynomial by a monomial.

You have used the distributive property to multiply a binomial by a monomial: $a(b + c) = ab + ac$. The distributive property is true for any number of terms inside the parentheses. For example, $a(b + c + d) = ab + ac + ad$. You can also use the distributive property when the order of the factors is reversed. For example, $(b + c)a = ba + ca$.

Multiplying a Polynomial by a Monomial

MULTIPLYING A POLYNOMIAL BY A MONOMIAL

Step 1 Use the distributive property to multiply the monomial by each term of the polynomial.

Step 2 Multiply each set of monomials. Use the product of powers property when necessary.

REMEMBER

The product of powers property states $a^m \cdot a^n = a^{m+n}$.

Example 1 Find each product.

A. $4x(x + 3)$

Solution

$4x(x + 3) = 4x \cdot x + 4x \cdot 3$ Distributive Property

$= 4x^2 + 12x$ Multiply. Use the product of powers property for the first term. ■

B. $7y(3y^3 - 4y^2 - y)$

Solution

$7y(3y^3 - 4y^2 - y) = 7y \cdot 3y^3 + 7y \cdot (-4y^2) + 7y \cdot (-y)$ Distributive Property

$= 21y^4 - 28y^3 - 7y^2$ Multiply. Use the product of powers property. ■

C. $(21ab^3 + 5ab^2 - 3ab - 7)a^2b$

Solution

$(21ab^3 + 5ab^2 - 3ab - 7)a^2b$

$= 21ab^3 \cdot a^2b + 5ab^2 \cdot a^2b - 3ab \cdot a^2b - 7 \cdot a^2b$ Distributive Property

$= 21a^1a^2b^3b^1 + 5a^1a^2b^2b^1 - 3a^1a^2b^1b^1 - 7a^2b^1$ Commutative Property of Multiplication

$= 21a^3b^4 + 5a^3b^3 - 3a^3b^2 - 7a^2b$ Product of Powers Property ■

Application: Area

Example 2 Write a polynomial that represents the area of the shaded region.

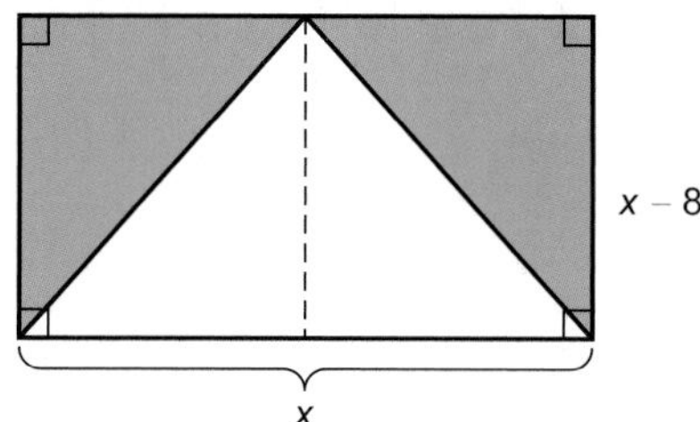

Solution Find the area of the shaded region by subtracting the area of the triangle from the area of the rectangle.

Step 1 Find the area of the triangle.

$A = \frac{1}{2}bh$	
$= \frac{1}{2}x(x - 8)$	The base of the triangle is x and the height is $x - 8$.
$= \frac{1}{2}x \cdot x - \frac{1}{2}x \cdot 8$	Distributive Property
$= \frac{1}{2}x^2 - 4x$	Simplify.

The area of the triangle is $\frac{1}{2}x^2 - 4x$.

Step 2 Find the area of the rectangle.

$A = lw$	
$= x(x - 8)$	The length of the rectangle is x and the width is $x - 8$.
$= x \cdot x - x \cdot 8$	Distributive Property
$= x^2 - 8x$	Simplify.

The area of the rectangle is $x^2 - 8x$.

Step 3 Find the area of the shaded region.

Area of the shaded region = Area of rectangle − Area of triangle

$= (x^2 - 8x) - \left(\frac{1}{2}x^2 - 4x\right)$	
$= x^2 - 8x - \frac{1}{2}x^2 + 4x$	Distributive Property
$= x^2 - \frac{1}{2}x^2 - 8x + 4x$	Commutative Property of Addition
$= \frac{1}{2}x^2 - 4x$	Simplify.

The area of the shaded region is $\frac{1}{2}x^2 - 4x$. ■

Problem Set

Multiply and simplify.

1. $x(x + 4)$
2. $a(a - 9)$
3. $3x(x - 1)$
4. $2y(y + 6)$
5. $7m(12 - m)$
6. $8x(6x + 2)$
7. $5z^3(2z - 10)$
8. $(3x + 7)8x^2$
9. $8n(2n^2 - n + 1)$
10. $a(3a^3 + 2a^2 + a)$
11. $y(2y^5 + 4y^3 + 5y^2)$
12. $10w(5w^6 + 4w^3 - 2w)$
13. $4x^3(6x^{10} - 10x^9 + 9x^2)$
14. $7a^3(-10a^3 - 18a^2 + a)$
15. $12x^3(3x^9 - 12x^8 - 8x^7)$
16. $-7p^6(-4p^5 - 9p^4 - 7p^3)$
17. $xy(3x^2y - 4xy^2 + 2xy - 8)$
18. $(9x^5y^4 + 6x^4y^3 + 7x^3y^2 + 12)x^2y$
19. $2mn^2(m^3n^2 + 7m^2n + 11mn - 20)$
20. $5xy^4(2x^4y^2 - 8x^3y + 14x^2y + 12)$
21. $(5a^{12}b^2 + 7a^{10}b^4 - 4a^3b^2 + 6) \cdot 3ab^5$
22. $(3x^7y - 13x^6y + 10xy - 30)4xy^6$
23. $a^4b^3c^2(3a^6b^{5c} - 11a^5b^4c^2 - 13a^4b^3c^3 - 14a^3b^2c^4 + ab)$
24. $4x^2y^3z(11x^5y^4z - 9x^3y^2z^2 - 10x^2yz^3 - 14z^4 + z^3)$

Solve.

25. A large rectangular box is constructed to hold shipping supplies. Write a polynomial to represent the volume of the box ($V = lwh$).

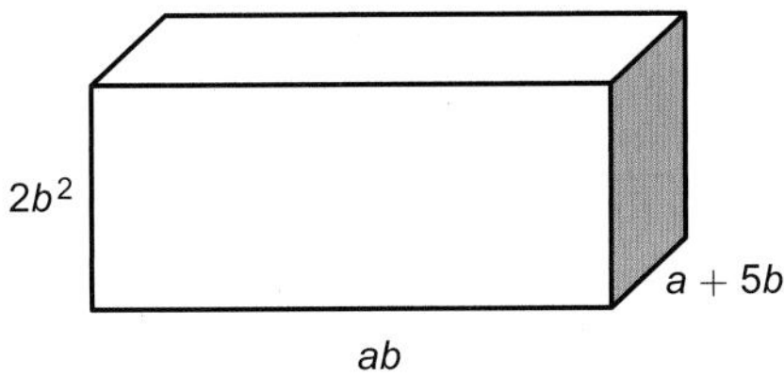

26. Luke is 5 years older than Olga and Condi is 4 years younger than Olga. Write a polynomial that represents Olga's age times Luke's age decreased by Condi's age.

27. Write a polynomial that represents the area of the shaded region formed by the two triangles.

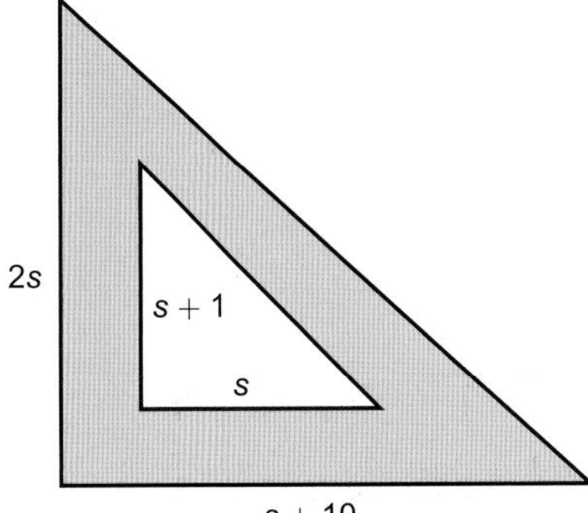

28. Write a polynomial that represents the area of the shaded walkway formed by these two rectangles.

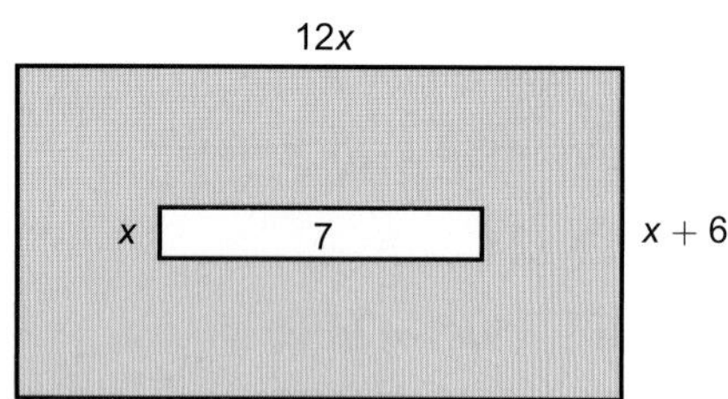

***29. Challenge** Write a polynomial that represents the area of the region formed by the rectangle and semicircle.

$x + 5$

x

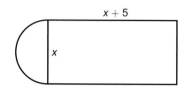

***30. Challenge** A quilt pattern is being constructed below. All diagrams are drawn to scale. A square is cut for the first step. In Step 2, a 1 unit square and a rectangle that is 1 unit wide are added to the original square. Find the area and perimeter of the resulting figure in each step.

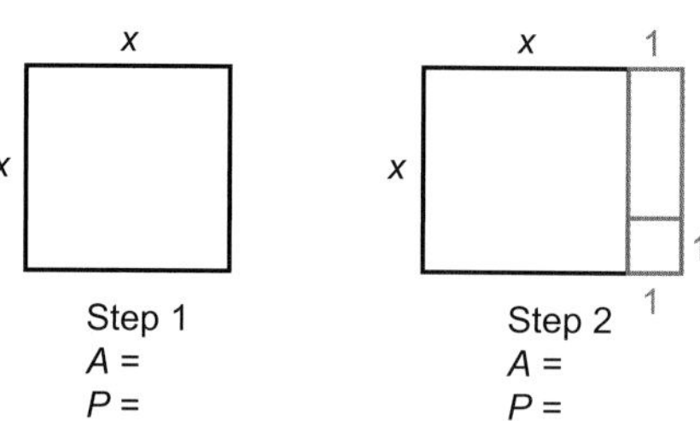

Multiplying Polynomials

Using the distributive property to multiply polynomials is similar to multiplying a polynomial by a monomial.

USING THE DISTRIBUTIVE PROPERTY TO MULTIPLY TWO POLYNOMIALS

Step 1 Use the distributive property to multiply each term of the first polynomial by the second polynomial.

Step 2 Use the distributive property to multiply the monomials by each term of the polynomial.

Step 3 Multiply each set of monomials.

Step 4 If necessary, combine like terms to simplify.

Multiplying a Binomial by a Binomial

REMEMBER

A binomial is a polynomial with two terms.

Example 1 Multiply $(3x + 2)(x - 5)$.

Solution Use the distributive property. Think of $(x - 5)$ as a single value. Multiply $3x$ by $(x - 5)$ and 2 by $(x - 5)$.

$$\begin{aligned}(3x + 2)(x - 5) &= 3x(x - 5) + 2(x - 5) && \text{Distributive Property}\\ &= 3x \cdot x + 3x \cdot (-5) + 2 \cdot x + 2 \cdot (-5) && \text{Distributive Property}\\ &= 3x^2 - 15x + 2x - 10 && \text{Multiply the monomials.}\\ &= 3x^2 - 13x - 10 && \text{Combine like terms.} \blacksquare\end{aligned}$$

Squaring a Binomial

When you multiply two binomials and both factors are equivalent, you are squaring the binomial. In the diagram below, each side of the square has a side length of $a + b$. Use the diagram to see that $(a + b)^2 = a^2 + 2ab + b^2$.

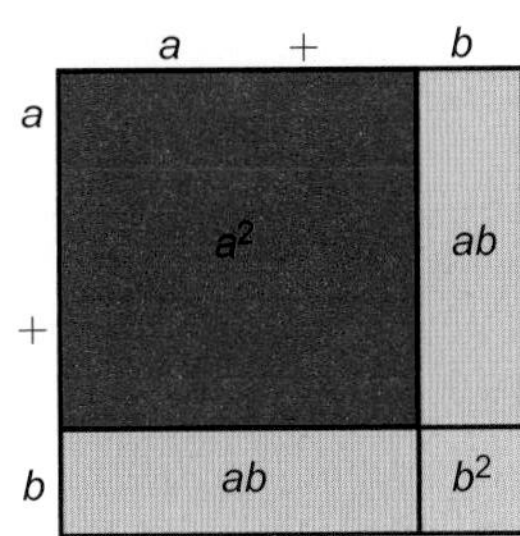

(continued)

SQUARE OF A BINOMIAL

$$(a + b)^2 = a^2 + 2ab + b^2$$

Example 2 Expand $(2x + 1)^2$.

Solution Use the pattern $(a + b)^2 = a^2 + 2ab + b^2$ to square the binomial.

$(a + b)^2 = a^2 + 2ab + b^2$

$(2x + 1)^2 = (2x)^2 + 2 \cdot 2x \cdot 1 + 1^2$ Substitute $2x$ for a and 1 for b.

$= 2x \cdot 2x + 4x + 1$ Multiply the monomials.

$= 4x^2 + 4x + 1$ Multiply. ■

Multiplying a Polynomial by a Polynomial

Example 3 Find each product.

A. $(a - 4)(2a^2 + 3a - 7)$

Solution

$(a - 4)(2a^2 + 3a - 7) = a(2a^2 + 3a - 7)$

$- 4(2a^2 + 3a - 7)$ Distributive Property

$= a \cdot 2a^2 + a \cdot 3a + a \cdot (-7) - 4 \cdot 2a^2 - 4 \cdot 3a - 4 \cdot (-7)$ Distributive Property

$= 2a^3 + 3a^2 - 7a - 8a^2 - 12a + 28$ Multiply the monomials.

$= 2a^3 - 5a^2 - 19a + 28$ Combine like terms. ■

B. $(x^2 + 6x + 9)(2x^2 - x - 1)$

Solution

$(x^2 + 6x + 9)(2x^2 - x - 1) = x^2(2x^2 - x - 1)$

$+ 6x(2x^2 - x - 1) + 9(2x^2 - x - 1)$ Distributive Property

$= x^2 \cdot 2x^2 + x^2 \cdot (-x) + x^2 \cdot (-1) + 6x \cdot 2x^2 + 6x \cdot (-x)$

$+ 6x \cdot (-1) + 9 \cdot 2x^2 + 9 \cdot (-x) + 9 \cdot (-1)$ Distributive Property

$= 2x^4 - x^3 - x^2 + 12x^3 - 6x^2 - 6x + 18x^2 - 9x - 9$ Multiply the monomials.

$= 2x^4 + 11x^3 + 11x^2 - 15x - 9$ Combine like terms. ■

C. $(x + 1)(x - 1)(5x + 2)$

Solution First multiply $(x + 1)(x - 1)$. Then multiply the product by $(5x + 2)$.

Step 1 $(x + 1)(x - 1) = x(x - 1) + 1(x - 1)$ Distributive Property

$= x \cdot x + x \cdot (-1) + 1 \cdot x + 1 \cdot (-1)$ Distributive Property

$= x^2 - x + x - 1$ Multiply the monomials.

$= x^2 - 1$ Combine like terms.

Step 2 $(x^2 - 1)(5x + 2) = x^2(5x + 2) - 1(5x + 2)$ Distributive Property

$= x^2 \cdot 5x + x^2 \cdot 2 - 1 \cdot 5x - 1 \cdot 2$ Distributive Property

$= 5x^3 + 2x^2 - 5x - 2$ Multiply the monomials. ■

Application: Area

Example 4

A. A garden is bordered on three sides by a tiled walkway. Write a polynomial that represents the total area of the garden and the walkway.

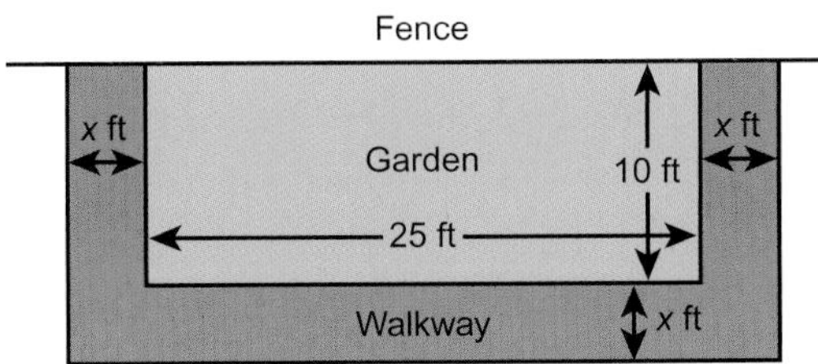

B. If the walkway is 3 feet wide, what is the total area of the garden and the walkway?

Solution

A.

Step 1 Write expressions for the outer length and width of the walkway.

The length of the walkway is $x + 25 + x = 2x + 25$.

The width of the walkway is $x + 10$.

Step 2 Use the formula for the area of a rectangle.

$A = lw$	
$= (2x + 25)(x + 10)$	Substitute $(2x + 25)$ for l and $(x + 10)$ for w.
$= 2x(x + 10) + 25(x + 10)$	Distributive Property
$= 2x^2 + 20x + 25x + 250$	Multiply.
$= 2x^2 + 45x + 250$	Combine like terms.

The total area of the garden and the walkway is $2x^2 + 45x + 250$. ■

B.

$A = 2x^2 + 45x + 250$	Write the expression found in Part A.
$= 2 \cdot 3^2 + 45 \cdot 3 + 250$	Substitute 3 for x.
$= 2 \cdot 9 + 45 \cdot 3 + 250$	Evaluate 3^2.
$= 18 + 135 + 250$	Multiply.
$= 403$	Add.

The total area of the garden and the walkway is 403 square feet. ■

Problem Set

Multiply and simplify.

1. $(x + 4)(x - 2)$
2. $(2u + 1)(u + 1)$
3. $(4x - 7)(x + 5)$
4. $(6c - 9)(2c - 4)$
5. $(5a + 7b)(3a - 8b)$
6. $(x + 2)^2$
7. $(3y - 1)^2$
8. $(4x + 3)^2$
9. $(10a - 7)^2$
10. $(3x + 5y)^2$
11. $(n + 1)(n^2 + 2n + 1)$
12. $(a - 2)(8a^2 - 5a + 3)$
13. $(x - 10)(4x^2 - 3x - 8)$
14. $(3a + 2)(5a^2 + 10a - 9)$
15. $(6x - 5y)(2x^2 - 7xy - 8y^2)$
16. $(x^2 + 3x + 1)(x^2 + 4x + 2)$
17. $(v^2 + 7v - 1)(v^2 - 5v + 3)$
18. $(x^2 + 2x - 4)(5x^2 - 2x - 11)$
19. $(10x^2 + 7x + 11)(2x^2 - 5x + 6)$
20. $(3y^2 + 2y - 7)(4y^2 - 9y + 3)$
21. $(z + 3)(z + 5)(z + 1)$
22. $(x + 2)(x - 6)(x - 3)$
23. $(d - 4)(d + 12)(2d + 5)$
24. $(2x + 5)(3x - 2)(4x - 1)$

Solve.

25. Write a polynomial that represents the area of a circle with a radius of $7x + 1$.

26. Find the volume of the package below. Use the formula $V = lwh$.

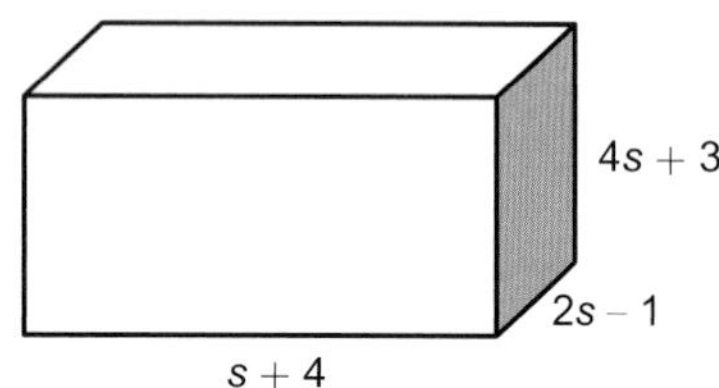

27. Given the right triangle below, use the Pythagorean theorem to write a polynomial expression for c^2.

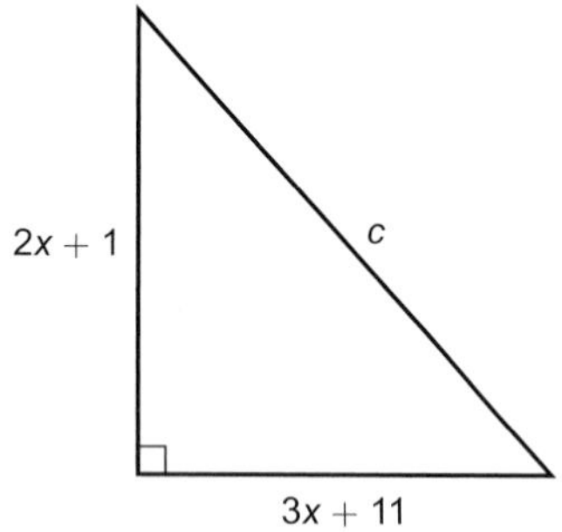

*28. **Challenge** A swimming pool in the shape of a trapezoid sits on a rectangular deck. Write a polynomial expression for the deck area surrounding the pool.

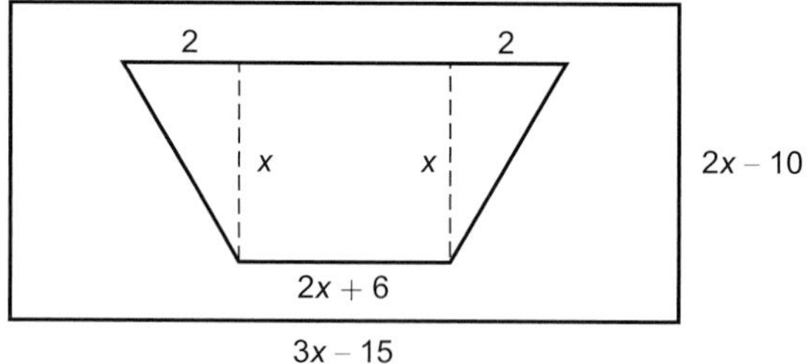

*29. **Challenge** Create a pattern for squaring a trinomial by multiplying $(a + b + c)^2$. Then use the pattern to multiply $(x + 2y + 3z)^2$.

The FOIL Method

When you use the distributive property to multiply two binomials, you are multiplying each term in the first binomial by each term in the second binomial. The FOIL method helps you organize the steps used to multiply two binomials.

Using the FOIL Method to Multiply a Binomial by a Binomial

The letters of the word **FOIL** stand for **F**irst, **O**uter, **I**nner, and **L**ast. These words tell you which terms to multiply.

First Outer Inner Last

$$(a + b)(c + d) = a \cdot c + a \cdot d + b \cdot c + b \cdot d$$

Example 1 Multiply.

A. $(x + 9)(3x - 4)$

Solution

First Outer Inner Last

$$\begin{aligned}(x + 9)(3x - 4) &= x \cdot 3x + x \cdot (-4) + 9 \cdot 3x + 9 \cdot (-4) && \text{FOIL}\\ &= 3x^2 - 4x + 27x - 36 && \text{Multiply.}\\ &= 3x^2 + 23x - 36 && \text{Combine like terms. ■}\end{aligned}$$

B. $(\sqrt{a} - 2)(\sqrt{a} + 4)$

Solution

First Outer Inner Last

$$\begin{aligned}(\sqrt{a} - 2)(\sqrt{a} + 4) &= \sqrt{a} \cdot \sqrt{a} + \sqrt{a} \cdot 4 + (-2) \cdot \sqrt{a} + (-2) \cdot 4 && \text{FOIL}\\ &= a + 4\sqrt{a} - 2\sqrt{a} - 8 && \text{Multiply.}\\ &= a + (4 - 2)\sqrt{a} - 8 && \text{Combine like terms.}\\ &= a + 2\sqrt{a} - 8 && \text{Simplify. ■}\end{aligned}$$

REMEMBER

$$\sqrt{a} \cdot \sqrt{a} = \sqrt{a^2}$$
$$= a$$

Using the FOIL Method to Multiply Conjugate Binomials

Conjugate binomials, $(a + b)$ and $(a - b)$, are two binomials with the same terms but opposite signs.

CONJUGATE BINOMIALS

For any real numbers a and b, $(a + b)(a - b) = a^2 - b^2$.

Example 2

A. Prove that $(a + b)(a - b) = a^2 - b^2$.

Solution

$(a + b)(a - b) = a \cdot a - a \cdot b + b \cdot a - b \cdot b$	FOIL
$= a^2 - ab + ba - b^2$	Multiply the monomials.
$= a^2 - ab + ab - b^2$	Commutative Property of Multiplication
$= a^2 - b^2$	Additive Inverse Property ■

B. Multiply $(5x - 7)(5x + 7)$.

Solution Use the pattern $(a + b)(a - b) = a^2 - b^2$ to find the product.

$(a - b)(a + b) = a^2 - b^2$

$(5x - 7)(5x + 7) = (5x)^2 - 7^2$	Substitute $5x$ for a and 7 for b.
$= 5x \cdot 5x - 7 \cdot 7$	Multiply the monomials.
$= 25x^2 - 49$	Simplify. ■

Cubing a Binomial

You know a pattern for squaring a binomial. There is also a pattern for cubing a binomial.

Example 3 Find the product.

A. $(x + y)^3$

Solution $(x + y)^3 = (x + y)\,(x + y)\,(x + y)$

Step 1 Use FOIL to expand $(x + y)(x + y)$.

$(x + y)(x + y) = x \cdot x + x \cdot y + y \cdot x + y \cdot y$	FOIL
$= x^2 + xy + yx + y^2$	Multiply the monomials.
$= x^2 + xy + xy + y^2$	Commutative Property of Multiplication
$= x^2 + 2xy + y^2$	Combine like terms.

Step 2 Use the distributive property to multiply the product found in Step 1 by $(x + y)$.

$(x + y)(x^2 + 2xy + y^2) = x(x^2 + 2xy + y^2) + y(x^2 + 2xy + y^2)$	Distributive Property
$= x \cdot x^2 + x \cdot 2xy + x \cdot y^2 + y \cdot x^2 + y \cdot 2xy + y \cdot y^2$	Distributive Property
$= x^3 + 2x^2y + xy^2 + x^2y + 2xy^2 + y^3$	Multiply the monomials.
$= x^3 + 3x^2y + 3xy^2 + y^3$	Combine like terms. ■

The expression $(x + y)^3$ is a perfect cube, and $(x + y)^3 = x^3 + 3x^2y + 3xy^2 + y^3$. You can use this fact to find any perfect cube.

B. $(a + 3)^3$

Solution Use the perfect cube pattern: $(x + y)^3 = x^3 + 3x^2y + 3xy^2 + y^3$.

$(x + y)^3 = x^3 + 3x^2y + 3xy^2 + y^3$

$(a + 3)^3 = a^3 + 3a^2 \cdot 3 + 3a \cdot 3^2 + 3^3$ Substitute a for x and 3 for y.

$= a^3 + 9a^2 + 27a + 27$ Simplify. ■

Problem Set

Multiply and simplify.

1. $(x + 4)(x + 2)$
2. $(j - 0.2)(0.13 + j)$
3. $(d - 5)(d - 10)$
4. $(x + 12)(x - 3)$
5. $(q + 1)(q + 5)$
6. $(v - 6)(v - 3)$
7. $(x - 7)(x + 3)$
8. $(a + 11)(a - 10)$
9. $\left(x + \frac{7}{8}\right)\left(x - \frac{7}{8}\right)$
10. $(p - \sqrt{2})(p - \sqrt{2})$
11. $(\sqrt{z} + 2)(18 + \sqrt{z})$
12. $(k + 3)(8k + 4)$
13. $(2a + 1)(a - 1)$
14. $(t - 7)(5t - 7)$
15. $(6.1 + n)(2n + 5)$
16. $(\sqrt{r} - 2)(3\sqrt{r} - 4)$
17. $\left(\frac{1}{4}y + \frac{2}{3}\right)\left(\frac{2}{5}y + 1\right)$
18. $(1 - 3u)(1 + 3u)$
19. $(3f + 2)(6f + 4)$
20. $(0.9 - 2g)(2.5g - 3)$
21. $(20x + \sqrt{21})(20x - \sqrt{21})$
22. $(2\sqrt{y} + 7)(1 - 2\sqrt{y})$
23. $(b + 7)(b^2 - 2)$
24. $(h^2 + 0.3)(1.4 - h)$
25. $(w^2 + 5)(2w + 1)$
26. $(6x^2 + 3)(4 - x)$
27. $(x + 6)^3$
28. $(5 - 3c)^3$

Challenge

*29. **A.** Find the product of $(3x + 1)(x - 2)$.

B. Use your work in Part A to find the product of $(3x + 1)(x - 2)(x + 4)$.

*30. **A.** Find the product of $(x + 4)(x - 4)$.

B. Use your work in Part A to find the product of $(x + 4)^2(x - 4)^2$.

UNIT 11 Factoring Polynomials

You can use polynomials to describe framing for art.

A polynomial is an expression that has variables that represent numbers. A number can be factored, so you should be able to factor a polynomial, right? Sometimes you can and sometimes you can't. Finding ways to write a polynomial as a product of factors can be quite useful.

Big Ideas

- Expressions, equations, and inequalities express relationships between different entities.
- The laws of arithmetic can be used to simplify algebraic expressions and equations. Solving an equation means finding values for the variable or variables that make the equation a true statement.
- A function is a correspondence between two sets, the domain and the range, that assigns to each member of the domain exactly one member of the range. Many events in the physical world can be modeled as functions. Many functions can be described by algebraic expressions.

Unit Topics

- Factoring Integers
- Dividing Monomials
- Common Factors of Polynomials
- Dividing Polynomials by Monomials
- Factoring Perfect Squares
- Factoring Differences of Squares
- Factoring Quadratic Trinomials
- Factoring Quadratic Trinomials, $a \neq 1$
- Factoring Completely
- Factoring Challenges
- Finding Roots of a Polynomial
- Applications: Using Factoring

Factoring Integers

You can factor integers into products of primes.

DEFINITION

A **prime number** is an integer greater than one that has exactly two factors, the number itself and 1.

REMEMBER

The set of integers, $\mathbb{Z} = \{\ldots, -2, -1, 0, 1, 2, \ldots\}$, is the set of natural numbers, their opposites, and zero.

Writing a Number as a Product of Prime Numbers

REMEMBER

A factor is a number or variable multiplied by one or more numbers or variables to get a product.

Example 1 Write 84 as the product of its prime factors.

Solution

Method 1 Use a factor tree. Write 84 at the top of your tree. Write 84 as the product of any two of its factors. Then write each factor that is not prime as the product of two factors. Continue until all the leaves on the factor tree are prime numbers.

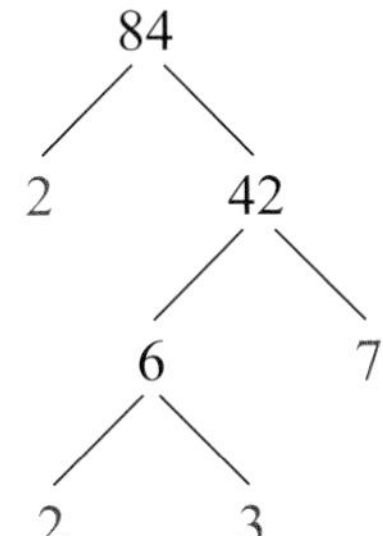

Now write 84 as the product of its prime factors found in the factor tree: $84 = 2 \cdot 2 \cdot 3 \cdot 7$. In exponential form, this is: $84 = 2^2 \cdot 3 \cdot 7$.

Method 2 Use a division ladder. Keep dividing 84 by prime numbers until the divisor and the quotient are both prime numbers.

$2\,\underline{|\,84}$ Divide 84 by the prime number 2. Write the quotient 42 below 84.

$2\,\underline{|\,42}$ Divide 42 by the prime number 2. Write the quotient 21 below 42.

$3\,\underline{|\,21}$ Divide 21 by the prime number 3. Write the quotient 7 below 21.

7 Since 7 is a prime number, the factorization is complete.

The prime factorization of 84 is $2 \cdot 2 \cdot 3 \cdot 7 = 2^2 \cdot 3 \cdot 7$. ■

Composite Numbers

A number that is not a prime number is a composite number. A composite number is an integer greater than one that has more than two factors. For example, 4 has factors of 1, 2, and 4, so it is a composite number.

Example 2 Determine whether each number is prime or composite.

A. 57

Solution The factors of 57 are 1, 3, 19, and 57, so 57 is a composite number. ■

B. 101

Solution The factors of 101 are 1 and 101, so 101 is a prime number. ■

Finding the GCF

DEFINITIONS

A **common factor** is a factor shared by two or more numbers. The **greatest common factor** (GCF) of two or more numbers is the greatest of the common factors of the numbers.

Example 3 Find the GCF of 72 and 48.

Solution

Method 1 List the factors of each number and find the greatest of the common factors.

Factors of 72: 1, 2, 3, 4, 6, 8, 9, 12, 18, 24, 36, 72

Factors of 48: 1, 2, 3, 4, 6, 8, 12, 16, 24, 48

The greatest common factor is 24.

Method 2 Find the prime factorization in exponential form of each number.

$72 = 2^3 \cdot 3^2$

$48 = 2^4 \cdot 3$

Look for the smallest common power of each prime factor and multiply: $2^3 \cdot 3 = 24$. ■

Determining Whether Numbers Are Relatively Prime

Two numbers are **relatively prime** if they share no common factors other than 1.

Example 4 Are 28 and 55 relatively prime?

Solution Find the prime factorization of each number and see if they share any common prime factors.

$28 = 2 \cdot 2 \cdot 7 = 2^2 \cdot 7$

$55 = 5 \cdot 11$

Since 28 and 55 share no common prime factors, they are relatively prime. ■

Application: Mersenne Primes

A Mersenne prime is a number of the form

$M = 2^n - 1$, where n and M are prime numbers.

Example 5 Find the first five Mersenne primes.

Solution Substitute consecutive prime numbers into the equation for n.

Prime Number, n	Apply Mersenne Equation: $M = 2^n - 1$	Mersenne Prime?
2	$M = 2^2 - 1$ $= 4 - 1$ $= 3$	Yes
3	$M = 2^3 - 1$ $= 8 - 1$ $= 7$	Yes
5	$M = 2^5 - 1$ $= 32 - 1$ $= 31$	Yes
7	$M = 2^7 - 1$ $= 128 - 1$ $= 127$	Yes
11	$M = 2^{11} - 1$ $= 2048 - 1$ $= 2047$	No $2047 = 23 \cdot 89$
13	$M = 2^{13} - 1$ $= 8192 - 1$ $= 8191$	Yes

■

THINK ABOUT IT

Not all Mersenne numbers are Mersenne primes. A Mersenne number is any number of the form $2^n - 1$, where n is an integer. A Mersenne prime is a number of the form $M = 2^n - 1$, where n and M are prime numbers.

THINK ABOUT IT

As n increases, Mersenne primes become very difficult to compute. Only 44 Mersenne primes have been discovered, the last in 2006.

Problem Set

Write each number as the product of its prime factors.

1. 76
2. 35
3. 36
4. 150
5. 180
6. 520

Determine whether each number is prime or composite.

7. 61
8. 91
9. 123
10. 193
11. 227

*12. **Challenge** 437

Find the greatest common factor (GCF) of each set of numbers.

13. 18 and 90
14. 45 and 60
15. 128 and 192
16. 16, 24, and 40
17. 42, 63, and 84
18. 68 and 170
19. 65 and 78
20. 140 and 196

Determine whether each pair of numbers is relatively prime. If they are not, find the GCF.

21. 34 and 44
22. 56 and 75
23. 124 and 165
24. 95 and 231
25. 126 and 175
26. 138 and 243
27. 108 and 245

Solve.

*28. **Challenge** Find the 6th Mersenne prime.

Dividing Monomials

Divide monomials using the quotient of powers property.

The quotient of powers property is just one of the many properties of exponents. To apply the properties of exponents, you will need to understand integer exponents.

DEFINITION OF INTEGER EXPONENTS

For any $a \in \mathbb{R}$:

1. If n is a positive integer, $a^n = \overbrace{a \cdot a \cdot a \cdot \ldots \cdot a}^{n \text{ factors}}$.
2. If $n = 0$ and $a \neq 0$, $a^n = 1$.
3. For any n and nonzero a, $a^{-n} = \frac{1}{a^n}$.

The following table lists properties of exponents.

PROPERTIES OF EXPONENTS

Let $a \in \mathbb{R}, b \in \mathbb{R}, a \neq 0, b \neq 0, m \in \mathbb{Z}, n \in \mathbb{Z}$.

Name	Definition	Examples
Product of Powers	$a^m \cdot a^n = a^{(m+n)}$	$2^2 \cdot 2^3 = 2^{2+3} = 2^5$ $x^3 \cdot x^{-2} = x^{3+(-2)} = x^1 = x$
Quotient of Powers	$\frac{a^m}{a^n} = a^{(m-n)}$	$\frac{x^9}{x^3} = x^{(9-3)} = x^6$ $\frac{b^7}{b^{10}} = b^{(7-10)} = b^{-3} = \frac{1}{b^3}$
Power of a Product	$(ab)^n = a^n b^n$	$(5x)^3 = 5^3 \cdot x^3 = 125x^3$
Power of a Quotient	$\left(\frac{a}{b}\right)^n = \frac{a^n}{b^n}$	$\left(\frac{2}{x}\right)^5 = \frac{2^5}{x^5} = \frac{32}{x^5}$
Power of a Power	$(a^m)^n = a^{mn}$	$(2^2)^3 = 2^{(2 \cdot 3)} = 2^6 = 64$

REMEMBER

The letter $\mathbb{R}$ denotes the set of real numbers. The letter $\mathbb{Z}$ denotes the set of integers.

Dividing Monomials

Example 1 Find each quotient.

A. $\dfrac{x^5}{x^2}$

Solution

$\dfrac{x^5}{x^2} = x^{(5-2)}$ Quotient of Powers Property

$= x^3$ Simplify. ■

B. $\dfrac{-9a^3b^4c}{3a^2b}$

Solution

$\dfrac{-9a^3b^4c}{3a^2b} = -3a^{(3-2)}b^{(4-1)}c$ Quotient of Powers Property

$= -3ab^3c$ Simplify. ■

C. $\dfrac{15x^3}{5x^9}$

Solution

$\dfrac{15x^3}{5x^9} = 3x^{(3-9)}$ Quotient of Powers Property

$= 3x^{-6}$ Simplify.

$= 3 \cdot \dfrac{1}{x^6}$ Definition of negative integer exponents

$= \dfrac{3}{x^6}$ Multiply. ■

THINK ABOUT IT

For Example 1C, the answer is not a monomial because the variable does not have a whole number exponent.

D. $\left(\dfrac{2xy}{4x^2}\right)^2$

Solution

$\left(\dfrac{2xy}{4x^2}\right)^2 = \dfrac{(2xy)^2}{(4x^2)^2}$ Power of a Quotient Property

$= \dfrac{2^2x^2y^2}{4^2x^{2\cdot 2}}$ Power of a Power Property

$= \dfrac{4x^2y^2}{16x^4}$ Simplify.

$= \dfrac{1}{4}x^{(2-4)}y^2$ Quotient of Powers Property

$= \dfrac{1}{4}x^{-2}y^2$ Simplify.

$= \dfrac{1}{4} \cdot \dfrac{1}{x^2} \cdot y^2$ Definition of negative integer exponents

$= \dfrac{y^2}{4x^2}$ Multiply. ■

Application: Ratio

Example 2

A. What is the ratio of the volume of a cube to its surface area?

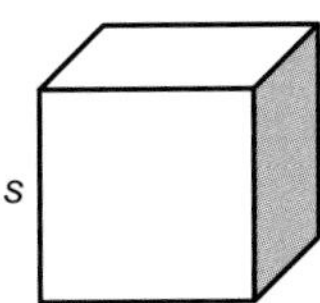

Solution The volume of a cube with side s is s^3. The surface area of a cube is the sum of the areas of the six sides or $6s^2$. The ratio of the volume of a cube to its surface area is $\frac{s^3}{6s^2}$. Simplify the ratio by dividing.

$\frac{s^3}{6s^2} = \frac{s^{(3-2)}}{6}$ Quotient of Powers Property

$= \frac{s}{6}$ Simplify.

The ratio of the volume of a cube to its surface area is $\frac{s}{6}$. ■

B. What is the ratio of the circumference of a circle to its area?

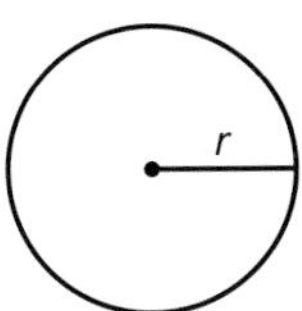

Solution The circumference of a circle with radius r is $2\pi r$. The area of a circle with radius r is πr^2. The ratio of the circumference of a circle to its area is represented by:

$\frac{2\pi r}{\pi r^2} = 2r^{(1-2)}$ Quotient of Powers Property

$= 2r^{-1}$ Simplify.

$= 2 \cdot \frac{1}{r^1}$ Definition of negative integer exponents

$= \frac{2}{r}$ Multiply.

The ratio of the circumference of a circle to its area is $\frac{2}{r}$. ■

Problem Set

Identify the property.

1. $(7a)^2 = 7^2 \cdot a^2$
2. $(4^3)^3 = 3^{3 \cdot 3}$
3. $2^3 \cdot 2^5 = 2^{3+5}$
4. $\left(\frac{a}{3}\right)^4 = \frac{a^4}{3^4}$
5. $\frac{6^5}{6^3} = 6^{5-3}$
6. $(2ab^3)^2 = 2^2 \cdot a^{1 \cdot 2} \cdot b^{3 \cdot 2}$

Find each quotient.

7. $\frac{a^7}{a^4}$

8. $\frac{x^9}{x^2}$

9. $\frac{y^3}{y^6}$

10. $\frac{3^5}{3^6}$

11. $\frac{16a^5}{4a^2}$

12. $\frac{m^2}{m^{-5}}$

13. $\frac{12x^2y^4}{-6xy^2}$

14. $\frac{3b^6}{18b^4}$

15. $\frac{x^3y^2z^8}{x^2yz^3}$

16. $\frac{28a^{-2}b^9c^2}{7a^{-6}b^{-2}}$

17. $\frac{a^{-2}b^8}{a^4b^5}$

18. $\frac{-56r^3s^5}{8r^5s^3}$

19. $\frac{a^2b^3c^4}{a^4b^3c^2}$

20. $\left(\frac{3x^4y^{-2}}{6x^3y^3}\right)^{-1}$

21. $\frac{4x^{-5}y^3z^2}{-8x^{-2}y^4z^{-3}}$

Challenge

*22. $\frac{-9x^6y^3}{6x^2yz^3}$

*23. $\frac{9x^2y}{24x^{-2}y^6}$

*24. $\left(\frac{-4x^2y^5z^{-2}}{32x^4y^6z^4}\right)^{-3}$

Solve.

25. What is the ratio of the area of this triangle to its perimeter?

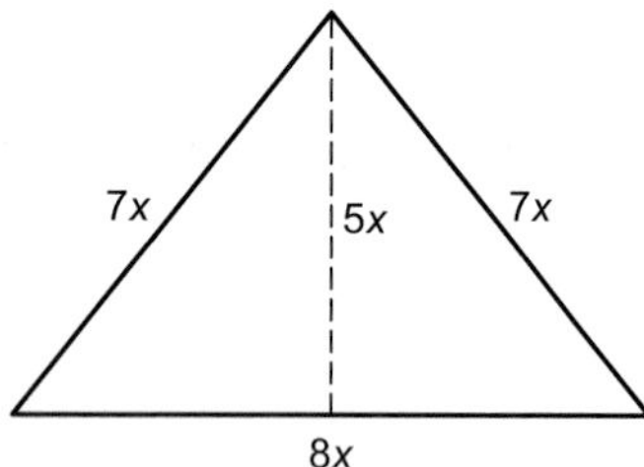

26. A group of $6p$ people are renting a vacation house together. The price of the rental is $3p^2$. If they split the cost evenly, what is each member's share of the price?

27. Barker's age can be represented by the expression $4x^2$.

   A. Karin's age can be represented by the expression $2x^4$.What is the ratio of Karin's age to Barker's age?

   B. Penny's age can be represented by the expression $3x^3$. What is the ratio of Barker's age to Penny's age?

28. Nasser has saved $2s^2t$ dollars. He wants to save a total of $4rs^3t^2$ dollars. What fraction of his total savings goal has he achieved so far?

*29. **Challenge** Hamilton bought a car for $7s^2t^3$ dollars. He paid s^2t^3 dollars as a down payment. Find the number of months it would take him to pay off the car completely if he made each of the following monthly payments.

   A. $3s^2t$ dollars

   B. $4st^2$ dollars

*30. **Challenge** What is the ratio of the surface area of a sphere to its volume?

Common Factors of Polynomials

When every term of a polynomial shares a common monomial factor, you can factor out the common factor from all the terms.

Identifying the Greatest Common Monomial Factor

The greatest common factor of the expression $18 + 27$ is 9, since 9 is the greatest factor that evenly divides 18 and 27.

Finding the greatest common monomial factor of polynomials with variables is similar to finding the greatest common factor of numerical expressions.

FINDING THE GREATEST COMMON MONOMIAL FACTOR

Step 1 Write each term of the polynomial as the product of its prime factors and look for the smallest power of each prime factor common to each term.

Step 2 Multiply the common factors found in Step 1.

REMEMBER

A factor of a monomial term can be a number or a monomial.

Example 1 Find the greatest common monomial factor of each polynomial.

A. $8x^5 + 12x^2$

Solution

Step 1 $8x^5 = 2^3 \cdot x^5$

$12x^2 = 2^2 \cdot 3 \cdot x^2$

Step 2 Multiply 2^2 and x^2. The greatest common monomial factor is $4x^2$. ■

B. $15a^3b + 25a^2bc - 100a^5b^4c^2$

Solution

Step 1 $15a^3b = 3 \cdot 5 \cdot a^3 \cdot b$

$25a^2bc = 5^2 \cdot a^2 \cdot b \cdot c$

$100a^5b^4c^2 = 2^2 \cdot 5^2 \cdot a^5 \cdot b^4 \cdot c^2$

Step 2 Multiply 5, a^2, and b: $5 \cdot a^2 \cdot b = 5a^2b$. The greatest common monomial factor is $5a^2b$. ■

Factoring Out the Greatest Common Monomial Factor

Since 9 is the greatest common factor of the expression $18 + 27$, you can use the distributive property to factor it out: $18 + 27 = 9(2 + 3)$.

Example 2 Factor the polynomial $14a^3b + 7a^2b^2 + 49ab^3$.

Solution

Step 1 Find the greatest common monomial factor.

$$14a^3b = 2 \cdot 7 \cdot a^3 \cdot b$$

$$7a^2b^2 = 7 \cdot a^2 \cdot b^2$$

$$49ab^3 = 7^2 \cdot a \cdot b^3$$

The greatest common monomial factor is $7ab$.

THINK ABOUT IT

You can check your work by multiplying the greatest common monomial factor by the new polynomial to get the original polynomial.

Step 2 Rewrite each term of the polynomial as a product of the greatest common monomial factor.

$$14a^3b + 7a^2b^2 + 49ab^3 = 7ab \cdot 2a^2 + 7ab \cdot ab + 7ab \cdot 7b^2$$

Step 3 Use the distributive property to factor out the greatest common monomial factor.

$$7ab \cdot 2a^2 + 7ab \cdot ab + 7ab \cdot 7b^2 = 7ab(2a^2 + ab + 7b^2). \blacksquare$$

You can also divide each term of a polynomial by its greatest common monomial factor to factor out the greatest common monomial factor.

Example 3 Factor the polynomial $12xy^4 - 21x^2y^5z + 36xy^3$.

Solution

Step 1 Find the greatest common monomial factor.

$$12xy^4 = 2^2 \cdot 3 \cdot x \cdot y^4$$

$$21x^2y^5z = 3 \cdot 7 \cdot x^2 \cdot y^5 \cdot z$$

$$36xy^3 = 2^2 \cdot 3^2 \cdot x \cdot y^3$$

The greatest common monomial factor is $3xy^3$.

Step 2 Factor out the greatest common monomial factor. Divide each term of the polynomial by the greatest common monomial factor.

$$\begin{aligned}\frac{12xy^4 - 21x^2y^5z + 36xy^3}{3xy^3} &= \frac{12xy^4}{3xy^3} - \frac{21x^2y^5z}{3xy^3} + \frac{36xy^3}{3xy^3} \\ &= 4x^{(1-1)}y^{(4-3)} - 7x^{(2-1)}y^{(5-3)}z + 12x^{(1-1)}y^{(3-3)} \\ &= 4y - 7xy^2z + 12\end{aligned}$$

Step 3 Multiply the greatest common monomial factor by the result in Step 2: $12xy^4 - 21x^2y^5z + 36xy^3 = 3xy^3(4y - 7xy^2z + 12)$. $\blacksquare$

Factoring Out a Binomial Factor

Example 4 Factor $7x(x + 3) - 5(x + 3)$.

Solution Notice that both terms of the polynomial contain the binomial factor $(x + 3)$.

Step 1 To factor out the common binomial factor, divide each term by the common binomial factor:

$$\frac{7x(x + 3) - 5(x + 3)}{(x + 3)} = \frac{7x(x + 3)}{(x + 3)} - \frac{5(x + 3)}{(x + 3)}$$
$$= 7x - 5$$

Step 2 Multiply the common binomial factor by the result in Step 1: $7x(x + 3) - 5(x + 3) = (x + 3)(7x - 5)$. ■

Application: Geometry

Example 5 A rectangle has an area of $6x + 4$ square feet and a width of 2 feet. What is the length of the rectangle?

Solution

$A = lw$	Write the formula for the area of a rectangle.
$6x + 4 = l \cdot 2$	Substitute 2 for w and $6x + 4$ for A.
$\underbrace{(3x + 2)}_{l} \cdot \underbrace{2}_{w} = l \cdot 2$	Factor 2 from $6x + 4$.

So, the length of the rectangle is $3x + 2$ feet. ■

Problem Set

Find the greatest common monomial factor.

1. $4x^3 + 20x^5$
2. $18a^6 + 36a^3$
3. $75y^2 + 200y^3$
4. $6m^3x^4 + 30m^5y^2 + 45m^3x^6y^2$
5. $14x^3y^5z^2 - 98x^2yz^2 + 28x^2y^3$
6. $10a^3b^6c^5 + 20a^2b^3 - 24b^2c^3$

Factor.

7. $3x^2 + 6x$
8. $4x + 8y$
9. $2a^2 + a$
10. $9r + 12s$
11. $5m^2 + 15m$
12. $4p^3 + 2p^2$
13. $18x^3y^4 + 24x^2y^5$
14. $12m^5n^5 - 15m^3n^2$
15. $32x^3y^4 - 12x^2y^5$
16. $15a^3bc^3 - 6a^2b^2c^3$
17. $6r^5s + 4r^4s^2 - 8r^2s$
18. $21x^4y^5z + 28x^2y^4z^4$
19. $3x(2x - 4) + 5(2x - 4)$
20. $6m(3m - 2) - 4(3m - 2)$

Challenge

***21.** $45m^4n^5 - 165m^5n^5p + 75m^3n^6p^4 - 105m^3n^5$

***22.** $(-14xy - 28y) + (6x^2y + 12xy)$

***23.** $(6r^5s^2t^3 - 15r^6s^2t^2 + 27r^5s^2) - (8t^4 - 20rt^3 + 36t) + (12t^3 - 30rt^2 + 54)$

Solve.

24. A rectangle has an area of $16x - 12$ square centimeters and a length of 4 centimeters. What is the width of the rectangle?

25. A triangle has a height of 6 inches and an area of $18y + 3$ square inches. What is the length of the base of the triangle?

26. A parallelogram has a base of 5 centimeters and an area of $12a - 10$ square centimeters. What is the height of the parallelogram?

27. Marta is planning a rectangular shaped perennial garden with a length of 9 feet. Find the width for each of the possible areas of Marta's garden.

A. $45 - 21x$ square feet

B. $60 + 18x$ square feet

28. Jacqui's monthly cell phone bill includes additional minutes at $3x$ per minute. How many additional minutes did Jacqui use for each month?

A. charge for additional minutes in January: $240x + 6x^3$

B. charge for additional minutes in July: $189x + 9x^2$

Dividing Polynomials by Monomials

Dividing a polynomial by a monomial is a good application of the distributive property.

When you have a sum of terms in the numerator of a fraction, the distributive property allows you to separate the fraction into the sum or difference of quotients.

$$\frac{a+b}{c} = \frac{a}{c} + \frac{b}{c} \text{ and } \frac{a-b}{c} = \frac{a}{c} - \frac{b}{c}$$

You can use these properties to divide polynomials by monomials.

Dividing a Polynomial by a Monomial

Example 1 Find each quotient.

A. $(21y^4 + 18y^3) \div 3y$

Solution

$(21y^4 + 18y^3) \div 3y = \dfrac{21y^4 + 18y^3}{3y}$ Write the division problem as a fraction.

$= \dfrac{21y^4}{3y} + \dfrac{18y^3}{3y}$ Divide each term by the denominator.

$= 7y^3 + 6y^2$ Simplify each term.

REMEMBER
Use the quotient of powers property of exponents to simplify the variables.

When dividing a polynomial by a monomial, it is always possible to check if your answer is correct by using related equations. You know that $\frac{6}{2} = 3$, $\frac{6}{3} = 2$, and $2 \cdot 3 = 6$. The same concept holds true for polynomials. If $n(x)$, $d(x)$, and $q(x)$ are polynomials and $\frac{n(x)}{d(x)} = q(x)$, then $n(x) = q(x) \cdot d(x)$. If you multiply the quotient found by the divisor, your answer should be the dividend. You can always make sure you have the correct solution using this answer check method.

TIP
If $\frac{n(x)}{d(x)} = q(x)$, then $n(x) = q(x) \cdot d(x)$.

Check If $\dfrac{21y^4 + 18y^3}{3y} = 7y^3 + 6y^2$, then $21y^4 + 18y^3 = (7y^3 + 6y^2) \cdot 3y$.

$21y^4 + 18y^3 = (7y^3 + 6y^2) \cdot 3y$

$21y^4 + 18y^3 = 3y \cdot 7y^3 + 3y \cdot 6y^2$

$21y^4 + 18y^3 = 21y^4 + 18y^3$ ✓

The answer is correct. ■

(continued)

B. $(25a^6b^5c + 20a^3b^3 - 60a^2b^2) \div 5a^2b^2$

Solution

$$(25a^6b^5c + 20a^3b^3 - 60a^2b^2) \div 5a^2b^2 = \frac{25a^6b^5c + 20a^3b^3 - 60a^2b^2}{5a^2b^2}$$ Write the division problem as a fraction.

$$= \frac{25a^6b^5c}{5a^2b^2} + \frac{20a^3b^3}{5a^2b^2} - \frac{60a^2b^2}{5a^2b^2}$$ Divide each term by the denominator.

$$= 5a^4b^3c + 4ab - 12$$ Simplify each term. ■

Application: Geometry

Example 2 The area of a rectangle is $2x^2 + 6x$ square inches. The length of the rectangle is $2x$ inches. What is the width of the rectangle?

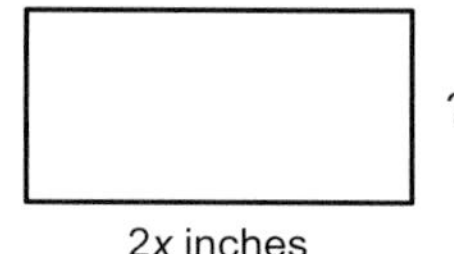

Solution

Step 1 Use the formula for the area of a rectangle to write an equation.

$$A = lw$$

$$2x^2 + 6x = 2x \cdot w$$ Substitute $2x^2 + 6x$ for A and $2x$ for l into the equation.

Step 2 Solve the equation for w by dividing each side by $2x$.

$$\frac{2x^2 + 6x}{2x} = \frac{2x \cdot w}{2x}$$

$$\frac{2x^2 + 6x}{2x} = w$$

Step 3 Simplify.

$$\frac{2x^2 + 6x}{2x} = w$$

$$\frac{2x^2}{2x} + \frac{6x}{2x} = w$$ Divide each term by the denominator.

$$x + 3 = w$$ Simplify each term.

The width of the rectangle is $x + 3$ inches.

Step 4 Check. If $\frac{2x^2 + 6x}{2x} = x + 3$, then $2x^2 + 6x = 2x \cdot (x + 3)$.

$$2x^2 + 6x = 2x \cdot (x + 3)$$

$$2x^2 + 6x = 2x \cdot x + 2x \cdot 3$$

$$2x^2 + 6x = 2x^2 + 6x \checkmark$$

The answer is correct. ■

Problem Set

Find the quotient.

1. $(x^2 + 2x) \div x$
2. $(9b^2 - 3b) \div b$
3. $(4a^3 + 2a^2) \div 2a$
4. $(x^6 - x^5) \div x^2$
5. $(3y^2 + 6y) \div 3y$
6. $(16x^9 + 8x^6) \div x^3$
7. $(12y^7 + 34y^2) \div 2y$
8. $(f^3 - 4f^6) \div f^3$
9. $(1.4a^9 + 0.21a^4) \div 0.07a^2$
10. $(50n^{44} + 25n^{22}) \div 5n^{11}$
11. $(9t^3 + 12t^5) \div 3t^3$
12. $(32h^{12} - 48h^{18}) \div -16h^6$
13. $(2a^3b + 6a^4b^2) \div 2a^2$
14. $(14p^2q^2 + 7p^6q^4) \div 7pq$
15. $(24g^8h^9 - 20g^4h^3) \div 4g^3h$
16. $(18v^{14}w^{12} - 36v^{12}w^{14}) \div 3v^2w^2$
17. $(8y^{10}z^4 + y^{10}z^6) \div -y^5z^3$
18. $\left(\frac{3}{2}m^2n^3 + \frac{8}{5}m^4n^2\right) \div 2mn^2$
19. $(50u^3v^6 + 250u^6v^8 + 100u^6v^6) \div 25v^6$
20. $(4l^3w^7 - 2l^5w^{12} + 8l^2w^2) \div 2l^2w$
21. $(3p^4q^4r^2 + 12p^2q^7r^3 + 9p^3q^9r^6) \div 3q^3$
22. $(42a^{12}b^{16}c^{15} + 14a^{23}b^{19}c^{25} + 28a^{14}b^{31}c^{27}) \div 7a^8b^{12}$
23. $(15f^7g^9h^8 + 25f^6g^2h^{10} + 10f^4gh^8) \div 5fh^3$
24. $(2.7l^2m^3n^5 - 18l^4m^6n^3 + 0.45l^5m^4n^2) \div 0.9lmn$
25. $(-42hj^7k^9 - 28h^3j^5k^8 + 14h^4j^2k^{12}) \div -14hj^2k^8$
26. $\left(\frac{1}{2}x^5y^4z^3 + \frac{3}{4}x^6y^4z^2 + \frac{4}{7}x^5y^5z^2\right) \div \frac{2}{3}x^5y^4z^2$

Solve.

*27. **Challenge**

A. A rectangular tile has width $3a$ and length $2ab$. Find the area of the rectangular tile.

B. Find an expression for the number of rectangular tiles needed to cover an area of $12a^5b^3 + 18a^4b^5 + 36a^7b^6$.

*28. **Challenge**

A. A rectangular tile has width $6p^4q^3r$ and length $3p^2q^7r^9$. Find the area of the rectangular tile.

B. Find an expression for the number of rectangular tiles needed to cover an area of $36p^{16}q^{12}r^{15} + 18p^{10}q^{13}r^{11} + 72p^8q^{16}r^{12}$.

Factoring Perfect Squares

REMEMBER

The pattern for squaring a binomial is $(a + b)^2 = a^2 + 2ab + b^2$.

When you square a binomial, the result is a perfect square trinomial. You can use this perfect square pattern to work the other way and find the squared binomial for a given trinomial.

When you expand the square of a binomial, you get a perfect square trinomial because it can be written as the square of a binomial, rather than the product of two different binomials. You can use the patterns of perfect squares to help you factor perfect square trinomials.

Identifying a Perfect Square

PERFECT SQUARE TRINOMIAL PATTERNS

$a^2 + 2ab + b^2 = (a + b)^2$

$a^2 - 2ab + b^2 = (a - b)^2$

Note that for a trinomial to be a perfect square, the first and last terms have to be perfect squares and the middle term has to equal twice the square root of the first and third terms.

Example 1 Determine if each is a perfect square trinomial.

A. $x^2 - 4x + 4$

Solution Try to write the polynomial in the form $a^2 + 2ab + b^2$ or $a^2 - 2ab + b^2$.

Substitute x for a and 2 for b. So, $x^2 - 4x + 4 = x^2 - 2 \cdot x \cdot 2 + 2^2$. The trinomial $x^2 - 4x + 4$ is a perfect square. ■

B. $x^2 - 1$

Solution Since there is no x term, the polynomial $x^2 - 1$ is not a perfect square. ■

C. $x^2 + 7x + 25$

Solution To write the trinomial in the form $a^2 + 2ab + b^2$, substitute x for a and 5 for b. The middle term $2ab$ must then be $2 \cdot x \cdot 5$ or $10x$. Since the middle term is $7x$, the trinomial is not a perfect square. ■

D. $4x^2 + 12x - 100$

Solution When you square a binomial, the sign of the constant term is always positive. Since the constant in the trinomial $4x^2 + 12x - 100$ has a negative sign, the trinomial is not a perfect square. ■

Factoring a Perfect Square

Example 2 Factor each trinomial.

A. $x^2 + 4x + 4$

Solution Write the polynomial in the form $a^2 + 2ab + b^2$.

$x^2 + 4x + 4 = x^2 + 2 \cdot x \cdot 2 + 2^2$ Substitute x for a and 2 for b.

$= (x + 2)^2$ Use the pattern $(a + b)^2$. ■

B. $4x^2 - 20xy + 25y^2$

Solution

$4x^2 - 20xy + 25y^2 = (2x)^2 - 2 \cdot 2x \cdot 5y + (5y)^2$ Substitute $2x$ for a and $5y$ for b.

$= (2x - 5y)^2$ Use the pattern $(a - b)^2$. ■

C. $4x^2 - \frac{4}{3}x + \frac{1}{9}$

Solution

$4x^2 - \frac{4}{3}x + \frac{1}{9} = (2x)^2 - 2 \cdot 2x \cdot \frac{1}{3} + \left(\frac{1}{3}\right)^2$ Substitute $2x$ for a and $\frac{1}{3}$ for b.

$= \left(2x - \frac{1}{3}\right)^2$ Use the pattern $(a - b)^2$. ■

Problem Set

Determine if the expression is a perfect square. If it is, factor it.

1. $x^2 + 2x + 1$
2. $c^2 - 6c + 9$
3. $j^2 + 40j + 400$
4. $n^2 - 26n - 169$
5. $y^2 - 16y + 64$
6. $x^2 + 8x + 16$
7. $4a^2 - 4a + 1$
8. $x^2 + 4x + 4$
9. $z^2 + 10z + 5$
10. $y^2 + y + 1$
11. $f^2 + 1.2f + 0.36$
12. $s^2 + s + \frac{1}{4}$
13. $p^2 + 3.4p + 2.89$
14. $z^2 + \frac{4}{5}z + \frac{4}{25}$
15. $9u^2 + 27u + 81$
16. $4d^2 + 8d - 4$
17. $225v^2 + 450v + 225$
18. $16m^2 + 56m + 49$
19. $169q^2 + 52q + 4$
20. $121t^2 - 22t + 1$
21. $4f^2 - 24f + 36$
22. $25k^2 + 25$
23. $x^2 + 9$
24. $y^2 - 19$
25. $0.64w^2 + 0.32w + 0.04$
26. $\frac{9}{16}h^2 - 4h + \frac{64}{9}$
27. $49r^2 + 140rs + 100s^2$
28. $u^2 + 10uv + 16v^2$
29. $196k^2 - 336kl + 144l^2$
30. $-\frac{169}{121}y^2 - \frac{26}{121}yz + \frac{1}{121}z^2$
31. $4.41c^2 - 4.2cd + d^2$

Solve.

***32. Challenge**

A. Factor $4a^2b^2 + 12abc + 9c^2$.

B. Verify that $4a^2b^2 + 12abc + 9c^2 \neq 9a^2b^2 + 12abc + 4c^2$.

***33. Challenge**

A. Factor $36j^4 + 60j^2 + 25$.

B. Verify your answer by factoring $36f^2 + 60f + 25$, then substituting $f = j^2$ into your answer.

Factoring Differences of Squares

You can use a pattern to factor a difference of squares.

Conjugate binomials, $(a + b)$ and $(a - b)$, are two binomials with the same terms but opposite signs. The product of conjugate binomials, $a^2 - b^2$, is called the difference of squares.

Identifying a Difference of Squares

Example 1 Determine if each is the difference of squares.

A. $x^2 - 1$

Solution Try to write the polynomial in the form $a^2 - b^2$.

Since $x^2 - 1 = x^2 - 1^2$, it is the difference of squares. ■

B. $x^2 + 1$

Solution Since the terms are added, the binomial is the sum of two squares, not the difference of two squares. ■

C. $x^4 - 9$

Solution Try to write the polynomial in the form $a^2 - b^2$. Use the power of a power property of exponents to rewrite x^4.

Since $x^4 - 9 = (x^2)^2 - 3^2$, it is the difference of squares. ■

TIP

The word "difference" in difference of squares means one square term is subtracted from the other square term.

REMEMBER

The power of a power property states

$$(a^m)^n = a^{mn}.$$

Factoring the Difference of Two Squares

You can use the sum and difference pattern to help you factor any binomial that is the difference of squares.

DIFFERENCE OF SQUARES PATTERN

$a^2 - b^2 = (a + b)(a - b)$

Example 2 Completely factor each difference of squares.

A. $144x^2 - z^2$

Solution First, write the polynomial in the form $a^2 - b^2$. Then apply the difference of squares pattern.

$144x^2 - z^2 = (12x)^2 - z^2$	Substitute $12x$ for a and z for b.
$= (12x + z)(12x - z)$	Difference of squares pattern ■

(continued)

> **TIP**
> Always look for perfect squares when a binomial has a minus sign and even powers of variables.

B. $p^{12} - q^{20}$

Solution

$p^{12} - q^{20} = (p^6)^2 - (q^{10})^2$ Power of a Power Property

$= (p^6 + q^{10})(p^6 - q^{10})$ Difference of squares pattern

The binomial $p^6 - q^{10}$ is also a difference of squares so the expression can be factored further.

$(p^6 + q^{10})(p^6 - q^{10})$

$= (p^6 + q^{10})[(p^3)^2 - (q^5)^2]$ p^6 and q^{10} are perfect squares.

$= (p^6 + q^{10})(p^3 + q^5)(p^3 - q^5)$ Difference of squares pattern ■

C. $4x^2 - \frac{4}{9}$

Solution

$4x^2 - \frac{4}{9} = (2x)^2 - \left(\frac{2}{3}\right)^2$ Substitute $2x$ for a and $\frac{2}{3}$ for b.

$= \left(2x + \frac{2}{3}\right)\left(2x - \frac{2}{3}\right)$ Difference of squares pattern ■

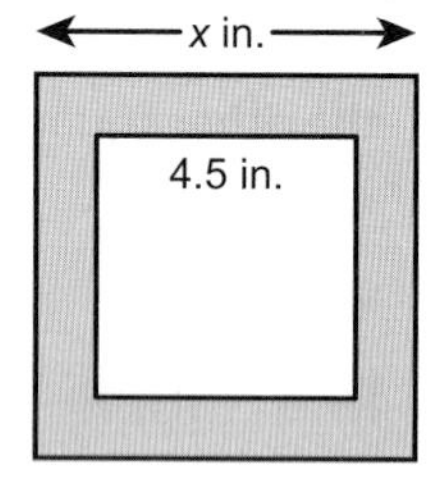

> **REMEMBER**
> The formula for the area of a square is $A = s^2$.

Application: Geometry

Example 3 A picture frame is created by cutting a 4.5-inch square piece from a square piece of plywood.

A. Write a polynomial expression that represents the area of the picture frame after the square piece is removed.

B. Write the area as the difference of squares.

Solution

A. Find the area of the original piece of plywood and subtract the area of the piece that was removed.

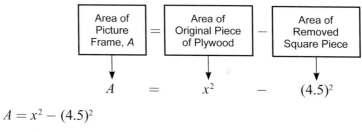

Area of Picture Frame, A	=	Area of Original Piece of Plywood	−	Area of Removed Square Piece
A	=	x^2	−	$(4.5)^2$

$A = x^2 - (4.5)^2$

$= x^2 - 20.25$

The area of the picture frame is $x^2 - 20.25$ inches.

B. Factor the binomial found in part A.

$x^2 - 20.25 = x^2 - (4.5)^2$ Substitute x for a and 4.5 for b.

$= (x + 4.5)(x - 4.5)$ Difference of squares pattern ■

Problem Set

Determine if the expression is a difference of squares. If it is, factor it.

1. $x^2 - 64$
2. $a^2 - 256$
3. $n^4 - 484$
4. $f^2 + 100$
5. $-d^6 + 1$
6. $s^4 - 81$
7. $z^2 - 15$
8. $p^2 - 36$
9. $r^2 - 4$
10. $k^2 - 0.25$
11. $u^2 - \frac{9}{169}$
12. $x^3 - 8$
13. $4 - x^2$
14. $4b^2 - 121$
15. $17q^2 - 289$
16. $16h^4 - 625$
17. $400g^{10} - 900$
18. $49w^2 + 49$
19. $9t^9 - 9$
20. $16m^4 - 1$
21. $361c^2 - 9d^2$
22. $4u^4 - 16v^{16}$
23. $9j^2 - 25k^6$
24. $25p^{36} - 36q^{64}$
25. $1.21y^2 - 0.81z^2$
26. $\frac{1}{4}r^4 - \frac{9}{25}s^2$
27. $0.16a^6 - 0.25b^6$
28. $\frac{81}{16}f^{12} - \frac{16}{625}g^{12}$

Solve.

29. Keena's framed bathroom mirror is square and has a side length of 36 inches. The mirrored portion measures x inches on each side.

    A. Write a polynomial expression that represents the area of the mirror frame.

    B. Write the area as a difference of squares.

30. A small circle has a radius of $9\sqrt{\pi}$. A larger circle has a radius of $x\sqrt{\pi}$.

    A. Write a polynomial expression that represents how much greater the area of the larger circle is than the smaller circle.

    B. Write this expression as a difference of squares.

31. A small rectangle has length n^3 inches and width $0.25n^5$ inches. A larger rectangle has length 0.8 inches and width 0.2 inches.

    A. Write a polynomial expression that represents how much greater the area of the larger rectangle is than the smaller rectangle.

    B. Write this expression as a difference of squares.

32. Remy is painting a mural on a wall that is 12 feet high and 27 feet wide.

    A. Write a polynomial expression that represents the area he has left to cover once he has painted an x by x square of the wall.

    B. Write this expression as a difference of squares.

*33. **Challenge**

    A. Determine if $4a^4b^6 - 14c^{11}d^8$ is a difference of squares.

    B. If so, factor it. If not, what change would make it a difference of squares?

*34. **Challenge**

    A. Determine if $4.9t^2u^8 - 0.0169v^{14}w^6$ is a difference of squares.

    B. If so, factor it. If not, what change would make it a difference of squares?

Factoring Quadratic Trinomials

You learned how to multiply two binomials using the distributive property and the FOIL method. You can reverse this process to factor a trinomial into two binomial factors.

The trinomial $x^2 + bx + c$ can be factored into the product $(x + d)(x + e)$ if $d + e = b$ and $de = c$.

FACTORING $x^2 + bx + c$

If $c > 0$ and $b > 0$, then the product can be written as $(x + \square)(x + \square)$.
If $c > 0$ and $b < 0$, then the product can be written as $(x - \square)(x - \square)$.
If $c < 0$, then the product can be written as $(x + \square)(x - \square)$.

Factoring Trinomials of the Form $x^2 + bx + c$

Example 1 Factor each trinomial.

A. $x^2 + 5x + 6$

Solution Find two binomials whose product is $x^2 + 5x + 6$. Both the x term and the constant term are positive so the binomials will have the form $(x + \square)(x + \square)$.

The coefficient of the x term is 5 and the constant term is 6, so you need to find two positive factors of 6 whose sum is 5.

Positive Factors of 6	Sum of the Factors
1, 6	7
2, 3	5

The factors 2 and 3 have a sum of 5, so $x^2 + 5x + 6 = (x + 2)(x + 3)$.

TIP

Use the FOIL method to check your answer when factoring.

Check

$x^2 + 5x + 6 \stackrel{?}{=} (x + 2)(x + 3)$

$x^2 + 5x + 6 \stackrel{?}{=} x \cdot x + x \cdot 3 + 2 \cdot x + 2 \cdot 3$ FOIL

$x^2 + 5x + 6 \stackrel{?}{=} x^2 + 3x + 2x + 6$ Multiply.

$x^2 + 5x + 6 = x^2 + 5x + 6$ ✓ Combine like terms.

The answer is correct. ■

B. $x^2 - 7x - 8$

Solution The constant term is negative so the factors have opposite signs. The binomials will have the form $(x + \square)(x - \square)$.

The coefficient of the x term is -7 and the constant term is -8, so you need to find two factors of -8 whose sum is -7.

Factors of -8	Sum of the Factors
$-1, 8$	7
$1, -8$	-7
$-2, 4$	2
$2, -4$	-2

The factors 1 and -8 have a sum of -7, so $x^2 - 7x - 8 = (x + 1)(x - 8)$. ■

TIP

If the signs of c (the constant term) and b (the coefficient of the x term) are negative, the factors will have opposite signs.

C. $x^2 + 6x - 27$

Solution The constant term is negative so the binomials will have the form $(x + \square)(x - \square)$.

The coefficient of the x term is 6 and the constant term is -27, so you need to find two factors of -27 whose sum is 6.

Factors of -27	Sum of the Factors
$-1, 27$	26
$1, -27$	-26
$-3, 9$	6
$3, -9$	-6

The factors -3 and 9 have a sum of 6, so $x^2 + 6x - 27 = (x + 9)(x - 3)$. ■

D. $x^2 - 9x + 20$

Solution The x term is negative and the constant term is positive so the factors will have the same sign as the x term. The binomials will have the form $(x - \square)(x - \square)$.

The coefficient of the x term is -9 and the constant term is positive 20, so you need to find two negative factors of 20 whose sum is -9.

Negative Factors of 20	Sum of the Factors
$-1, -20$	-21
$-2, -10$	-12
$-4, -5$	-9

The factors -4 and -5 have a sum of -9, so $x^2 - 9x + 20 = (x - 4)(x - 5)$. ■

Prime Polynomials

Just as a prime number cannot be broken down into the product of two other numbers, a prime polynomial cannot be broken down into the product of two other polynomials.

REMEMBER

A prime number is a positive integer greater than 1 that has exactly two factors, the number itself and 1.

DEFINITION

A polynomial that cannot be factored is a **prime polynomial.**

In this book, all polynomials have rational coefficients. For our purposes, a polynomial is factorable if you can write it as the product of at least two other polynomials with rational coefficients.

Example 2 Factor $x^2 + 8x + 9$.

Solution Both the x term and the constant term are positive so the binomials will have the form $(x + \square)(x + \square)$.

The coefficient of the x term is 8 and the constant term is 9, so you need to find two positive factors of 9 whose sum is 8.

Positive Factors of 9	Sum of the Factors
1, 9	10
3, 3	6

Since there are no factors of 9 whose sum is 8, the trinomial is prime. ■

Finding a Value to Make a Polynomial Factorable

Example 3 Find the value of k, for $k > 0$, that makes each polynomial factorable.

A. $x^2 + kx + 7$

Solution Both the x term and the constant term are positive so the binomials will have the form $(x + \square)(x + \square)$.

The only factors of 7 are 1 and 7, so the only possible factorization is $(x + 1)(x + 7)$.

$$
\begin{aligned}
(x + 1)(x + 7) &= x^2 + 7x + x + 1 \cdot 7 && \text{FOIL} \\
&= x^2 + 8x + 7 && \text{Combine like terms.}
\end{aligned}
$$

So, $k = 8$. ■

B. $x^2 - kx + 10$

Solution The x term is negative and the constant is positive, so the binomials will have the form $(x - \square)(x - \square)$.

The factor pairs of 10 are 1 and 10, and 2 and 5. The possible factorizations are $(x - 1)(x - 10)$ and $(x - 2)(x - 5)$.

$$\begin{aligned}(x - 1)(x - 10) &= x^2 - 10x - x - 1 \cdot (-10) \\ &= x^2 - 11x + 10\end{aligned}$$

$$\begin{aligned}(x - 2)(x - 5) &= x^2 - 5x - 2x - 2 \cdot (-5) \\ &= x^2 - 7x + 10\end{aligned}$$

So, $k = 11$ or $k = 7$. ■

Problem Set

Factor. If the polynomial cannot be factored, write *prime*.

1. $x^2 + 7x + 10$
2. $x^2 - 6x + 5$
3. $x^2 + 5x + 6$
4. $x^2 + 5x - 6$
5. $x^2 + 12x + 13$
6. $x^2 + 9x - 22$
7. $x^2 - 5x - 24$
8. $x^2 + 10x + 8$
9. $x^2 + 15x + 56$
10. $x^2 - 16x - 36$
11. $x^2 + 13x + 42$
12. $x^2 - 11x - 80$
13. $x^2 + 9x - 90$
14. $x^2 - x - 110$
15. $x^2 + 5x - 36$
16. $x^2 + 8x - 21$
17. $x^2 + 23x + 132$

Find the value of k that makes each equation true.

18. $x^2 + kx + 5 = (x + 5)(x + 1)$
19. $x^2 - kx - 11 = (x - 11)(x + 1)$
20. $x^2 - kx - 23 = (x - 23)(x + 1)$
21. $x^2 + kx - 3 = (x + 3)(x - 1)$

Find the value of k, for $k > 0$, that makes each equation factorable.

22. $x^2 + kx + 1$
23. $x^2 - kx - 17$
24. $x^2 - kx + 53$

*25. **Challenge** $x^2 + kx + 8$

Solve.

*26. **Challenge** If the area of Bianca's rectangular backyard patio is represented by the expression $x^2 - 18x + 81$, and the length of the patio is represented by the expression $x - 9$, what is the expression for the width of the patio and what special rectangular shape is the patio?

*27. **Challenge** If the area of Susie's rectangular backyard garden is represented by the expression $x^2 + 16x + 64$, and the length of the garden is represented by the expression $x + 8$, what is the expression for the width of the garden and what special rectangular shape is the garden?

Factoring Quadratic Trinomials, $a \neq 1$

You may need to factor a trinomial where the coefficient of the x^2 term is not equal to 1.

You learned how to factor trinomials of the form $x^2 + bx + c$. Now you will learn how to factor trinomials of the form $ax^2 + bx + c$, where $a \neq 1$.

Factoring Trinomials of the Form $ax^2 + bx + c$

When factoring trinomials of the form $ax^2 + bx + c$, it is not enough to consider only the factors of the constant. You must also consider the factors of the coefficient of the x^2 term. The rules for the signs of the binomial factors are the same as for trinomials of the form $x^2 + bx + c$.

Example 1 Factor each trinomial.

A. $2x^2 + 7x + 3$

Solution You need to find two binomials whose product is $2x^2 + 7x + 3$. Both the x term and the constant term are positive so the binomials will have the form (x +)(x +).

You must think about the order of the factors of the constant term or the order of the factors of the x^2 term because different orders result in different coefficients for the x term.

Positive Factors of 2 (coefficient of x^2)	Positive Factors of 3 (constant term)	Possible Factorization	Product of the Factors
1, 2	1, 3	$(x + 1)(2x + 3)$	$2x^2 + 5x + 3$
1, 2	3, 1	$(x + 3)(2x + 1)$	$2x^2 + 7x + 3$

$2x^2 + 7x + 3 = (x + 3)(2x + 1)$ ■

B. $3x^2 - 6x + 5$

Solution The x term is negative and the constant term is positive so the binomials will have the form $(\ \ x - \ \ )(\ \ x - \ \ )$.

Positive Factors of 3 (coefficient of x^2)	Negative Factors of 5 (constant term)	Possible Factorization	Product of the Factors
1, 3	−1, −5	$(x - 1)(3x - 5)$	$3x^2 - 8x + 5$
1, 3	−5, −1	$(x - 5)(3x - 1)$	$3x^2 - 16x + 5$

Since there are no possible factorizations that produce the correct product, the trinomial $3x^2 - 6x + 5$ is prime. ■

REMEMBER

A prime polynomial is a polynomial that cannot be factored.

C. $4x^2 - 12x - 7$

Solution The constant term is negative so the binomials will have the form $(\ \ x + \ \ )(\ \ x - \ \ )$ or $(\ \ x - \ \ )(\ \ x + \ \ )$.

Positive Factors of 4 (coefficient of x^2)	Factors of −7 (constant term)	Possible Factorization	Product of the Factors
1, 4	−1, 7	$(x - 1)(4x + 7)$	$4x^2 + 3x - 7$
1, 4	1, −7	$(x + 1)(4x - 7)$	$4x^2 - 3x - 7$
1, 4	−7, 1	$(x - 7)(4x + 1)$	$4x^2 - 27x - 7$
1, 4	7, −1	$(x + 7)(4x - 1)$	$4x^2 + 27x - 7$
2, 2	−1, 7	$(2x - 1)(2x + 7)$	$4x^2 + 12x - 7$
2, 2	1, −7	$(2x + 1)(2x - 7)$	$4x^2 - 12x - 7$

$4x^2 - 12x - 7 = (2x + 1)(2x - 7)$ ■

Finding a Value to Make a Polynomial Factorable

Example 2 Find the values of k that make $5x^2 + kx + 7$ factorable.

Solution Both the x term and the constant term are positive so the binomials will have the form $(\ \ x + \ \ )(\ \ x + \ \ )$.

Since 5 and 7 are both prime, the only possible factorizations are $(5x + 1)(x + 7)$ or $(x + 1)(5x + 7)$. Find the product of each pair of binomials.

$$(5x + 1)(x + 7) = 5x^2 + 35x + x + 1 \cdot 7$$
$$= 5x^2 + 36x + 7$$

$$(x + 1)(5x + 7) = 5x^2 + 7x + 5x + 1 \cdot 7$$
$$= 5x^2 + 12x + 7$$

The trinomial is factorable when $k = 36$ or $k = 12$. ■

Problem Set

Factor. If the polynomial is not factorable, write *prime*.

1. $3x^2 + 16x + 20$
2. $3x^2 - 4x - 32$
3. $2x^2 + 10x + 9$
4. $2x^2 + 4x - 6$
5. $4x^2 - 8x - 45$
6. $4x^2 + 12x + 3$
7. $5x^2 + 22x + 21$
8. $5x^2 - 14x + 8$
9. $6x^2 + 8x - 8$
10. $9x^2 + 6x + 1$
11. $12x^2 + 7x - 10$
12. $4x^2 + 33x - 27$
13. $10x^2 - 14x - 12$
14. $5x^2 + 3x - 11$
15. $8x^2 + 38x - 60$
16. $15x^2 - 13x + 2$
17. $15x^2 - 67x + 72$
18. $8x^2 - 22x - 6$

Find the values of *k* that make each polynomial factorable.

19. $3x^2 + kx + 7$
20. $2x^2 + kx + 3$
21. $2x^2 + kx + 7$
22. $3x^2 + kx + 11$
23. $5x^2 + kx + 3$
24. $7x^2 + kx + 11$
25. $3x^2 + kx + 13$
26. $5x^2 + kx + 5$

Factoring Completely

Factoring a trinomial into two binomials does not necessarily mean that the trinomial is completely factored.

Sometimes you will need to repeatedly factor a polynomial until it is factored completely. A polynomial is factored completely when it is written as the product of prime polynomials with integer coefficients. It is not always easy to know if a polynomial is completely factored. Here are some suggestions:

TIPS FOR FACTORING POLYNOMIALS COMPLETELY

1. Look for common monomial factors.
2. Look for trinomials that are perfect square trinomials and for other trinomials that are not prime.
3. Look for binomials that are the difference of two squares.

Factoring Polynomials Completely

Example 1 Factor each trinomial.

A. $3x^2 + 18x + 27$

Solution The terms in the trinomial have a common monomial factor 3. First factor out the 3, then factor the trinomial into two binomials.

$3x^2 + 18x + 27 = 3(x^2 + 6x + 9)$	Factor out 3.
$= 3(x + 3)(x + 3)$	Factor the perfect square trinomial.
$= 3(x + 3)^2$	Simplify. ■

B. $x^4 - 1$

Solution The binomial $x^4 - 1$ is the difference of two squares.

$x^4 - 1 = (x^2)^2 - (1)^2$	Write $x^4 - 1$ as the difference of two squares.
$= (x^2 - 1)(x^2 + 1)$	Factor.
$= (x - 1)(x + 1)(x^2 + 1)$	$x^2 - 1$ is also the difference of two squares. Factor it into two binomials. ■

(continued)

REMEMBER

The binomial $x^2 + 1$ is prime.

C. $x^2 - 4x + 4 - z^2$

Solution The first three terms of the polynomial form a perfect square trinomial.

$x^2 - 4x + 4 - z^2 = (x^2 - 4x + 4) - z^2$	Use the associative property to group the perfect square trinomial.
$= (x - 2)(x - 2) - z^2$	Factor the perfect square trinomial.
$= (x - 2)^2 - z^2$	Simplify.

The resulting polynomial is the difference of two squares and can be factored further.

$(x - 2)^2 - z^2 = [(x - 2) - z][(x - 2) + z]$	Factor the difference of two squares.
$= (x - z - 2)(x + z - 2)$	Simplify. ■

D. $4x^2 + 20x + 24$

Solution The terms in the trinomial have a common monomial factor 4. First factor out the 4, then factor the trinomial into two binomials.

$4x^2 + 20x + 24 = 4(x^2 + 5x + 6)$	Factor out the common monomial factor 4.
$= 4(x + 2)(x + 3)$	Factor the trinomial. ■

Problem Set

Factor completely.

1. $2x^2 + 18x + 40$
2. $2x^2 - 12x - 14$
3. $2x^2 - 2$
4. $3x^3 - 27x$
5. $4m^2 - 81$
6. $27x^3 - 1$
7. $16s^4 - 1$
8. $2x^2 - 2x - 12$
9. $24x^2 + 26x - 28$
10. $45x^2 + 3x - 6$
11. $3x^2 - 12$
12. $t^4 - 1$
13. $5x^3 - 40$
14. $4x^2 - 44x + 72$
15. $-x^2 + 3x - 2$
16. $8x^2 + 16x - 198$
17. $5x^2 + 80x + 320$
18. $9x^2 + 54x + 81$
19. $x^4 - 9$
20. $2x^3 + 6x^2 - 20x$
21. $x^2 + 10x + 25 + y^3$
22. $10y^2 + x^2 - 100$
23. $16x^2 + 72x + 81$
24. $169x^2 - 52x + 4$
25. $256y^4 - 10{,}000$
26. $25x^2 - 4y^2$

*27. **Challenge** $100y^2 + 40xy + 4x^2$

*28. **Challenge** $125x^2 - 100xy + 20y^2$

Factoring Challenges

Factoring polynomials completely can be challenging. Some clever strategies will help.

When you come across a polynomial that is difficult to factor, use one of these methods: grouping or splitting the middle term.

Factoring by Grouping

Example 1 Factor each polynomial by grouping.

A. $xy + 2x - yz - 2z$

Solution In the polynomial $xy + 2x - yz - 2z$, two terms have the variable x and two terms have the variable z. Group the terms of the polynomial so you can divide out a common monomial from each grouping. Then use the distributive property.

$xy + 2x - yz - 2z = (xy + 2x) - (yz + 2z)$	Associative Property
$= x(y + 2) - z(y + 2)$	Factor a common monomial from each binomial.
$= (y + 2)(x - z)$	Distributive Property ■

B. $x^4 - 9y^2 - 6x^2 + 9$

Solution Use the commutative property to change the order of the terms. Group the x terms together and look for a pattern. Since the x terms and the constant form a perfect square trinomial, group these three terms together.

$x^4 - 9y^2 - 6x^2 + 9 = x^4 - 6x^2 + 9 - 9y^2$	Commutative Property
$= (x^4 - 6x^2 + 9) - 9y^2$	Associative Property
$= (x^2 - 3)(x^2 - 3) - 9y^2$	Factor the perfect square trinomial.
$= (x^2 - 3)^2 - 9y^2$	Simplify.
$= (x^2 - 3)^2 - (3y)^2$	Write as the difference of two squares.
$= [(x^2 - 3) + 3y][(x^2 - 3) - 3y]$	Factor.
$= (x^2 + 3y - 3)(x^2 - 3y - 3)$	Simplify. ■

Factoring by Splitting the Middle Term

Another technique you can use when factoring trinomials, especially trinomials where $a \neq 1$, is called splitting the middle term.

THINK ABOUT IT

If you cannot find two factors of *ac* whose sum is *b*, then the polynomial cannot be factored and the polynomial is prime.

FACTORING $ax^2 + bx + c$ BY SPLITTING THE MIDDLE TERM

Step 1 Find the product *ac*.

Step 2 Find two factors of *ac* whose sum is *b*.

Step 3 Split the middle term of the trinomial into two terms using the factors found in Step 2 as the coefficients of the terms.

Step 4 Group the terms into two binomials.

Step 5 Factor out the common monomial in each group.

Step 6 Factor out the common binomial.

Example 2 Factor each polynomial by splitting the middle term.

A. $2x^2 + 7x + 3$

Solution

Step 1	Find the product of 2 and 3.	$2 \cdot 3 = 6$
Step 2	Find two factors of 6 whose sum is the coefficient of the middle term 7.	6 and 1
Step 3	Split the middle term $7x$ into $6x + 1x$.	$2x^2 + 6x + x + 3$
Step 4	Group the terms using the associative property.	$(2x^2 + 6x) + (x + 3)$
Step 5	Factor out the common monomial term in each group.	$2x(x + 3) + 1(x + 3)$
Step 6	Factor out the common binomial.	$(x + 3)(2x + 1)$ ■

B. $8x^2 - 16x - 10$

Solution

Step 1	Find the product of $8 \cdot (-10)$.	$8 \cdot (-10) = -80$
Step 2	Find two factors of –80 whose sum is -16.	-20 and 4
Step 3	Split the middle term $-16x$ into $-20x + 4x$.	$8x^2 - 20x + 4x - 10$
Step 4	Group the terms using the associative property.	$(8x^2 - 20x) + (4x - 10)$
Step 5	Factor out the common monomial term in each group.	$4x(2x - 5) + 2(2x - 5)$
Step 6	Factor out the common binomial.	$(2x - 5)(4x + 2)$ ■

Problem Set

Use grouping to factor. If the polynomial is not factorable, write *prime*.

1. $xy + 3y + xz + 3z$
2. $ac + ad + bc + bd$
3. $x^2 - y^2 - 10x + 25$
4. $x^2 - 100y^2 + 8x + 16$
5. $2xz + xy + 10z + 5y$
6. $4xy - 12xz + yz - 3z^2$

Split the middle term to factor. If the polynomial is not factorable, write *prime*.

7. $3x^2 + 7x + 4$
8. $2x^2 - x - 10$
9. $4x^2 - x - 3$
10. $12x^2 - 5x - 2$
11. $10x^2 + 21x + 9$
12. $8x^2 + 14x - 15$

Determine the method of factoring to use: grouping or splitting the middle term. Factor each polynomial. If the polynomial is not factorable, write *prime*.

13. $ab - 2ac + 2b - 4c$
14. $5x^2 + 7x - 3$
15. $3x^2 + 7x + 2$
16. $xy - xz - 4y + 4z$
17. $x^2 - 4y^2 - 2x + 1$
18. $6xz - 10x - 3yz + 5y$
19. $x^2 - 25y^2 + 4x + 4$
20. $21x^2 - 25x - 4$
21. $x^2 - 81y^2 + 6x + 9$
22. $x^2 + y^2 + 14x + 49$
23. $4x^2 - 9y^2 + 4x + 1$
24. $ac + 2ab - 3bc - 6b^2$
25. $x^4 - 4x^2 - 121y^2 + 4$
26. $12x^2 + 16x + 5$
27. $a^4 - c^2 + b^2 - 2a^2b$
28. $x^4 - 169y^2 + 12x^2 + 36$

*29. **Challenge** $24x^2 - 46x + 7$

*30. **Challenge** $16x^4 + 81y^4 + 72x^2y^2 - 16z^2$

Finding Roots of a Polynomial

Use the zero product property to find the root of a polynomial.

THINK ABOUT IT

For any real number a, $a \cdot 0 = 0$. You can also say for any real numbers a and b, if $a = 0$ or $b = 0$, then $ab = 0$. The zero product property is the converse of this statement.

ZERO PRODUCT PROPERTY

For any real numbers a and b, if $ab = 0$, then $a = 0$ or $b = 0$ or both $a = 0$ and $b = 0$.

You can use the zero product property to solve polynomial equations where one side of the equation is a factored polynomial and the other side of the equation is equal to zero. The solutions to a polynomial equation of this form are called the **roots of the polynomial.**

Solving Polynomial Equations

Example 1 Find the roots.

A. $x^2 + 5x - 6 = 0$

Solution Factor the left side of the equation. Then use the zero product property to find the solutions.

$x^2 + 5x - 6 = 0$			
$(x + 6)(x - 1) = 0$			Factor.
$x + 6 = 0$	or	$x - 1 = 0$	Zero Product Property
$x + 6 - 6 = 0 - 6$		$x - 1 + 1 = 0 + 1$	Solve each equation for x.
$x = -6$		$x = 1$	Simplify.

The roots of the polynomial are −6 and 1.

Check You can check your solutions by substituting each root into the equation for x.

$x^2 + 5x - 6 = 0$	$x^2 + 5x - 6 = 0$
$(-6)^2 + 5 \cdot (-6) - 6 \stackrel{?}{=} 0$	$1^2 + 5 \cdot 1 - 6 \stackrel{?}{=} 0$
$36 - 30 - 6 \stackrel{?}{=} 0$	$1 + 5 - 6 \stackrel{?}{=} 0$
$0 = 0$ ✓	$0 = 0$ ✓

The solutions are correct. ■

B. $x^2 + 6x = -9$

Solution To use the zero product property, one side of the equation must equal 0. The first step in solving the equation $x^2 + 6x = -9$ is to write an equivalent equation where one side of the equation is equal to 0.

$x^2 + 6x = -9$

$x^2 + 6x + 9 = -9 + 9$ Add 9 to each side of the equation.

$x^2 + 6x + 9 = 0$ Simplify.

Now solve the polynomial equation.

$x^2 + 6x + 9 = 0$

$(x + 3)(x + 3) = 0$ Perfect squares pattern

The factors are the same, so this equation has only one solution.

$x + 3 = 0$ Solve the equation for x.

$x = -3$ Subtract 3 from both sides of the equation.

The root of the polynomial is -3. ■

C. $2x^3 - 7x^2 - 15x = 0$

Solution Factor the polynomial.

$2x^3 - 7x^2 - 15x = 0$

$x(2x^2 - 7x - 15) = 0$ Factor out the common monomial x.

$x(2x + 3)(x - 5) = 0$ Factor the trinomial.

$x = 0$ or $2x + 3 = 0$ or $x - 5 = 0$ Zero Product Property

$2x = -3$ $x = 5$ Solve each equation for x.

$x = -\frac{3}{2}$ Simplify.

The roots of the polynomial are $0, -\frac{3}{2}$, and 5. ■

Finding the Zeros of a Polynomial Function

A zero of a function $f(x)$ is a solution to the equation $f(x) = 0$. The zeros of the function are the x-intercepts of the graph of the function.

> **REMEMBER**
> The x-intercept of a graph is the x-coordinate of the point where the graph intersects the x-axis.

Example 2 Use the zeros of the polynomial function $f(x) = 25x^2 - 9$ to find the x-intercepts of the function.

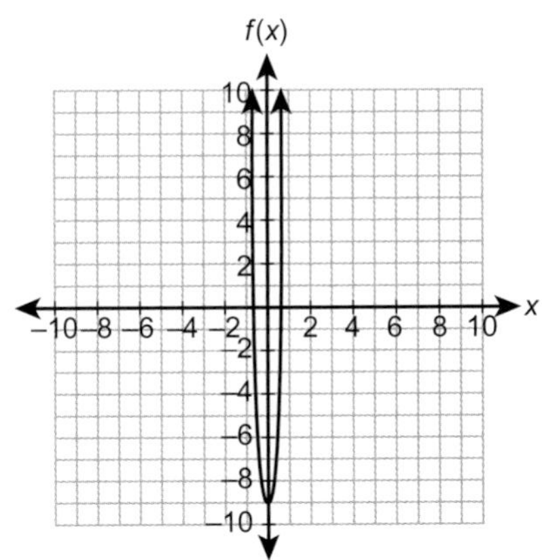

(continued)

Solution On the graph, the x-intercepts appear to be about halfway between 0 and 1. The zeros of the polynomial function are the values of x where $f(x) = 0$. Set the function equal to zero and solve to find the exact values of the x-intercepts. Factor the right side of the equation. Then use the zero product property.

$0 = 25x^2 - 9$			Set the function equal to 0.
$0 = (5x - 3)(5x + 3)$			Difference of squares pattern
$5x - 3 = 0$	or	$5x + 3 = 0$	Zero Product Property
$5x = 3$		$5x = -3$	Solve each equation for x.
$x = \frac{3}{5}$		$x = -\frac{3}{5}$	Simplify.

The zeros are $\frac{3}{5}$ and $-\frac{3}{5}$, so the x-intercepts are $\frac{3}{5}$ and $-\frac{3}{5}$. ■

Application: Measurement

Example 3 A rectangular fishpond is surrounded by a border with a uniform width of x feet. The length of the fishpond including the border is 12 feet and the width including the border is 10 feet. The area of the fishpond is 48 square feet. What are the length and width of the fishpond?

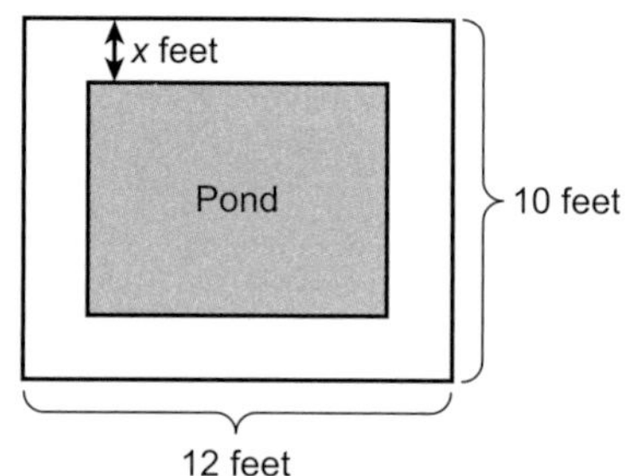

Solution Use the diagram to help you write an equation to solve the problem.

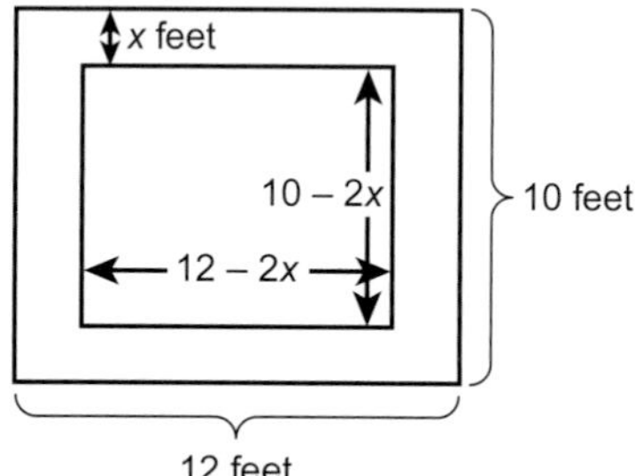

The length of the fishpond is $12 - x - x = 12 - 2x$.

The width of the fishpond is $10 - x - x = 10 - 2x$.

Use the formula for the area of a rectangle to write an equation that represents the area of the fishpond.

$A = lw$

$48 = (12 - 2x)(10 - 2x)$	Substitute 48 for A, $12 - 2x$ for l, and $10 - 2x$ for w.
$48 = 120 - 24x - 20x + 4x^2$	Multiply the two binomials using the FOIL method.
$48 = 120 - 44x + 4x^2$	Combine like terms.
$0 = 72 - 44x + 4x^2$	Subtract 48 from each side.

Now factor the polynomial and solve for x using the zero product property to find the zeros.

$4x^2 - 44x + 72 = 0$

$4(x^2 - 11x + 18) = 0$	Factor out the common monomial 4.
$4(x - 9)(x - 2) = 0$	Factor the trinomial.

Solve each binomial for x.

$x - 9 = 0$ or $x - 2 = 0$

$x = 9$ $\quad$ $x = 2$

The zeros of the function are 9 and 2.

The length and width of the fishpond are $12 - 2x$ and $10 - 2x$. If you substitute 9 into each expression to find the length and width, the values are negative, so 9 is not a valid solution.

$12 - 2x = 12 - 2 \cdot 9$ and $10 - 2x = 10 - 2 \cdot 9$

$= 12 - 18$ $\quad$ $= 10 - 18$

$= -6$ $\quad$ $= -8$

Substitute 2 into the expressions to find the length and width of the fishpond.

$12 - 2x = 12 - 2 \cdot 2$ and $10 - 2x = 10 - 2 \cdot 2$

$= 12 - 4$ $\quad$ $= 10 - 4$

$= 8$ $\quad$ $= 6$

The length of the fishpond is 8 feet and the width is 6 feet. ■

Problem Set

Find the roots of the polynomial equation.

1. $x^2 + x - 12 = 0$
2. $x^2 - 10x + 9 = 0$
3. $x^2 - x - 2 = 0$
4. $x^2 + 7x + 12 = 0$
5. $x^2 - 2x - 35 = 0$
6. $x^2 + 16x + 64 = 0$
7. $x^2 - 12x = -36$
8. $x^2 + 100 = -20x$
9. $2x^2 - 11x - 6 = 0$
10. $9x^2 + 6x + 1 = 0$
11. $x^3 - 8x^2 + 16x = 0$
12. $x^3 - 4x = 0$
13. $10x^3 + 13x^2 = 3x$
14. $27x^3 + 42x^2 = -8x$

Find the zeros of each polynomial function.

15. $f(x) = x^2 - 6x + 5$

16. $f(x) = x^2 + 3x - 10$

17. $f(x) = x^2 + 2x - 80$

18. $f(x) = 3x^2 + x - 10$

19. $f(x) = x^2 - 5x$

20. $f(x) = x^2 - 49$

21. $f(x) = x^2 - 22x + 121$

22. $f(x) = 16x^3 + 6x^2 - x$

23. $f(x) = 4x^2 - 9$

24. $f(x) = x^3 - 20x^2 + 100x$

25. $f(x) = 15x^3 + 46x^2 + 16x$

26. $f(x) = 2x^3 + 52x^2 + 338x$

27. $f(x) = x^3 - 144x$

28. $f(x) = 40x^3 + 6x^2 - x$

Solve.

29. Amar has a coin collection containing dimes and nickels. The number of dimes is 3 more than the number of nickels. If the product of the number of all coins equals 180, find the number of dimes and nickels in his collection.

30. A school has designated a rectangular plot of land for student award plaques. The entire rectangular plot has been reserved except for a small rectangular area in the lower right hand corner. The dimensions are shown below. If the area of this small rectangle is 24 square feet, find the dimensions of the small rectangle and the larger rectangular plot.

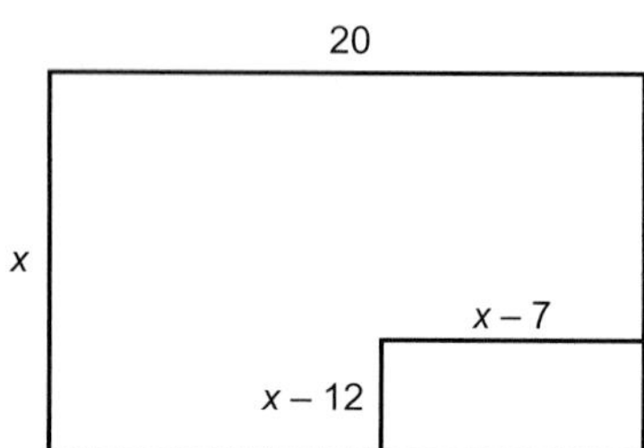

31. In a flag shaped like a right triangle, one leg is 2 less than the hypotenuse and the other leg is 11 less than 3 times the length of the hypotenuse. If the area of the flag is 6 square feet, find the length of the legs and the hypotenuse.

32. Find three consecutive odd integers if the product of the second and third odd integer is 63.

***33.** **Challenge** A box is being constructed to ship a flat panel television. The television's width is 5 times its length and its height is 4 more than 5 times its length. To make the box large enough to store the television and packing materials, 6 inches must be added to the dimensions of the television. If the area of one face of the box, width by height, is 780 square inches, what are the dimensions of the box?

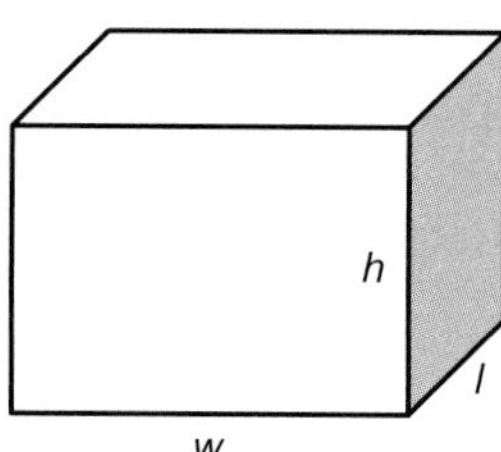

***34.** **Challenge** Lee just celebrated a birthday. Her friend Juanita is 8 years less than twice as old as Lee is now. If the sum of the squares of the two friends ages is 400, find both ages.

Applications: Using Factoring

You can use factoring to solve many problems involving polynomials.

Application: Age

Example 1 Kiersten is k years old. Kiersten's brother Don is 1 year older than twice Kiersten's age. The product of their ages is 300. How old are Kiersten and Don?

Solution

Step 1 *Identify* Find the ages of Kiersten and Don.

Step 2 *Strategize* Let k represent Kiersten's age in years and let $2k + 1$ represent Don's age.

Step 3 *Set Up* Write an equation to solve the problem.

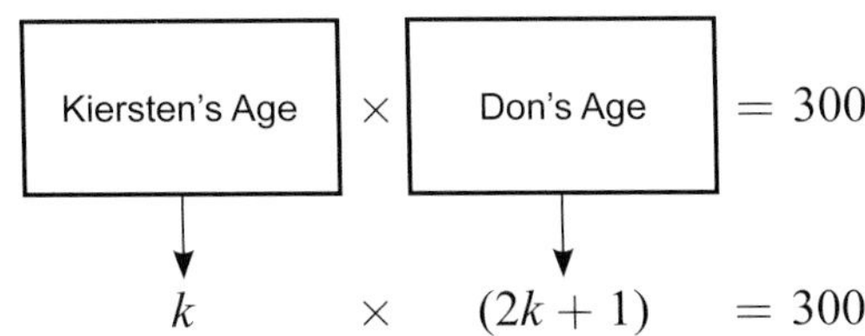

Step 4 *Solve* Transform the equation into an equivalent equation equal to zero so you can use the zero product property. Then solve the equation.

$$k(2k + 1) = 300$$

$$2k^2 + k = 300 \qquad \text{Distributive Property}$$

$$2k^2 + k - 300 = 0 \qquad \text{Subtract 300 from each side of the equation.}$$

$$(2k + 25)(k - 12) = 0 \qquad \text{Factor the trinomial into two binomials.}$$

$$2k + 25 = 0 \quad \text{or} \quad k - 12 = 0 \qquad \text{Zero Product Property}$$

$$2k = -25 \qquad k = 12 \qquad \text{Solve each equation for } k.$$

$$k = -\frac{25}{2}$$

(continued)

TIP

Use the problem-solving plan.

TIP

Choose a variable that reminds you of what it stands for. Here, *k* stands for Kiersten's age.

REMEMBER

The zero product property states: For any real numbers *a* and *b*, if $ab = 0$, then $a = 0$ or $b = 0$ or both $a = 0$ and $b = 0$.

One of the roots is negative and cannot be a solution to an age problem. The only reasonable solution is 12.

$k = 12$ and $2k + 1 = 2 \cdot 12 + 1 = 25$

Kiersten is 12 years old and Don is 25 years old.

Step 5 *Check* You can check your solution by finding the product of their ages: $12 \cdot 25 = 300$. The answer is correct. ■

Application: Numbers

You have probably seen number problems before. With factoring, you can solve more difficult problems.

REMEMBER

Consecutive integers increase by 1 and you can represent them with n, $n + 1$, and so on. Even and odd consecutive integers increase by 2 and you can represent them with n, $n + 2$, and so on.

Example 2 The product of two consecutive odd integers is 195. What are the integers?

Solution

Step 1 *Identify* Find two consecutive odd integers whose product is 195.

Step 2 *Strategize* Let n and $n + 2$ represent the consecutive odd integers.

Step 3 *Set Up* Write an equation to solve the problem.

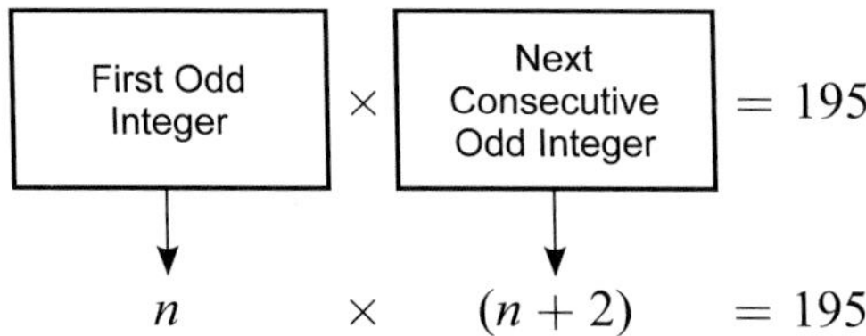

$$n \times (n + 2) = 195$$

Step 4 *Solve* Transform the equation into an equivalent equation equal to zero so you can use the zero product property. Then solve the equation.

$n(n + 2) = 195$	
$n^2 + 2n = 195$	Multiply.
$n^2 + 2n - 195 = 0$	Subtract 195 from each side of the equation.
$(n + 15)(n - 13) = 0$	Factor the trinomial into two binomials.
$n + 15 = 0$ or $n - 13 = 0$	Zero Product Property
$n = -15$ or $n = 13$	Solve each equation for n.

There are two solutions for the first odd integers, -15 and 13. The next consecutive odd integers are -13 and 15, respectively. So, the consecutive odd integers are -15 and -13, and 13 and 15.

Step 5 *Check* You can check your solutions by finding the product of each pair of consecutive odd integers: $-15 \cdot (-13) = 195$ and $13 \cdot 15 = 195$.

The answer is correct. ■

Application: Measurement

When the dimensions of a figure are unknown, you can represent the unknown dimensions with variable expressions. If you multiply two variable dimensions to calculate an area, you end up with a quadratic equation. If you multiply three variable dimensions to calculate a volume, you end up with a cubic (third degree) equation.

Example 3 A rectangular box has the dimensions shown in the diagram. The volume of the box is 12 cubic feet. Find the dimensions of the box.

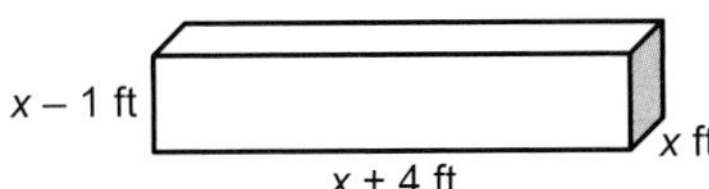

Solution

Step 1 *Identify* Find the length, width, and height of the rectangular box.

Step 2 *Strategize* The diagram shows that $x + 4$ represents the length, x represents the width, and $x - 1$ represents the height.

Step 3 *Set Up* Write an equation to solve the problem. Use the formula for the volume of a rectangular prism.

$V = lwh$

$12 = (x + 4) \cdot x \cdot (x - 1)$

Step 4 *Solve* Transform the equation into an equivalent equation equal to zero so you can use the zero product property. Then solve the equation.

$12 = (x + 4) \cdot x \cdot (x - 1)$	
$12 = (x^2 + 4x)(x - 1)$	Multiply the first two factors.
$12 = x^3 - x^2 + 4x^2 - 4x$	Use the FOIL method.
$12 = x^3 + 3x^2 - 4x$	Combine like terms.
$0 = x^3 + 3x^2 - 4x - 12$	Subtract 12 from each side of the equation.
$0 = (x^3 + 3x^2) - (4x + 12)$	Associative Property
$0 = x^2(x + 3) - 4(x + 3)$	Factor each binomial.
$0 = (x + 3)(x^2 - 4)$	Distributive Property
$0 = (x + 3)(x + 2)(x - 2)$	Factor the difference of two squares.
$x + 3 = 0$ or $x + 2 = 0$ or $x - 2 = 0$	Zero Product Property
$x = -3$ $\quad$ $x = -2$ $\quad$ $x = 2$	Solve each equation for x.

Two of the roots are negative and are not reasonable solutions for the dimensions of a box. So, the solution is 2.

Use the solution to find the dimensions of the box.

Length: $x + 4 = 2 + 4 = 6$

Width: $x = 2$

Height: $x - 1 = 2 - 1 = 1$

The box is 6 feet by 2 feet by 1 foot.

(continued)

Step 5 *Check* You can check the solutions for the dimensions of the box by substituting each solution into the equation for V.

$$V = lwh$$
$$12 = 6 \cdot 2 \cdot 1$$
$$= 12 \checkmark$$

The answer is correct. ■

Problem Set

Solve.

1. The product of two numbers is 232. If the second number is 5 more than 3 times the first, find both numbers.
2. Find two consecutive integers if the product of the first and 5 times the second equals 210.
3. A number times itself equals 529. Find the number.
4. Find two numbers if the second number equals 4 less than the square of the first number and their sum is 38.
5. The sum of the squares of two consecutive odd integers is 290. Find the 2 integers.
6. Find three consecutive even integers if the product of the second and third consecutive even integers is 168.
7. Find three consecutive integers if twice the second plus the square of the third is 22.
8. The sum of the squares of two numbers is 74. If the second number is 2 more than the first number, find both numbers.
9. A gold coin is in a square cardboard pocket to protect its value. The side length of the pocket is 5 centimeters greater than the radius of the coin and the area of the pocket is 81 square centimeters. Find the dimensions of the pocket.

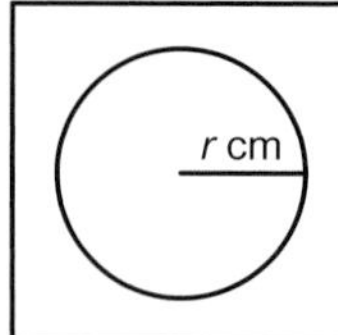

10. The height of a rectangular crate is 2 feet more than the width and the length is 6 feet more than the width. If the area of one face (length by height) is 45 square feet, what are the dimensions of the crate?

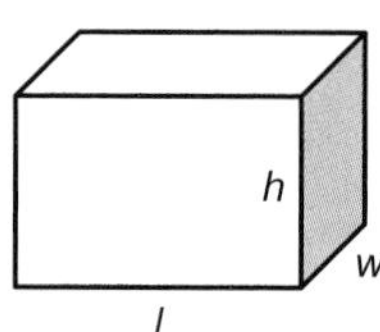

11. A rectangular piece of fabric is divided into three strips. The second strip is 4 inches wider than the first and the third strip is 8 inches wider than the first. Find the width of each strip if the width of the second strip times the width of the third strip is 320 square inches.

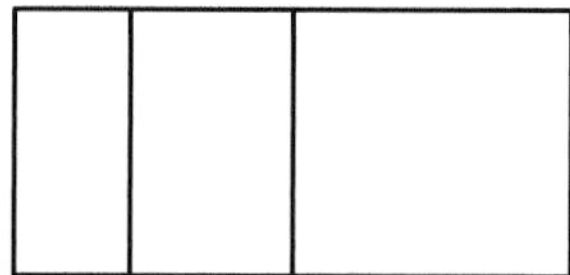

12. A decorative coffee table top is cut from a rectangle by cutting equal sized triangles from each corner. The length of the original rectangle is 8 more than its width. The base and height of each triangle is $\frac{1}{4}$ the widh of the rectangle. If the area of the finished top is 352, find the length and width of the original rectangle.

13. The length of a photograph is 2 inches more than its width. The width of the photograph with a frame is 6 inches more than the photograph's width and the length of the photograph with a frame is 6 inches more than the photograph's length. If the area of the framed photograph is 224 square inches, find the area of the frame.

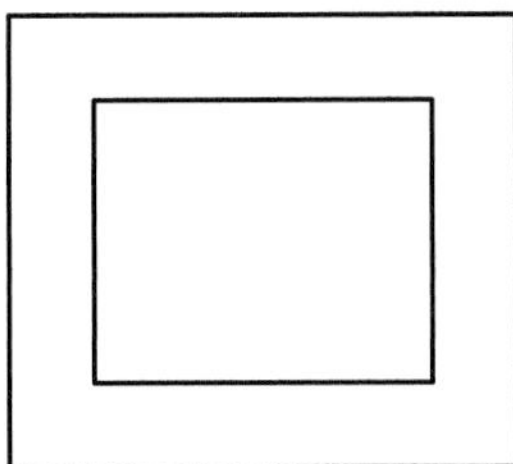

14. The volume of a rectangular box is 96 cubic units. Using the dimensions shown, find the numeric dimensions of the box.

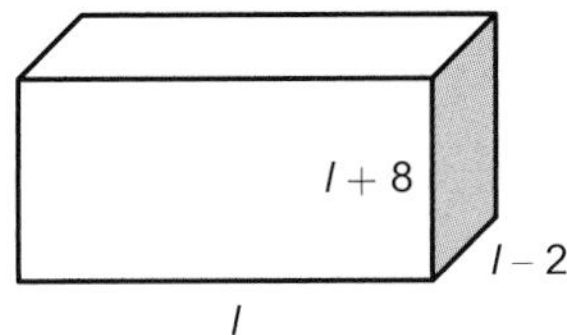

15. Juki, Edde, and Sami play baseball. Edde has hit 6 more homeruns than Juki, and Sami has hit 5 fewer than twice the number that Juki has hit. How many homeruns has each boy hit if the product of Edde's and Sami's homeruns equals 240?

16. Devon, Ben, and Cyrus want to buy concert tickets for all of their friends. Devon bought 3 times as many tickets as Ben, and Cyrus bought 3 less than twice the number that Ben bought. The product of Devon's and Cyrus's tickets is 60. Find the number of tickets each boy bought.

17. Kianna and Sienna are mother and daughter. Kianna's age is 3 less than 4 times Sienna's age. If the product of their ages is 370, how old are Kianna and Sienna?

18. The sum of the numerical values of a circle's area and circumference is 120π. What is the radius of the circle?

19. The Willnout family has three girls. The oldest is 4 years older than the middle child and the youngest girl is 4 years younger than the middle child. If the product of the youngest and oldest girls' ages is 65, find the age of each girl.

20. Olson, Burton, and Jamal are brothers. Jamal is the youngest, Burton is 3 more than twice Jamal's age, and Olson is 1 more than 3 times Jamal's age. If the product of Burton's and Olson's ages equal 143, find the age of each boy.

***21.** **Challenge** The height of a launched rocket is modeled by the function $h(t) = -16t^2 + 32t$. If t represents time, find the time in seconds when the rocket took off and hit the ground. (Hint: Find the zeros of the function.)

***22.** **Challenge** A baseball player hits a baseball and its height is modeled by the function $h(t) = -16t^2 + 12t + 4$. If t represents time, in seconds, find the time in seconds when the ball hit the ground.

UNIT 12 Quadratic Equations

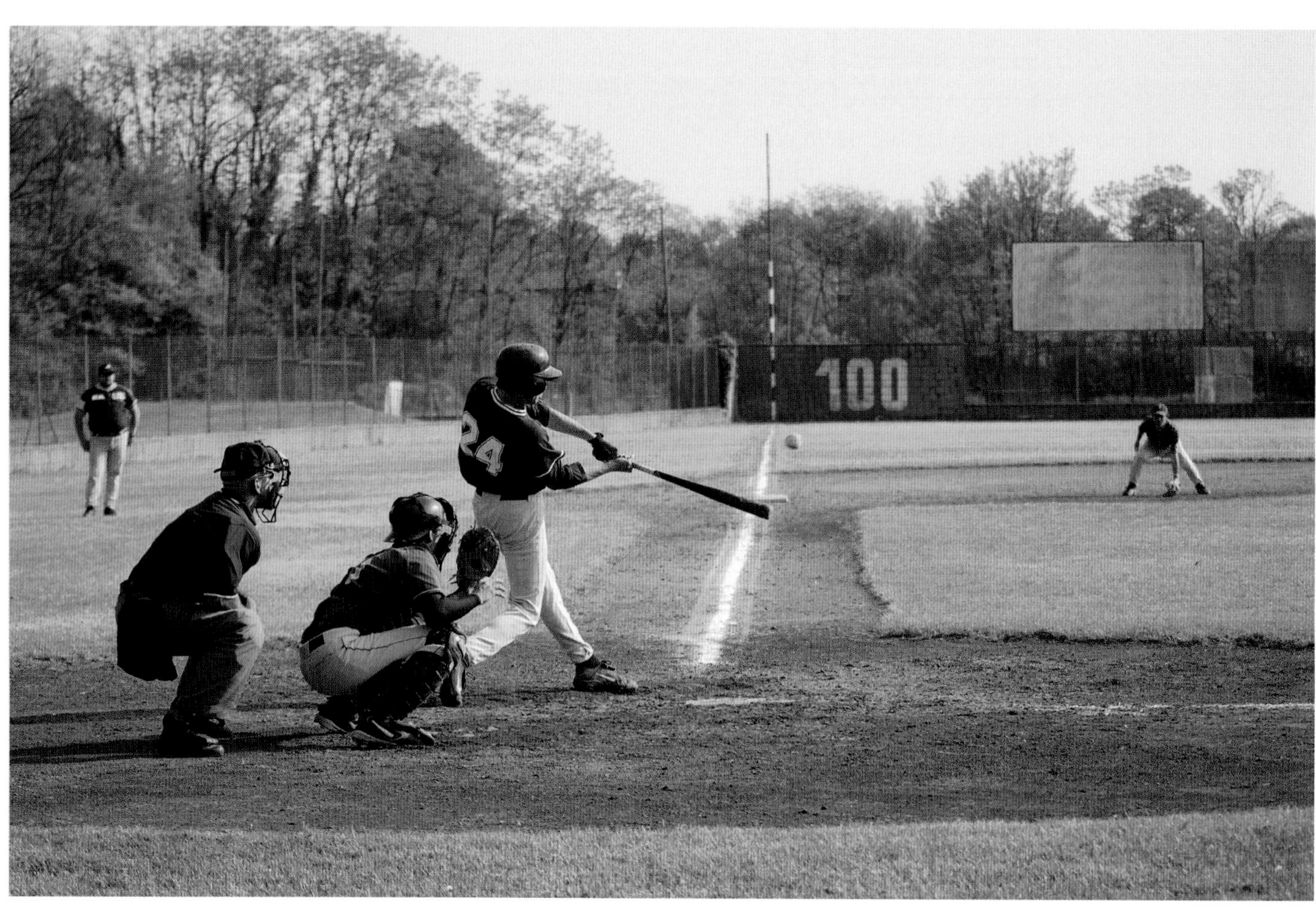

A quadratic equation can model the trajectory of a batted baseball.

Solving equations can help you find answers to many kinds of problems in your daily life. Linear equations usually have one solution, but what about quadratic equations? How can you solve them and what do the solutions look like?

Big Ideas

- Expressions, equations, and inequalities express relationships between different entities.
- If you can create a mathematical model for a situation, you can use the model to solve other problems that you might not be able to solve otherwise. Algebraic equations can capture key relationships among quantities in the world.
- A function is a correspondence between two sets, the domain and the range, that assigns to each member of the domain exactly one member of the range. Many events in the physical world can be modeled as functions. Many functions can be described by algebraic expressions.

Unit Topics

- Solving Perfect Square Equations
- Completing the Square
- The Quadratic Formula
- Solving Quadratic Equations
- Equations and Graphs: Roots and Intercepts
- Applications: Area Problems
- Applications: Projectile Motion

Solving Perfect Square Equations

Some of the simplest quadratic equations involve perfect squares.

An equation of the form $ax^2 + bx + c = 0$, where $a \neq 0$, is a quadratic equation in standard form. There are different methods for solving a quadratic equation, and the values of a, b, and c determine which method is most appropriate.

REMEMBER

A quadratic polynomial is a polynomial of degree two.

Solving by Taking the Square Root of Each Side

To solve a perfect square equation, take the square root of both sides of the equation.

Example 1 Solve $x^2 = 4$.

Solution

$$x^2 = 4$$

$$|x| = \sqrt{4}$$

$x = \sqrt{4}$ or $x = -\sqrt{4}$

$x = 2$ or $x = -2$

The equation is true when $x = 2$ or $x = -2$. The solution set is $\{2, -2\}$. ■

Example 1 suggests a property that can make solving quadratic equations a bit simpler.

PROPERTY

If $x^2 = a$, then $x = \pm\sqrt{a}$.

Example 2 Solve each equation.

A. $16x^2 = 9$

Solution

$16x^2 = 9$

$x^2 = \frac{9}{16}$ Divide each side by 16.

$x = \pm\sqrt{\frac{9}{16}}$ Take the square root of each side.

$x = \pm\frac{3}{4}$ Simplify.

The solution set is $\left\{\frac{3}{4}, -\frac{3}{4}\right\}$.

(continued)

Check

$16x^2 = 9$	$16x^2 = 9$
$16\left(\frac{3}{4}\right)^2 \stackrel{?}{=} 9$	$16\left(-\frac{3}{4}\right)^2 \stackrel{?}{=} 9$
$\cancel{16} \cdot \frac{9}{\cancel{16}} \stackrel{?}{=} 9$	$\cancel{16} \cdot \frac{9}{\cancel{16}} \stackrel{?}{=} 9$
$9 = 9$ ✓	$9 = 9$ ✓ ■

B. $(x - 6)^2 = 4$

Solution

$(x - 6)^2 = 4$

$(x - 6) = \pm\sqrt{4}$ Take the square root of each side.

$x - 6 = \pm 2$ Simplify.

$x = 6 \pm 2$

The expression 6 ± 2 means that there are two answers: $6 + 2$ and $6 - 2$. The solution set is $\{8, 4\}$. ■

C. $5t^2 - 3 = 4$

Solution

$5t^2 - 3 = 4$

$5t^2 = 7$ Add 3 to each side.

$t^2 = \frac{7}{5}$ Divide each side by 5.

$t = \pm\sqrt{\frac{7}{5}}$ Take the square root of each side.

$t = \pm\frac{\sqrt{35}}{5}$ Rationalize the denominator.

The solution set is $\left\{\frac{\sqrt{35}}{5}, -\frac{\sqrt{35}}{5}\right\}$. ■

REMEMBER

To rationalize a denominator, multiply the numerator and denominator of the expression by the radical in the denominator of the expression.

Identifying and Using Perfect Square Factoring Patterns

Some quadratic equations have perfect squares hidden in a trinomial. If you know the factoring pattern, you can use it to simplify and solve equations that look complicated at first.

PERFECT SQUARE TRINOMIAL PATTERNS

$a^2 + 2ab + b^2 = (a + b)^2$

$a^2 - 2ab + b^2 = (a - b)^2$

When solving a quadratic equation, you may need to start by factoring one side of the equation.

Example 3 Solve $x^2 + 16x + 64 = 49$.

Solution The left side is a perfect square trinomial.

$x^2 + 16x + 64 = 49$	
$x^2 + 2 \cdot x \cdot 8 + 8^2 = 49$	Write the polynomial in the form $a^2 + 2ab + b^2$.
$(x + 8)^2 = 49$	Perfect square trinomial pattern
$(x + 8) = \pm\sqrt{49}$	Take the square root of each side.
$x = -8 \pm 7$	Subtract 8 from both sides and simplify.

The solutions are $-8 + 7$ and $-8 - 7$. The solution set is $\{-1, -15\}$.

Check

$x^2 + 16x + 64 = 49$	$x^2 + 16x + 64 = 49$
$(-1)^2 + 16 \cdot (-1) + 64 \stackrel{?}{=} 49$	$(-15)^2 + 16 \cdot (-15) + 64 \stackrel{?}{=} 49$
$1 - 16 + 64 \stackrel{?}{=} 49$	$225 - 240 + 64 \stackrel{?}{=} 49$
$49 = 49$ ✓	$49 = 49$ ✓ ■

REMEMBER

Perfect square trinomial patterns:

$a^2 + 2ab + b^2 = (a + b)^2$

$a^2 - 2ab + b^2 = (a - b)^2$

Application: Geometry

Example 4 The surface area S of a cube is equal to the sum of the areas of the six square faces that form the cube. If each face has side length s, then the formula $S = 6s^2$ can be used to find the surface area of a cube. The surface area of the cube below is 1350 square units. What is the value of x?

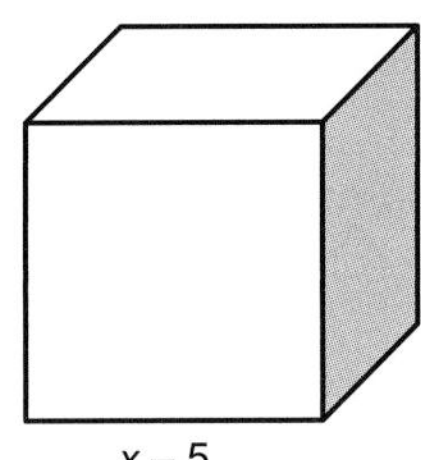

Solution Substitute the given information into the formula and isolate the perfect square to solve.

$S = 6s^2$	
$1350 = 6(x - 5)^2$	Substitute 1350 for S and $(x - 5)$ for s.
$225 = (x - 5)^2$	Divide each side by 6.
$\pm\sqrt{225} = x - 5$	Take the square root of each side.
$5 \pm 15 = x$	Add 5 to both sides and simplify.

The solutions are -10 and 20. Since a side length cannot be a negative value, the only value of x is 20. ■

Problem Set

Solve.

1. $x^2 = 25$
2. $y^2 = 144$
3. $4x^2 = 1$
4. $9y^2 = 4$
5. $2t^2 + 1 = 19$
6. $25x^2 - 7 = 9$
7. $(a - 2)^2 = 9$
8. $(y - 3)^2 = 36$
9. $(2x - 6)^2 = 16$
10. $(5x + 4)^2 = 25$
11. $(4x + 4.1)^2 = 36.75$
12. $\left(\frac{1}{3}y + 2\right)^2 = 121$
13. $5x^2 - 2 = 43$
14. $4m^2 - 9 = 7$
15. $4x^2 - 5 = 12$
16. $6t^2 + 2 = 11$
17. $3x^2 + 4 = 8$

*18. **Challenge** $6y^2 - 7 = 3$

Solve using perfect square factoring patterns.

19. $x^2 + 4x + 4 = 25$
20. $y^2 - 6y + 9 = 16$
21. $t^2 - 12t + 36 = 9$
22. $m^2 + 10m + 25 = 49$
23. $x^2 - 8x + 16 = 4$
24. $4x^2 - 36x + 81 = 9$
25. $9p^2 + 24p + 16 = 100$
26. $\frac{1}{4}y^2 - 5y + 25 = 4$

Solve.

27. Kelly's garden has a 3-foot-wide path on two sides, making a square with sides measuring $x + 3$ feet. If the area of the garden, including the path, is 225 square feet, what are the dimensions of the garden not including the path?

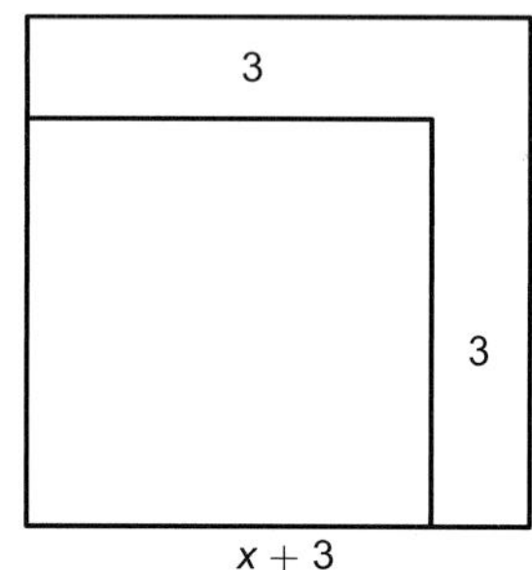

28. The length of a rectangle is 3 times the side of a square. The width of the rectangle is 5 inches greater than the side of the square. If the area of the square is $4x^2 - 12x + 9$ square inches, what are the dimensions of the rectangle?

29. Shar has framed a square painting in a 6-inch wide frame. Including the frame, the painting measures 20.25 square feet. Each side of the frame is $x + 1$ feet long. What is the length of each side of the painting, without the frame?

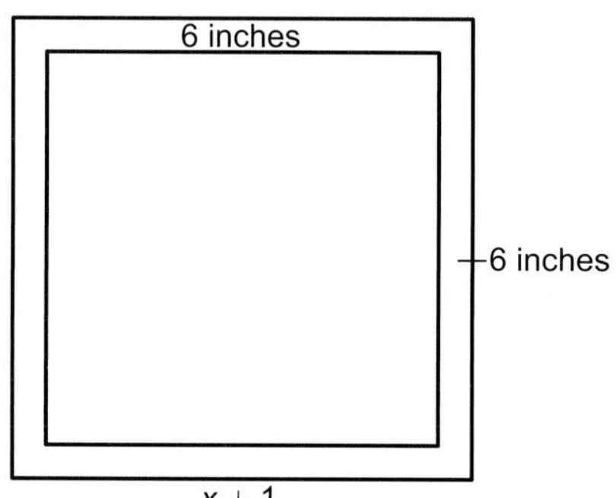

30. Find the value of x for each cube.

    A. Total surface area 486 square centimeters; side length $x + 3$

    B. Total surface area 3456 square centimeters; side length $x - 7$

Completing the Square

You can write any quadratic equation as a perfect square equation.

In a perfect square trinomial, the constant term is always equal to the square of half the coefficient of the x term, as shown in the examples below.

$$(x + 5)^2 = x^2 + 10x + 25 = x^2 + 10x + \left(\frac{10}{2}\right)^2$$

$$(x - 4)^2 = x^2 - 8x + 16 = x^2 - 8x + \left(\frac{-8}{2}\right)^2$$

You can use this fact to turn a quadratic expression into a perfect square trinomial.

Completing the Square

Complete the square by finding the number that should be added to each expression to change it into a perfect square trinomial.

DEFINITION

Completing the square is the process of transforming an expression of the form $x^2 + bx$ into a perfect square trinomial by adding the term $\left(\frac{b}{2}\right)^2$ to it.

Example 1 Find the number that should be added to the expression $x^2 + 14x$ to change it into a perfect square trinomial.

Solution Take half of 14 and square the result: $\left(\frac{14}{2}\right)^2 = 7^2 = 49$. The number is 49.

Check Determine if $x^2 + 14x + 49$ is a perfect square trinomial.

$x^2 + 14x + 49 = (x + 7)(x + 7) = (x + 7)^2$. ■

THINK ABOUT IT

The last term in a perfect square trinomial is always positive.

Solving a Quadratic Equation by Completing the Square

Completing the square makes it possible to write any quadratic equation as a perfect square equation. Use the following steps to solve any quadratic equation by completing the square.

HOW TO USE COMPLETING THE SQUARE TO SOLVE A QUADRATIC EQUATION

Step 1 Write the equation in the form $x^2 + bx = c$.

Step 2 Add $\left(\frac{b}{2}\right)^2$ to each side of the equation and simplify.

Step 3 Factor the perfect square trinomial and solve for x.

REMEMBER

Before completing the square, the coefficient of the squared term must be 1.

TIP

Do not multiply out the $\left(\frac{b}{2}\right)^2$ term on the left side. That way, the trinomial is easier to factor and you are less likely to make a mistake.

Example 2 Transform each equation into a perfect square equation and solve.

A. $4x^2 = 3 + 4x$

Solution

Step 1 Write the equation in the form $x^2 + bx = c$ by subtracting $4x$ from each side of the equation, then dividing each side by 4.

$$4x^2 = 3 + 4x$$

$$4x^2 - 4x = 3 \qquad \text{Subtract } 4x \text{ from each side.}$$

$$x^2 - x = \frac{3}{4} \qquad \text{Divide each side by 4.}$$

Step 2 Add $\left(\frac{-1}{2}\right)^2$ to each side.

$$x^2 - x = \frac{3}{4}$$

$$x^2 - x + \left(-\frac{1}{2}\right)^2 = \frac{3}{4} + \frac{1}{4} \qquad \text{Add } \left(\frac{-1}{2}\right)^2 = \frac{1}{4} \text{ to each side.}$$

$$x^2 - x + \left(-\frac{1}{2}\right)^2 = 1 \qquad \text{Simplify.}$$

Step 3 Factor the perfect square trinomial and solve for x.

$$x^2 - x + \left(-\frac{1}{2}\right)^2 = 1$$

$$\left(x - \frac{1}{2}\right)^2 = 1 \qquad \text{Factor the perfect square trinomial.}$$

$$\left(x - \frac{1}{2}\right) = \pm\sqrt{1} \qquad \text{Take the square root of each side.}$$

$$x = \frac{1}{2} \pm 1 \qquad \text{Add } \frac{1}{2} \text{ to each side and simplify.}$$

The solution set is $\left\{\frac{3}{2}, -\frac{1}{2}\right\}$. ■

B. $x^2 + 20x + 8 = 0$

Solution

Step 1 $x^2 + 20x + 8 = 0$

$x^2 + 20x = -8$ Subtract 8 from each side.

Step 2 $x^2 + 20x + 10^2 = -8 + 100$ Add $\left(\frac{20}{2}\right)^2 = 10^2 = 100$ to each side.

$x^2 + 20x + 10^2 = 92$ Simplify.

Step 3 $(x + 10)^2 = 92$ Factor the perfect square trinomial.

$x + 10 = \pm\sqrt{92}$ Take the square root of each side.

$x + 10 = \pm 2\sqrt{23}$ Simplify.

$x = -10 \pm 2\sqrt{23}$ Subtract 10 from each side.

The solution set is $\{-10 + 2\sqrt{23}, -10 - 2\sqrt{23}\}$. ■

THINK ABOUT IT

Sometimes quadratic equations have solutions that are irrational numbers.

Application: Art

Example 3 An 8 inch by 10 inch painting is framed so the total area of the painting with the frame is 100 square inches. Find the width of the frame to the nearest hundredth of an inch.

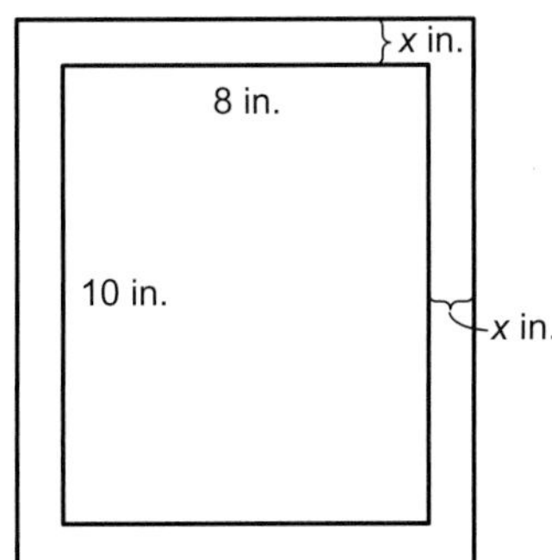

Solution Use the problem-solving plan.

Step 1 *Identify* Find the width of the frame.

Step 2 *Strategize* The length and width of the frame is x inches. Write the length and width of the painting with the frame, in terms of x.

The total width in inches is $8 + x + x = 8 + 2x$.

The total length in inches is $10 + x + x = 10 + 2x$.

Step 3 *Set Up* Use the length and width to write and solve an equation for the area.

$(8 + 2x)(10 + 2x) = 100$ Area is length times width.

(continued)

Step 4 *Solve*

$$(8 + 2x)(10 + 2x) = 100$$

$$80 + 36x + 4x^2 = 100 \quad \text{Multiply the binomials.}$$

$$20 + 9x + x^2 = 25 \quad \text{Divide each side by 4.}$$

$$9x + x^2 = 5 \quad \text{Subtract 20 from each side.}$$

$$x^2 + 9x = 5 \quad \text{Rearrange the terms.}$$

$$x^2 + 9x + \left(\frac{9}{2}\right)^2 = 5 + \frac{81}{4} \quad \text{Add } \left(\frac{9}{2}\right)^2 = \frac{81}{4} \text{ to each side.}$$

$$\left(x + \frac{9}{2}\right)^2 = \frac{101}{4} \quad \text{Factor the perfect square trinomial and simplify.}$$

$$\left(x + \frac{9}{2}\right) = \pm\sqrt{\frac{101}{4}} \quad \text{Take the square root of each side.}$$

$$x = -\frac{9}{2} \pm \frac{\sqrt{101}}{2} \quad \text{Subtract } \frac{9}{2} \text{ from each side.}$$

$$x = -\frac{9}{2} + \frac{\sqrt{101}}{2} \quad \text{or} \quad x = -\frac{9}{2} - \frac{\sqrt{101}}{2} \quad \text{Simplify.}$$

$$x \approx 0.5249 \qquad x \approx -9.5249$$

The width of the frame must be positive, so you can disregard the negative solution. The width is about 0.52 inches.

Step 5 *Check*

$$(8 + 2x)(10 + 2x) = 100$$

$$(8 + 2 \cdot 0.52)(10 + 2 \cdot 0.52) \stackrel{?}{=} 100$$

$$9.04 \cdot 11.04 \stackrel{?}{=} 100$$

$$99.80 \approx 100 \checkmark$$

The approximate solution is accurate. ■

Problem Set

Find the number that should be added to each expression to change it into a perfect square trinomial. Then write the expression as a perfect square trinomial.

1. $x^2 + 6x$

2. $x^2 - 8x$

3. $x^2 - 7x$

4. $y^2 + \frac{2}{5}y$

5. $a^2 - 2.4a$

***6.** **Challenge** $4x^2 + 16x$

Transform each equation into a perfect square equation and solve.

7. $x^2 + 4x = 5$
8. $x^2 + 2x = 3$
9. $t^2 - 8t = -15$
10. $y^2 - 6y = -5$
11. $x^2 + 14x = 15$
12. $3x^2 - 18x = 21$
13. $2x^2 - x = 3$
14. $3x^2 - 9x = 30$
15. $5p^2 + 18p = -16$
16. $2x^2 - 48 = -20x$
17. $20m = 13.8 - 5m^2$
18. $9 + 4.5y = -\frac{1}{2}y^2$
19. $\frac{4}{9}t^2 - \frac{8}{3}t = 32$
20. $8 + x^2 = 9x + 26 - x^2$
21. $y^2 - 4 = -2y$
22. $x^2 - 6 + 2x = 4 - x^2 - 4x$
23. $2x^2 - 5x = -1$
24. $x^2 - 1 = \frac{7}{3}x$

Solve.

25. A contractor is constructing a concrete patio off the back of Sarabel's house. The contractor is placing square tiles that are 2 feet by 2 feet along the edges of the patio. If the area of the patio and the tiles is 216 square feet and the width is 6 feet greater than the length, what are the dimensions of the patio?

26. Seana is hanging a rectangular mirror with a width of 24 inches and a length of 76 inches centered on her door. If the area of the door is 2688 square inches, what are the width and length of the door?

27. Sam's corkboard has a 1-inch frame border. If the area of the corkboard including the frame is 864 square inches, and the width of the corkboard is 12 inches greater than the length, what are the dimensions of the corkboard, excluding the frame?

28. Mandi and Aaron are playing in a rectangular sandbox that is surrounded by a wooden walkway with a width of x feet. If the area of the sandbox and walkway is 63 square feet and the sandbox measures 4.5 feet by 6.5 feet, how wide is the walkway?

The Quadratic Formula

You can solve any quadratic equation in standard form using the quadratic formula.

Use completing the square on the standard form of a quadratic equation, $ax^2 + bx + c = 0$, to derive the **quadratic formula**.

$ax^2 + bx + c = 0$	
$ax^2 + bx = -c$	Subtract c from each side.
$x^2 + \frac{b}{a}x = -\frac{c}{a}$	Divide each side by a.
$x^2 + \frac{b}{a}x + \left(\frac{b}{2a}\right)^2 = -\frac{c}{a} + \frac{b^2}{4a^2}$	Add $\left(\frac{b}{2a}\right)^2 = \frac{b^2}{4a^2}$ to each side.
$x^2 + \frac{b}{a}x + \left(\frac{b}{2a}\right)^2 = -\frac{4ac}{4a^2} + \frac{b^2}{4a^2}$	Multiply $\frac{c}{a}$ by $\frac{4a}{4a}$ to get a common denominator.
$x^2 + \frac{b}{a}x + \left(\frac{b}{2a}\right)^2 = \frac{b^2 - 4ac}{4a^2}$	Simplify.
$\left(x + \frac{b}{2a}\right)^2 = \frac{b^2 - 4ac}{4a^2}$	Factor the perfect square trinomial.
$\left(x + \frac{b}{2a}\right) = \pm\sqrt{\frac{b^2 - 4ac}{4a^2}}$	Take the square root of each side.
$x + \frac{b}{2a} = \pm\frac{\sqrt{b^2 - 4ac}}{2a}$	Simplify.
$x = -\frac{b}{2a} \pm \frac{\sqrt{b^2 - 4ac}}{2a}$	Subtract $\frac{b}{2a}$ from each side.
$x = \frac{-b \pm \sqrt{b^2 - 4ac}}{2a}$	Simplify.

Using the Quadratic Formula

PROPERTY

For a quadratic equation written in standard form, $ax^2 + bx + c = 0$, where $a \neq 0$, the solutions of the equation can be found using the **quadratic formula**.

$$x = \frac{-b \pm \sqrt{b^2 - 4ac}}{2a}$$

To use the quadratic formula, write the quadratic equation you are trying to solve in standard form, then identify the values of a, b, and c.

Example 1 Solve each equation. Estimate irrational solutions to nearest tenth.

A. $x^2 + 9x - 22 = 0$

Solution Since the equation is in standard form, identify a, b, and c: $a = 1$, $b = 9$, and $c = -22$.

$$x = \frac{-b \pm \sqrt{b^2 - 4ac}}{2a}$$

$$x = \frac{-9 \pm \sqrt{9^2 - 4 \cdot 1 \cdot (-22)}}{2 \cdot 1}$$ Substitute values for a, b, and c.

$$x = \frac{-9 \pm \sqrt{81 - (-88)}}{2}$$ Simplify the radicand.

$$x = \frac{-9 \pm \sqrt{169}}{2}$$ Simplify.

$$x = \frac{-9 \pm 13}{2}$$ Evaluate the square root.

$$x = \frac{-9 + 13}{2} \quad \text{or} \quad x = \frac{-9 - 13}{2}$$ Write $x = \frac{-9 \pm 13}{2}$ as two equations.

$$x = \frac{4}{2} \qquad x = \frac{-22}{2}$$ Simplify each numerator.

$$x = 2 \qquad x = -11$$ Divide.

The solution set is $\{2, -11\}$. ■

> **TIP**
> Parentheses help to avoid sign errors when using the quadratic formula.

> **REMEMBER**
> The radicand is the expression under the radical sign.

B. $x^2 + 3x = 5$

Solution Write the equation in standard form by subtracting 5 from each side.

$$x^2 + 3x = 5$$

$$x^2 + 3x - 5 = 0$$ Subtract 5 from each side.

Identify a, b, and c: $a = 1$, $b = 3$, and $c = -5$.

$$x = \frac{-b \pm \sqrt{b^2 - 4ac}}{2a}$$

$$x = \frac{-3 \pm \sqrt{3^2 - 4 \cdot 1 \cdot (-5)}}{2 \cdot 1}$$ Substitute values for a, b, and c.

$$x = \frac{-3 \pm \sqrt{9 - (-20)}}{2}$$ Simplify the radicand.

$$x = \frac{-3 \pm \sqrt{29}}{2}$$ Simplify.

$$x = \frac{-3 + \sqrt{29}}{2} \approx 1.2 \quad \text{or} \quad x = \frac{-3 - \sqrt{29}}{2} \approx -4.2$$ Write $x = \frac{-3 \pm \sqrt{29}}{2}$ as two equations.

The solution set is $\{1.2, -4.2\}$. ■

Using the Discriminant

The **discriminant** is the radicand $b^2 - 4ac$ in the quadratic formula. If you know the value of the discriminant, you can determine how many solutions the equation has, and whether the solutions are rational, irrational, or nonreal.

PROPERTY

The equation, $ax^2 + bx + c = 0$, where $a \neq 0$, has

2 rational solutions	if $b^2 - 4ac > 0$ and $b^2 - 4ac$ is a perfect square.
2 irrational solutions	if $b^2 - 4ac > 0$ and $b^2 - 4ac$ is not a perfect square.
1 rational solution	if $b^2 - 4ac = 0$.
0 real solutions	if $b^2 - 4ac < 0$.

REMEMBER

A number is a perfect square if it can be written as the square of a rational number.

Example 2 Use the discriminant to determine the number and type of solutions each equation has.

A. $2x^2 + 13x + 15 = 0$

Solution Identify a, b, and c: $a = 2$, $b = 13$, and $c = 15$.

$b^2 - 4ac = 13^2 - 4 \cdot 2 \cdot 15 = 169 - 120 = 49$

The discriminant, 49, is positive and is a perfect square. So, the equation has two rational solutions. ■

B. $x^2 - \frac{1}{2}x + \frac{1}{16} = 0$

Solution Identify a, b, and c: $a = 1$, $b = -\frac{1}{2}$, and $c = \frac{1}{16}$.

$b^2 - 4ac = \left(-\frac{1}{2}\right)^2 - 4 \cdot 1 \cdot \frac{1}{16} = \frac{1}{4} - \frac{1}{4} = 0$

The discriminant is zero, so the equation has one rational solution. ■

C. $x^2 + 5 = 0$

Solution Identify a, b, and c: $a = 1$, $b = 0$, and $c = 5$.

$b^2 - 4ac = 0^2 - 4 \cdot 1 \cdot 5 = 0 - 20 = -20$

The discriminant, –20, is negative. So, the equation has no real solutions. ■

Application: Determining Whether or Not a Polynomial Is Factorable

The expression $ax^2 + bx + c$ is factorable if the solutions to the equation $ax^2 + bx + c = 0$ are rational. So, the expression $ax^2 + bx + c$ is factorable if the discriminant is either a perfect square or zero.

Example 3 Determine if each trinomial is factorable.

A. $30x^2 - 31x - 44$

Solution Find the discriminant.

$a = 30$, $b = -31$, and $c = -44$

$$\begin{aligned} b^2 - 4ac &= (-31)^2 - 4 \cdot 30 \cdot (-44) \\ &= 961 + 5280 \\ &= 6241 \end{aligned}$$

Because 6241 is a perfect square, $30x^2 - 31x - 44$ is factorable. ■

B. $27x^2 + 14x - 15$

Solution Find the discriminant.

$a = 27$, $b = 14$, and $c = -15$

$$\begin{aligned} b^2 - 4ac &= 14^2 - 4 \cdot 27 \cdot (-15) \\ &= 196 + 1620 \\ &= 1816 \end{aligned}$$

Because 1816 is not a perfect square, $27x^2 + 14x - 15$ is not factorable. ■

Problem Set

Use the quadratic formula to solve each equation. Round your answer to the nearest tenth.

1. $x^2 + 7x - 4 = 0$

2. $v^2 - v - 1 = 0$

3. $d^2 - 4d + 3 = 0$

4. $x^2 + 3x - 6 = 0$

5. $2x^2 - 5x + 3 = 0$

6. $y^2 + 2y + 1 = 0$

7. $3x^2 + 3x - 1 = 0$

8. $2h^2 + 7h + 4 = 0$

9. $5p^2 + 10p - 3 = 0$

10. $x^2 - 3x = -2$

11. $s^2 - 6s = 3$

12. $m^2 = -40m - 400$

13. $u^2 = 13 - 8u$

14. $6j^2 - 4j = 3$

15. $14r^2 = 5 - 7r$

16. $0.1z^2 + 0.5z + 0.4 = 0$

17. $f^2 + \frac{3}{2}f + \frac{1}{2} = 0$

18. $-0.69y^2 = 2.7y + 1.8$

19. $\frac{3}{5}g^2 - \frac{5}{4} = -\frac{9}{5}g$

Use the discriminant to determine the number and type of solutions each equation has.

20. $12t^2 + 4t - 9 = 0$

21. $-3n^2 - 2n - 6 = 0$

22. $k^2 - 10k + 25 = 0$

23. $23w^2 + 13w = 0$

24. $7q^2 - q = 9$

25. $4 + 12d = -9d^2$

26. $-13n = 6 + 5n^2$

27. $0.2t^2 - 0.3t = -0.01$

28. $3f - 9f^2 = 6$

Determine if each trinomial is factorable.

29. $16x^2 + 7x + 3 = 0$

30. $-h^2 + h = 1$

31. $36p^2 - 49 = 0$

32. $\frac{1}{4}v^2 + \frac{1}{3}v + \frac{1}{9} = 0$

Solve.

*33. **Challenge**

A. Show that $\frac{-b + \sqrt{b^2 - 4ac}}{2a}$ is a solution of $ax^2 + bx + c = 0$ by substituting.

B. Show that $\frac{-b - \sqrt{b^2 - 4ac}}{2a}$ is a solution of $ax^2 + bx + c = 0$ by substituting.

*34. **Challenge**

A. Verify that $r^2x^2 + 4rsx + 3s^2 = 0$ is factorable when r and s are whole numbers.

B. Under what circumstances would the equation have one rational solution?

Solving Quadratic Equations

To determine the best method for solving a quadratic equation, first examine the equation.

METHODS FOR SOLVING QUADRATIC EQUATIONS

1. Take the square root of each side.	Use only with perfect square equations.
2. Factor and use the zero product property.	Use when one side of an equation is equal to 0, and the other side is easily factored.
3. Complete the square.	Use when an equation is of the form $x^2 + bx + c = 0$, where b is an even number and $x^2 + bx + c$ is not factorable.
4. Use the quadratic formula.	Use when other methods are too difficult or cannot be used.

Choosing a Method for Solving a Quadratic Equation

Example 1 Determine the best method for solving each equation.

A. $x^2 + 4x - 1 = 0$

Solution Complete the square or use the quadratic formula. The equation is of the form $x^2 + bx + c = 0$, where b is an even number and $x^2 + bx + c$ is not factorable. ■

B. $x^2 + 6x + 9 = 49$

Solution Take the square root of each side. Since you can the write the equation as $(x + 3)^2 = 49$, it is a perfect square equation. ■

C. $x^2 + 5x - 6 = 3$

Solution Use the quadratic formula. You can write the equation as $x^2 + 5x - 9 = 0$, and the trinomial $x^2 + 5x - 9$ is not factorable. Since b is not an even number, completing the square would be cumbersome. ■

REMEMBER

Use the discriminant to determine if a quadratic expression is factorable.

Solving Quadratic Equations

Example 2 Use the best method to solve each equation.

A. $x^2 = -9x$

Solution Use the zero product property.

$$x^2 = -9x$$

$x^2 + 9x = 0$ Add $9x$ to each side.

$x(x + 9) = 0$ Factor the left side.

$x = 0$ or $x + 9 = 0$ Zero Product Property

$x = -9$

The solution set is $\{0, -9\}$. ■

THINK ABOUT IT

You cannot divide both sides of the equation by *x* because you would lose a solution. Division by zero is undefined, so be careful when dividing by any variable expression.

B. $x^2 + 4x = 6$

Solution Complete the square.

$$x^2 + 4x = 6$$

$x^2 + 4x + 2^2 = 6 + 4$ Add $\left(\frac{4}{2}\right)^2 = 2^2 = 4$ to each side.

$(x + 2)^2 = 10$ Factor the left side.

$(x + 2) = \pm\sqrt{10}$ Take the square root of each side.

$x = -2 \pm \sqrt{10}$ Subtract 2 from each side.

The solution set is $\{-2 + \sqrt{10}, -2 - \sqrt{10}\}$. ■

C. $-x^2 - 6 = 0$

Solution Isolate the perfect square, and then take the square root of each side.

$$-x^2 - 6 = 0$$

$-x^2 = 6$ Add 6 to each side.

$x^2 = -6$ Divide each side by -1.

The square of a real number cannot be negative. The equation has no real solutions. This can be verified by finding the discriminant:

$b^2 - 4ac = 0^2 - 4 \cdot (-1) \cdot (-6) = -24$. ■

D. $3x^2 - x + 1 = 0$

Solution Use the quadratic formula with $a = 3$, $b = -1$, and $c = 1$.

$$x = \frac{-b \pm \sqrt{b^2 - 4ac}}{2a}$$

$$= \frac{-(-1) \pm \sqrt{(-1)^2 - 4 \cdot 3 \cdot 1}}{2 \cdot 3}$$

$$= \frac{1 \pm \sqrt{1 - 12}}{6}$$

$$= \frac{1 \pm \sqrt{-11}}{6}$$

The discriminant is -11, so there is no real solution. ■

Application: Geometry

Example 3 The length of a rectangular window is 6 feet longer than its width w. Find the width if the area is 10 square feet. Round your answer to the nearest hundredth.

Solution Use w for width and $w + 6$ for length.

$$A = lw$$

$10 = (w + 6) \cdot w$	Area is length times width.
$10 = w^2 + 6w$	Distributive Property
$10 + 9 = w^2 + 6w + 9$	Complete the square.
$19 = (w + 3)^2$	Factor the perfect square.
$\pm\sqrt{19} = (w + 3)$	Take the square root of each side.
$-3 \pm \sqrt{19} = w$	Subtract 3 from each side.

The solutions are $w = -3 + \sqrt{19} \approx 1.36$ and $w = -3 - \sqrt{19} \approx -7.36$. Since width cannot be negative, the width of the rectangle to the nearest hundredth is 1.36 feet.

Check

$$10 = w(w + 6)$$

$$10 \stackrel{?}{=} 1.36(1.36 + 6)$$

$$10 \stackrel{?}{=} 1.36 \cdot 7.36$$

$$10 \approx 10.00096 \checkmark$$

The answer is correct. ■

Problem Set

Determine the best method for solving each equation.

1. $x^2 - 5x + 4 = 0$
2. $n^2 + 18n + 9 = 0$
3. $f^2 - 13f = 13$
4. $h^2 - 7h - 20 = -32$
5. $z^2 - 10z + 25 = 16$
6. $2v^2 + 4v - 2 = 5$

Use the best method to solve each equation.

7. $q^2 - 10q - 20 = 0$
8. $d^2 - 21d + 20 = 0$
9. $m^2 + 22m + 121 = 64$
10. $j^2 + 10j - 28 = 11$
11. $7x^2 - 9x - 18 = 3$
12. $2y^2 - 3y = -1$
13. $g^2 + 18g + 50 = 0$
14. $s^2 - 7s + 25 = 85$
15. $u^2 - 22u = 9$
16. $p^2 - 2p + 1 = 0$
17. $w^2 + 4 = 0$
18. $4 - y^2 = 8y$
19. $r^2 + 17r + 15 = 15$
20. $k^2 + \frac{2}{3}k + \frac{4}{9} = \frac{1}{4}$
21. $t^2 - 28t + 86 = -74$
22. $d^2 + 40d - 56 = 0$
23. $g^2 + 0.8g + 0.16 = 0.25$
24. $p^2 - p - 42 = 0$

Write a quadratic equation to model the problem. Then use the equation to solve.

25. The width of a rectangular frame is 6 inches shorter than its length l. Find the length if the area is 216 square inches.

26. Brian wants to increase the size of his 3 feet by 6 feet garden. He wants to increase each side by the same amount to double the area. Find the amount by which he should increase each side. Round your answer to the nearest tenth.

27. Two sides of a square are increased by 2 meters, and two sides are decreased by 2 meters to create a rectangle. The new area is 10 times the original area. Find the original length of each side of the square. Round your answer to the nearest tenth.

28. The legs of a right triangle measure 12 inches and 16 inches. Each side is decreased by the same length, resulting in an area of 45 square inches. Find the amount by which each side was decreased. Round your answer to the nearest tenth.

***29. Challenge** The original sides of a square were changed and the new area can be represented by the quadratic equation $4x^2 + 12x + 9$, where x is the original side length.

A. Determine the original measure of each side if the new area is 100 square inches. Round your answer to the nearest tenth.

B. What changes were made to the original sides of the square to get the new area?

***30. Challenge** One side of a square is increased by 4 feet, and another side is increased by 6 feet, resulting in a rectangle with three times the area.

A. What was the original side length of the square? Round your answer to the nearest tenth.

B. What is the new area?

Equations and Graphs: Roots and Intercepts

The x-intercepts of the graph of a function $y = f(x)$ are the same as the roots of the related equation $f(x) = 0$.

The graph of any quadratic function is a symmetric curve called a **parabola**. You can graph a quadratic function by making a table of ordered pairs, plotting the points, and connecting the points with a smooth curve. The graph of $y = x^2 - 3x - 4$ is shown below.

x	y	(x, y)
-2	$(-2)^2 - 3 \cdot (-2) - 4 = 6$	$(-2, 6)$
-1	$(-1)^2 - 3 \cdot (-1) - 4 = 0$	$(-1, 0)$
0	$0^2 - 3 \cdot 0 - 4 = -4$	$(0, -4)$
1	$1^2 - 3 \cdot 1 - 4 = -6$	$(1, -6)$
2	$2^2 - 3 \cdot 2 - 4 = -6$	$(2, -6)$
3	$3^2 - 3 \cdot 3 - 4 = -4$	$(3, -4)$
4	$4^2 - 3 \cdot 4 - 4 = 0$	$(4, 0)$
5	$5^2 - 3 \cdot 5 - 4 = 6$	$(5, 6)$

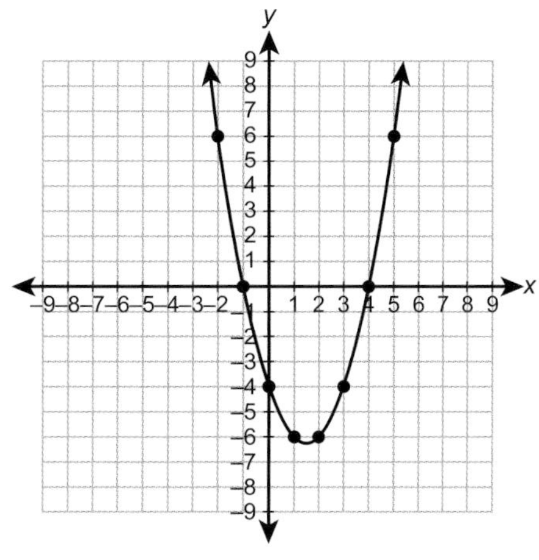

Notice that there are two x-intercepts: $(-1, 0)$ and $(4, 0)$. So, -1 and 4 are the roots of the related equation $x^2 - 3x - 4 = 0$. You can verify this by solving the related equation algebraically.

$$x^2 - 3x - 4 = 0$$

$$(x - 4)(x + 1) = 0 \qquad \text{Factor.}$$

$$x - 4 = 0 \quad \text{or} \quad x + 1 = 0 \qquad \text{Zero Product Property}$$

$$x = 4 \qquad x = -1 \qquad \text{Solve.}$$

The "turning point" of a parabola is called the **vertex**. The vertex can lie below the x-axis, on the x-axis, or above the x-axis. The direction the parabola opens can also vary. It can open upward, as the graph of $y = x^2 - 3x - 4$ does, or it can open downward. Where the vertex lies and the direction a parabola opens determine the number of x-intercepts the graph has.

THINK ABOUT IT

The vertex will be the highest or lowest point of the parabola. If the parabola opens upward, the vertex is the lowest point. If the parabola opens downward, the vertex is the highest point.

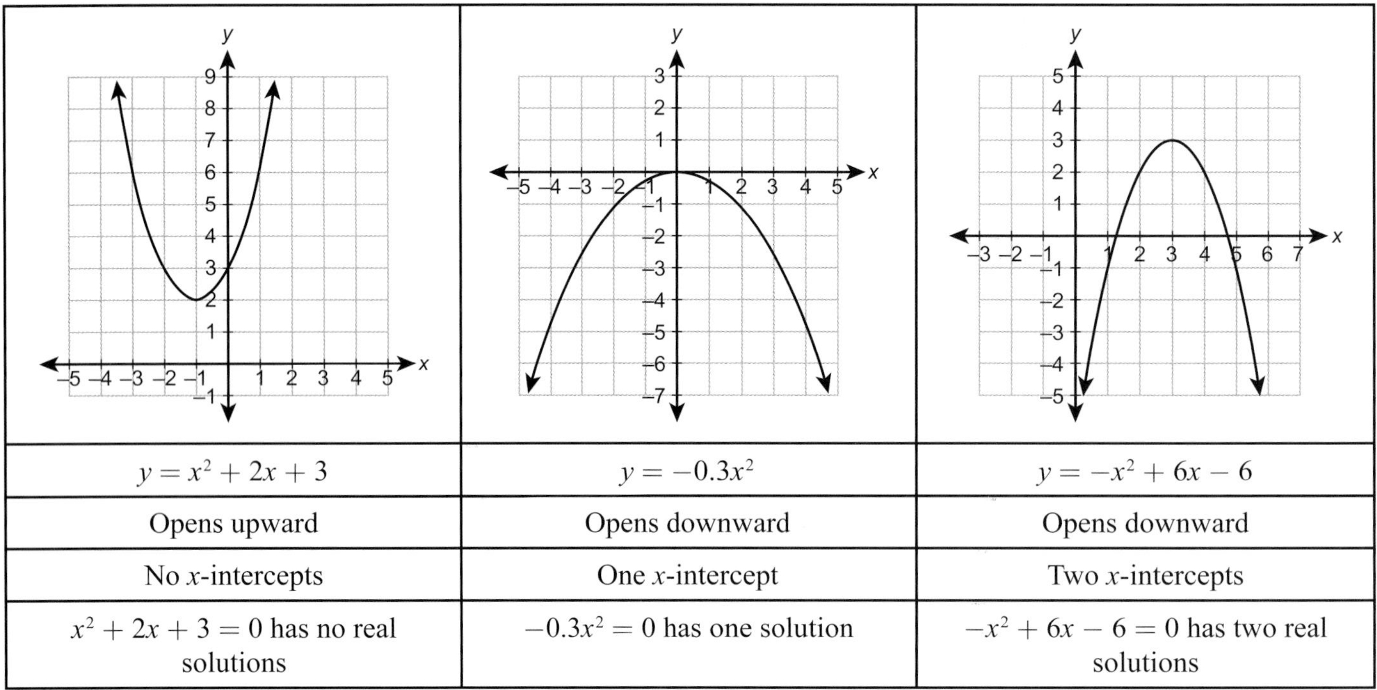

$y = x^2 + 2x + 3$	$y = -0.3x^2$	$y = -x^2 + 6x - 6$
Opens upward	Opens downward	Opens downward
No x-intercepts	One x-intercept	Two x-intercepts
$x^2 + 2x + 3 = 0$ has no real solutions	$-0.3x^2 = 0$ has one solution	$-x^2 + 6x - 6 = 0$ has two real solutions

There is a relationship between the value of a and the direction a parabola opens.

PROPERTY

For $y = ax^2 + bx + c$, $a \neq 0$, if a is positive, the graph opens upward. If a is negative, the graph opens downward.

Describing a Parabola from the Related Equation

You can determine information about the graph of a quadratic function without actually drawing the graph.

THINK ABOUT IT

If the graph opens upward and has two x-intercepts, the vertex is below the x-axis. The vertex is also below the x-axis when the graph opens downward and has no x-intercepts.

Example 1 For each function, determine the number of x-intercepts of the graph, and whether the parabola opens upward or downward.

A. $y = x^2 - 5x - 12$

Solution The related equation is $x^2 - 5x - 12 = 0$. Find the value of the discriminant for $a = 1$, $b = -5$, and $c = -12$.

$b^2 - 4ac = (-5)^2 - 4 \cdot 1 \cdot (-12) = 25 + 48 = 73$

Since the discriminant is positive, the equation has two roots, so the graph of the function has two x-intercepts. Since a is positive, the graph opens upward. The vertex is below the x-axis and directly halfway between the two x-intercepts. ■

B. $y = -5x^2 + 2x - 1$

Solution The related equation is $-5x^2 + 2x - 1 = 0$. Find the value of the discriminant for $a = -5$, $b = 2$, and $c = -1$.

$b^2 - 4ac = 2^2 - 4 \cdot (-5) \cdot (-1) = 4 - 20 = -16$

Since the discriminant is negative, the equation has no roots, so the graph of the function has no x-intercepts. Since a is negative, the graph opens downward. The vertex is below the x-axis. ■

C. $y = -x^2 + 6x - 9$

Solution The related equation is $-x^2 + 6x - 9 = 0$. Find the value of the discriminant for $a = -1$, $b = 6$, and $c = -9$.

$b^2 - 4ac = 6^2 - 4 \cdot (-1) \cdot (-9) = 36 - 36 = 0$

Since the discriminant is zero, the equation has one root, so the graph of the function has one x-intercept. Since a is negative, the graph opens downward. The vertex is on the x-axis. ■

Graphing Quadratic Functions

Knowing the x-intercepts and the direction that the parabola faces is helpful for drawing the graph of a parabola.

Example 2 Graph $y = x^2 - 4x - 21$.

Solution Since a is positive, the parabola opens upward. Solve the related equation $x^2 - 4x - 21 = 0$ to find the x-intercepts.

$$x^2 - 4x - 21 = 0$$

$$(x + 3)(x - 7) = 0$$

$$x + 3 = 0 \quad \text{or} \quad x - 7 = 0$$

$$x = -3 \qquad\qquad x = 7$$

The x-intercepts are $(-3, 0)$ and $(7, 0)$.

Use a table of ordered pairs to find additional points on the graph. Then, plot and connect the points to graph.

x	y	(x, y)
-4	$(-4)^2 - 4 \cdot (-4) - 21 = 11$	$(-4, 11)$
2	$2^2 - 4 \cdot 2 - 21 = -25$	$(2, -25)$
4	$4^2 - 4 \cdot 4 - 21 = -21$	$(4, -21)$
8	$8^2 - 4 \cdot 8 - 21 = 11$	$(8, 11)$

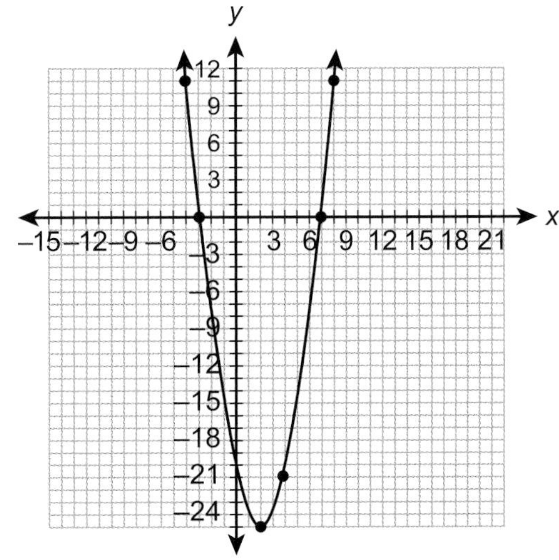

The vertex is located on the x-axis when there is a single x-intercept. When there are two x-intercepts, the x-coordinate of the vertex is halfway between the x-intercepts. Since the graph of $y = x^2 - 4x - 21$ has x-intercepts -3 and 7, the x-coordinate of the vertex is $\frac{(-3 + 7)}{2} = 2$. So, the vertex lies at $(2, -25)$. ■

Problem Set

For each quadratic function, determine:

A. the number of x-intercepts.
B. whether the parabola opens upward or downward.
C. if the vertex lies on, below, or above the x-axis.

1. $y = -x^2 + 3x - 7$

2. $y = x^2 + 4x - 1$

3. $y = x^2 - 4x + 4$

4. $y = 2x^2 - 3x - 2$

5. $y = 3x^2 - 8$

6. $y = -2x^2 - 4x - 5$

7. $y = 3x^2$

8. $y = 10x^2 - 6x - 3$

9. $y = -4x^2 - 2$

10. $y = -5x^2 + 10x - 5$

11. $y = -3x^2 + 7x - 5$

12. $y = 9x^2 - 6x + 1$

Graph each quadratic function. Find the x-intercepts and graph at least one other point.

13. $y = x^2 - x - 2$

14. $y = x^2 + 8x + 15$

15. $y = 4x^2$

16. $y = x^2 - 9x + 14$

17. $y = x^2 + 12x + 36$

18. $y = x^2 - 4$

19. $y = 2x^2 - 7x - 4$

20. $y = 3x^2 - 3$

21. $y = 3x^2 + x - 2$

22. $y = 9x^2 - 25$

23. $y = 4x^2 + 21x + 5$

24. $y = 12x^2 + 16x + 5$

25. $y = 30x^2 - 43x + 4$

26. $y = 15x^2 - 19x - 10$

Solve.

27. The square of a number decreased by 25 is -9. Find the number. Graph the parabola that models this problem.

28. Find two numbers if one number is 10 less than the other and their product is -16. Graph the parabola that models this problem.

***29. Challenge** A firecracker is launched from ground level. The model of the firecracker's height is $y = -16t^2 + 32t$. Find the t-intercepts of this parabola. If t represents time, what do the t-intercepts represent in this problem?

***30. Challenge** Write the equation of the parabola whose x-intercepts are $\left(-\frac{4}{3}, 0\right)$ and $(5, 0)$.

Applications: Area Problems

You can solve many area problems by using quadratic equations.

Application: Rectangles

The area of a rectangle is $A = lw$. When l and w are variables, the area is a quadratic.

Example 1

A. The length of a rectangle is 5 more than 3 times its width. Find the length and width of the rectangle with an area of 182 square units.

Solution Write expressions for the length and width and use the formula for the area of a rectangle. Let w represent the width of the rectangle. Let l represent the length of the rectangle: $l = 3w + 5$.

$A = lw$

$182 = (3w + 5)w$ Substitution Property

$182 = 3w^2 + 5w$ Distributive Property

$0 = 3w^2 + 5w - 182$ Subtract 182 from each side.

Find the value of the discriminant for $a = 3$, $b = 5$, and $c = -182$ to find the number of roots.

$b^2 - 4ac = 5^2 - 4 \cdot 3 \cdot (-182) = 25 + 2184 = 2209$

Since the discriminant is positive, there are two roots. Since the quadratic equation cannot be easily factored, use the quadratic formula to find the roots of the equation.

$w = \frac{-b \pm \sqrt{b^2 - 4ac}}{2a}$ Quadratic Formula

$w = \frac{-5 \pm \sqrt{5^2 - 4 \cdot 3 \cdot (-182)}}{2 \cdot 3}$ Substitute 3 for a, 5 for b, and -182 for c.

$w = \frac{-5 \pm \sqrt{2209}}{6}$ Simplify.

$w = \frac{-5 + \sqrt{2209}}{6}$ or $w = \frac{-5 - \sqrt{2209}}{6}$ Write $w = \frac{-5 \pm \sqrt{2209}}{6}$ as two equations.

$w = \frac{-5 + 47}{6} = 7$ or $w = \frac{-5 - 47}{6} \approx -8.67$ Simplify.

$w = 7$ and $3w + 5 = 3 \cdot 7 + 5 = 26$

(continued)

REMEMBER

Distance is always positive.

Notice there are two answers, 7 and –8.67. Since width can only be positive, discard the negative answer. The width is 7 units and the length is 26 units.

Check $7 \cdot 26 = 182$ and 26 is 5 more than 3 times 7. ■

B. The length of a rectangle is twice its width. If the width is tripled and the length is decreased by 5, the area is increased by 4. Find the width.

Solution For the original rectangle: Let w represent the width of the rectangle. Let l represent the length of the rectangle: $l = 2w$.

Arrange the information in a table.

	Original Rectangle	**New Rectangle**
Width	w	$3w$
Length	$2w$	$2w - 5$
Area	$2w \cdot w = 2w^2$	$3w(2w - 5) = 6w^2 - 15w$

$$\underbrace{\text{The new area}}_{6w^2 - 15w}\ \underbrace{\text{is}}_{=}\ \underbrace{\text{the area of the original rectangle}}_{2w^2}\ \underbrace{\text{increased by 4.}}_{+4}$$

$$6w^2 - 15w = 2w^2 + 4$$

$4w^2 - 15w - 4 = 0$ Simplify so one side of the equation equals 0.

$(4w + 1)(w - 4) = 0$ Factor.

$w = -\frac{1}{4}$ or $w = 4$ Zero Product Property

Discard the negative solution because width can only be positive. The width of the rectangle is 4 units.

Check Original area: $4 \cdot 8 = 32$, New area: $12 \cdot 3 = 36$, and $36 = 32 + 4$. ■

Application: Triangles and Circles

The area of a triangle is $A = \frac{1}{2}bh$. When b and h are variables, the area is a quadratic.

Example 2 The height of a triangle is 3 times the length of its base. A new triangle is formed by lengthening the base by 1 and dividing the height by 3. The area is 60 less than the area of the original triangle. What are the length of the base and the height of the original triangle?

Solution Let b represent the base of the original triangle. Let h represent the height of the original triangle: $h = 3b$.

Arrange the information in a table.

	Original Triangle	New Triangle
Base	b	$b + 1$
Height	$3b$	b
Area	$\frac{1}{2} \cdot b \cdot 3b = \frac{1}{2}(3b^2)$	$\frac{1}{2}(b + 1) \cdot b = \frac{1}{2}(b^2 + b)$

REMEMBER

The formula for the area of a triangle is $A = \frac{1}{2}bh$, where b is the base and h is the height of the triangle.

$$\underbrace{\text{The new area}}_{\frac{1}{2}(b^2 + b)} \quad \underbrace{\text{is}}_{=} \quad \underbrace{\text{the area of the original triangle}}_{\frac{1}{2} \cdot 3b^2} \quad \underbrace{\text{decreased by 60.}}_{-\ 60}$$

$$\frac{1}{2}(b^2 + b) = \frac{1}{2} \cdot 3b^2 - 60$$

$b^2 + b = 3b^2 - 120$ Multiply each side by 2 to eliminate the fractions.

$-2b^2 + b + 120 = 0$ Simplify so one side of the equation equals 0.

Use the quadratic formula to solve.

$b = \frac{-b \pm \sqrt{b^2 - 4ac}}{2a}$ Quadratic Formula

$b = \frac{-1 \pm \sqrt{1^2 - 4 \cdot (-2) \cdot (120)}}{2 \cdot (-2)}$ Substitute -2 for a, 1 for b, and 120 for c in the quadratic formula.

$b = \frac{-1 \pm \sqrt{961}}{-4}$ Simplify.

$b = \frac{-1 + \sqrt{961}}{-4}$ or $b = \frac{-1 - \sqrt{961}}{-4}$ Write $b = \frac{-1 \pm \sqrt{961}}{-4}$ as two equations.

$b = 8$ or $b = -7.5$ Simplify.

REMEMBER

Don't confuse the variable b in the area formula with the b in the quadratic formula.

$b = 8$ and $h = 3b = 3 \cdot 8 = 24$.

Remember to discard the negative solution because the base of a triangle can only be positive. The original triangle has a base of 8 units and a height of 24 units. ■

The area of a circle is $A = \pi r^2$. When the radius or diameter is variable, the area is a quadratic.

Example 3 The area of the shaded region is 56π in^2. Find the width of the shaded region.

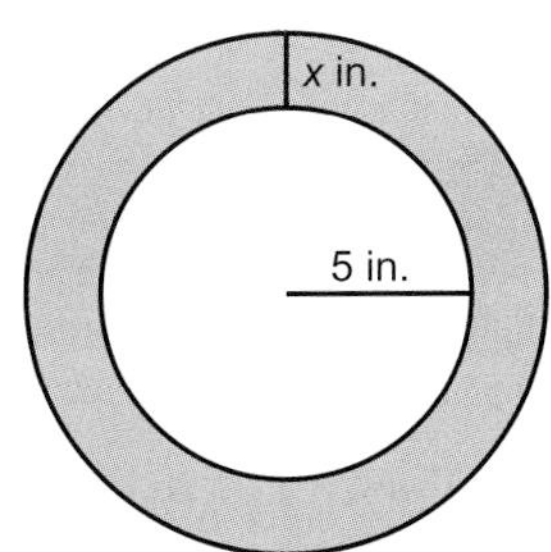

(continued)

Solution The area of the shaded region is the difference between the area of the larger circle and the area of the unshaded region.

$56\pi = (5 + x)^2\, \pi - 25\pi$	The width of the shaded area is x.
$56 = (5 + x)^2 - 25$	Divide each side by π.
$56 = 25 + 10x + x^2 - 25$	Square the binomial.
$56 = 10x + x^2$	Simplify the right side.
$0 = x^2 + 10x - 56$	Subtract 56 from each side.
$0 = (x + 14)(x - 4)$	Factor.
$x = -14$ or $x = 4$	Zero Product Property

Discard the negative solution because width is always positive. The shaded region has a width of 4 inches. ■

Problem Set

Solve. Use the following area formulas when needed:
parallelogram: $A = bh$, circle: $A = \pi r^2$, rectangle: $A = lw$, triangle: $A = \frac{1}{2}bh$

1. The length of a particular rectangle is 2 inches less than twice its width. If the area of the rectangle is 40 square inches, find the length and width.

2. In the diagram, the radius of the outer circle is 5 centimeters and the area of the shaded region is 16π square centimeters. Find the radius of the inner circle.

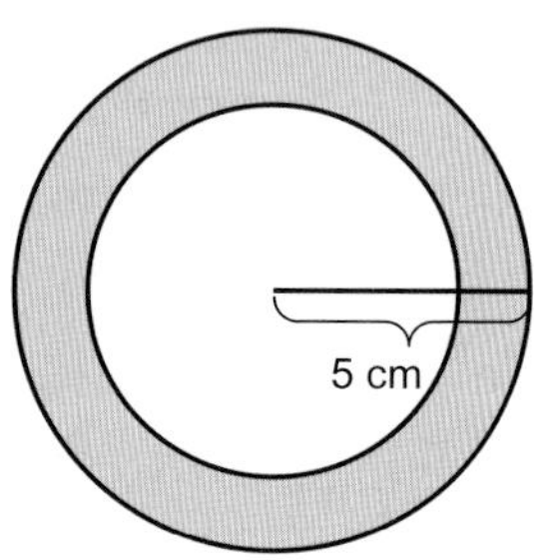

3. The base length of a particular triangle is 4 inches more than its height. A new triangle is formed by doubling the base and increasing the height by 5 inches. The area of the new triangle is 45.5 square inches more than the area of the original triangle. Find the base length and height of the original triangle.

4. The height of a particular triangle equals its base length. A new triangle is formed by dividing the height by 2. The area is 36 square inches less than the area of the original triangle. Find the height and base length of the original triangle.

5. In the diagram, the radius of the inner circle is 4 meters. The area of the shaded region is 48π square meters. Find the radius of the outer circle.

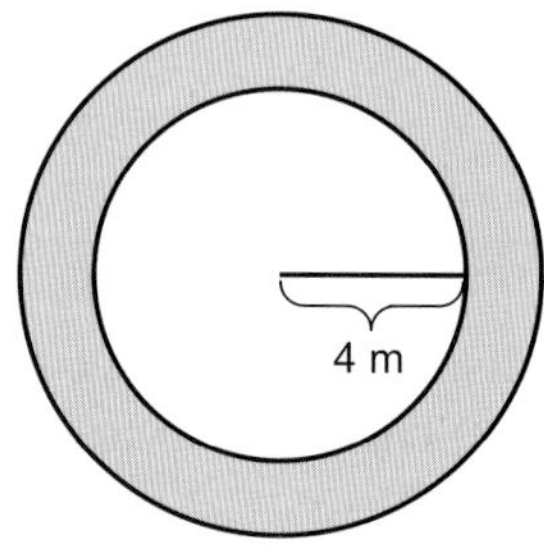

6. A circle is inscribed in a square. The side length of the square is x inches. If the area of the shaded region is 20π, find the radius of the circle.

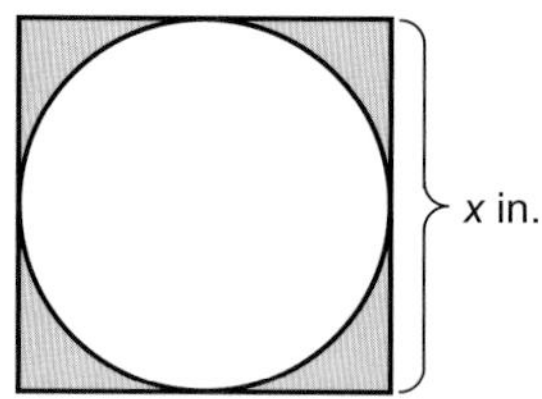

7. The base of a particular parallelogram is 4 times its height. If the base and height are doubled, the new area is 972 square inches greater than the area of the original parallelogram. Find the base and height of the original parallelogram.

8. The height of a particular parallelogram is 5 millimeters more than twice its base length. If the height is decreased by 3 millimeters and the base length is increased by 7 millimeters, the area is 14 square millimeters more than twice the original area. Find the height and base length of the original parallelogram.

9. The length of a particular rectangle is 8 inches more than 2 times its width. A new rectangle is formed by tripling the width. The area is 30 square inches more than the area of the original rectangle. Find the dimensions of the original rectangle.

10. The base length of a particular triangle is 8 meters more than twice its height. A new triangle is formed by increasing the base by 10 meters and increasing the height by 5 meters. The area is 65 square meters more than the area of the original triangle. Find the base length and height of the original triangle.

11. The length of a particular rectangle is 6 times its width. If the width is decreased by 1 millimeter and the length is doubled, the area is increased by 18 square millimeters. Find the dimensions of the original rectangle.

12. The base length of a particular triangle is 5 times its height. A new triangle is formed by multiplying the base by 4 and decreasing the height by 1 inch. The area is 10 square inches more than the area of the original triangle. Find the base length and height of the original triangle.

13. The length of a particular rectangle is 7 meters less than 5 times its width. A new rectangle is formed by doubling the width and increasing the length by 2 meters. The new area is 8 square meters more than the original area. Find the length and width of the original rectangle.

14. The base of a particular parallelogram is 5 times its height. A new parallelogram is formed by decreasing the base by 2 centimeters and dividing the height by 3. The new area is 20 square centimeters less than the area of the original parallelogram. Find the base and height of the original parallelogram.

15. The length of a particular rectangle is 10 feet more than 4 times its width. Find the length and width if the area of the rectangle is 103 square feet.

16. In the diagram, the radius of the inner circle is 1 inch and the area of the shaded region is 24π square inches. Find the radius of the outer circle.

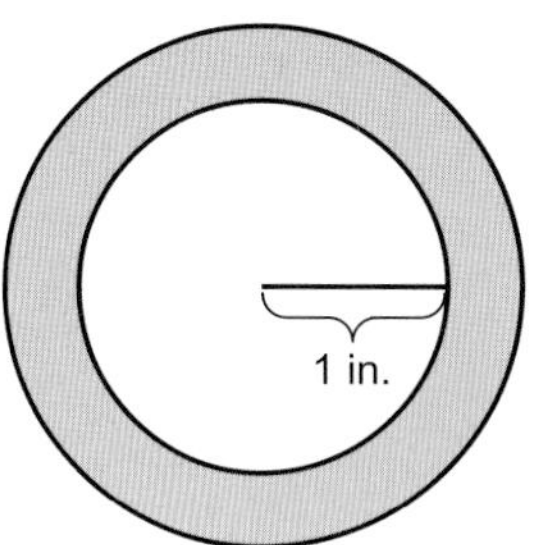

17. The base of a particular parallelogram is 2 times its height. A new parallelogram is formed by decreasing the base by 3 inches and dividing the height by 2. The new area is 10 square inches less than the area of the original parallelogram. Find the base and height of the original parallelogram.

18. The base of a particular parallelogram is 4 times its height. If the base is doubled and the height is changed to 3 meters more than 2 times the original height, the area is increased by 36 square meters. Find the base and height of the original parallelogram.

*19. **Challenge** Determine the radius of each circle if the area of the shaded region is 16π square meters and the dimensions of the rectangle are x meters by 25π meters. Assume that the circles are the same size.

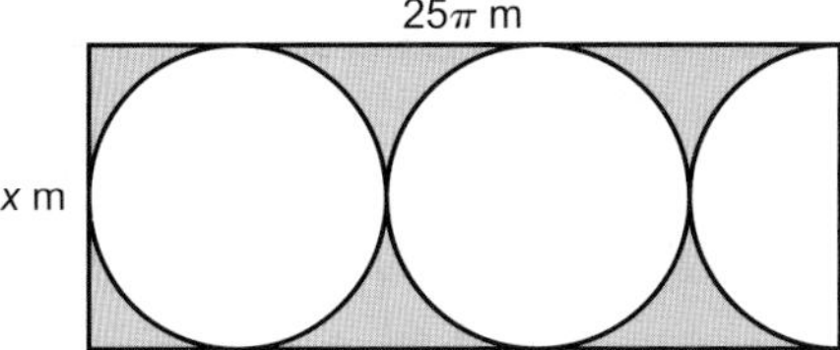

*20. **Challenge** A trapezoid can be formed by drawing triangles on opposite sides of a rectangle. In the diagram below, the rectangle's length is 3 inches more than twice its width. If the base of both triangles is 1 inch more than the rectangle's width and the rectangle's area has increased by 6 square inches when the triangles' areas are added, find the width of the rectangle.

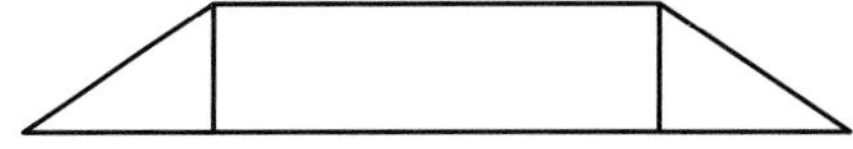

Applications: Projectile Motion

A projectile is an object that is only under the influence of gravity once it has been launched. The vertical height of a projectile can be modeled with a quadratic equation.

Formulas can model the height of a projectile shot straight up after a given number of seconds. These formulas account for constant acceleration due to gravity, initial vertical velocity v_0, and initial height h_0.

PROJECTILE MOTION FORMULAS

The height of an object, *in meters*, after *t* seconds, with initial vertical velocity v_0, and initial height h_0, is given by

$$h(t) = -4.9t^2 + v_0t + h_0.$$

The height of an object, *in feet*, after *t* seconds, with initial vertical velocity v_0, and initial height h_0, is given by

$$h(t) = -16t^2 + v_0t + h_0.$$

Sports

Example 1

A. A football is kicked with an initial vertical velocity of 80 feet per second. After how many seconds will the football hit the ground?

Solution The ball will be on the ground twice: before it is kicked and when it returns to the ground. For each of these, the height $h(t)$ is 0.

$h(t) = -16t^2 + v_0t + h_0$	Use the formula that gives height in feet.
$0 = -16t^2 + 80t + 0$	Substitute 0 for $h(t)$, 80 for v_0, and 0 for h_0.
$0 = -16t^2 + 80t$	Simplify.
$0 = 16t(-t + 5)$	Factor.
$0 = 16t$ or $0 = -t + 5$	Zero Product Property
$0 = t$ $\quad t = 5$	Solve.

The answers indicate that the ball is on the ground at 0 seconds and at 5 seconds. Since the first instance is when the ball is kicked, the answer is 5 seconds.

Check Graph the function. The x-intercepts are the solutions of $0 = 80t - 16t^2$.

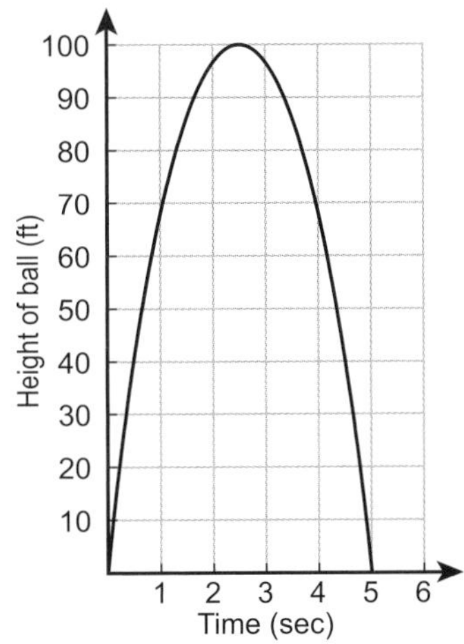

B. A baseball is thrown into the air from an initial height of 5.25 feet with an initial vertical velocity of 40 feet/second. After how many seconds will the baseball hit the ground?

$$h(t) = -16t^2 + v_0t + h_0$$ Use the formula that gives height in feet.

$$0 = -16t^2 + 40t + 5.25$$ Substitute 0 for $h(t)$, 40 for v_0, and 5.25 for h_0.

$$t = \frac{-b \pm \sqrt{b^2 - 4ac}}{2a}$$ Quadratic Formula

$$t = \frac{-40 \pm \sqrt{(40)^2 - 4 \cdot (-16) \cdot 5.25}}{2 \cdot (-16)}$$ Substitute -16 for a, 40 for b, and 5.25 for c.

$$t = \frac{-40 \pm \sqrt{1936}}{-32}$$ Simplify the radicand.

$$t = \frac{-40 + \sqrt{1936}}{-32} \quad \text{or} \quad t = \frac{-40 - \sqrt{1936}}{-32}$$ Write $t = \frac{-40 \pm \sqrt{1936}}{-32}$ as two equations.

$$t = \frac{-40 + 44}{-32} = -0.125 \quad \text{or} \quad t = \frac{-40 - 44}{-32} = 2.625$$ Simplify.

Since time cannot be negative, the baseball will hit the ground after about 2.6 seconds. ■

Rocketry

Example 2

A. The initial vertical velocity of a rocket shot straight up from the ground is 35 meters per second. Estimate the maximum height of the rocket and the time the maximum height occurs.

Solution The formula to use when the velocity is given in meters is $h(t) = -4.9t^2 + v_0t + h_0$. Because the question is asking for an estimate and the initial height is 0, use $h(t) = -5t^2 + v_0t$.

Solve the equation $0 = -5t^2 + 35t$ by factoring to find the t-intercepts of $h(t) = -5t^2 + 35t$. Then graph the function to find the maximum height.

THINK ABOUT IT

Whenever the initial height is equal to 0, you can exclude h_0 from the formula.

(continued)

$$0 = -5t^2 + 35t$$

$$0 = 5t(-t + 7) \quad \text{Factor.}$$

$$0 = 5t \quad \text{or} \quad 0 = -t + 7 \quad \text{Zero Product Property}$$

$$0 = t \qquad t = 7 \quad \text{Solve.}$$

The t-intercepts are 0 and 7. Use a table to find additional points.

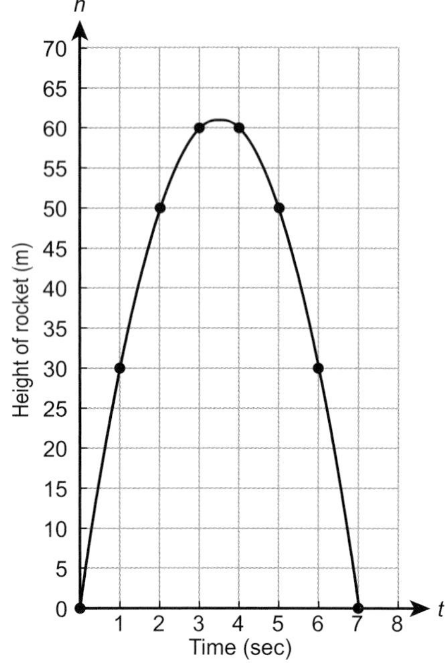

t	$h(t) = 5t(7 - t)$
1	$5 \cdot 1 \cdot (7 - 1) = 30$
2	$5 \cdot 2 \cdot (7 - 2) = 50$
3	$5 \cdot 3 \cdot (7 - 3) = 60$
4	$5 \cdot 4 \cdot (7 - 4) = 60$
5	$5 \cdot 5 \cdot (7 - 5) = 50$
6	$5 \cdot 6 \cdot (7 - 6) = 30$

The maximum height is about 62 meters. Remember the vertex is half-way between the two t-intercepts. Since the t-intercepts occur at $t = 0$ and $t = 7$, the t-coordinate of the vertex is $t = 3.5$. The maximum height occurs at about 3.5 seconds. ■

B. The initial vertical velocity of a rocket shot straight up is 42 meters per second. How long does it take for the rocket to return to Earth? Round your answer to the nearest tenth of a second.

Solution Use the formula $h(t) = -4.9t^2 + v_0t$. Solve $0 = -4.9t^2 + 42t$ by using the quadratic formula.

$$t = \frac{-b \pm \sqrt{b^2 - 4ac}}{2a} \quad \text{Quadratic Formula}$$

$$t = \frac{-42 \pm \sqrt{(42)^2 - 4 \cdot (-4.9) \cdot 0}}{2 \cdot (-4.9)} \quad \text{Substitute } -4.9 \text{ for } a, 42 \text{ for } b, \text{ and } 0 \text{ for } c.$$

$$t = \frac{-42 \pm \sqrt{1764}}{-9.8} \quad \text{Simplify the radicand.}$$

$$t = \frac{-42 + \sqrt{1764}}{-9.8} \quad \text{or} \quad t = \frac{-42 - \sqrt{1764}}{-9.8} \quad \text{Write } t = \frac{-42 \pm \sqrt{1764}}{-9.8} \text{ as two equations.}$$

$$t = \frac{-42 + 42}{-9.8} = 0 \quad \text{or} \quad t = \frac{-42 - 42}{-9.8} \approx 8.6 \quad \text{Simplify.}$$

You can also use factoring to solve this problem.

$$-4.9t^2 + 42t = 0$$

$$t(-4.9t + 42) = 0$$

So, $t = 0$ or $-4.9t + 42 = 0$

$$-4.9t = -42$$

$$t = \frac{-42}{-4.9}$$

$$t = \frac{60}{7} \approx 8.6$$

It takes about 8.6 seconds for the rocket to return to Earth. ■

Problem Set

Solve. Round your answers to the nearest hundredth.

1. Sira launches an object with an initial vertical velocity of 19.6 meters per second from a 58-meter-tall platform. How long will it take to land at the base of the platform?

2. Tyrese attempts a field goal with an initial vertical velocity of 49 meters per second from the ground. How long will the football be in the air?

3. A javelin thrower releases a javelin 1.5 meters from the ground with an initial vertical velocity of 25 meters per second. How long will it take the javelin to hit the ground?

4. Julie throws a ball into the air from a 60-foot high cliff with an initial vertical velocity of 12 feet per second. How long will it take the ball to hit the ground at the base of the cliff?

5. If a batter hits a baseball from a height of 0.9 meters with an initial vertical velocity of 20 meters per second, how long will it take the ball to hit the ground?

6. Sam launches a bottle rocket with an initial vertical velocity of 39 meters per second from a 79-meter-tall platform. How long will the bottle rocket be in the air?

7. Tamra attempts a field goal with an initial vertical velocity of 12 feet per second from a tee set on the ground. How long will the football be in the air?

8. A javelin thrower releases a javelin 5 feet from the ground with an initial vertical velocity of 16 feet per second. How long will it take the javelin to land?

9. At a track meet, Jona puts a shot with an initial vertical velocity of 40 feet per second from a height of 4 feet. How long will it take the shot to land?

10. Jiran hit a golf ball from the ground with an initial vertical velocity of 117 feet per second. After how many seconds will the ball land?

11. Bret kicks a soccer ball straight up into the air with an initial vertical velocity of 25 meters per second from a height of 0.75 meters. After how many seconds will the soccer ball land?

12. Bin bounces a soccer ball from his head with an initial vertical velocity of 6 meters per second from an initial height of 1.8 meters. When will the ball reach the ground?

13. A field hockey player makes a pass and the ball is projected into the air with an initial vertical velocity of 28 feet per second. When will the ball land?

14. Cyrus throws a baseball into the air with an initial vertical velocity of 52.8 feet per second from an initial height of 3.5 feet. For how long will the baseball be in the air?

15. Ezra throws a stone into the air from the edge of a 300-meter cliff with an initial vertical velocity of 12 meters per second. When will the stone reach the ground at the base of the cliff?

16. If a hurdler jumps with an initial vertical velocity of 12 feet per second, will she have any chance of clearing a 3-foot hurdle?

17. A juggler tosses a ball into the air with an initial vertical velocity of 10 feet per second from an initial height of 4 feet.

    A. If the juggler does not catch the ball, how long will the ball be in the air?

    B. The juggler cannot catch the ball if it falls below 1 foot. How long does the juggler have to catch the ball?

18. Max is playing hopscotch and jumps with an initial vertical velocity of 2 meters per second. How long is Max in the air?

*19. **Challenge** A batter hits a ball from an initial height of 4 feet. The vertical speed of the batted ball is 90 feet per second.

    A. If the ball is not caught, how long will it be in the air?

    B. How far will the ball travel? (Hint: Use the formula $d(t) = vt$.)

*20. **Challenge** A kicker punts a football at 36 feet per second from an initial height of 3 feet.

    A. What is the hang time? (Hint: Hang time is the amount of time the punted football is in the air.)

    B. To the nearest foot, what is the maximum height the football will reach?

UNIT 13 Rational Expressions

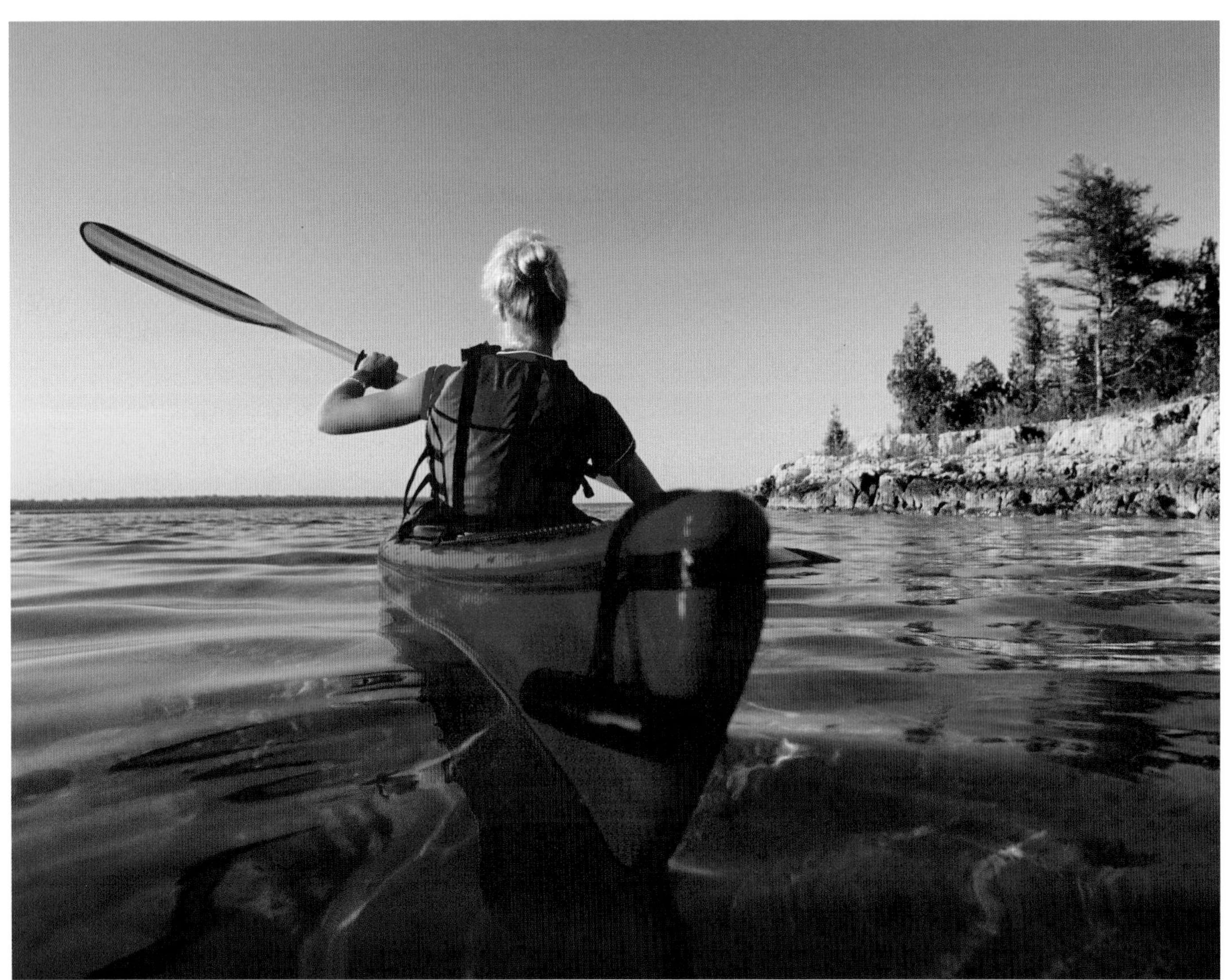

A kayaker's speed is a rate that can be modeled with a rational expression.

A fraction always has a number in the numerator and in the denominator. However, those numbers can actually be expressions that represent numbers, which means you can do all sorts of interesting things with fractions. Fractions with variable expressions in the numerator and denominator can help you solve many kinds of problems.

Big Ideas

- The laws of arithmetic can be used to simplify algebraic expressions and equations.
- Expressions, equations, and inequalities express relationships between different entities.

Unit Topics

- Simplifying Rational Expressions
- Multiplying Rational Expressions
- Dividing Rational Expressions
- Like Denominators
- Adding and Subtracting Rational Expressions

Simplifying Rational Expressions

Fractions may include variable expressions in the numerator or denominator.

DEFINITION

A **rational expression** is a quotient of two polynomials.

The following are rational expressions.

$$\frac{6}{2x+1} \qquad \frac{x^2+8}{x^2+x-12} \qquad \frac{x^3-8x}{4x} \qquad 3x^2-6x+9$$

REMEMBER

When no denominator is given, the denominator is understood to be 1.

Identifying Restricted Values of Rational Expressions

A fraction is undefined when its denominator is 0. Therefore, any value that produces a value of 0 in the denominator of a rational expression must be removed from the allowable domain. For example, the expression $\frac{4-x}{x+5}$ has a domain of all real numbers except −5. Because −5 makes the denominator 0, it is a *restricted value.*

Example 1 Identify the restricted values of the expression.

THINK ABOUT IT

There are no restrictions on the numerator of a rational expression.

A. $\frac{5x-4}{x^2-9}$

Solution Set the denominator equal to 0, and solve for x.

$x^2-9=0$	Set the denominator equal to 0.
$x^2=9$	Add 9 to each side.
$x=\pm\sqrt{9}=\pm3$	Take the square root of each side and simplify.

The restricted values are 3 and −3. ■

B. $\frac{x^2+8}{x^2+x-12}$

Solution Set the denominator equal to 0. Then factor to solve for x.

$x^2+x-12=0$	Set the denominator equal to 0.
$(x+4)(x-3)=0$	Factor.
$x=-4$ or $x=3$	Zero Product Property

The restricted values are −4 and 3. ■

Simplifying Rational Expressions

As with numerical fractions, if the same factor appears in both the numerator and denominator of a rational expression, you can divide it out.

Fractions	Rational Expressions
$\frac{4}{8}=\frac{\cancel{4}}{2\cdot\cancel{4}}=\frac{1}{2}$	$\frac{x+2}{x^2+7x+10}=\frac{\cancel{(x+2)}}{(x+5)\cancel{(x+2)}}=\frac{1}{x+5}$

TIP

Always determine restricted values before simplifying.

You must determine restricted values before you divide out any factors from the expression. The restricted values for $\frac{(x+2)}{(x+5)(x+2)}$ are -5 and -2 because both values produce a 0 in the denominator. You would not be able to see that -2 is a restricted value by looking at the simplified expression alone.

Example 2 Identify any restrictions on the domain and simplify the expression.

A. $\frac{4x^3+12x}{2x^2}$

Solution Always start by identifying any restrictions.

$2x^2=0$ Set the denominator equal to 0.

$x^2=0$ Divide each side by 2.

$x=0$ Take the square root of each side and simplify.

The value 0 is restricted from the domain.

Factor the numerator. The denominator is already simplified.

$\frac{4x^3+12x}{2x^2}=\frac{4x(x^2+3)}{2x^2}$ The GCF of the numerator is $4x$.

$=\frac{{}^{2}\cancel{4x}(x^2+3)}{\cancel{2x^2}}$ Divide out the common factor $2x$.

$=\frac{2(x^2+3)}{x}, x\neq 0$ Simplify and restate the restriction. ■

B. $\frac{x^2+5x-36}{x^2-81}$

Solution Identify any restrictions. Then factor and simplify.

$x^2-81=0$ Set the denominator equal to 0.

$x^2=81$ Add 81 to each side.

$x=\pm\sqrt{81}=\pm 9$ Take the square root of each side and simplify.

The values -9 and 9 are restricted from the domain.

$\frac{x^2+5x-36}{x^2-81}=\frac{\cancel{(x+9)}(x-4)}{\cancel{(x+9)}(x-9)}$ Factor the numerator and denominator.

$=\frac{x-4}{x-9}, x\neq\pm 9$ Divide out the common factor $x+9$ and restate the restrictions. ■

C. $\dfrac{6x^2 - 17x + 5}{4 - 17x + 15x^2}$

Solution Identify any restrictions. Then factor and simplify.

$4 - 17x + 15x^2 = 0$	Set the denominator equal to 0.
$(1 - 3x)(4 - 5x) = 0$	Factor.
$1 - 3x = 0$ or $4 - 5x = 0$	Zero Product Property
$-3x = -1$ $\quad -5x = -4$	Solve for x.
$x = \frac{-1}{-3} = \frac{1}{3}$ $\quad x = \frac{-4}{-5} = \frac{4}{5}$	Simplify.

The values $\frac{1}{3}$ and $\frac{4}{5}$ are restricted from the domain.

$\dfrac{6x^2 - 17x + 5}{4 - 17x + 15x^2} = \dfrac{(2x - 5)(3x - 1)}{(1 - 3x)(4 - 5x)}$	Factor both polynomials.
$= \dfrac{(2x - 5)(3x - 1)}{-1(-1 + 3x)(4 - 5x)}$	Factor -1 out of $(1 - 3x)$.
$= \dfrac{(2x - 5)(3x - 1)}{-1(3x - 1)(4 - 5x)}$	Commutative Property of Addition
$= \dfrac{2x - 5}{-(4 - 5x)}, x \neq \frac{1}{3}, \frac{4}{5}$	Divide out the common factor and restate the restrictions. ■

TIP

$(1 - 3x)$ and $(3x - 1)$ are opposites.

$$-(3x - 1) = -1(3x - 1)$$
$$= -3x + 1$$
$$= 1 - 3x$$

Problem Set

Identify the values restricted from the domain of the expression.

1. $\dfrac{7x - 5}{2x}$
2. $\dfrac{x + 8}{3x + 1}$
3. $\dfrac{x^2 - 5}{x^2 - 4}$
4. $\dfrac{x^2 + 3x - 5}{x^2 + 6x + 9}$
5. $\dfrac{x + 6}{x^2 + 7x - 8}$
6. $\dfrac{x^2 - 10}{2x^2 - 3x - 20}$

Identify any restrictions on the domain and simplify the expression.

7. $\dfrac{6x^2 + 6x}{3x^2}$
8. $\dfrac{x^2 + x - 12}{x^2 - 16}$
9. $\dfrac{8x^2 - 12x}{4x^2}$
10. $\dfrac{x^2 - 49}{3x - 21}$
11. $\dfrac{16x^3 + 64x}{16x^3}$
12. $\dfrac{x^2 - 36}{2x^2 - 12x}$
13. $\dfrac{x^2 + 10x + 16}{x^2 + 7x - 8}$
14. $\dfrac{x^2 + 3x + 2}{x^2 - x - 6}$
15. $\dfrac{x^2 + 7x + 12}{x^2 - 2x - 15}$
16. $\dfrac{6x^2 + x - 12}{3x^2 + 14x - 24}$
17. $\dfrac{x^2 - 4x - 5}{x^2 - 25}$
18. $\dfrac{9x^2 - 90x}{18x}$
19. $\dfrac{12x^2 - 19x + 5}{21x^2 - 13x + 2}$
20. $\dfrac{20x^6 - 100x^4}{10x^5}$
21. $\dfrac{2x^2 + 21x - 11}{x^2 - 121}$

22. $\frac{7x - 30x^2 + 2}{30x^2 + 17x + 2}$

23. $\frac{x^3 + 8}{2x + 4}$

24. $\frac{x^3 - 27}{3x - 9}$

25. $\frac{24x^2 - 8x - 10}{40 - 36x^2 - 18x}$

26. $\frac{4x^2 + 14x + 6}{2x^2 - 18}$

27. $\frac{8x^2 + 30x + 18}{6 - 12x^2 - x}$

Solve.

28. **Challenge** The surface area of a cylinder is $2\pi r^2 + 2\pi rh$ and the volume of a cylinder is $\pi r^2 h$, where r is the radius and h is the height. Write a rational expression that represents the ratio of the volume to the surface area of a cylinder.

***29.** **Challenge** The surface area of a cube is $6s^2$, where s represents side length. Find the ratio of the surface area of a cube with a side length of $3x$ inches to a cube with a side length of $2x^2$ inches.

Multiplying Rational Expressions

To multiply rational expressions, follow the same rules you use to multiply fractions.

MULTIPLYING FRACTIONS

The general equation for multiplying fractions is $\frac{a}{b} \cdot \frac{c}{d} = \frac{ac}{bd}$.

To multiply fractions, multiply the numbers in the numerator and the numbers in the denominator. Divide out common factors in the numerator and denominator when possible.

Here is how it works with a couple numerical fractions.

$$\frac{3}{5} \cdot \frac{1}{4} = \frac{3 \cdot 1}{5 \cdot 4} = \frac{3}{20} \qquad \frac{\cancel{4}^{1}}{5} \cdot \frac{1}{\cancel{12}_{3}} = \frac{1 \cdot 1}{5 \cdot 3} = \frac{1}{15}$$

Multiplying Rational Expressions Without Factoring

Common variable factors can be divided out of numerators and denominators.

$$\frac{x}{y^2} \cdot \frac{y^3}{x^5} = \frac{\cancel{x} \cdot \cancel{y} \cdot \cancel{y} \cdot y}{\cancel{y} \cdot \cancel{y} \cdot \cancel{x} \cdot x \cdot x \cdot x \cdot x} = \frac{y}{x^4} \quad \text{or} \quad \frac{x}{y^2} \cdot \frac{y^3}{x^5} = \frac{\cancel{x}}{\cancel{y^2}} \cdot \frac{y^{\cancel{3}1}}{x^{\cancel{5}4}} = \frac{y}{x^4}$$

You can also use properties of exponents to divide out common variable factors.

$$\frac{x}{y^2} \cdot \frac{y^3}{x^5} = \frac{xy^3}{x^5y^2} = x^{1-5}y^{3-2} = x^{-4}y = \frac{y}{x^4}$$

REMEMBER

$\frac{a^m}{a^n} = a^{m-n}$ and $a^{-m} = \frac{1}{a^m}$

Example 1 Simplify. Assume that no denominator equals zero.

A. $\frac{y^4}{3x} \cdot \frac{3}{5xy^2}$

Solution Multiply the numerators and multiply the denominators.

$$\frac{y^4}{3x} \cdot \frac{3}{5xy^2} = \frac{3y^4}{15x^2y^2}$$

$$= \frac{y^2}{5x^2} \qquad \text{Divide out the common factor } 3y^2. \blacksquare$$

B. $\frac{n^5}{m^4} \cdot \frac{m^3}{n^2}$

Solution Multiply the numerators and multiply the denominators. Then use the properties of exponents.

$$\frac{n^5}{m^4} \cdot \frac{m^3}{n^2} = \frac{n^5m^3}{m^4n^2} = n^{5-2}m^{3-4} = n^3m^{-1} = \frac{n^3}{m} \blacksquare$$

(continued)

C. $\frac{2}{x+3} \cdot \frac{x+3}{4}$

Solution Divide out the common factors $(x + 3)$ and 2.

$\frac{{}^{1}\cancel{2}}{\cancel{x+3}} \cdot \frac{\cancel{x+3}}{\cancel{4}_{2}} = \frac{1}{2}$ ■

Multiplying Rational Expressions with Factoring

When numerators and/or denominators can be factored, it is much easier to divide out common factors before multiplying.

REMEMBER

Identify the restrictions on the domain before dividing out common factors.

HOW TO MULTIPLY RATIONAL EXPRESSIONS

1. Factor all numerators and denominators if possible.
2. Divide out factors common in any numerator and any denominator.
3. Multiply the numerators and multiply the denominators.

Example 2 Identify the domain and multiply the expressions.

A. $\frac{2x-6}{x+6} \cdot \frac{x^2-36}{2}$

Solution Factor the numerators.

$\frac{2(x-3)}{x+6} \cdot \frac{(x+6)(x-6)}{2}$

The expression $x + 6$ is in the denominator, so the domain is all real numbers except -6.

$$\frac{\cancel{2}(x-3)}{\cancel{x+6}} \cdot \frac{\cancel{(x+6)}(x-6)}{\cancel{2}} = \frac{(x-3)(x-6)}{1}$$

$$= (x-3)(x-6)$$

$$= x^2 - 9x + 18, x \neq -6$$ ■

B. $\frac{-8}{x^2+8x+16} \cdot \frac{x^2-3x-28}{4x-28}$

Solution Factor the polynomials.

$\frac{-8}{(x+4)(x+4)} \cdot \frac{(x+4)(x-7)}{4(x-7)}$

The domain is all real numbers except -4 and 7.

$$\frac{{}^{-2}\cancel{-8}}{(x+4)\cancel{(x+4)}} \cdot \frac{\cancel{(x+4)}\cancel{(x-7)}}{{}_{1}\cancel{4}\cancel{(x-7)}} = \frac{-2}{x+4}, x \neq -4, 7$$ ■

C. $\frac{x^3-4x^2}{x^2+3x} \cdot \frac{x^2+x-6}{4-x}$

Solution Factor.

$$\frac{x^2(x-4)}{x(x+3)} \cdot \frac{(x+3)(x-2)}{4-x} = \frac{x^2(-1)(4-x)}{x(x+3)} \cdot \frac{(x+3)(x-2)}{4-x}$$

The domain is all real numbers except 0, −3, and 4.

$$\frac{x^{2}(-1)(4-x)}{x(x+3)} \cdot \frac{(x+3)(x-2)}{4-x} = \frac{x(-1)(x-2)}{1}$$

$$= -x(x-2)$$

$$= -x^2 + 2x$$

$$= 2x - x^2, x \neq 0, -3, 4 \ \blacksquare$$

D. $(4x^2 - 100) \cdot \frac{3}{x^2 - 3x - 40}$

Solution Write the first expression as a rational expression and factor both expressions.

$$\frac{4(x+5)(x-5)}{1} \cdot \frac{3}{(x+5)(x-8)}$$

The domain is all real numbers except −5 and 8.

$$\frac{4(x+5)(x-5)}{1} \cdot \frac{3}{(x+5)(x-8)} = \frac{12(x-5)}{x-8}, x \neq -5, 8 \ \blacksquare$$

Problem Set

Multiply. Assume no denominator is equal to zero.

1. $\frac{x^2}{4y} \cdot \frac{8y}{xy}$
2. $\frac{a^4}{b^7} \cdot \frac{b^2}{a^3}$
3. $\frac{x+1}{5} \cdot \frac{10}{x+1}$
4. $\frac{a^9}{b^3} \cdot \frac{b^{12}}{a^{11}}$
5. $\frac{m}{n^2} \cdot \frac{n^{12}}{m^9}$
6. $\frac{5x^3}{x^2} \cdot \frac{1}{25y^5}$
7. $\frac{x-4}{12} \cdot \frac{6}{x-4}$
8. $\frac{x+7}{x-6} \cdot \frac{x-6}{x+7}$
9. $\frac{12y^5}{3x} \cdot \frac{6x^{10}}{y^4}$
10. $\frac{m^{13}}{n^5} \cdot \frac{n^4}{m^{20}}$
11. $\frac{x-10}{12} \cdot \frac{24}{10-x}$
12. $\frac{d^8}{10c^6} \cdot \frac{2cd}{c^2d}$

Identify the domain and multiply the expressions.

13. $\frac{x^2-16}{3x-12} \cdot \frac{6}{x+4}$
14. $\frac{12-x}{x^2+2x-35} \cdot \frac{x^2+7x}{x^2-12x}$
15. $\frac{8r-8}{r^2+8r+7} \cdot \frac{r^2+10r+21}{-2r+2}$
16. $(3x^2-3) \cdot \frac{2x}{x^2-9x-10}$
17. $\frac{-5}{10s+20} \cdot \frac{s^2+8s+12}{s^2+12s+36}$
18. $\frac{x^4-3x^3}{x^3-10x^2} \cdot \frac{x^2-12x+20}{3-x}$
19. $(2x^2-50) \cdot \frac{x}{4x^2-20x-200}$
20. $\frac{4v-8}{20} \cdot \frac{5v+10}{v^2-4}$
21. $\frac{2}{x^2-121} \cdot \frac{3x-33}{12x+132}$
22. $(2c^2-9c-35) \cdot \frac{9}{3c^2-6c-105}$
23. $\frac{7x+21}{-x-5} \cdot \frac{9x+45}{3x+9}$
24. $\frac{72+x-x^2}{x^3+3x^2} \cdot \frac{x^2+3x}{x^2-x-72}$

Dividing Rational Expressions

To divide rational expressions, follow the same rules you use to divide fractions.

When dividing fractions, you rewrite the division as multiplication by the reciprocal. If possible, divide out common factors once you have rewritten division as multiplication.

$$\frac{3}{4} \div \frac{2}{5} = \frac{3}{4} \cdot \frac{5}{2} = \frac{15}{8} \qquad \frac{4}{21} \div \frac{2}{7} = \frac{\cancel{4}^{2}}{\cancel{21}_{3}} \cdot \frac{\cancel{7}^{1}}{\cancel{2}_{1}} = \frac{2}{3}$$

Dividing Rational Expressions Without Factoring

Dividing rational expressions that contain monomials or polynomials is similar to dividing fractions.

Example 1 Divide and simplify.

A. $\frac{c^3}{cd} \div \frac{2}{d^4}$

Solution Rewrite division as multiplication by the reciprocal and divide out common factors.

$$\frac{c^3}{cd} \div \frac{2}{d^4} = \frac{c^3}{cd} \cdot \frac{d^4}{2} = \frac{c^3d^4}{2cd} = \frac{c^{3-1}d^{4-1}}{2} = \frac{c^2d^3}{2} \blacksquare$$

REMEMBER

The expression $\frac{x+3}{x+2}$ does not simplify to $\frac{3}{2}$ because you cannot factor the x from the numerator or the denominator.

B. $\frac{x-1}{x+2} \div \frac{x-1}{x+3}$

Solution Rewrite division as multiplication by the reciprocal and divide out common factors.

$$\frac{x-1}{x+2} \div \frac{x-1}{x+3} = \frac{\cancel{x-1}}{x+2} \cdot \frac{x+3}{\cancel{x-1}} = \frac{x+3}{x+2} \blacksquare$$

Dividing Rational Expressions with Factoring

HOW TO DIVIDE RATIONAL EXPRESSIONS

1. Change the division sign to a multiplication sign and take the reciprocal of the divisor.
2. Factor all numerators and denominators if possible.
3. Divide out factors common in any numerator and any denominator.
4. Multiply the numerators and multiply the denominators.

Example 2 Identify the domain and divide the expressions.

A. $\frac{3t-18}{9} \div \frac{t^2-12t+36}{t+2}$

Solution Rewrite division as multiplying by the reciprocal. Then factor.

$$\frac{3t-18}{9} \div \frac{t^2-12t+36}{t+2} = \frac{3t-18}{9} \cdot \frac{t+2}{t^2-12t+36} = \frac{3(t-6)}{9} \cdot \frac{t+2}{(t-6)^2}$$

The domain is all real numbers except 6.

$$\frac{{}^{1}\cancel{3}\cancel{(t-6)}}{\cancel{9}_{3}} \cdot \frac{t+2}{(t-6)^{\cancel{2}}} = \frac{t+2}{3(t-6)} \quad ■$$

B. $\frac{x^2+6x-16}{3x+24} \div \frac{x^2-4x+4}{15x+15}$

Solution Rewrite division as multiplication by the reciprocal and factor.

$$\frac{x^2+6x-16}{3x+24} \cdot \frac{15x+15}{x^2-4x+4} = \frac{(x-2)(x+8)}{3(x+8)} \cdot \frac{15(x+1)}{(x-2)^2}$$

The domain is all real numbers except −8 and 2.

$$\frac{\cancel{(x-2)}\cancel{(x+8)}}{{}_{1}\cancel{3}\cancel{(x+8)}} \cdot \frac{{}^{5}\cancel{15}(x+1)}{(x-2)^{\cancel{2}}} = \frac{5(x+1)}{x-2} \quad ■$$

When dividing rational expressions, identify the domain after you change the division problem to a multiplication problem.

Multiplying and Dividing Rational Expressions

Example 3 Simplify. $\frac{x^2-36}{12} \cdot \frac{x^2-1}{5x+30} \div \frac{x-1}{18x^3+30x^2}$

Solution Rewrite the division as multiplication and factor.

$$\frac{(x+6)(x-6)}{12} \cdot \frac{(x+1)(x-1)}{5(x+6)} \cdot \frac{6x^2(3x+5)}{x-1}$$

The domain is all real numbers except −6 and 1.

Divide out common factors. Then multiply the numerators and multiply the denominators.

$$\frac{\cancel{(x+6)}(x-6)}{{}_{2}\cancel{12}} \cdot \frac{(x+1)\cancel{(x-1)}}{5\cancel{(x+6)}} \cdot \frac{{}^{1}\cancel{6}x^2(3x+5)}{\cancel{x-1}} = \frac{x^2(x-6)(x+1)(3x+5)}{10} \quad ■$$

Problem Set

Divide the expressions. Assume no denominator is equal to zero.

1. $\frac{a^4}{bc^2} \div \frac{a^3}{5}$
2. $\frac{7}{a^8} \div \frac{b^6}{14ab}$
3. $\frac{x+9}{x-5} \div \frac{x+9}{x+2}$
4. $\frac{2m}{n^3} \div \frac{m^5}{m^7n}$
5. $\frac{x-7}{x-3} \div \frac{x-7}{x}$
6. $\frac{x+10}{2x+3} \div \frac{x+10}{2x+3}$
7. $\frac{4m}{mn^2} \div \frac{m^9}{n^8}$
8. $\frac{x-12}{x-16} \div \frac{x+12}{x-16}$
9. $\frac{10y^2}{xy} \div \frac{y^4}{x^6}$

Identify the domain and divide the expressions.

10. $\frac{3x - 21}{18x - 18} \div \frac{x^2 - 49}{x - 1}$

11. $\frac{x^2 + 3x - 54}{2x - 12} \div \frac{x^2 + 18x + 81}{8x - 24}$

12. $\frac{t^2 + 20t + 100}{20} \div \frac{5t + 50}{10t - 90}$

13. $\frac{2x - 16}{27x + 54} \div \frac{x^2 - 64}{9}$

14. $\frac{x^2 - 144}{x^2 + 7x - 60} \div \frac{3x - 36}{9x - 45}$

15. $\frac{4t + 12}{t^2 + 6t + 9} \div \frac{t^2 - 6t + 9}{t - 3}$

16. $\frac{x^2 - 8x + 16}{34x + 136} \div \frac{2x^2 - 7x - 4}{34x + 17}$

17. $\frac{t^2 - 4}{t + 2} \div \frac{15t + 135}{5}$

18. $\frac{x^2 + 5x - 14}{x^2 + 5x - 14} \div \frac{6x^2 - 13x + 2}{6x - 12}$

Simplify.

19. $\frac{9x^2 - 117x}{x^2 - 3x - 40} \cdot \frac{x^2 + 4x - 5}{x^3 + 8x^2} \div \frac{3x - 39}{x^2 - 64}$

20. $\frac{x^2 - 64}{7x^2 - 42x} \cdot \frac{x^2 - 36}{x^2 + 14x + 48} \div \frac{x - 8}{x^4 + 8x^3}$

21. $\frac{38}{3x^3 + 45x^2} \cdot \frac{x^3 + 15x^2}{2x^2 + 11x + 14} \div \frac{19}{2x^2 + 17x + 35}$

22. $\frac{x^2 - 4}{4x^2 + 33x - 27} \cdot \frac{x^2 + 11x + 28}{8x - 16} \div \frac{x^2 + 8x + 16}{8x - 6}$

23. $\frac{12x^2 - 11x - 5}{9x + 9} \cdot \frac{x^2 + 11x + 10}{4x^4 - 5x^3} \div \frac{9x^2 - 1}{18x^2}$

24. $\frac{56x^2 + 13x - 3}{x^2 + 26x + 169} \div \frac{24x^2 + 9x}{2x^2 + 27x + 13} \cdot \frac{6x^5}{7x^2 - x}$

Like Denominators

As with numbers, algebraic expressions can have common multiples.

A common multiple of a set of numbers is a number that is a multiple of every number in the set. For example, a common multiple of 9 and 12 is 72 because $9 \cdot 8 = 72$ and $12 \cdot 6 = 72$. The easiest way to find a common multiple is to multiply the numbers together. For instance, $9 \cdot 12 = 108$ is a common multiple of 9 and 12, but there are limitless other common multiples of 9 and 12 including 36 and 144.

DEFINITION

The **least common multiple (LCM)** of a set of numbers is the least, or smallest, number that is a common multiple of all the numbers.

Identifying Least Common Multiples

To find the LCM of a set of numbers, list the prime factorization of each number. Then multiply each factor that appears, including common factors only once.

$9 = 3 \cdot 3 = 3^2$

$12 = 2 \cdot 2 \cdot 3 = 2^2 \cdot 3$

LCM: $3^2 \cdot 2^2 = 9 \cdot 4 = 36$

THINK ABOUT IT

The LCM of a set of numbers may be the product of the numbers or one of the numbers itself.

You can also find the least common multiple of algebraic expressions.

$4x^3 = 2 \cdot 2 \cdot x^3 = 2^2 \cdot x^3$

$8x = 2 \cdot 2 \cdot 2 \cdot x = 2^3 \cdot x$

LCM: $2^3 \cdot x^3 = 8x^3$

Example 1 Find the LCM.

A. 28 and 30

Solution Write the prime factorization of each number. Multiply each factor that appears, including common factors only once.

$28 = 2^2 \cdot 7$

$30 = 2 \cdot 3 \cdot 5$

The LCM is $2^2 \cdot 3 \cdot 5 \cdot 7 = 420$. ■

(continued)

B. 6, 10, and 18

Solution Write the prime factorization of each number.

$6 = 2 \cdot 3$

$10 = 2 \cdot 5$

$18 = 2 \cdot 3^2$

The LCM is $2 \cdot 3^2 \cdot 5 = 90$. ■

THINK ABOUT IT

The LCM is the smallest number that every number in the set divides into.

C. $12a^3b$ and $15b^2$

Solution Write the prime factorization of each expression.

$12a^3b = 2^2 \cdot 3 \cdot a^3 \cdot b$

$15b^2 = 3 \cdot 5 \cdot b^2$

The LCM is $2^2 \cdot 3 \cdot 5 \cdot a^3 \cdot b^2 = 60a^3b^2$. ■

Identifying Least Common Denominators

The fractions $\frac{2}{3}$ and $\frac{1}{3}$ have the **like denominator** 3. Because they have like denominators, you can add or subtract the fractions by adding or subtracting the numerators and keeping the denominator.

To add or subtract fractions that do not have like denominators, such as $\frac{1}{2}$ and $\frac{1}{3}$, you must find the **least common denominator (LCD)** by multiplying each fraction by a form of 1 that will make the denominators the same.

$$\frac{1}{2} \cdot \frac{3}{3} = \frac{3}{6} \quad \text{and} \quad \frac{1}{3} \cdot \frac{2}{2} = \frac{2}{6}$$

Notice that the like denominator 6 is the LCM of the original denominators 2 and 3.

THINK ABOUT IT

The LCM of the denominators is the LCD of the fractions.

Example 2 Find the LCD.

A. $\frac{3}{2x}$ and $\frac{5}{6x^4y}$

Solution Find the LCM of the denominators.

$2x = 2 \cdot x$

$6x^4y = 2 \cdot 3 \cdot x^4 \cdot y$

The LCD is $2 \cdot 3 \cdot x^4 \cdot y = 6x^4y$. ■

B. $\frac{6w}{w-4}$, $\frac{3}{w^2}$, and $\frac{9}{w^2 - 3w - 4}$

Solution Factor the denominator of the third expression to find the LCM of the denominators.

$w^2 - 3w - 4 = (w - 4)(w + 1)$

The LCD is $w^2(w - 4)(w + 1)$. ■

Using the Least Common Denominator to Rewrite Fractions

To rewrite fractions so they have like denominators, first find the LCD of the fractions. Then multiply each fraction that does not have the LCD by a form of 1 so that the denominator becomes the LCD.

Example 3 Rewrite the fractions using like denominators.

A. $\frac{6}{5x^3}, \frac{3}{10x},$ and $\frac{1}{4x^2}$

Solution The LCD is $5 \cdot 4 \cdot x^3 = 20x^3$. Multiply the numerator and denominator of each fraction by the missing factors.

$$\frac{6}{5x^3} \cdot \frac{4}{4} = \frac{24}{20x^3}, \quad \frac{3}{10x} \cdot \frac{2x^2}{2x^2} = \frac{6x^2}{20x^3}, \quad \frac{1}{4x^2} \cdot \frac{5x}{5x} = \frac{5x}{20x^3} \quad \blacksquare$$

B. $\frac{x-1}{x^2-4}$ and $\frac{2x}{x^2-3x-10}$

Solution Factor the denominators to determine the LCD.

$$\frac{x-1}{x^2-4} = \frac{x-1}{(x+2)(x-2)} \text{ and } \frac{2x}{x^2-3x-10} = \frac{2x}{(x+2)(x-5)}$$

The LCD is $(x+2)(x-2)(x-5)$.

$$\frac{x-1}{(x+2)(x-2)} \cdot \frac{x-5}{x-5} = \frac{(x-1)(x-5)}{(x+2)(x-2)(x-5)}$$

$$\frac{2x}{(x+2)(x-5)} \cdot \frac{x-2}{x-2} = \frac{2x(x-2)}{(x+2)(x-2)(x-5)} \quad \blacksquare$$

Application: Distance, Rate, and Time

Example 4 Trevah kayaked 7 miles with the current and 4 miles against it. Her average kayaking rate is 3 mph. Write rational expressions with like denominators to represent the time of each part of the trip. If the average current was 2 miles per hour, what was Trevah's total travel time?

Solution Use $t = \frac{d}{r}$, letting c represent the rate of the current.

With current: $t = \frac{7}{3+c}$, Against current: $t = \frac{4}{3-c}$, LCD: $(3+c)(3-c)$

With current: $\frac{7}{3+c} \cdot \frac{3-c}{3-c} = \frac{7(3-c)}{(3+c)(3-c)}$.

Against current: $\frac{4}{3-c} \cdot \frac{3+c}{3+c} = \frac{4(3+c)}{(3+c)(3-c)}$.

The total time is the sum of the expressions.

(continued)

THINK ABOUT IT

When with the current, the rate is faster than the kayaking rate, so add c. When against the current, the rate is slower than the kayaking rate, so subtract c.

$$\frac{7(3-c)}{(3+c)(3-c)} + \frac{4(3+c)}{(3+c)(3-c)} = \frac{7(3-c)+4(3+c)}{(3+c)(3-c)}$$

$$= \frac{7(3-2)+4(3+2)}{(3+2)(3-2)}$$ Substitute 2 for c.

$$= \frac{7 \cdot 1 + 4 \cdot 5}{5 \cdot 1}$$ Perform the operations inside the parentheses.

$$= \frac{7+20}{5}$$ Multiply.

$$= \frac{27}{5} = 5.4$$ Simplify.

It took Trevah 5.4 hours. ■

Problem Set

Find the LCM.

1. 5 and 175
2. 12 and 16
3. 8, 14, and 28
4. 9, 18, and 21
5. $14x^2y^3$ and $22xy$
6. $6g^4h$ and $75g^2$

Find the LCD.

7. $\frac{3}{4a^3b}$ and $\frac{5}{2ab^2}$
8. $\frac{4}{50a^2b^2}$ and $\frac{2}{100ab^3}$
9. $\frac{5}{9uv^2}, \frac{10}{21u^5v^2},$ and $\frac{12u}{v^4}$
10. $\frac{75p}{p+2}$ and $\frac{20}{75p^3}$
11. $\frac{30t}{t^2-4}$ and $\frac{t}{2t+4}$
12. $\frac{2}{3c+3c^2}, \frac{1}{3c},$ and $\frac{8}{9c+9}$

Rewrite the fractions using like denominators.

13. $\frac{2}{3y^2}$ and $\frac{7}{6y^3}$
14. $\frac{9}{14h^6}$ and $\frac{6}{35h^2}$
15. $\frac{z+1}{z^3}$ and $\frac{7}{18z^7}$
16. $\frac{23}{21f^9}, \frac{2}{15f^8},$ and $\frac{8}{9f^{15}}$
17. $\frac{5-j}{13j^2}, \frac{11}{3j^3},$ and $\frac{8}{12j^6}$
18. $\frac{17}{x^2+3x+2}$ and $\frac{23}{x^2-x-2}$
19. $\frac{8}{x^2+2x-3}$ and $\frac{2}{x^2+3x-4}$
20. $\frac{w}{w^2+12w+36}$ and $\frac{w}{w^2-36}$
21. $\frac{a+15}{a^9-a^{11}}, \frac{a}{1-a^3},$ and $\frac{4}{a^2+2}$
22. $\frac{1}{h^5-49h}, \frac{8}{h},$ and $\frac{14}{h^6-49h^2}$
23. $\frac{c}{cd+d^2}, \frac{1}{d^2},$ and $\frac{cd}{c^2+2cd+d^2}$
24. $\frac{10}{x^2+12}$ and $\frac{25}{x^4-144}$

Solve.

A. For each problem, write rational expressions with like denominators to represent the time of each part of the trip.

B. Answer the question.

25. Eliza sailed her boat 9 miles against the current and 7 miles with the current. The boat traveled at an average speed of 12 mph. If the speed of the current was 2 mph, what was the total travel time?

26. A boat traveled 15 miles with the current and 12 miles against it. The boat's average speed was 14 mph. Find the total travel time if the speed of the current is 1 mph.

27. An airplane made a roundtrip flight between two cities 2000 miles apart. The airplane flew against the wind in one direction and with the wind in the opposite direction, and the airplane's average speed was 320 mph. If the average wind speed was 10 mph, what was the total travel time?

28. A bird flies 10 miles with the wind and 7 miles against the wind. The bird's average speed was 25 mph. If the average wind speed was 3 mph, what was the total travel time?

29. Mario and Felipa took a 250-mile road trip. Mario drove the first half of the distance, and Felipa drove the second half of the distance. Felipa's average speed was 7 mph more than Mario's. If Mario's average speed was 58 mph, how many additional minutes did it take him to drive his half of the trip?

***30.** **Challenge** Marko and Jon took a 120-mile road trip. Marko drove three-quarters of the distance, and Jon drove the rest of the distance. Marko's average speed was 4 mph less than Jon's. Write a rational expression to represent how much longer Marko spent driving.

Adding and Subtracting Rational Expressions

Fractions with like denominators can be added or subtracted.

Once the fractions have like denominators, add or subtract the numerators and write this sum or difference over the like denominator. Then simplify if possible.

Here is how it works with a couple numerical fractions.

$$\frac{3}{4}+\frac{2}{5}=\frac{3}{4}\cdot\frac{5}{5}+\frac{2}{5}\cdot\frac{4}{4}=\frac{15}{20}+\frac{8}{20}=\frac{23}{20}$$

Adding Rational Expressions

Adding rational expressions is similar to adding numerical fractions.

Example 1 Add and simplify. Identify the domain.

A. $\frac{3}{2x}+\frac{1}{x^2}$

Solution The least common denominator is $2x^2$. The domain is all real numbers except 0.

$\frac{3}{2x}+\frac{1}{x^2}=\frac{3}{2x}\cdot\frac{x}{x}+\frac{1}{x^2}\cdot\frac{2}{2}$ Multiply each rational expression by a form of 1 to make the denominators the same.

$=\frac{3x}{2x^2}+\frac{2}{2x^2}$ Multiply.

$=\frac{3x+2}{2x^2}$ Add the numerators. ■

B. $\frac{x^2}{x+4}+\frac{3}{x^2-16}$

REMEMBER

The LCD is the least common multiple of the denominators. Each denominator divides into it.

Solution Factor to determine the LCD.

$$\frac{x^2}{x+4}+\frac{3}{x^2-16}=\frac{x^2}{x+4}+\frac{3}{(x+4)(x-4)}$$

The LCD is $(x+4)(x-4)$. The domain is all real numbers except -4 and 4.

$\frac{x^2}{x+4}+\frac{3}{(x+4)(x-4)}=\frac{x^2}{x+4}\cdot\frac{x-4}{x-4}+\frac{3}{(x+4)(x-4)}$ Multiply by a form of 1 to get common denominators.

$=\frac{x^3-4x^2}{(x+4)(x-4)}+\frac{3}{(x+4)(x-4)}$ Multiply.

$=\frac{x^3-4x^2+3}{(x+4)(x-4)}$ Add the numerators. ■

C. $\dfrac{3}{x+3} + \dfrac{x+9}{x^2+4x+3}$

Solution Factor to determine the LCD.

$$\frac{3}{x+3} + \frac{x+9}{x^2+4x+3} = \frac{3}{x+3} + \frac{x+9}{(x+3)(x+1)}$$

The LCD is $(x+3)(x+1)$. The domain is all real numbers except -3 and -1.

$\dfrac{3}{x+3} + \dfrac{x+9}{(x+3)(x+1)} = \dfrac{3}{x+3} \cdot \dfrac{x+1}{x+1} + \dfrac{x+9}{(x+3)(x+1)}$	Multiply by a form of 1 to get common denominators.
$= \dfrac{3x+3}{(x+3)(x+1)} + \dfrac{x+9}{(x+3)(x+1)}$	Multiply.
$= \dfrac{3x+3+x+9}{(x+3)(x+1)}$	Add the numerators.
$= \dfrac{4x+12}{(x+3)(x+1)}$	Combine like terms.
$= \dfrac{4(x+3)}{(x+3)(x+1)}$	Factor the numerator.
$= \dfrac{4\cancel{(x+3)}}{\cancel{(x+3)}(x+1)}$	Divide out the common factor $x+3$.
$= \dfrac{4}{x+1}$	Simplify. ■

Subtracting Rational Expressions

When subtracting rational expressions, be sure to subtract the entire numerator of the subtrahend and not just the first term. It helps to use parentheses.

Example 2 Subtract. Identify the domain.

A. $\dfrac{x}{x+3} - \dfrac{x-2}{4x^2+12x}$

Solution Factor to determine the LCD.

$$\frac{x}{x+3} - \frac{x-2}{4x^2+12x} = \frac{x}{x+3} - \frac{x-2}{4x(x+3)}$$

The LCD is $4x(x+3)$. The domain is all real numbers except -3 and 0.

$\dfrac{x}{x+3} - \dfrac{x-2}{4x(x+3)} = \dfrac{x}{x+3} \cdot \dfrac{4x}{4x} - \dfrac{x-2}{4x(x+3)}$	Multiply by a form of 1 to get common denominators.
$= \dfrac{4x^2}{4x(x+3)} - \dfrac{x-2}{4x(x+3)}$	Multiply.
$= \dfrac{4x^2-(x-2)}{4x(x+3)}$	Subtract the numerators.
$= \dfrac{4x^2-x+2}{4x(x+3)}$	Distribute -1 and simplify. ■

(continued)

B. $\dfrac{x-5}{x+3} - \dfrac{2x+1}{x-8}$

Solution The LCD is $(x+3)(x-8)$. The domain is all real numbers except -3 and 8.

$$\frac{x-5}{x+3} - \frac{2x+1}{x-8} = \frac{x-5}{x+3} \cdot \frac{x-8}{x-8} - \frac{2x+1}{x-8} \cdot \frac{x+3}{x+3}$$ Multiply by a form of 1 to get common denominators.

$$= \frac{x^2 - 13x + 40}{(x+3)(x-8)} - \frac{2x^2 + 7x + 3}{(x+3)(x-8)}$$ Multiply.

$$= \frac{x^2 - 13x + 40 - (2x^2 + 7x + 3)}{(x+3)(x-8)}$$ Subtract the numerators.

$$= \frac{x^2 - 13x + 40 - 2x^2 - 7x - 3}{(x+3)(x-8)}$$ Distribute -1.

$$= \frac{-x^2 - 20x + 37}{(x+3)(x-8)}$$ Combine like terms. ■

Application: Aviation

Example 3 A plane flies with a headwind 1200 miles to its destination at an average speed of 300 mph. It makes the return trip back to its starting point, with a tailwind, at the same average speed. Write a simplified rational expression for the total time the plane was in the air.

Solution Use $t = \frac{d}{r}$, letting w represent the rate of the wind.

Flying with a headwind means flying into the wind, which slows the plane down, so subtract w from 300. Flying with a tailwind means flying in the same direction as the wind, which speeds the plane up, so add w to 300.

To destination: $\dfrac{1200}{300 - w}$, From destination: $\dfrac{1200}{300 + w}$

The total time is the sum of the expressions.

$$\frac{1200}{300 - w} + \frac{1200}{300 + w}$$

The LCD is $(300 - w)(300 + w)$.

$$\frac{1200}{300 - w} + \frac{1200}{300 + w} = \frac{1200}{300 - w} \cdot \frac{300 + w}{300 + w} + \frac{1200}{300 + w} \cdot \frac{300 - w}{300 - w}$$ Multiply by a form of 1 to get common denominators.

$$= \frac{360{,}000 + 1200w}{(300 - w)(300 + w)} + \frac{360{,}000 - 1200w}{(300 - w)(300 + w)}$$ Multiply.

$$= \frac{720{,}000}{(300 - w)(300 + w)}$$ Add the numerators.

The expression $\dfrac{720{,}000}{(300 - w)(300 + w)}$ represents the total time the plane was in the air. ■

Problem Set

Add or subtract the expressions.

1. $\frac{6}{5p^3} + \frac{3}{8p^4}$
2. $\frac{1}{4a} - \frac{7}{9a^5}$
3. $\frac{12}{5x^2} + \frac{1}{15x^6}$
4. $\frac{7}{6v^5} + \frac{4}{3v^{15}}$
5. $\frac{11}{8f^4} - \frac{5}{2f^3}$
6. $\frac{14}{n^{22}} + \frac{12}{n^{11}}$
7. $\frac{z}{2} - \frac{2}{z}$
8. $\frac{16}{g^2} + \frac{3}{g}$
9. $\frac{1}{3c^4} - \frac{c}{c^2 + 1}$
10. $\frac{r}{r - 4} - \frac{4}{4 - r}$
11. $\frac{9}{32m + 8} + \frac{7}{8m - 32}$
12. $\frac{w}{w^2 + 14w + 49} - \frac{w}{w^2 - 36}$
13. $\frac{4}{s^4 - s^3} + \frac{5}{3s + 9}$
14. $\frac{1}{4z + 2z^2} + \frac{2}{z}$
15. $\frac{j}{5 + j} + \frac{6}{12j - 3}$
16. $\frac{2}{x + 2} + \frac{x + 4}{x^2 + 3x + 2}$
17. $\frac{4}{x + 4} - \frac{x + 8}{x^2 + 9x + 20}$
18. $\frac{2u}{u^2 + 2u + 1} - \frac{u^2}{u - 1}$
19. $\frac{5}{g^2 - 10g + 25} - \frac{g}{g - 5}$
20. $\frac{1}{x} + \frac{3x}{x^4 + 6x^2 + 9}$
21. $\frac{a + 13}{a^{11} - a^{13}} + \frac{a}{1 - a^2} + \frac{11}{a + 1}$
22. $\frac{1}{h^5 - 64h} + \frac{4}{h} + \frac{12}{h^8 - 64h^4}$
23. $\frac{1}{q^2 + q} + \frac{1}{q^2 - q} - \frac{1}{q^2 - 1}$
24. $\frac{y}{y^2 - 4} - \frac{y^2}{y^2 + 2y} + \frac{y^2}{y^2 - 2y}$

Solve.

25. An airplane started a trip between two cities with a tailwind. The cities are 1600 miles apart. Halfway through the trip, the tailwind became a headwind. The airplane's average speed was 300 mph. Write a simplified rational expression to represent the total time of the trip.

26. Franco drove round-trip to the mall, which is 30 miles away. On his way there, his average speed was 10 mph greater than on his way home. Write a simplified expression to represent how much longer his trip home was.

27. Dawn drove to and from her class, which is 12 miles away. On her way there, her average speed was 8 mph greater than on her way home. Write a simplified expression to represent how much longer her trip home took.

28. Two buses left a bus station at the same time to travel to the same destination, which is 15 miles away. The average speed of Bus 1 was 10 mph greater than Bus 2. Write a simplified expression to represent how much longer it took Bus 2 to reach the destination.

29. Marion was running laps on a one-mile track. Her average speed on her first lap was 3 mph faster than her average speed on her second lap. Write a simplified expression to represent how much longer it took her to run her second lap.

30. A boat traveled 10 miles with the current and 10 miles against it. The boat's average speed was 10 mph.

    A. Write a simplified rational expression to represent how much longer it took to travel against the current.

    B. Find the difference in travel time if the speed of the current is 1 mph.

UNIT 14 Logic and Reasoning

Lawyers use logic and reasoning to make convincing arguments in court.

Just as lawyers use logical reasoning to formulate convincing arguments, mathematicians use logical reasoning to formulate and prove theorems. Once you have mastered the uses of inductive and deductive reasoning, you will be able to make and understand arguments in many areas.

Big Idea

- Mathematical reasoning involves making convincing arguments to justify or prove mathematical statements. The result of mathematical reasoning is often a proof. A proof is a convincing argument that conforms to the rules of logic and relies on accepted axioms or already proven results.

Unit Topics

- Reasoning and Argument
- Hypothesis and Conclusion
- Forms of Conditional Statements
- Inductive and Deductive Reasoning
- Analyzing and Writing Proofs
- Counterexample

Reasoning and Argument

You use reasoning in daily life and in mathematics.

Suppose a student listening to a news broadcast hears the following.

Anchorman to anchorwoman: "Whenever it rains, morning traffic becomes a mess."
Traffic reporter: "Traffic is slow throughout the metropolitan area. All the major roads are jammed."

The student might reason that it is raining outside. But based on what was actually said, that may or may not be true. It cannot be assumed that because traffic is a mess it is raining. When you understand some basic rules of logic and reasoning, you can avoid making bad assumptions.

Logical reasoning uses *statements,* which are sentences that tell an idea. A statement can either be true or false.

DEFINITIONS

An **argument** is a set of statements, called *premises*, that are used to reach a *conclusion*.

Syllogism is a logical argument that always contains two premises and a conclusion.

Syllogisms

Syllogisms take several forms. The most common syllogism forms are shown in the table, where *a, b,* and *c* represent phrases.

NOTATION

The symbol $\therefore$ means *therefore*.

Syllogisms	
If a, then b. If b, then c. Therefore, if a, then c.	All a are b. All c are a. $\therefore$ all c are b.
If a number is a whole number, then it is an integer. If a number is an integer, then it is a real number. Therefore, if a number is a whole number, then it is a real number.	All integers are real numbers. All whole numbers are integers. Therefore, all whole numbers are real numbers.

(continued)

Example 1 Complete the syllogisms.

A. If it is the month of May, then lilacs are blooming.

If lilacs are blooming, then tulips are blooming.

Therefore, if ______, then ______.

Solution Identify the parts of the syllogism. Determine that a is "it is the month of May," b is "lilacs are blooming," and c is "tulips are blooming." The completed conclusion is this: Therefore, if it is the month of May, then tulips are blooming. ■

B. All polynomials are mathematical expressions.

All ______ are ______.

Therefore, all quadratics are mathematical expressions.

Solution Identify the parts of the syllogism. Determine that a is "polynomials," b is "mathematical expressions," and c is "quadratics." The completed premise is this: All quadratics are polynomials. ■

Determining if an Argument Is Valid or Invalid

An argument may not be valid. In a **valid** argument, if the premises are true, then the conclusion must be true. In an **invalid** argument, it is possible for the conclusion to be false when all the premises are true.

Example 2 Determine if the argument is valid or invalid. Explain your answer.

If it is a car, then it has an engine.

If it has an engine, then you can drive it.

Therefore, if it is a car, then you can drive it.

THINK ABOUT IT

The argument has three statements and three terms, but the placement of the terms does not form a valid syllogism.

Solution The premises are each true: Cars have engines and an engine enables you to drive a car. The conclusion is also true that cars can be driven. However, the argument is flawed. Other factors can make a car immobile. For example, if a car has a flat tire, you cannot drive it even though it has a working engine. Sometimes even though the premise statements in an argument are true, they do not necessarily lead to a true conclusion, as the example above shows. ■

Identifying the Flaw in an Argument

Example 3 Sean sees four paw prints in the snow and states, "An animal with four legs has walked through here." Suzy says, "All dogs have four legs, so the animal must be a dog." What is the flaw in Suzy's argument?

Solution The argument is flawed because Suzy assumes that all animals with four legs are dogs. That statement is not true. Other animals with four legs are not dogs, such as wildebeests, elephants, and cats. ■

Problem Set

Complete the syllogism.

1. If x is an even number, then $x + 1$ is an odd number.

   If $x + 1$ is an odd number, then $x + 2$ is an even number.

   Therefore, if ________, then ________.

2. If a regular polygon has three sides, then it is a triangle.

   If a regular polygon is a triangle, then the sum of the measures of its interior angles is 180°.

   Therefore, if ________, then ________.

3. All students that receive a zero are students that fail.

   All students that cheat are students that receive a zero.

   Therefore, ________.

4. If it snows, then school will be canceled.

   If school is canceled, then you can sleep in.

   Therefore, if ________, then ________.

5. If two lines are cut by a transversal and corresponding angles are congruent, then the lines are parallel.

   If two lines are parallel, then alternate-interior angles around a transversal that intersects the lines are congruent.

   Therefore, if ________, then ________.

6. If two lines are perpendicular, then the two lines form a right angle.

   If the two lines form a right angle, then the two lines meet at a 90° angle.

   Therefore, if ________, then ________.

7. If a measurement is 36 inches, then it is 3 feet.

   If ________, then ________.

   Therefore, if a measurement is 36 inches, then it is 1 yard.

8. All mammals are warm-blooded.

   All dogs are mammals.

   Therefore, ________.

9. If it is hot outside, then I will turn on the air conditioning.

   If ________, then ________.

   Therefore, if it is hot outside, the electric bill will be high.

10. If it is November, then the leaves will be falling.

    If ________, then ________.

    Therefore, if it is November, I will have to rake the leaves.

11. If the discriminant of a quadratic function is positive, then the function has two real solutions.

    If a function has two real solutions, then it will cross the x-axis twice.

    Therefore, if ____________, then ____________.

12. If a triangle is isosceles, then the triangle has two congruent sides.

    If a triangle has two congruent sides, then the base angles are congruent.

    Therefore, if ____________, then ____________.

Determine if the argument is valid or invalid.

13. If a student plays football, then the student is an athlete.

    If a student plays soccer, then the student is an athlete.

    Therefore, if a student plays football, then the student plays soccer.

14. If a shape is a rectangle, then it has four right angles.

    If a shape is a square, then it has four right angles.

    Therefore, if a shape is a rectangle, then it is a square.

15. If a shape is a square, then it has four sides.

    If a shape has four sides, then it is a quadrilateral.

    Therefore, if a shape is a square, then it is a quadrilateral.

16. If a person enjoys playing the guitar, then that person likes music.

    If a person likes music, then that person can appreciate all genres of music.

    Therefore, if a person enjoys playing the guitar, then that person can appreciate all genres of music.

17. If a number is divisible by 6, then it is divisible by 3.

    If a number is divisible by 9, then it is divisible by 3.

    Therefore, if a number is divisible by 6, then it is divisible by 9.

18. Some vehicles are cars.

    A bus is a vehicle.

    Therefore, a bus has four wheels.

19. Some fruit is red.

    A banana is a fruit.

    Therefore, a banana is red.

20. If a vehicle is a car, then it has four wheels.

    If a vehicle is a truck, then it has four wheels.

    Therefore, all cars are trucks.

Identify the flaw in the argument.

21. Bobby thought that there was a football game tonight. Bobby sees that his friend Jason, who is a member of the football team, is not wearing his jersey. Bobby says, "Since Jason isn't wearing his jersey, then tonight's game must be canceled."

22. Stanley's dad is the soccer coach for his little brother's soccer team. Stanley asked his dad who won the game. His dad replied, "We outscored them 4 to 3 in the second half," so Stanley congratulates his little brother on getting a win.

23. Keri knows that her mother is buying her a new car for her birthday. When Keri goes outside on her birthday, she sees a new red car on the street. Keri runs to her mother to thank her for the car.

24. Danitza needs to know the length of a string of spaghetti. Since her father told her that they were having spaghetti for dinner tonight, Danitza will wait for dinner and measure one that she gets on her plate.

25. The cover of Stewart's book has four right angles. Stewart thinks his book's shape must be a square.

26. Malika learned that every member of the cheerleading squad from last year is on this year's squad as well. When she sees a girl with a cheerleading uniform on, she says to herself, "She must have been on the squad last year."

27. Kara knows that an equilateral triangle has three 60° angles. Kara measures one angle of a triangle and the measure is 60°. Kara says the triangle must be an equilateral triangle.

28. Jessica needs to construct a triangular base for her table. She takes the first three pieces that she sees in her dad's workshop because you can make a triangle out of any three sizes of wood.

Hypothesis and Conclusion

Conditional statements are the foundation of logical reasoning.

THINK ABOUT IT

Notice in the definition that a statement is conditional if it *can* be expressed in if-then form. Not all conditional statements use the words *if* and *then*.

DEFINITION

A **conditional statement** is a statement that can be written in if-then form.

In a conditional statement, the part that follows *if* is the **hypothesis** and the part that follows *then* is the **conclusion**. Sometimes the word *then* is not written, but is implied. It is also possible for a conditional statement to include a phrase that is neither the hypothesis nor the conclusion.

Identifying the Hypothesis and Conclusion of a Conditional Statement

THINK ABOUT IT

A conditional statement can also be called an *implication*, because the hypothesis implies the conclusion.

THINK ABOUT IT

The statement in Example 1B is equivalent to "If a number is divisible by 4, then it is divisible by 2."

Example 1 Identify the hypothesis and conclusion of each conditional statement.

A. If it is Wednesday, then I have a piano lesson.

Solution The words following *if* are the hypothesis. The words following *then* are the conclusion.

Hypothesis: it is Wednesday

Conclusion: I have a piano lesson ■

B. A number is divisible by 2 if it is divisible by 4.

Solution In this statement, the conclusion is written before the hypothesis.

Hypothesis: it is divisible by 4

Conclusion: a number is divisible by 2 ■

C. For $a \geq 0$, if $x^2 = a$, then $x = \pm\sqrt{a}$.

Solution In identifying the hypothesis and conclusion, disregard the premise, for $a \geq 0$.

Hypothesis: $x^2 = a$

Conclusion: $x = \pm\sqrt{a}$ ■

Writing a Conditional Statement

When writing a conditional in if-then form, it may be necessary to add extra words for clarity.

TIP

A conditional statement is sometimes just called a conditional.

Example 2 Write each statement as a conditional statement in if-then form. Then identify the hypothesis and conclusion.

A. All cats like to eat salmon.

Solution The statement implies that if an animal is a cat, then it would like to eat salmon. The conditional is:

If an animal is a cat, then it likes to eat salmon.

Hypothesis: an animal is a cat

Conclusion: it likes to eat salmon ■

B. Parallel lines have equal slopes.

Solution If two or more lines are parallel, then their slopes are equal.

Hypothesis: two or more lines are parallel

Conclusion: their slopes are equal ■

Identifying Conditional Statements

Example 3 Determine if each statement is a conditional statement.

A. Shar will drive to the movie theater.

Solution The statement does not give any condition for when Shar will drive to the movie theater, nor does it give any conclusion about what would happen if she does. The statement is not a conditional statement. ■

B. Numbers that end in 5 are divisible by 5.

Solution The statement implies that if a number ends in 5, then it is divisible by 5. The statement is a conditional. ■

Application: Real-World Conditional Statements

Example 4

A. A merchant prints the words *"All products come with a money-back guarantee"* on each sales receipt. How can the merchant write the words as a conditional statement in if-then form?

Solution If you buy any product, then you get a money-back guarantee. ■

B. One of the key recommendations for healthy living is *"To maintain body weight in a healthy range, balance calories from foods and beverages with calories expended."* How can you write the recommendation as a conditional statement in if-then form?

Solution If you balance calories from foods and beverages with calories expended, then you will maintain a body weight in a healthy range. ■

Problem Set

Identify the hypothesis and conclusion of each statement.

1. If it is Saturday, then I have a soccer game.
2. You can find the decimal equivalent of a fraction if you divide the numerator by the denominator.
3. For all of values of a, b, and c, if $a \cdot b = a \cdot c$, then $b = c$.
4. If the temperature is below 32°F, then water will turn from a liquid to a solid.
5. If you were born in 2000, then you turned 5 in 2005.
6. If you live in Los Angeles, then you live in California.
7. If a word is a proper noun, then it starts with a capital letter.
8. If a triangle is a right triangle, then it has a 90° angle.

Write each statement as a conditional statement in if-then form. Then identify the hypothesis and conclusion.

9. All photographers take pictures.
10. The sum of 12 and 14 is 26.
11. Every quadratic function has a graph that is shaped like a parabola.
12. Any number whose last two digits are divisible by 4 is divisible by 4.
13. The product of two negative numbers is a positive number.
14. All doctors must go to medical school.

Determine if the statement is a conditional statement.

15. Any student that cheats will fail.
16. I am going to walk my dog.
17. We can go to the pool after 10 a.m.
18. We don't have school when it snows.
19. All mammals are warm-blooded.
20. Tasha wants to get her driver's license.
21. Accidentally spilling bleach on your clothing will leave a stain.
22. Today is the last day of January.

Rewrite each statement as a conditional statement.

23. The sum of the measures of the angles of a triangle is 180°.
24. A federal guideline regarding education states that students are required to pass tests in English, algebra, biology, and social studies before they can receive a diploma.
25. The local middle school publishes a student handbook outlining the rules of the school. One statement reads "Chronic lateness to school will result in suspension."
26. State University has installed a filter to block school offices from accessing sports websites. The school issued a rule stating that employees who bypass the filter will be terminated.

Forms of Conditional Statements

You can form a new conditional statement from any conditional statement by switching the hypothesis and conclusion, negating the hypothesis and conclusion, or both switching and negating the hypothesis and conclusion.

Determining if a Converse Is True or False

DEFINITION

The **converse** is a conditional statement that switches the hypothesis and conclusion of the original conditional statement.

Conditional: If a, then b.

Converse: If b, then a.

When a conditional statement is true, the converse of that statement may or may not be true.

Example 1 Write the converse of each conditional statement. Then determine if the converse is true or false.

A. If a number is an irrational number, then it is a real number.

Solution The converse is: If a number is a real number, then it is an irrational number.

The converse is false because real numbers are made up of both rational and irrational numbers. ■

B. If $ab = 0$, then $a = 0$ or $b = 0$.

Solution The converse is: If $a = 0$ or $b = 0$, then $ab = 0$.

The converse is true. If any factor in a multiplication expression is 0, then the product is 0. ■

C. All percents are ratios with denominators of 100.

Solution It sometimes helps to first write the statement as a conditional statement: If an expression is a percent, then it is a ratio with a denominator of 100.

The converse is: If an expression is a ratio with a denominator of 100, then it is a percent.

The converse is true. This is the definition of a percent. ■

(continued)

D. An expression can be factored if it is a difference of squares.

Solution Be careful: The conclusion is written before the hypothesis. Write the conditional in if-then form to see the hypothesis and conclusion.

Conditional: If an expression is a difference of squares, then it can be factored.

Converse: If an expression can be factored, then it is a difference of squares.

The converse is false. Expressions other than differences of squares can be factored. ■

Writing Converses, Inverses, and Contrapositives

To *negate* a statement means to write that the statement is *not* true. Negating hypotheses and conclusions gives us two more forms of conditional statements.

DEFINITIONS

The **inverse** is a conditional statement that negates the hypothesis and the conclusion of the original conditional statement. The **contrapositive** is a conditional statement that both switches and negates the hypothesis and conclusion of the original conditional statement.

Conditional: If a, then b.

Converse: If b, then a.

Inverse: If not a, then not b.

Contrapositive: If not b, then not a.

THINK ABOUT IT

The contrapositive can be defined as the inverse of the converse.

When a conditional statement is true, the inverse of that statement may or may not be true but the contrapositive will always be true.

Example 2 Write the converse, inverse, and contrapositive of the conditional statement.

Conditional: If it is raining, then I will go to the movies.

Solution Identify the hypothesis and conclusion of the conditional.

Hypothesis: it is raining

Conclusion: I will go to the movies

Converse: If I go to the movies, then it is raining.

Inverse: If it is not raining, then I will not go to the movies.

Contrapositive: If I do not go to the movies, then it is not raining. ■

Determining if Converses, Inverses, and Contrapositives Are True or False

Example 3 Determine if the converse, inverse, and contrapositive of the conditional statement is true or false.

Conditional: All numbers that are divisible by 5 end in 0 or 5.

Solution Write the statement in if-then form to identify the hypothesis and conclusion.

If a number is divisible by 5, then it ends in 0 or 5.

Hypothesis: A number is divisible by 5.

Conclusion: It ends in 0 or 5.

Converse: If a number ends in 0 or 5, then it is divisible by 5.
True

Inverse: If a number is not divisible by 5, then it does not end in 0 or 5.
True

Contrapositive: If a number does not end in 0 or 5, then it is not divisible by 5.
True ■

Using the Law of Contrapositives

THE LAW OF CONTRAPOSITIVES

If a conditional statement is true, then its contrapositive is also true.

The law of contrapositives can help you prove statements because sometimes it is easier or simpler to show the truth value of the contrapositive than the truth value of the conditional statement.

TIP

The *truth value* of a statement is either *true* or *false.*

Example 4 Use the law of contrapositives to determine whether the following statements are true.

A. If a given triangle is not a right triangle, then $a^2 + b^2 \neq c^2$.

Solution Identify the hypothesis and conclusion of the statement. Then write the contrapositive.

Hypothesis: A given triangle is not a right triangle.

Conclusion: $a^2 + b^2 \neq c^2$

Contrapositive: If $a^2 + b^2 = c^2$, then the triangle is a right triangle.

The Pythagorean theorem guarantees that the contrapositive is true. So, the conditional statement is true. ■

(continued)

B. If the discriminant is irrational, then the polynomial is not factorable.

Hypothesis: the discriminant is irrational

Conclusion: the polynomial is not factorable

Contrapositive: If the polynomial is factorable, then the discriminant is not irrational.

The contrapositive is true since a polynomial is only factorable when the discriminant is a perfect square or 0. The contrapositive is true, so the original conditional is true ■

Application: Advertising

Example 5 Alberto sees a billboard that reads, *"Eat Green's Granola Bars for a healthier you."* Alberto said, "Wow, if I don't eat Green's Granola Bars, then I won't be healthy." Explain the error in Alberto's thinking.

Solution The statement on the billboard can be written as the conditional,

If you eat Green's Granola Bars, then you will be healthy.

Alberto's statement is the inverse of the original statement and the inverse of a conditional statement is not always true. ■

Problem Set

Write the converse of each conditional statement. Then determine if the converse is true or false.

1. If a number is a rational number, then it can be written as a fraction.
2. If a function is a constant function, then the graph of the function is a horizontal line.
3. If a triangle is equilateral, then it is isosceles.
4. If n is prime, then it has n and 1 as factors.
5. All negative integers are less than 0.
6. All squares are rectangles.
7. If a polygon has three sides, then it is a triangle.
8. An expression cannot be factored if it is a sum of two squares.

Identify the hypothesis and conclusion. Then write the converse, inverse, and contrapositive of the conditional statement.

9. If it is Tuesday, then I have swimming lessons.
10. If I study, then I will pass the math test.
11. If I learn to cook, then I will stop eating at restaurants.
12. If I like this course, then I will be motivated to study.
13. If the football team wins the game this week, then they will be in the championship game.
14. If a number is even, then it is divisible by 2.
15. If the dog gets sick, then I have to take him to the vet.
16. If I graduate from college, then I will have a college degree.

Identify the hypothesis and conclusion of the conditional statement. Then determine if the converse, inverse, and contrapositive of the conditional statement are true or false.

17. If a number is an integer, then it can be positive, negative, or 0.

18. If an equation of a line is in slope-intercept form, then it is in the form $y = mx + b$.

19. All vertical lines have undefined slope.

20. All rational numbers are real numbers.

21. An expression is simplified correctly if the order of operations is followed.

22. A year is a leap year if February has 29 days.

Identify the hypothesis and conclusion of the statement. Then write the contrapositive, and determine if the conditional statement and contrapositive are true or false.

23. If $5x \neq 10$, then $x \neq 2$.

24. If an equation is quadratic, then it has two real roots.

25. If the discriminant is 0, then the graph of the quadratic function has one x-intercept.

26. If a function is linear, then its graph is a line.

***27. Challenge** All quadratic variation equations have a constant of variation.

***28. Challenge** If a number is a perfect number, then it is equal to half of the sum of all of its positive divisors.

Inductive and Deductive Reasoning

Inductive and deductive reasoning are commonly used to reach a conclusion.

Using Inductive Reasoning

DEFINITION

Inductive reasoning is a type of reasoning based on observations of patterns or past events to reach a conclusion.

Inductive reasoning does not always result in a true conclusion and it is not considered "proof" in mathematics. However, it does have an important place in mathematics.

THINK ABOUT IT

We are assuming in Example 1A that the pattern remains "multiply by 3," but it could be "multiply by 3 four times, then add 1." Our conclusion is an educated guess only.

Example 1 Use inductive reasoning to complete each problem.

A. Find the next term in the sequence 5, 15, 45, 135, 405, ...

Solution Each term is 3 times the preceding term. Based on this pattern, the next term is $405 \cdot 3 = 1215$. ■

B. Find the next term in the sequence 40, 39, 37, 34, 30, ...

Solution Each term decreases by one more than the preceding term.

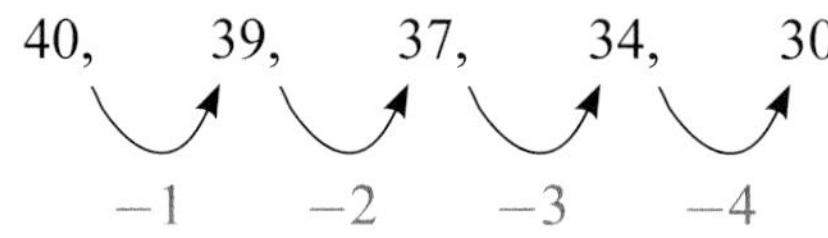

Based on this pattern, the next term is $30 - 5 = 25$. ■

THINK ABOUT IT

You can use inductive reasoning to generate new ideas to test deductively.

C. Every Tuesday since he moved to town, Juan's neighbor mows his lawn. Today is Tuesday. Draw a conclusion.

Solution Based on past events, Juan's neighbor will mow his lawn today. ■

Using Deductive Reasoning

DEFINITION

Deductive reasoning is a type of reasoning that uses proven or accepted properties to reach a conclusion.

Deductive reasoning uses logical reasoning, such as syllogisms, to move from one statement to another. Mathematical proofs use deductive reasoning.

REMEMBER

A syllogism is a type of argument that uses exactly three statements.

Example 2 Use deductive reasoning to draw a conclusion from the given statements.

A. If a number ends in 0, then it is divisible by 10.

If a number is divisible by 10, then it is divisible by 5.

Solution The statements are premises of a syllogism. The conclusion is, "If a number ends in 0, then it is divisible by 5." ■

B. If you study, then you will pass the test.

Daisy studied for the test.

Solution Since anyone who studies will pass the test, Daisy will pass the test. ■

C. If a number is prime, then it is not divisible by 2.

The number 1032 is divisible by 2.

Solution The second statement is the negation of the conclusion of the first statement. A valid conclusion can be made by using the contrapositive of the first statement:

"If a number is divisible by 2, then it is not a prime number."

Since we are given that the number 1032 is divisible by 2, we can conclude that it is not a prime number. ■

The solution to Example 2C uses the Law of Detachment.

DEFINITION

Law of Detachment is a valid argument of the form:

If a, then b.
a.
Therefore, b.

Identifying Inductive and Deductive Reasoning

Example 3 Determine whether inductive or deductive reasoning was used.

A. Julio wrote the following.

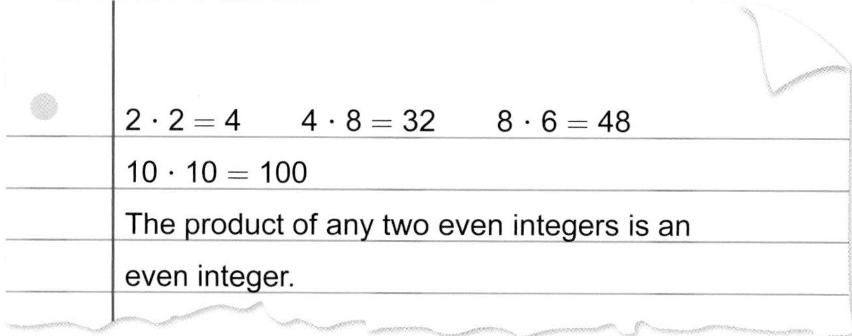

$2 \cdot 2 = 4 \quad 4 \cdot 8 = 32 \quad 8 \cdot 6 = 48$
$10 \cdot 10 = 100$
The product of any two even integers is an
even integer.

Solution Julio used a set of observations to create a conjecture. This is inductive reasoning. ■

B. Lisa said that all equations have an equals sign, and all identities are equations, so all identities must have equals signs.

Solution Lisa used logical reasoning. Specifically, she used a form of syllogism. This is deductive reasoning. ■

Example 4 Tyrell and Lee are each trying to prove that the product of a number plus 1 and the same number minus 1 equals 1 less then the square of the number.

Tyrell wrote:

$(5 + 1)(5 - 1) = 6 \cdot 4 = 24 = 5^2 - 1$

$(0 + 1)(0 - 1) = 1 \cdot (-1) = -1 = 0^2 - 1$

$(-6 + 1)(-6 - 1) = (-5) \cdot (-7) = 35 = (-6)^2 - 1$

It is true for a positive number, zero, and a negative number, so it is true for all numbers.

Lee wrote:

$(n + 1)(n - 1) = n^2 - n + n - 1 = n^2 - 1$

by the FOIL method of polynomial multiplication.

Whose reasoning is considered mathematically sound proof?

Solution Tyrell gave three examples while Lee used an accepted property of mathematics. Lee's reasoning is deductive. Since deductive reasoning is accepted as proof in mathematics, Lee's proof is mathematically sound. ■

Problem Set

Use inductive reasoning to complete each problem.

1. Find the next term in the sequence 1, 3, 5, 7, 9, ...
2. Find the next term in the sequence 1, 5, 9, 13, 17, ...
3. Every Friday Mr. Juarez gives a math quiz. Today is Friday. Draw a conclusion.
4. Find the next term in the sequence –5, –2, 1, 4, 7, ...
5. Find the next term in the sequence 250, 50, 10, 2, $\frac{2}{5}$, ...
6. When it is not raining, Sami walks his dog. It is not raining today. Draw a conclusion.
7. The cafeteria closes the snack line on Thursday. Today is Thursday. Draw a conclusion.
8. Find the next term in the sequence 1, 1, 2, 3, 5, ...
9. Find the next term in the sequence 2, 4, 8, 16, 32, ...
10. Find the next term in the sequence 1, 4, 9, 16, 25, ...

Use deductive reasoning to draw a conclusion from the given statements.

11. If $3x - 2 = 6$, then $3x = 8$. If $3x = 8$, then $x = \frac{8}{3}$.
12. If a number is even, then it is divisible by 2. $g = 14$.
13. If the slope of a line equals 4, then the slope is positive. If the slope is positive, then the graph of the line rises from left to right.
14. If a number is divisible by 6, then it is also divisible by 3. The number 104 is not divisible by 3.
15. If the study session began at 4 p.m., then I am late. If I am late, then I will miss the discussion.
16. If a triangle is a right triangle, then it has one right angle. Triangle *ABC* does not have a right angle.
17. If it snows today, then the team practices indoors. The team is not practicing indoors today.
18. If a polygon has four sides, then it is a quadrilateral. A triangle is not a quadrilateral.

Determine whether inductive or deductive reasoning was used.

19. Joaquin wrote the following statements:

    $-1 \cdot 2 = -2$ $\quad$ $-3 \cdot 5 = -15$

    $6 \cdot (-2) = -12$ $\quad$ $4 \cdot (-2) = -8$

    A negative number times a positive number equals a negative number.

20. Su Young said that all integers are rational numbers, and all rational numbers are real numbers, so all integers are real numbers.
21. Jon saw the following sequence: 2, 4, 8, 16, 32, ... He concluded that the sequence represented the powers of 2 and wrote the next three numbers: 64, 128, and 256.
22. Micah examined the following sequence: O, T, T, F, ... He concluded that the sequence represented the numbers One, Two, Three, Four, ... and wrote the next four terms F, S, S, E, ...
23. If a number is a perfect square, then its square root is rational. The square root of 19 is not rational. Therefore, if a number's square root is not rational, then the number is not a perfect square.

24. Sang wrote the following:

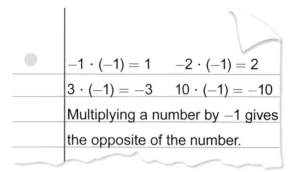

$-1 \cdot (-1) = 1$ $-2 \cdot (-1) = 2$

$3 \cdot (-1) = -3$ $10 \cdot (-1) = -10$

Multiplying a number by -1 gives the opposite of the number.

25. Amara noticed that $x = 2$ in the second problem of her quiz. The value of x was also 2 in the fourth and sixth problems. Therefore, Amara reasoned that the answer to the eighth problem was $x = 2$.

26. If $P = 2l + 2w$, then $2l = P - 2w$. If $2l = P - 2w$, then $l = \frac{P - 2w}{2}$. Therefore, if $P = 2l + 2w$, then $l = \frac{P - 2w}{2}$.

27. Jamal's best friend has gone to the library after school on Wednesday every week for the past month. Today is Wednesday. Jamal concludes that his friend will go to the library after school.

Solve.

28. Caleb and Thea are trying to prove that the square of a binomial equals a trinomial in the form of the sum of the square of the first term, twice the product of the first and second terms, and the square of the second term. Whose reasoning is considered a mathematically sound proof?

Caleb's method:

$(x + y)^2 = (x + y)(x + y) = x^2 + xy + xy + y^2$

$= x^2 + 2xy + y^2$ by the FOIL method. This is true for all values of x and y.

Thea's method:

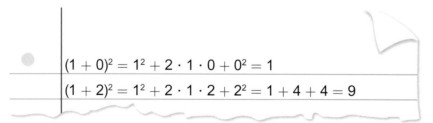

$(1 + 0)^2 = 1^2 + 2 \cdot 1 \cdot 0 + 0^2 = 1$

$(1 + 2)^2 = 1^2 + 2 \cdot 1 \cdot 2 + 2^2 = 1 + 4 + 4 = 9$

***29. Challenge** Ed and Jeb are trying to prove that the factored form of $x^3 + y^3 = (x + y)(x^2 - xy + y^2)$. Whose reasoning is considered a mathematically sound proof?

Jeb's method:

$(2^3 + 3^3) = (2 + 3)(2^2 - 2 \cdot 3 + 3^2)$

$= 5 \cdot (4 - 6 + 9)$

$= 5 \cdot 7 = 35$

$(5^3 + 0^3) = (5 + 0)(5^2 - 5 \cdot 0 + 0^2) = 5 \cdot 25 = 125$

Ed's method: Using the distributive property and the laws of multiplication,

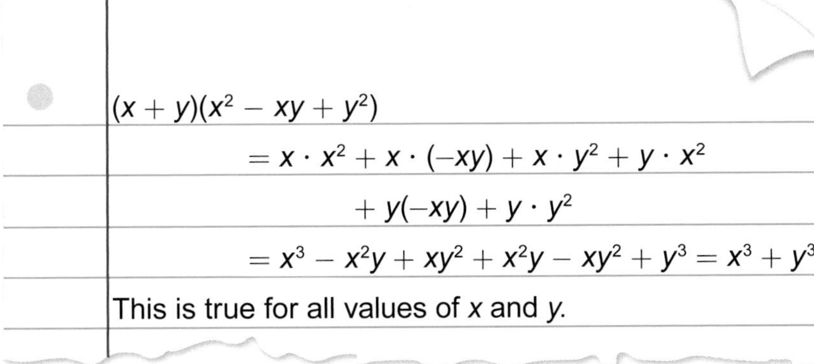
$(x + y)(x^2 - xy + y^2)$
$= x \cdot x^2 + x \cdot (-xy) + x \cdot y^2 + y \cdot x^2$
$+ y(-xy) + y \cdot y^2$
$= x^3 - x^2y + xy^2 + x^2y - xy^2 + y^3 = x^3 + y^3$
This is true for all values of x and y.

***30.** **Challenge** Jill and Tyne are trying to prove that the product of the slopes of two perpendicular lines equals −1. Whose reasoning is considered a mathematically sound proof?

Jill's method:

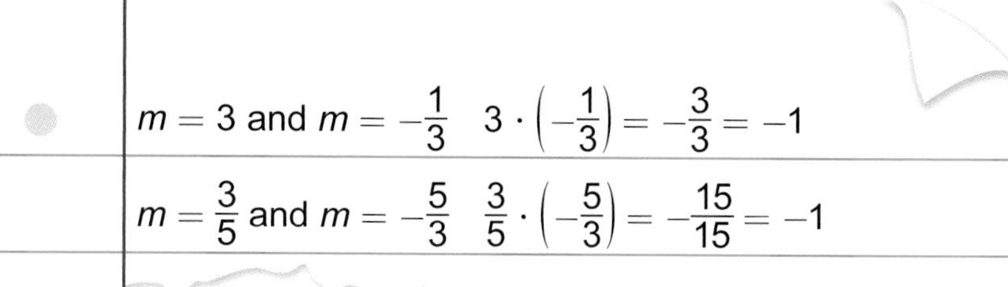

$m = 3$ and $m = -\frac{1}{3}$ $3 \cdot \left(-\frac{1}{3}\right) = -\frac{3}{3} = -1$
$m = \frac{3}{5}$ and $m = -\frac{5}{3}$ $\frac{3}{5} \cdot \left(-\frac{5}{3}\right) = -\frac{15}{15} = -1$

Tyne's method:

The slopes of two perpendicular lines are opposite reciprocals. Suppose that the first line's slope is $\frac{a}{b}$ and the line perpendicular to the first line has a slope of $-\frac{b}{a}$ where a and b do not equal 0.

$\frac{a}{b} \cdot \left(-\frac{b}{a}\right) = -\frac{ab}{ba} = -1.$

Therefore, the product of the slopes of two perpendicular lines equals −1.

Analyzing and Writing Proofs

You use deductive reasoning in proofs.

A **proof** is a clear, logical structure of reasoning that begins from accepted ideas and proceeds through logic to reach a conclusion. You will see most proofs written either in a two-column format or a paragraph format.

Justifying Steps in an Algebraic Proof

Regardless of the format, each step in an algebraic proof must be justified. The justification can be a mathematical property, such as the associative property of multiplication or a definition, such as the definition of a rational number.

Justification can also come from postulates and theorems. **Postulates** are mathematical statements that have not been proven but are understood to be true. Some people say that postulates are self-evident. One well-known postulate is that the whole is greater than the part. Unlike postulates, **theorems** are statements that have been or are to be proven on the basis of established definitions and properties.

When proving a conditional statement, the hypothesis is the given statement. The last line in the proof is the conclusion of the conditional statement.

TIP

Postulates are sometimes called axioms.

Example 1 Justify each step of the proof.

Conjecture: If $2x^2 + 6 = 22$, then $x = \pm 2\sqrt{2}$

$2x^2 + 6 = 22$	
$2x^2 = 16$	
$x^2 = 8$	
$x = \pm\sqrt{8}$	
$x = \pm\sqrt{4 \cdot 2}$	
$x = \pm 2\sqrt{2}$	

Solution

$2x^2 + 6 = 22$	Given
$2x^2 = 16$	Subtraction Property of Equality
$x^2 = 8$	Division Property of Equality
$x = \pm\sqrt{8}$	Square Root Property
$x = \pm\sqrt{4 \cdot 2}$	Product Rule for Radicals
$x = \pm 2\sqrt{2}$	Simplify.

QED ■

TIP

QED is an abbreviation for the Latin phrase "quod erat demonstrandum." Some mathematicians use QED at the end of an argument to show that the proof is complete.

Identifying the Given in an Algebraic Proof

Example 2 Determine the given statement in the proof of each conditional.

A. $y = 0$ if $5y = 0$.

Solution The given statement is the hypothesis of the conditional, that is, the words following *if.* Therefore, $5y = 0$ is the given statement. ■

B. All whole numbers are rational numbers.

Solution Write the statement in if-then form: If a number is a whole number, then the number is a rational number. The given statement would be: x is a whole number. ■

Proving a Conjecture

Although mathematicians use deductive reasoning to prove results, they use inductive reasoning to find conjectures to prove. For example, suppose a student writes the following equations.

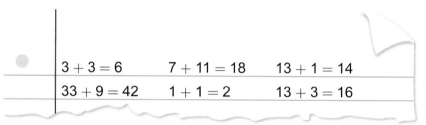

$3 + 3 = 6$	$7 + 11 = 18$	$13 + 1 = 14$
$33 + 9 = 42$	$1 + 1 = 2$	$13 + 3 = 16$

THINK ABOUT IT

Listing more sums of odd numbers does not prove the conjecture. There are infinite pairs of numbers, and you can't test all of them.

The student observes that all the addends are odd and all the sums are even and makes the following *conjecture:* the sum of two odd numbers is an even number. A **conjecture** is an educated guess. While the student found the conjecture by using inductive reasoning, she can only prove it with deductive reasoning.

Example 3 Prove the conjecture: the sum of two odd numbers is an even number.

Solution For any integer n, $2n$ is an even number. Because adding 1 to any even number results in an odd number, any odd number can be expressed in the form $2n + 1$.

Let $2a + 1$ and $2b + 1$ be any two odd numbers, where a and b are integers. Then their sum is $2a + 1 + 2b + 1$.

$2a + 1 + 2b + 1 = 2a + 2b + 1 + 1$	Commutative Property of Addition
$= 2a + 2b + 2$	Combine like terms.
$= 2(a + b + 1)$	Distributive Property of Multiplication

By the closure property of integers, $a + b + 1$ is an integer.

Since 2 times any integer is an even number, $2(a + b + 1)$ is an even number. Therefore, the sum of two odd numbers is an even number. ■

Identifying the Flaw in a Mathematical Argument

Example 4 Find the flaw in each proof.

A. Given that $a = 1$, prove that $1 = 0$.

$a = 1$	Given
$a^2 = a$	Multiplication Property of Equality
$a^2 - a = 0$	Subtraction Property of Equality
$\frac{a^2 - a}{a - 1} = \frac{0}{a - 1}$	Division Property of Equality
$\frac{a(a - 1)}{a - 1} = \frac{0}{a - 1}$	Factor.
$a = 0$	Simplify.
$1 = 0$	Substitution Property of Equality

Solution The error is in the fourth line when the division property of equality is used. Since $a = 1$, $a - 1 = 0$, and division by 0 is undefined. ■

B. $3 = \sqrt{9} = \sqrt{(-3) \cdot (-3)} = \sqrt{(-3)^2} = -3$

Solution The product rule for radicals only applies when the factors are nonnegative. ■

Problem Set

Justify each step of the proof.

1. Conjecture: If $2(x + 6) = 10$, then $x = -1$.

$2(x + 6) = 10$	**A.**
$2x + 12 = 10$	**B.**
$2x = -2$	**C.**
$x = -1$	**D.**

QED

2. Conjecture: If $3x^2 + 10 = 100$, then $x = \pm\sqrt{30}$.

$3x^2 + 10 = 100$	**A.**
$3x^2 = 90$	**B.**
$x^2 = 30$	**C.**
$x = \pm\sqrt{30}$	**D.**

QED

3. Conjecture: If $x^2 + 13x + 42 = 0$, then $x = -6$ or $x = -7$.

$x^2 + 13x + 42 = 0$	**A.**
$(x + 6)(x + 7) = 0$	**B.**
$x + 6 = 0$ or $x + 7 = 0$	**C.**
$x = -6$ or $x = -7$	**D.**

QED

4. Conjecture: If $\frac{2}{3}x^2 - 40 = 0$, then $x = \pm 2\sqrt{15}$.

$\frac{2}{3}x^2 - 40 = 0$	**A.**
$\frac{2}{3}x^2 = 40$	**B.**
$\frac{3}{2} \cdot \frac{2}{3}x^2 = \frac{3}{2} \cdot 40$	**C.**
$x^2 = 60$	**D.**
$x = \pm\sqrt{60}$	**E.**
$x = \pm\sqrt{4 \cdot 15}$	**F.**
$x = \pm 2\sqrt{15}$	**G.**

QED

5. Conjecture: If $4(x^2 + 7) = 100$, then $x = \pm 3\sqrt{2}$.

$4(x^2 + 7) = 100$	**A.**
$4x^2 + 28 = 100$	**B.**
$4x^2 = 72$	**C.**
$x^2 = 18$	**D.**
$x = \pm\sqrt{18}$	**E.**
$x = \pm\sqrt{9 \cdot 2}$	**F.**
$x = \pm 3\sqrt{2}$	**G.**

QED

6. Conjecture: If $y = mx + b$, then $m = \frac{y - b}{x}$.

$y = mx + b$	**A.**
$mx + b = y$	**B.**
$mx = y - b$	**C.**
$m = \frac{y - b}{x}$	**D.**

QED

Write the *given* statement you would use when proving the conditional.

7. $x = \pm 2$ if $x^2 = 4$.

8. If $3x + 5 = 20$, then $x = 5$.

9. A statement is true if its contrapositive is true.

10. All linear functions have lines as graphs.

11. An equation has three roots, if it is a cubic function.

12. If the converse of a statement is true, then the inverse is also true.

Prove each conjecture.

13. The product of two even numbers is an even number.

14. The sum of an odd and even number is an odd number.

15. If $\frac{a}{b} = \frac{c}{d}$, then $\frac{a + b}{b} = \frac{c + d}{d}$.

16. The square of an odd is an odd number.

17. If $\frac{a}{b} = \frac{c}{d}$, then $ad = bc$.

18. If $\frac{a}{b} = \frac{c}{d}$, then $\frac{a}{c} = \frac{b}{d}$.

Find the flaw in each proof.

19. $-2^2 + 5 = 4 + 5 = 9$

20. $(-1)^{100} = (-1)^{99} \cdot (-1)^1 = 1 \cdot -1 = -1$

21. Prove: If $x^2 = x^3$, then $x = 0$, 1, or -1

$x^2 = x^3$	Given
$x^2 - x^3 = 0$	Subtraction Property of Equality
$x(1 - x^2) = 0$	Distributive Property of Multiplication
$x(1 - x)(1 + x) = 0$	Factoring a Difference of Two Squares
$x = 0$ or $1 - x = 0$ or $1 + x = 0$	Zero Product Property
$x = 0$ or $x = 1$ or $x = -1$	Addition and Subtraction Properties of Equality

22. Prove $(x + 2)^2 = x^2 - 4$

$(x + 2)^2 = x^2 - 4$	Given
$= (x + 2)(x - 2)$	Laws of Exponents
$= x^2 + 2x - 2x - 4$	FOIL
$= x^2 - 4$	Additive Inverse Property

***23.** **Challenge** The sum of the integers from 1 to 50 is 1275. Pairing the integers,

$1 + 50 = 51$

$2 + 49 = 51$

$3 + 48 = 51$

$4 + 47 = 51$

...

There are 24 pairs so $24 \cdot 51 = 1275$. Therefore, the sum of the integers from 1 to 50 is 1275.

***24.** **Challenge** $|-3| = -3$

The definition of absolute value is

$|x| = \begin{cases} x \text{ if } x \geq 0 \\ -x \text{ if } x < 0 \end{cases}$. Applying the definition,

$|2| = 2$ since $2 \geq 0$

$|0| = 0$ since $0 \geq 0$

$|-3| = -3$ since $-3 < 0$

Counterexample

It takes only one example to prove that a statement is false.

DEFINITION

A **counterexample** is an example that shows a conjecture, statement, or theory is not a valid generalization.

REMEMBER

A conjecture is a guess. It is often a conclusion of inductive reasoning.

TIP

It is sometimes easier to prove a statement false than it is to prove a statement true.

TIP

For Example 1C, any number between 0 and 1 would also work.

Finding Counterexamples for Conjectures

A conjecture can either be true or false. Deductive reasoning can prove a conjecture true. A single counterexample can prove a conjecture false. Note however, that just because nobody has found a counterexample does not mean a conjecture is proven.

Example 1 Find a counterexample that disproves each conjecture.

A. A student observes that 3, 5, 7, and 11 are all prime numbers that are also odd. The student conjectures: All odd numbers are prime numbers.

Solution Find an odd number that is not prime. One possible counterexample is 9. The number 9 is not prime because $3 \cdot 3 = 9$. ■

B. A student observes the following: $(-3)^2 > 3$, $\left(-\frac{1}{2}\right)^2 > -\frac{1}{2}$, and $10^2 > 10$.

The student then conjectures: The square of any number is greater than the number.

Solution When trying to find a counterexample, try the values 0, 1, and fractions between 0 and 1. One possible counterexample is 0: $0^2 = 0$. ■

C. It is given that the points (0, 0) and (1, 1) are both contained in the graph of a function. A student conjectures that the graph must be the graph of the function $y = x$.

Solution There are other functions that contain the points (0, 0) and (1, 1). Two possible counterexamples are shown below.

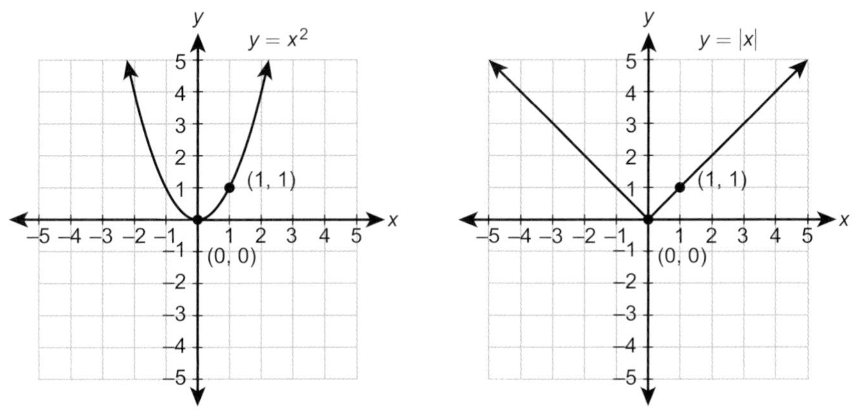

■

Finding Counterexamples for Conditionals

You can also prove that a conditional statement is false using a counterexample. When finding a counterexample for a conditional, look for an example that makes the hypothesis true and the conclusion false.

Example 2 Find a counterexample that disproves each conditional statement.

A. If $x^2 = 100$, then $x = 10$.

Solution -10 is a counterexample because $(-10)^2 = 100$ and $-10 \neq 10$. ■

B. If a number is divisible by 3, then it is divisible by 6.

Solution The number 3 is a counterexample because 3 is divisible by 3 but 3 is not divisible by 6. ■

C. All prime numbers are odd numbers.

Solution Write the conditional in if-then form: If a number is a prime number, then it is an odd number. A counterexample is the number 2 because 2 is both prime and even. ■

Determining if a Counterexample Is Valid

Example 3 Determine if each counterexample disproves the conjecture. If not, provide a counterexample that does.

A. Conjecture: All parabolas intersect the x-axis.

Counterexample:

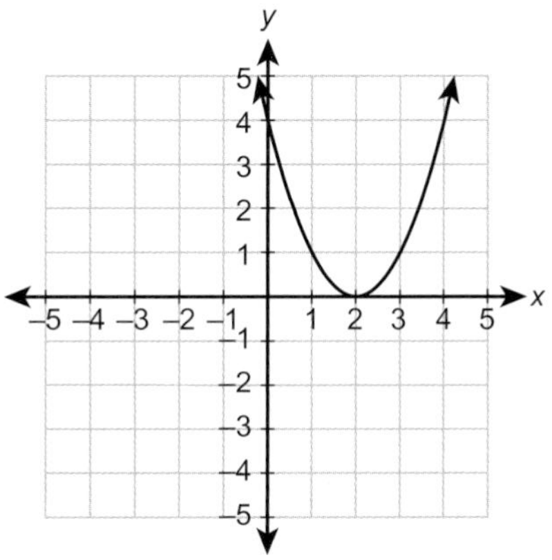

Solution No, a counterexample must be a parabola that does not intersect the x-axis.

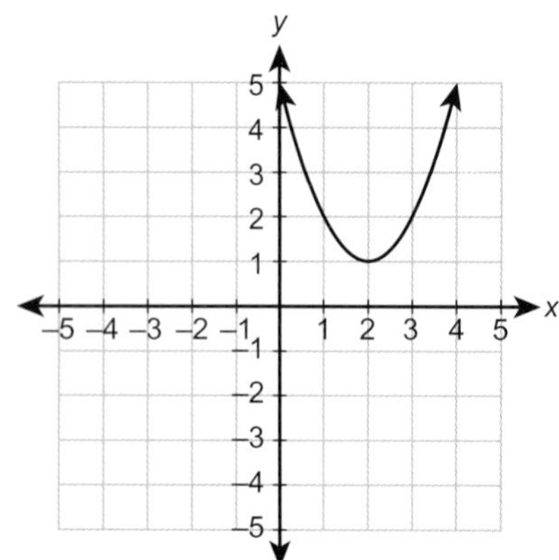

■

B. Conjecture: If a polynomial can be factored, then its terms share a GCF other than 1.

Counterexample: $x^2 - 4$

Solution Yes, the counterexample disproves the conjecture because it can be factored by a difference of squares but the terms do not have a GCF other than 1. ■

Problem Set

Find a counterexample that disproves each conjecture.

1. A student observes that 1, 2, and 3 are integers and positive numbers. The student conjectures: All integers are positive.

2. A student observes the following: $3^3 = 27$, $(-2)^3 = -8$, $4^3 = 64$, and $5^3 = 125$. The student conjectures: Cubing an integer results in a multiple of that integer.

3. If $3x^2 = 27$, then $x = -3$.

4. It is given that the points (2, 4) and (–2, 4) are both contained in the graph of a function. A student conjectures that the graph must be the graph of the function $y = 4$.

5. If a number is divisible by 5, then it is divisible by 10.

6. If $x^2 - 4 = 0$, then $x = 2$.

7. A student compares the following values:

1	$\frac{1}{1}$
2	$\frac{1}{2}$
3	$\frac{1}{3}$

   The student conjectures: For all integers x, $\frac{1}{x} \leq x$.

8. If a number is divisible by 7, then it is divisible by 14.

9. It is given that the points (0, 0) and (4, 2) are both contained in the graph of a quadratic function. A student conjectures that the graph must be the graph of a parabola opening up.

10. All rational numbers are in the form $\frac{p}{q}$ where $q \neq 0$.

11. A student notices that $\sqrt{2}$ and $\sqrt{3}$ are square roots and irrational numbers. The student conjectures: All square roots are irrational numbers.

12. All binomials can be factored.

13. A student observes that 4, 6, 8, and 16 are even and composite numbers. The student conjectures: All composite numbers are even.

14. If a number is divisible by 4, then it is divisible by 8.

15. A student compares the following values: 2 and 4, 3 and 9, and −4 and 16. The student conjectures: $x^2 > x$.

16. It is given that the points (0, 5) and (1, 5) are both contained in the graph of a function. A student conjectures that the graph must be the graph of a horizontal line.

Determine if each counterexample disproves the conjecture. If not, provide a counterexample that does.

17. All triangles are right triangles.

Counterexample: an equilateral triangle

18. All equations containing an x with a power (or implied power) of 1 are examples of direct variation equations.

Counterexample: $y = 14x$

19. All lines have positive slope.

Counterexample: $y = -3x + 5$

20. The set of irrational numbers is closed under division.

Counterexample: $\frac{\sqrt{14}}{\sqrt{7}} = \sqrt{2}$

21. All rectangles are squares.

Counterexample:

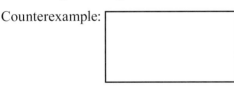

22. All linear systems of equations have one solution.

Counterexample: $\begin{array}{l} 2x + 3y = 9 \\ 8x + 12 = 36 \end{array}$

23. If you are given a slope and a point, you can always use the point-slope form to write an equation of the line.

Counterexample: $m = 2, (-1, 5)$

***24.** **Challenge** All quadratic functions have two real roots.

Counterexample:

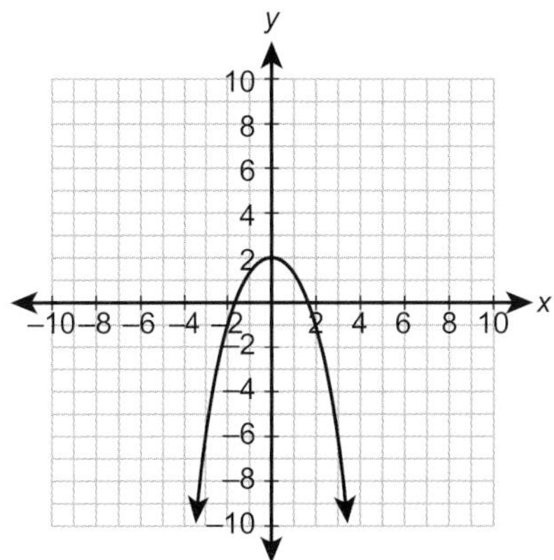

***25.** **Challenge** All absolute value functions open upward.

Counterexample:

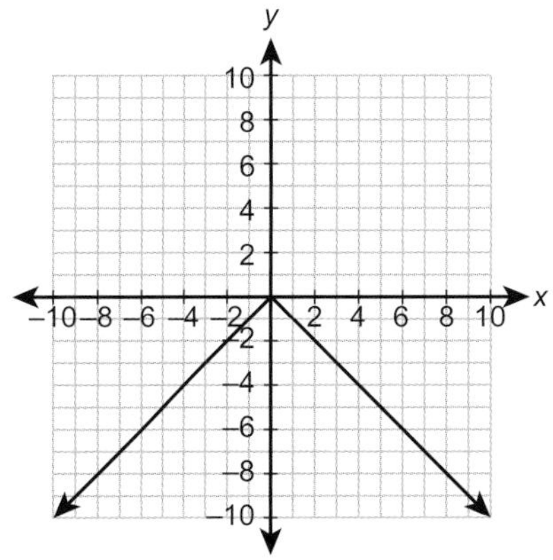

Pronunciation Guide

The table below provides sample words to explain the sounds associated with specific letters and letter combinations used in the respellings in this book. For example, *a* represents the short "a" sound in *cat*, while *ay* represents the long "a" sound in *day*.

Letter combinations are used to approximate certain more complex sounds. For example, in the respelling of *trapezoid*—TRA-puh-zoyd—the letters *uh* represent the vowel sound you hear in *shut* and *other*.

Vowels

a	short a: apple, cat
ay	long a: cane, day
e, eh	short e: hen, bed
ee	long e: feed, team
i, ih	short i: lip, active
iy	long i: try, might
ah	short o: hot, father
oh	long o: home, throw
uh	short u: shut, other
yoo	long u: union, cute

Letter Combinations

ch	chin, ancient
sh	show, mission
zh	vision, azure
th	thin, health
th	then, heather
ur	bird, further, word
us	bus, crust
or	court, formal
ehr	error, care
oo	cool, true, rule
ow	now, out
ou	look, pull, would
oy	coin, toy
aw	saw, maul, fall
ng	song, finger
air	Aristotle, barrister
ahr	cart, martyr

Consonants

b	butter, baby
d	dog, cradle
f	fun, phone
g	grade, angle
h	hat, ahead
j	judge, gorge
k	kite, car, black
l	lily, mile
m	mom, camel
n	next, candid
p	price, copper
r	rubber, free
s	small, circle, hassle
t	ton, pottery
v	vase, vivid
w	wall, away
y	yellow, kayak
z	zebra, haze

Glossary

abscissa (ab-SIH-suh) the x-coordinate; the first number in an ordered pair of numbers that designates the location of a point on the coordinate plane

absolute value the positive number of any pair of opposite nonzero real numbers; the absolute value of a number is the distance of its graph from the origin; the absolute value of 0 is 0; the absolute value of a number a is denoted by $|a|$

additive identity a number such that the sum of it and any given number is the given number; the additive identity for the set of real numbers is 0

additive inverse the opposite of a number; the sum of a pair of additive inverses is 0

argument a set of statements, called *premises*, that are used to reach a conclusion

Babylonian method a method that uses division and averages to approximate a square root

binomial a polynomial with exactly two terms

boundary line a line that divides the coordinate plane into two half-planes

coefficient the numerical factor of a term

coincident also *consistent dependent*; a system of linear equations where the graphs of the equations are the same line, resulting in infinite solutions

collinear (kuh-LIH-nee-uhr) lying on the same line

combined inequalities a number sentence that contains two inequalities combined by *and* or *or*

common factor a factor shared by two or more terms

completing the square to transform an expression of the form $x^2 + bx$ into a perfect square trinomial by adding the term $\left(\frac{b}{2}\right)^2$ to it

conclusion in an argument, the answer that is reached at the end of the statement of premises; in a conditional statement, the words following the word *then*

conditional statement a statement that can be written in if-then form in which the hypothesis implies the conclusion

conjecture an educated guess; a mathematical statement that has not been proven

conjugate binomials two binomials, $(a + b)$ and $(a - b)$, that have the same terms but opposite signs

conjunction a compound statement that has two statements connected by the word *and*; a conjunction is true only if both statements are true

consecutive integers integers that follow a sequence of increasing by 1

consistent system of equations having at least one solution in common (the system has a nonempty solution set)

consistent dependent system of equations also *coincident*; having the same graph and thus having infinite solutions

consistent independent system of equations having exactly one point of intersection, resulting in exactly one solution

constant a monomial consisting of a numeral only; a term with no variable factor

constant of variation the nonzero constant k used in direct, quadratic, and inverse variation

contradiction an equation that is true for no values of the variable; a statement that is inconsistent with itself or with the known truth

contrapositive a conditional statement that both switches and negates the hypothesis and conclusion of the original conditional statement; for example, if the conditional statement is "if a, then b," then the contrapositive statement is "if not b, then not a"

converse a conditional statement that switches the hypothesis and conclusion of the original conditional statement; for example, if the conditional statement is "if a, then b," then the converse statement is "if b, then a"

coordinate a number on a number line or axis, giving the location of a point

coordinate axis a reference line in a coordinate system; for example, the x-axis and y-axis in the coordinate plane

coordinate plane a plane in which the coordinates of a point are its distances from two intersecting perpendicular lines called *axes*

counterexample an example that shows that a conjecture, statement, or theory is not a valid generalization

counting number any whole number greater than zero $\{1, 2, 3, 4, \ldots\}$; the set of counting numbers is denoted by $\mathbb{N}$; also a *natural number*

deductive reasoning use of proven or accepted properties to reach a conclusion

degree of a monomial the sum of the exponents of the variables in the monomial

degree of a polynomial the degree of the monomial with the greatest degree in a polynomial

dependent variable the output variable for a function

direct linear variation a function where y varies directly with x following the equation $y = kx$, where k is a nonzero constant

discount a decrease in the price of an item

discriminant a value used to determine the number and types of roots for a given polynomial; for a quadratic of the form $ax^2 + bx + c$, the discriminant is $b^2 - 4ac$

disjunction a compound statement that has two statements connected by the word *or*; a disjunction is false only when both statements are false

domain in a relation, the set of allowable inputs

element a member of a set

empty set the set with no members

equation a number sentence that indicates that two expressions have the same value

equivalent equations equations with the same solution or solutions

equivalent inequalities inequalities with the same solutions

expression a group of mathematical symbols that represent a numerical value; most expressions contain numerals as well as operation signs or grouping symbols or a combination of these elements; an expression containing one or more variables is called a *variable expression* or *algebraic expression*

extremes in a proportion, the first and last numbers or variables; in $a{:}b = c{:}d$ or $\frac{a}{b} = \frac{c}{d}$, a and d are the extremes

factor a number, monomial, or polynomial used in an expression as a multiplicand

FOIL mnemonic used for the method to perform the distributive property when multiplying binomials: first-outer-inner-last

function a relation that assigns to each member of the domain exactly one member of the range

greatest common factor (GCF) the greatest integer that is a factor of two or more given integers

grouping symbols symbols (such as parentheses, brackets, and fraction bars) used to set apart an expression that should be simplified before other operations are performed

hypotenuse (hiy-PAH-tn-oos) the side opposite the right angle in a right triangle

hypothesis in an argument, the beginning statement; in a conditional statement, the words following the word *if*

identity an equation that is true for every value of the variable

improper fraction a fraction where the numerator is greater than or equal to the denominator

inconsistent system of equations having an empty solution set; the graph of an inconsistent system of linear equations is two parallel lines

independent variable the input variable for a function

inductive reasoning to reach a conclusion based on observations of patterns or past events

inequality a mathematical sentence that includes one of the symbols $<$, $>$, $\leq$, or $\geq$

integer any whole number, its opposite, or zero $\{\ldots, -3, -2, -1, 0, 1, 2, 3, \ldots\}$; the set of integers is denoted by $\mathbb{Z}$

interest the cost to borrow money

interest rate the percentage of the original amount of money that the interest is based on

inverse a conditional statement that negates the hypothesis and conclusion of the original conditional statement; if the conditional statement is "if a, then b," then the inverse statement is "if not a, then not b"

inverse variation a function where y varies inversely with x following the equation $y = \frac{k}{x}$, where k is a nonzero constant

irrational number any decimal number that cannot be written in the form $\frac{a}{b}$ for any integers a and b; in decimal form, all irrational numbers are nonterminating and nonrepeating; the set of irrational numbers is denoted by $\mathbb{I}$

least common denominator (LCD) the least common multiple of two or more denominators

least common multiple (LCM) the least number that is a common multiple of all numbers in a set

leg of a right triangle one of the two sides of a right triangle that form the right angle

like radicals two or more radical expressions having the same radicand

like terms terms that contain the same variables raised to the same powers

linear combination a method of solving a system of equations using addition or subtraction to eliminate a variable

markup an increase in the price of an item

means in a proportion, the second and third numbers or variables; in $a:b = c:d$ or $\frac{a}{b} = \frac{c}{d}$, b and c are the means

Mersenne number a number that is one less than a power of two

Mersenne prime a Mersenne number that is prime

mixed number a number consisting of both a whole number and a fraction or the opposite of such a number

monomial a number, a variable, or the product of a number and one or more variables

multiplicative identity a number such that the product of it and any given number is the given number; the multiplicative identity for the set of real numbers is 1

multiplicative inverse also the *reciprocal* of a number; the product of a pair of multiplicative inverses is 1; for example, the multiplicative inverse of 4 is $\frac{1}{4}$

natural number any whole number greater than zero $\{1, 2, 3, 4, \ldots\}$; the set of natural numbers is denoted by $\mathbb{N}$; also a *counting number*

nonrepeating decimal a decimal that does not have a repeating pattern of nonzero digits

nonterminating decimal a decimal that continues without end; however many digits there are to the right of the decimal point in a nonterminating decimal, there are always more nonzero digits farther to the right

n*th root of *a any number x such that $x^n = a$ for a natural number $n > 1$

number line a line that has equally spaced intervals labeled with coordinates

numerical expression an expression that names a particular number; for example, the numerical expression $10 + 2$ names the number 12

open sentence an equation or inequality that contains one or more variables

order of operations mathematical order that should be followed to simplify an expression when there is more than one operation

ordered pair a pair of numbers in which the first number is the x-coordinate and the second number is the y-coordinate of the location of a point

ordinate (OR-duh-nuht) the y-coordinate; the second number in an ordered pair of numbers that designates the location of a point on the coordinate plane

origin the point on a coordinate plane where the x-axis and y-axis intersect, with coordinates (0, 0); on a number line, the point with coordinate 0

parabola the graph of a quadratic function

parallel lines coplanar lines that never intersect

percent a ratio that compares a number to 100

perfect cube a number whose cube root is rational

perfect square a number whose square root is rational; a polynomial that is the product of two polynomials

perpendicular lines lines that meet at right angles

point-slope form (of a linear equation) an equation of a line that passes through the points (x_1, y_1) and has a slope of m is $y - y_1 = m(x - x_1)$

polynomial a monomial or the sum or difference of two or more monomials

postulate a mathematical statement that is understood to be true without proof; also called an *axiom*

premise a statement that is presumed to be true in the course of a logical argument

prime number an integer greater than 1 that has exactly two factors, the number itself and 1

prime polynomial a polynomial that cannot be factored

principal money that earns interest at a given rate over time

proof a clear, logical structure of reasoning that begins from accepted ideas and proceeds through logic to reach a conclusion

proper fraction a fraction where the numerator is less than the denominator

proportion an equation stating that two ratios are equal

Pythagorean theorem (puh-tha-guh-REE-uhn) the mathematical relationship between side lengths in a triangle with one 90° angle that states the sum of the squares of the lengths of the two legs of the triangle is equal to the square of the length of the hypotenuse, $a^2 + b^2 = c^2$

quadrant one of the four regions into which the coordinate axes separate the coordinate plane

quadratic formula a formula for finding the solutions of a quadratic equation in the form $ax^2 + bx + c = 0$, where a is not zero; $x = \frac{-b \pm \sqrt{b^2 - 4ac}}{2a}$

quadratic variation a function defined by an equation of the form $y = kx^2$, where k is a nonzero constant

radicand an expression under a radical sign

range in a relation, the set of possible outputs

rate of change the ratio of a change in one quantity to a change in a second quantity

ratio a comparison of two quantities using division

rational number any number that can be expressed as a ratio $\frac{a}{b}$, where a and b are integers and $b \neq 0$; the set of rational numbers is represented by $\mathbb{Q}$

rationalizing a denominator writing an equivalent rational expression that does not have a radical in the denominator

rational expression a quotient of two algebraic expressions

real number any number that can be written as a decimal; the set of real numbers is denoted by $\mathbb{R}$

reciprocal also *multiplicative inverse*; a number that when multiplied by the number gives the multiplicative identity 1

relation any set of ordered pairs

relatively prime having no common factors other than 1

repeating decimal a decimal that does not end but shows a repeating pattern of nonzero digits after the decimal point; the block of digits that repeat is represented with an overbar

replacement set a set of values allowable as a solution to an open sentence

right triangle a triangle with a right angle

rise the distance between two points on a vertical line or a line parallel to the y-axis on a coordinate grid

root of a function for a function $f(x)$, any value of the variable x that makes $f(x) = 0$ a true statement

run the distance between two points on a horizontal line or a line parallel to the x-axis on a coordinate grid

set a collection of objects

simple interest interest earned at a fixed percent of the initial deposit

simplified radical form a radical expression that contains no radicands with factors that are perfect squares other than 1

slope a number that describes the steepness of a line, computed as the ratio of the change in the y-coordinates to the change in the x-coordinates when moving from one point on a line to another point on the same line

slope-intercept form (of a linear equation) an equation of the form $y = mx + b$, where m is the slope of the line and b is the y-intercept

solution a value for the variable that makes the equation or open sentence a true statement

solve to find all the solutions for an equation

solution set the elements of the replacement set that make an open sentence true

specific equation an equation that applies a general equation to a problem by substituting values for variables; for example, if $y = kx$ is the general equation, then $y = 2x$ would be the specific equation for some problem

square root the factor of a number that when multiplied by itself results in the number

standard form (of a linear equation) an equation of the form $Ax + By = C$, where A, B, and C are integers and A and B are not both zero

standard form of a polynomial the arrangement of a polynomial expression where the monomials are listed from the highest to the lowest power and no two terms are like terms

substitution method a method used to solve a system of equations by replacing one variable in one of the equations to solve in terms of another variable

syllogism a logical argument that always contains two premises and a conclusion; syllogisms have the following form: If a, then b. If b, then c. Therefore, if a, then c.

system of linear equations two or more linear equations with the same variables

term part of an expression that is added or subtracted

terminating decimal decimal with a finite number of nonzero digits

theorem a mathematical statement that has been or is to be proven on the basis of established definitions and properties

transformation a one-to-one correspondence between two sets of points

translation the sliding of a figure in a straight path

trinomial a polynomial with three terms

valid argument an argument where the premises are all true, then the conclusion must also be true

variable a symbol that represents a value

variable expression a combination of variables, numbers, and operations; also *algebraic expression*

vertical line test defines if a relation is a function by verifying that there is only one y value for every x value by sliding a vertical line across the function from left to right; if a vertical line can hit the graph at more than one point, then the relation is not a function

whole number any number that is a natural number or zero $\{0, 1, 2, 3, 4, \ldots\}$; the set of whole numbers is denoted by $\mathbb{W}$

***x*-axis** the horizontal number line in the coordinate plane

***x*-coordinate** the first number in an ordered pair of numbers that designates the location of a point on the coordinate plane; also called *abscissa* (ab-SIH-suh)

***x*-intercept** the x-coordinate of a point where a graph intersects the x-axis

***y*-axis** the vertical number line in a coordinate plane

***y*-coordinate** the second number in an ordered pair of numbers that designates the location of a point on the coordinate plane; also called *ordinate* (OR-duh-nuht)

***y*-intercept** the y-coordinate of a point where a graph intersects the y-axis

zero of a function a solution to the equation $f(x) = 0$; the x-intercepts of the graph of the function

Symbols

$\mid$	such that
$\in$	is an element of
$\varnothing$ or $\{\ \}$	null or empty set
$\cap$	intersection
$\cup$	union
$\sqrt{x}$	principal square root of x
$\sqrt[n]{x}$	nth root of x
$\mathbb{N}$	the set of natural numbers
$\mathbb{W}$	the set of whole numbers
$\mathbb{Z}$	the set of integers
$\mathbb{Q}$	the set of rational numbers
$\mathbb{I}$	the set of irrational numbers
$\mathbb{R}$	the set of real numbers
π	pi
( )	parentheses
[ ]	brackets
{ }	braces
$\approx$	is approximately equal to
$=$	is equal to
$\neq$	is not equal to
$<$	is less than
$>$	is greater than
$\leq$	is less than or equal to
$\geq$	is greater than or equal to
$f(x)$	f of x; f is a function of x
$\lvert x\rvert$	absolute value of x
$-a$	the opposite of a
$\{\ldots\}$	description or list of all elements in a set; roster notation
$\{x\mid \text{condition}\}$	the set of all x that satisfy the given condition; set-builder notation
%	percent
$\overline{}$	placed over a block of digits in a decimal to show that the digits repeat
$\pm$	plus or minus
$a:b$	ratio of a to b
$^\circ$	degree

Properties

Real Number Properties

Let a, b, and c be any real numbers.

Addition Property of Equality	If $a = b$, then $a + c = b + c$ and $c + a = c + b$.	
Addition Property: Addends with Like Signs	For all $a > 0$ and $b > 0$, $a + b = \|a\| + \|b\|$. For all $a < 0$ and $b < 0$, $a + b = -(\|a\| + \|b\|)$.	
Addition Property: Addends with Unlike Signs	For all $a > 0$ and $b < 0$, If $\|a\| > \|b\|$, then $a + b = \|a\| - \|b\|$. If $\|a\| < \|b\|$, then $a + b = -(\|b\| - \|a\|)$.	
Subtraction Property of Equality	If $a = b$, then $a - c = b - c$.	
Substitution Property of Equality	If $a = b$, then a may be replaced with b in any expression or equation.	
Multiplication Property of Equality	If $a = b$, then $c \cdot a = c \cdot b$ and $a \cdot c = b \cdot c$.	
Division Property of Equality	If $a = b$ and $c \neq 0$ then $\frac{a}{c} = \frac{b}{c}$.	
Reflexive Property of Equality	$a = a$	
Symmetric Property of Equality	If $a = b$, then $b = a$.	
Transitive Property of Equality	If $a = b$ and $b = c$, then $a = c$.	
Closure Property	For all $a, b \in$ S, and an operation #, then $a \# b \in S$.	
Zero Product Property	$ab = 0$ if and only if $a = 0$ or $b = 0$.	
	Addition	**Multiplication**
Commutative Properties	$a + b = b + a$	$a \cdot b = b \cdot a$
Associative Properties	$(a + b) + c = a + (b + c)$	$(a \cdot b) \cdot c = a \cdot (b \cdot c)$
Inverse Properties	$a + (-a) = 0$ and $(-a) + a = 0$	$a \cdot \frac{1}{a} = 1$ and $\frac{1}{a} \cdot a = 1, a \neq 0$
Identity Properties	$a + 0 = a$ and $0 + a = a$	$a \cdot 1 = a$ and $1 \cdot a = a$
Distributive Property	$a(b + c) = ab + ac$	

Sets of Numbers

Natural Numbers	the counting numbers $\{1, 2, 3, 4, \ldots\}$; denoted by $\mathbb{N}$
Whole Numbers	the set of natural numbers and zero $\{0, 1, 2, 3, 4, \ldots\}$; denoted by $\mathbb{W}$
Integers	the set of natural numbers, their opposites, and zero $\{\ldots -3, -2, -1, 0, 1, 2, 3, \ldots\}$; denoted by $\mathbb{Z}$
Real Numbers	the set of numbers that can be written as decimals; denoted by $\mathbb{R}$
Rational Numbers	any number that can be expressed as a ratio $\frac{a}{b}$, where a and b are integers and $b \neq 0$; denoted by $\mathbb{Q}$
Irrational Numbers	a decimal number that can*not* be written in the form $\frac{a}{b}$, for any integers a and b; denoted by $\mathbb{I}$

Properties of Absolute Value Equations and Inequalities

If $|x| = a$ for some positive number a, then $x = a$ *or* $x = -a$.

If $|x| > a$ for some positive number a, then $x > a$ *or* $x < -a$.

If $|x| \geq a$ for some positive number a, then $x \geq a$ *or* $x \leq -a$.

If $|x| < a$ for some positive number a, then $x < a$ *and* $x > -a$.

If $|x| \leq a$ for some positive number a, then $x \leq a$ *and* $x \geq -a$.

Properties of Exponents

Let a and b be nonzero real numbers. Let m and n be integers.

If n is a positive integer, $a^n = a \cdot a \cdot a \cdot \ldots \cdot a$ (n factors).

Name of Property	**Statement of Property**
Zero Exponent Property	$a^0 = 1, a \neq 0$
Negative Exponent Property	$a^{-m} = \frac{1}{a^m}, a \neq 0$
Product of Powers Property	$a^m \cdot a^n = a^{m+n}$
Power of a Power Property	$(a^m)^n = a^{mn}$
Power of a Product Property	$(ab)^m = a^m b^m$
Quotient of Powers Property	$\frac{a^m}{a^n} = a^{m-n}, a \neq 0$
Power of a Quotient Property	$\left(\frac{a}{b}\right)^m = \frac{a^m}{b^m}, b \neq 0$

Square Root Property

For nonnegative values of a if $x^2 = a$, then $x = \pm\sqrt{a}$.

Properties of Radicals

Let a and b be real numbers.

For nonnegative values of m, n, and p, if $m < n < p$, then $\sqrt{m} < \sqrt{n} < \sqrt{p}$.

If b is a perfect nth power, then b can be factored so that the exponent on each factor is n.

If b is not a perfect nth power, then the nth root of b is irrational.

Real *n*th roots of *b*		
Values for *b*	***n* is even**	***n* is odd**
$b > 0$	two real roots (one positive and one negative)	one real root
$b < 0$	no real roots	one real root
$b = 0$	one real root, $\sqrt[n]{0} = 0$	
Any real number *b*	$\sqrt[n]{b^n} = \lvert b \rvert$	$\sqrt[n]{b^n} = b$

Other radical properties	
Product Property of Radicals	$\sqrt[n]{ab} = \sqrt[n]{a} \cdot \sqrt[n]{b}$ and $\sqrt[n]{a} \cdot \sqrt[n]{b} = \sqrt[n]{ab}$, when n is an integer greater than 1
Quotient Property of Radicals	$\sqrt[n]{\frac{a}{b}} = \frac{\sqrt[n]{a}}{\sqrt[n]{b}}$

For all a when n is odd, and for all nonnegative a when n is even, $a^{\frac{1}{n}} = \sqrt[n]{a}$ and $a^{\frac{m}{n}} = \sqrt[n]{a^m} = (\sqrt[n]{a})^m$, where m and n are integers greater than or equal to 1.

Reciprocal Properties

Reciprocal Property of Multiplication For any nonzero real number a, $a \cdot \frac{1}{a} = 1$.

For all nonzero real numbers a and b, the reciprocal of $\frac{a}{b}$ is $\frac{b}{a}$.

For any nonzero real number a, $\frac{1}{-a} = \frac{-1}{a} = -\frac{1}{a}$.

For all nonzero real numbers a and b, $\frac{1}{ab} = \frac{1}{a} \cdot \frac{1}{b}$.

Division Properties

For any real number a and nonzero real number b, $a \div b = a \cdot \frac{1}{b}$.

For all real numbers a and b and nonzero real number c, $\frac{a+b}{c} = \frac{a}{c} + \frac{b}{c}$.

For all $a > 0$ and $b > 0$, $a \div b > 0$.

For all $a < 0$ and $b < 0$, $a \div b > 0$.

For all $a < 0$ and $b > 0$, $a \div b < 0$.

Properties of Order

Comparison Property of Order	If $a > b$, then $b < a$. If $a < b$, then $b > a$.
Transitive Property of Order	If $a > b$ and $b > c$, then $a > c$. If $a < b$ and $b < c$, then $a < c$.
Addition Property of Order	If $a > b$, then $a + c > b + c$. If $a < b$, then $a + c < b + c$.
Subtraction Property of Order	If $a > b$, then $a - c > b - c$. If $a < b$, then $a - c < b - c$.
Multiplication Property of Order, Positive Multiplier	If $a > b$ and $c > 0$, then $ca > cb$ and $ac > bc$. If $a < b$ and $c > 0$, then $ca < cb$ and $ac < bc$.
Multiplication Property of Order, Negative Multiplier	If $a > b$ and $c < 0$, then $ca < cb$ and $ac < bc$. If $a < b$ and $c < 0$, then $ca > cb$ and $ac > bc$.
Division Property of Order, Positive Multiplier	If $a > b$ and $c > 0$, then $\frac{a}{c} > \frac{b}{c}$. If $a < b$ and $c > 0$, then $\frac{a}{c} < \frac{b}{c}$.
Division Property of Order, Negative Multiplier	If $a > b$ and $c < 0$, then $\frac{a}{c} < \frac{b}{c}$. If $a < b$ and $c < 0$, then $\frac{a}{c} > \frac{b}{c}$.

Comparison Property of Rational Numbers

For positive integers a and c and nonzero integers b and d,

$\frac{a}{b} > \frac{c}{d}$ if and only if $ad > bc$;

$\frac{a}{b} < \frac{c}{d}$ if and only if $ad < bc$;

$\frac{a}{b} = \frac{c}{d}$ if and only if $ad = bc$.

Properties of Proportions

Means-Extremes Product Property	If $\frac{a}{b} = \frac{c}{d}$, then $ad = bc$, given that b and d are not 0.
Reciprocal Property	If $\frac{a}{b} = \frac{c}{d}$, then $\frac{b}{a} = \frac{d}{c}$, given that a, b, c, and d are not 0.
Exchange Property	If $\frac{a}{b} = \frac{c}{d}$, then $\frac{a}{c} = \frac{b}{d}$, given that b, c, and d are not 0.
Add-One Property	If $\frac{a}{b} = \frac{c}{d}$, then $\frac{a+b}{b} = \frac{c+d}{d}$, given that b and d are not 0.

Line Properties

Parallel Lines

If two lines have the same slope, then the lines are parallel.

If two lines are parallel, then the lines have the same slope.

Perpendicular Lines

If two lines have slopes that are negative reciprocals, then the lines are perpendicular.

If two lines are perpendicular, then their slopes are negative reciprocals.

Translations

If (x, y) is translated h units to the right, then $(x, y) \rightarrow (x + h, y)$.

If (x, y) is translated h units to the left, then $(x, y) \rightarrow (x - h, y)$.

If (x, y) is translated k units up, then $(x, y) \rightarrow (x, y + k)$.

If (x, y) is translated k units down, then $(x, y) \rightarrow (x, y - k)$.

Triangles

Pythagorean Theorem In a right triangle, the sum of the squares of the lengths of the legs equals the square of the length of the hypotenuse. $a^2 + b^2 = c^2$

Converse of the Pythagorean Theorem If the sum of the squares of the lengths of the shorter sides of a triangle equals the square of the length of the longest side, then the triangle is a right triangle.

For a triangle with side lengths of a, b, and c, where $c > a$ and $c > b$,

if $c^2 > a^2 + b^2$, then the angle opposite side c has a measure greater than 90°;

if $c^2 < a^2 + b^2$, then the angle opposite side c has a measure less than 90°.

Polynomials

Perfect Square Trinomial Patterns $a^2 + 2ab + b^2 = (a + b)^2$

$a^2 - 2ab + b^2 = (a - b)^2$

Difference of Squares Patterns $a^2 - b^2 = (a + b)(a - b)$

Conditional Statements

a: hypothesis, b: conclusion

Conditional	If *a*, then *b*.
Converse	If b, then a.
Inverse	If *not* a, then *not* b.
Contrapositive	If *not* b, then *not* a.

Formulary

Geometric Formulas

Circle

Circumference $C = \pi d = 2\pi r$

Area $A = \pi r^2$

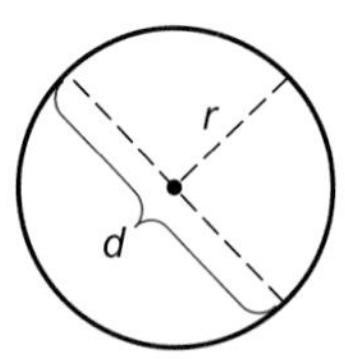

Cone

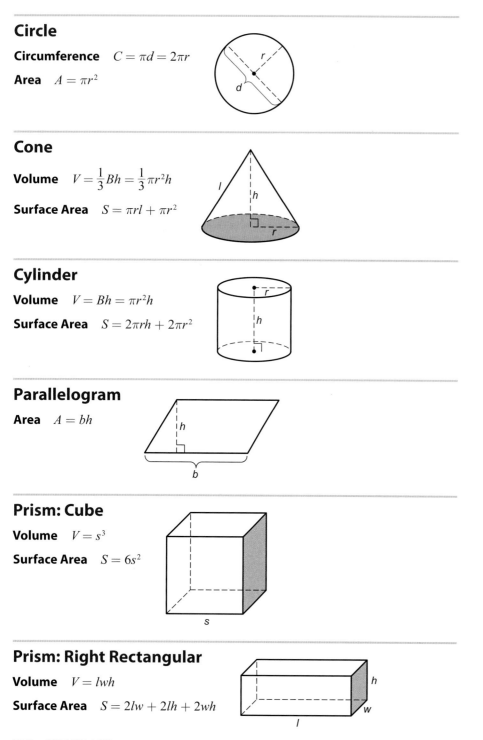

Volume $V = \frac{1}{3}Bh = \frac{1}{3}\pi r^2 h$

Surface Area $S = \pi rl + \pi r^2$

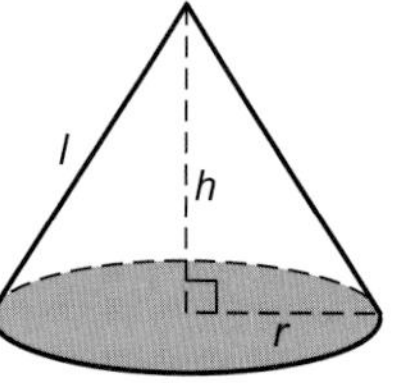

Cylinder

Volume $V = Bh = \pi r^2 h$

Surface Area $S = 2\pi rh + 2\pi r^2$

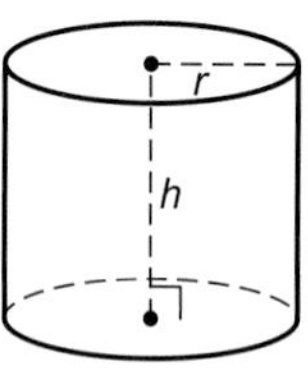

Parallelogram

Area $A = bh$

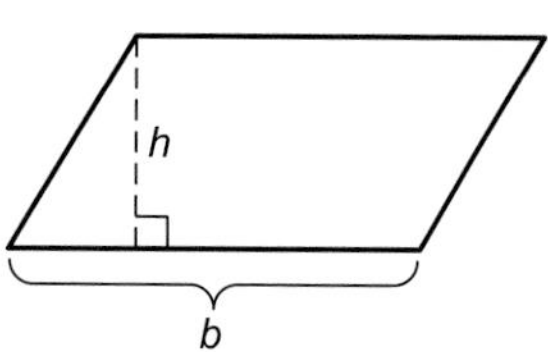

Prism: Cube

Volume $V = s^3$

Surface Area $S = 6s^2$

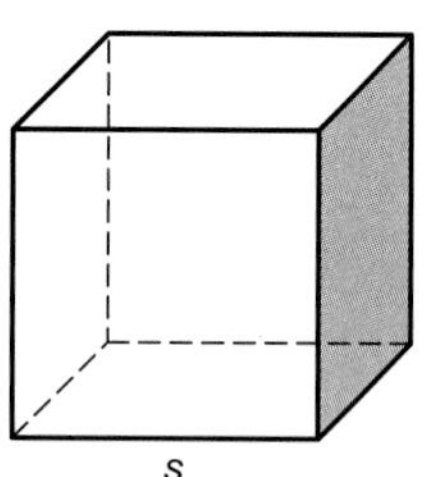

Prism: Right Rectangular

Volume $V = lwh$

Surface Area $S = 2lw + 2lh + 2wh$

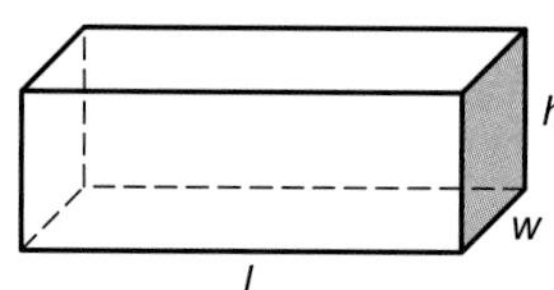

Rectangle

Area $A = lw$

Perimeter $P = 2l + 2w$

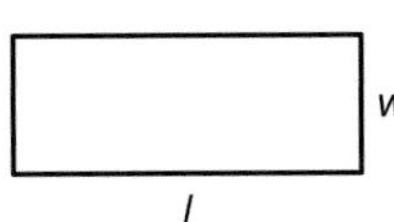

Sphere

Volume $V = \frac{4}{3}\pi r^3$

Surface Area $S = 4\pi r^2$

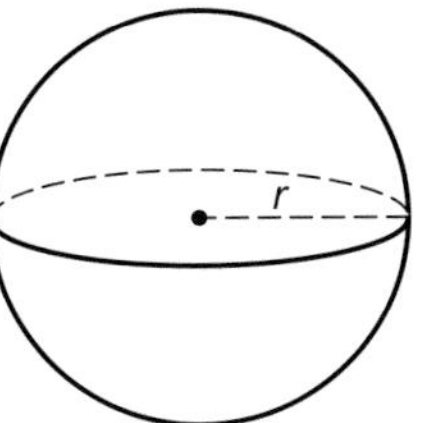

Square

Area $A = s^2$

Perimeter $P = 4s$

Trapezoid

Area $A = \frac{1}{2}h(b_1 + b_2)$

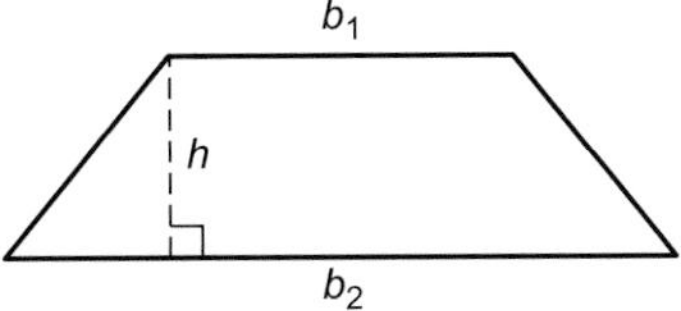

Triangle: General

Area $A = \frac{1}{2}bh$

Perimeter $a + b + c$

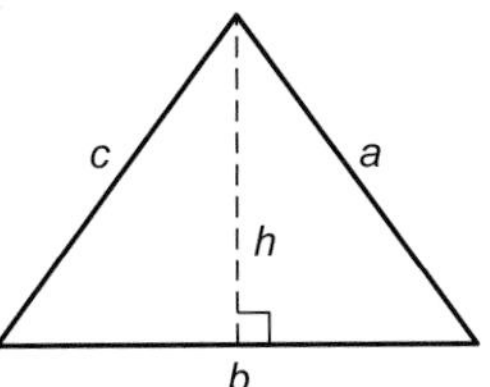

Triangle: Right

Pythagorean Theorem $a^2 + b^2 = c^2$

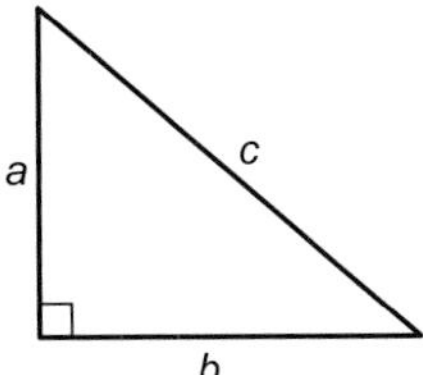

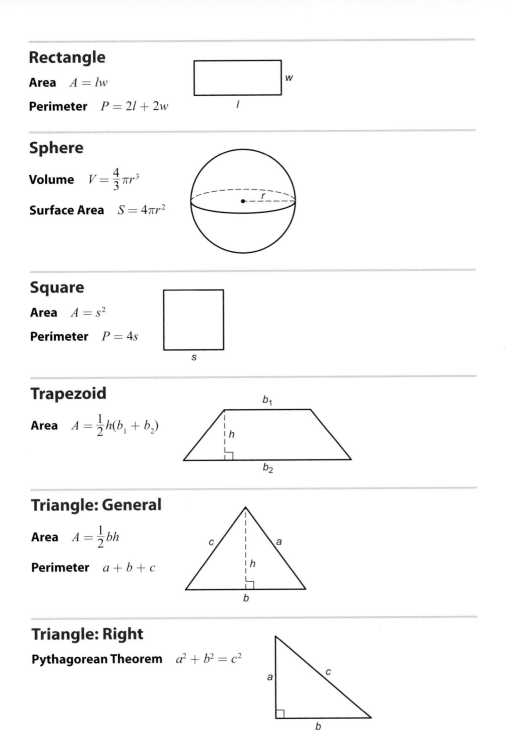

Line

Slope $m = \frac{\text{rise}}{\text{run}} = \frac{\text{vertical change}}{\text{horizontal change}} = \frac{y_2 - y_1}{x_2 - x_1}$

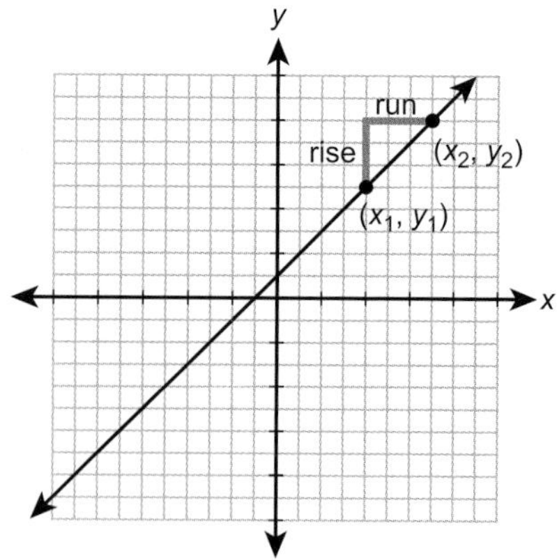

Linear Equation: standard form $Ax + By = C$

Linear Equation: slope-intercept form $y = mx + b$

Linear Equation: point-slope form $y - y_1 = m(x - x_1)$

Translations

Shift Left	$(x, y) \rightarrow (x - h, y)$
Shift Right	$(x, y) \rightarrow (x + h, y)$
Shift Up	$(x, y) \rightarrow (x, y + k)$
Shift Down	$(x, y) \rightarrow (x, y - k)$

Variation

Direct Linear Variation $f(x) = kx$ or $y = kx$

Inverse Variation $f(x) = \frac{k}{x}$ or $y = \frac{k}{x}$

Quadratic Variation $f(x) = kx^2$ or $y = kx^2$

Other Formulas

Completing the square add $\left(\frac{b}{2a}\right)^2$ to both sides of the equation $ax^2 + bx = c$

Discriminant $b^2 - 4ac$ given the equation $ax^2 + bx + c = 0$

Quadratic Formula $x = \frac{-b \pm \sqrt{b^2 - 4ac}}{2a}$ given the equation $ax^2 + bx + c = 0$, where $a \neq 0$

Percent of Change percent of change $= \frac{\text{amount of change}}{\text{original amount}}$

Projectile Motion The height of an object, *in meters*, after t seconds, with initial vertical velocity v_0 and initial height h_0, is given by

$$h(t) = -4.9t^2 + v_0t + h_0.$$

The height of an object, *in feet*, after t seconds, with initial vertical velocity v_0 and initial height h_0, is given by

$$h(t) = -16t^2 + v_0t + h_0.$$

Simple Interest: $I = Prt$, where I is the amount of interest, P is the principal, r is the interest rate, and t is the time in years.

Sample Graphs

Linear Function

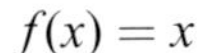

$f(x) = x$

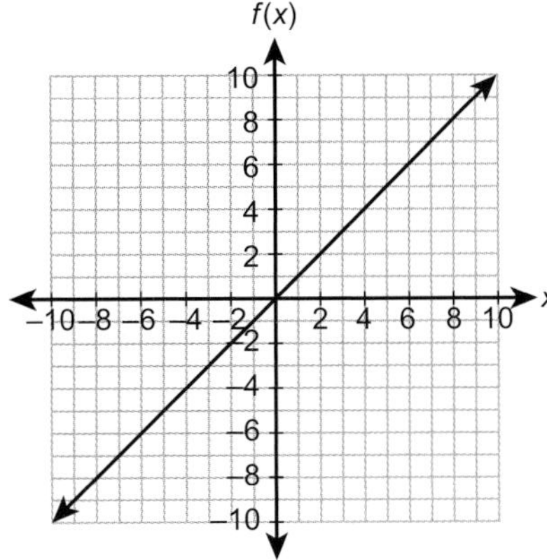

Quadratic Function

$f(x) = x^2$

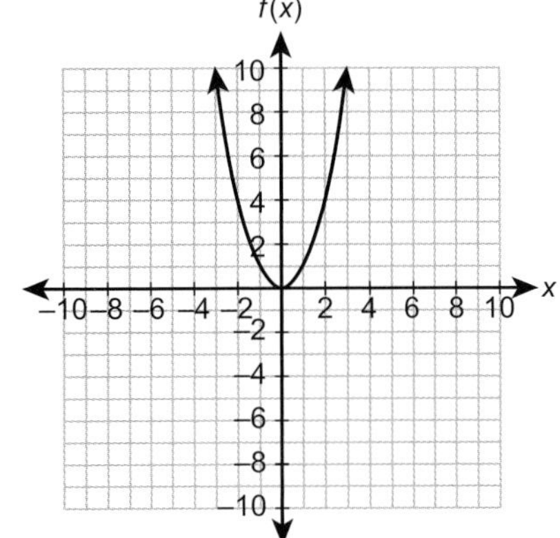

Absolute Value Function

$f(x) = |x|$

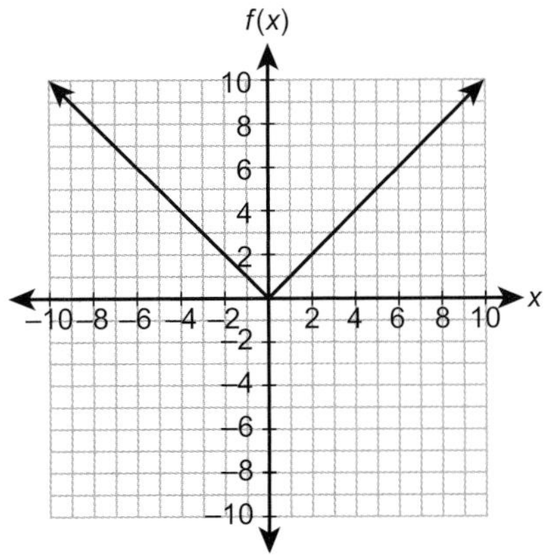

System of Inequalities

$f(x) \leq x$

$f(x) < 3$

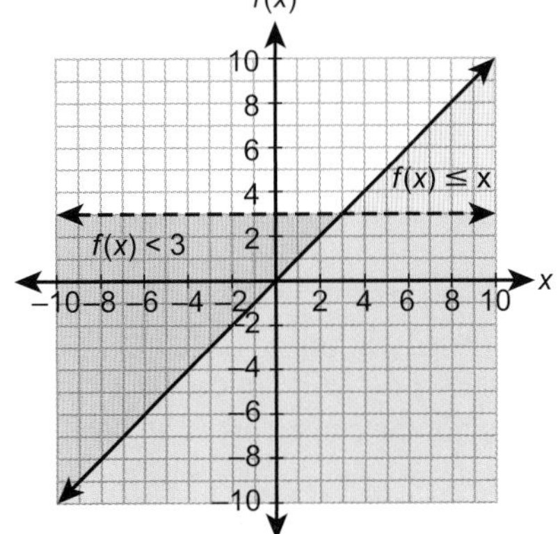

Selected Answers

UNIT 1 Algebra Basics

Pages 7–8

1. 28 **3.** 21 **5.** 48 **7.** 3 **9.** 146 **11.** 0.088 **13.** $0.1\overline{6}$ **15.** 7 **17.** 10 **19.** 20 **21.** 1 **23.** 3 **25.** $\frac{4}{7}$
27. A. $(8 + 9^2 - 7) \cdot 10$ **B.** $8 + (9^2 - 7) \cdot 10$
29. A. $720 \div [(2 + 7) \cdot 2^3]$ **B.** $(720 \div 2 + 7) \cdot 2^3$
31. $2 \cdot 3 + 7^3 - 18 \div 9$

Pages 11–12

1. 6 **3.** 0.5 **5.** 16 **7.** $0.\overline{3}$ **9.** 313 **11.** $1\frac{13}{14}$ **13.** $5x^2$, $3y$ **15.** coefficient: $\frac{2}{3}$; factors: $\frac{2}{3}$, x **17.** coefficient: $\frac{3}{7}$; factors: $\frac{3}{7}$, x, y **19.** terms: z^3, $6x$, 4; constant: 4 **21.** terms: $\frac{3m}{2n}$, 12; constant: 12 **23.** terms: $\frac{47}{3x}$, $2y$, $\frac{19}{51}$; constant: $\frac{19}{51}$
25. A. 72 centimeters **B.** 315 square centimeters
27. 153 square feet **29.** 1925 miles

Pages 15–17

1. $12n$ **3.** $4(5 + n)$ **5.** $n - 7$ **7.** $\frac{n}{10}$ **9.** CDs: c; DVDs: $c - 12$ **11.** trucks: t; cars: $109 - t$ **13.** afternoon distance: a; morning distance: $2a - 25$ **15.** men: m; women: $4 + m$ **17. A.** 24; **B.** 72; **C.** $12x$ **19. A.** 300; **B.** 420; **C.** $120y$ **21.** $1000 \cdot \frac{5}{n} = \frac{5000}{n}$ **23. A.** $10n$ **B.** 30 **C.** $4n^2$ **D.** 36 square units **25. A.** $7b$ **B.** 63 square centimeters **27. A.** $2n + 17$ **B.** 29 **29. A.** $35t$ **B.** 280 miles

Page 20

1. $\neq$ **3.** $=$ **5.** $\neq$ **7.** $=$ **9.** $\neq$ **11.** $=$ **13.** True. **15.** True. **17.** True. **19.** False. **21.** False. **23.** Yes, they are charged the same. **25.** No, a car will not cost the same at both agencies. **27.** No, it is not the same cost. **29.** Yes, they received the same score.

Pages 23–24

1. $4n + 3 = 12$ **3.** $\frac{n}{12} = 8 + n$ **5.** $n + 6 = 7n$ **7.** $n - 7 = 2$ **9.** $6n - 12 = 3n$ **11.** 9 **13.** 9 **15.** 40 **17.** 6 **19.** $\frac{9}{8}$ **21.** $D = 55t$ **23.** $A = 3h$ **25.** $W = 9.8m$ **27.** $A = s^2$ **29. A.** $A = 11h$ **B.** 55 square units

Pages 27–28

1. $\{4\}$ **3.** $\varnothing$ **5.** $\{-1, 1\}$ **7.** $\{4\}$ **9.** $\{2\}$ **11.** $\{1\}$ **13.** $\{15\}$ **15.** $\{11, 12, 13, 14\}$ **17.** $\{-4\}$ **19.** $\{3\}$ **21.** $\{9\}$ **23.** $\{3.5\}$ **25.** $\{25\}$ **27.** $\{20\}$ **29.** $\{0.375\}$

Pages 31–33

1. A. Let g represent the number of girls and b represent the number of boys. **B.** $b = g + 10$ **C.** $b = 24$ **D.** There are 24 boys. **3. A.** Let A represent area, P represent perimeter, l represent length, and w represent width. **B.** $A = lw$, $P = 2l + 2w$ **C.** $P = 48$ **D.** The perimeter of the rectangle is 48 units. **5. A.** Let d represent distance, r represent rate, and t represent time. **B.** $d = rt$ **C.** $t = 4$ **D.** It took 4 hours to travel the 200-mile distance. **7. A.** The variables are defined. **B.** $I = prt$ **C.** $p = 300$ **D.** Amida deposited \$300. **9. A.** Let P represent the perimeter and s represent the length of a side. **B.** $P = 3s$ **C.** $s = 13$ **D.** Each side measures 13 centimeters. **11. A.** Let d represent distance, r represent rate, and t represent time. **B.** $d = rt$ **C.** $d = 175$ **D.** Zahira drove 175 miles. **13. A.** Let z represent the number of students in Ms. Zambia's class and p represent the number of students in Mr. Powan's class. **B.** $z = p + 3$ **C.** $z = 25$ **D.** There are 25 students in Ms. Zambia's class. **15. A.** Let b represent the number of hours he plays baseball and s represent the number of hours he plays soccer. **B.** $b = 3s$ **C.** $b = 18$ **D.** Benoit plays baseball 18 hours per week. **17. A.** Let m represent the measure each angle. **B.** $2m = 110$ **C.** $m = 55$ **D.** Each angle measures 55°. **19. A.** Let d represent distance, r represent rate, and t represent time. **B.** $d = rt$ **C.** $t = 0.5$ **D.** Sarabi drove for a half hour. **21. A.** Let g represent Gita's age and let a represent Ajeet's age. **B.** $g = 3a$ **C.** $12 = a$ **D.** Ajeet is 12 years old. **23. A.** The variables are defined. **B.** $C = \frac{5}{9}(F - 32)$ **C.** $C \approx 26.7$ **D.** The Celsius temperature is approximately 26.7°. **25. A.** Let t represent total amount earned, a represent the amount he earns per hour, and h represent the hours worked. **B.** $t = ha$ **C.** $t = 105$ **D.** Jamal earned \$105. **27. A.** Let P represent perimeter, l represent length, and w represent width. **B.** $P = 8w$ **C.** $P = 40$ **D.** The amount of fencing needed to enclose the garden is 40 feet. **29. A.** Let b represent the number of bills, q represent the number of quarters, n represent the number of nickels, and c represent the other coins Cerise has. **B.** $5.67 = 1.00b + 0.25q + 0.05n + c$ **C.** $c = 0.02$ **D.** Since the value of the other coins Cerise has is \$0.02, she also has pennies.

UNIT 2 Properties of Real Numbers

Pages 40–41

1. A: -5, B: -2, C: 5, D: 9 **3.** A: -2, B: $-1\frac{1}{10}$, C: $\frac{3}{10}$, D: 1.25 **5.** A: -10, B: -7, C: 6, D: 15 **7.** A: -9, B: -3, C: 4, D: 12

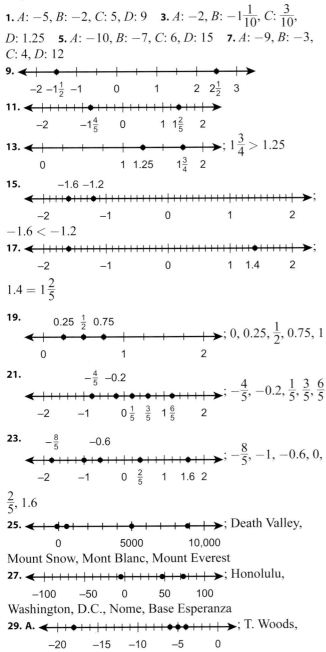

9. 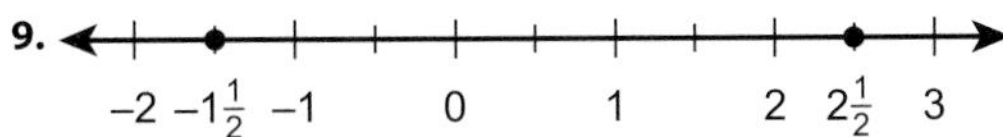

11.
−2 $-1\frac{4}{5}$ 0 1 $1\frac{2}{5}$ 2

13. ; $1\frac{3}{4} > 1.25$
0 1 1.25 $1\frac{3}{4}$ 2

15. −1.6 −1.2 ;
−2 −1 0 1 2
$-1.6 < -1.2$

17. ;
−2 −1 0 1 1.4 2
$1.4 = 1\frac{2}{5}$

19. 0.25 $\frac{1}{2}$ 0.75 ; 0, 0.25, $\frac{1}{2}$, 0.75, 1
0 1 2

21. $-\frac{4}{5}$ −0.2 ; $-\frac{4}{5}$, -0.2, $\frac{1}{5}$, $\frac{3}{5}$, $\frac{6}{5}$
−2 −1 0 $\frac{1}{5}$ $\frac{3}{5}$ 1 $\frac{6}{5}$ 2

23. $-\frac{8}{5}$ −0.6 ; $-\frac{8}{5}$, -1, -0.6, 0,
−2 −1 0 $\frac{2}{5}$ 1 1.6 2
$\frac{2}{5}$, 1.6

25. ; Death Valley,
0 5000 10,000
Mount Snow, Mont Blanc, Mount Everest

27. ; Honolulu,
−100 −50 0 50 100
Washington, D.C., Nome, Base Esperanza

29. A. ; T. Woods,
−20 −15 −10 −5 0
T. Kite, T. Tolles, and T. Watson **B.** Answers will vary. Sample answer: The 2007 tournament was more competitive since T. Woods dominated the score board in the 1997 tournament.

Pages 45–47

1. {3, 5, 7, 9, 11, 13} **3.** {6, 8, 10, 12, ...} **5.** {3, 5, 7, 9, 11, 13, 15, 17, 19} **7.** {30, 32} **9.** {10, 15, 20, 25, 30, 35, 40, 45, 50} **11.** 27: natural numbers, whole numbers, integers, real numbers; 2.6, $\frac{7}{10}$, $\frac{1}{5}$: real numbers; $-\frac{24}{12}$: integers, real numbers **13.** $\frac{5}{15}$, 0.001, -1.4: real numbers; -13: integers, real numbers; $\frac{30}{3} = 10$: natural numbers, whole numbers, integers, real numbers **15. A.** {1, 3, 5, 6, 7, 8, 9, 10, 11} **B.** {3, 9} **C.** {3, 5, 6, 7, 8, 9, 10, 12} **17. A.** {2, 4}; **B.** { } **C.** {−4, −3, −2, −1, 0, 2, 4, 6, 8, 10} **19. A.** {−1, 0, 1, 2, 3, 4, 6, 8, 10} **B.** {−1, 0} **C.** {6} **21. A.** {4, 8} **B.** { } **C.** {−5, −3, −1, 1, 3, 4, 5, 8, 9, 12, 15, 16} **23. A.** {3} **B.** {−5, −3, −1, 1, 2, 3, 4, 5, 6, 8, 9, 10, 12, 15} **C.** { } **25. A.** {J. Adams}; The intersection represents the president liked by Bo and Jericho. **B.** No **C.** intersection **27. A.** {Billings, Clove, Eddger, Humphrey, Ibsen, Klopfer, Riser, Vaughn, Williams} **B.** The union represents the top players that play lacrosse or soccer. **C.** {Clove, Humphrey, Ibsen, Klopfer, Vaughn} **D.** ∩ **29.** Honor Role: Morgan; Service: Fuller, Lowe, Morgan, Smith

Pages 50–51

1. < **3.** > **5.** < **7.** > **9.** > **11.** < **13.** True. **15.** False. **17.** True. **19.** False. **21.** False. **23. A.** Let c represent the number of star charts. **B.** $91 + 9 \cdot c \le 135$ **C.** $c = 1$: $91 + 9 \cdot 1 \overset{?}{\le} 135$; $91 + 9 \overset{?}{\le} 135$; $100 \le 135$; $c = 2$: $91 + 9 \cdot 2 \overset{?}{\le} 135$; $91 + 18 \overset{?}{\le} 135$; $109 \le 135$; $c = 3$: $91 + 9 \cdot 3 \overset{?}{\le} 135$; $91 + 27 \overset{?}{\le} 135$; $118 \le 135$; $c = 4$: $91 + 9 \cdot 4 \overset{?}{\le} 135$; $91 + 36 \overset{?}{\le} 135$; $127 \le 135$; $c = 5$: $91 + 9 \cdot 5 \overset{?}{\le} 135$; $91 + 45 \overset{?}{\le} 135$; $136 \not\le 135$ **D.** Mr. Le could buy 4 star charts. **25. A.** Let t represent the number of teachers. **B.** $240 + 8 \cdot t \le 265$ **C.** $c = 1$: $240 + 8 \cdot 1 \overset{?}{\le} 265$; $240 + 8 \overset{?}{\le} 265$; $248 \le 265$; $c = 2$: $240 + 8 \cdot 2 \overset{?}{\le} 265$; $240 + 16 \overset{?}{\le} 265$; $256 \le 265$; $c = 3$: $240 + 8 \cdot 3 \overset{?}{\le} 265$; $240 + 24 \overset{?}{\le} 265$; $264 \le 265$; $c = 4$: $240 + 8 \cdot 4 \overset{?}{\le} 265$; $240 + 32 \overset{?}{\le} 265$; $272 \not\le 265$ **D.** Three adults could attend, not including the teacher. **27. A.** Let t represent the number of t-shirts. **B.** $288 + 9 \cdot t \le 320$ **C.** $c = 1$: $288 + 9 \cdot 1 \overset{?}{\le} 320$; $288 + 9 \overset{?}{\le} 320$; $297 \le 320$; $c = 2$: $288 + 9 \cdot 2 \overset{?}{\le} 320$; $288 + 18 \overset{?}{\le} 320$; $306 \le 320$; $c = 3$: $288 + 9 \cdot 3 \overset{?}{\le} 320$; $288 + 27 \overset{?}{\le} 320$; $315 \le 320$; $c = 4$: $288 + 9 \cdot 4 \overset{?}{\le} 320$; $288 + 36 \overset{?}{\le} 320$; $324 \not\le 320$ **D.** Bruce could pay for 3 t-shirts. 29. **A.** Let c represent the cost of the cheese. **B.** $6 + c \cdot 4 \le 21$ **C.** $c = 2$: $6 + 2 \cdot 4 \overset{?}{\le} 21$; $6 + 8 \overset{?}{\le} 21$; $14 \le 21$; $c = 3$: $6 + 3 \cdot 4 \overset{?}{\le} 21$; $6 + 12 \overset{?}{\le} 21$; $18 \le 21$; $c = 4$: $6 + 4 \cdot 4 \overset{?}{\le} 21$; $6 + 16 \overset{?}{\le} 21$; $22 \not\le 21$ **D.** The most expensive cheese Harlan can buy is cheddar.

Pages 54–55

1. Reflexive Property **3.** Commutative Property of Multiplication **5.** Commutative Property of Addition **7.** Transitive Property **9.** Symmetric Property **11.** Commutative Property of Addition **13.** Transitive Property **15.** Associative Property of Multiplication **17. A.** Not all products are an element of the set. Sample answer: $2 \cdot (-2) = -4$ and -4 is not in the set. So, the set is not closed under multiplication.
B. Not all quotients are an element of the set. Sample answer: $1 \div 2 = \frac{1}{2}$ and $\frac{1}{2}$ is not in the set. So, the set is not closed under division. **19.** The sum of any negative numbers is negative. So, the set is closed under addition. **21.** The product of any numbers from the set will be a number from the set. So,

the set is closed under multiplication. **23.** Sample answer: The product of any two negative numbers is a positive number. So, the set is not closed under multiplication. **25.** The sum of two or more natural numbers is a natural number, so the set is closed under addition. **27.** Sample answer: The differences between the numbers in the set range from $0.1 - 0.9 = -0.8$ to $1.9 - 0.1 = 1.8$. The set does not contain negative tenths, so the set is not closed under subtraction. **29.** The quotient of any positive real numbers will be a positive number, so the set is closed under division.

Pages 58–59

1. A. $12 \cdot 53 = (10 + 2)53$ **B.** 636 **3. A.** $17 \cdot 43 = (10 + 7)43$ **B.** 731 **5. A.** $16 \cdot 34 = (10 + 6)34$ or $16 \cdot (30 + 4)$ **B.** 544 **7. A.** $3(y + 7) + 8y = 3 \cdot y + 3 \cdot 7 + 8y$ **B.** $11y + 21$ **9. A.** $11(x + 8) + 17x = 11 \cdot x + 11 \cdot 8 + 17x$ **B.** $28x + 88$ **11. A.** $4(y + 6) + 5y = 4 \cdot y + 4 \cdot 6 + 5y$ **B.** $9y + 24$ **13.** $16x$, $12x$ **15.** $10x$, $8x$ **17.** $12y^2 + 28x + 4a$ **19.** $2y^3 + 20x + 9a$ **21.** $3xy^2 + 25x + 18$ **23.** $4x$ **25.** $5x$ **27.** $C = 52 + 30h$ **29. A.** $C = 15 + 10d$ **B.** $85

Pages 62–66

1. A. Distributive Property **B.** Definition of subtraction **3. A.** Commutative Property of Multiplication **B.** Multiplication **5. A.** Associative Property of Multiplication **B.** Associative Property of Multiplication **C.** Commutative Property of Multiplication **7.** Commutative Property of Multiplication **9.** $(18t + 72t) + 20$ **11.** $13 + (2 + a)$ **13. A.** $45y + 12 + 2 \cdot 6 + 2 \cdot y$ **B.** Commutative Property of Addition **15. A.** $2v + (14 + 29) + 4v$ **B.** Distributive Property **17. A.** $7 \cdot [1 + (-l)] \cdot 2$ **B.** Commutative Property of Multiplication

Pages 70–71

1. $\frac{40}{7}$ **3.** $<$ **5.** $>$ **7.** $=$ **9.** 43,249 **11.** $\frac{100}{9}$ **13.** 6275 **15.** 26 **17.** -1 **19.** $\frac{11}{5}$ **21.** $\{-76, 76\}$ **23.** $\{-3.3, 5.3\}$ **25.** $\{244, -236\}$ **27.** The stop light caused the largest change in her speed. **29.** Round 3 had the greatest effect on her score.

UNIT 3 Operations with Real Numbers

Pages 78–79

1. 9.5 **3.** -20.6 **5.** -3.4 **7.** 11.7 **9.** -14.4 **11.** -10.9 **13.** 34.2 **15.** -4.1 **17.** -34.2 **19.** -61 **21.** -27 **23. A.** Additive Inverse Property **B.** Identity Property for Addition **25. A.** Answers will vary. Sample answer: $99.6 + (-8.6)$ **B.** 91 **C.** The world's tallest living woman is 91 inches tall. **27. A.** Answers will vary. Sample answer: $21.6 + 4.6 + (-24)$ **B.** 2.2 **C.** Fiona has 2.2 miles left to run in the marathon.

Page 83

1. 4.9 **3.** -10 **5.** $6t + 1.5$ **7.** 126.23 **9.** $431 - 100n$ **11.** 14.3 **13.** 0 **15.** 91 **17.** 1 **19.** 9 **21.** -7.5 **23.** not associative **25. A.** Answers will vary. Sample answer: $88.9 - 78.2$ **B.** 10.7 **C.** Buffalo received 10.7 more inches of snow during 2006–2007 than during 2005–2006. **27. A.** Answers will vary. Sample answer: $-5000 - (-56{,}000)$ **B.** 51,000 **C.** The company was worth $51,000 more after the second year than after the first year. **29. A.** Answers will vary. Sample answer: $-25 - (-15)$ **B.** -10 **C.** Her change in speed was -10 mph greater, or a 10 mph greater decrease from point 3 to 4 than from point 1 to 2.

Pages 86–87

1. 30 **3.** 26 **5.** 60 **7.** -22 **9.** -12 **11.** -496 **13.** 15 **15.** 22 **17.** $3x + 28a + 23$ **19.** -128 **21.** $-5y + 2a + b - 17$ **23.** $-7x + 3a - 23$ **25.** $-9x - 3a + 4b - 79$ **27. A.** $8.99 \cdot 5 + 6.99 - 0.60 \cdot 6 = 48.34$ **B.** Sang will pay $48.34 for his 6th order. **29. A.** $100 + |-20 \cdot 9| + 10 \cdot 8 = 360$ **B.** The total distance traveled per one ride is 360 feet. **31. A.** $1.50 \cdot 4 + 7 \cdot 2 + 4 = 24$ **B.** Uri and Will spent $24.

Page 91

1. $\frac{1}{3}$ **3.** $\frac{4}{9}$ **5.** $\frac{1}{2b}$ **7.** $-\frac{8}{49}$ **9.** -68 **11.** $-9y$ **13.** -12 **15.** $-\frac{5}{7}$ **17.** $-\frac{9}{16}$ **19.** $-\frac{5}{2x}$ **21.** $\frac{2s - 3p}{3}$ **23.** $-\frac{4}{5}$ **25.** 6 **27.** Meaghan grew an average of 3.25 inches per year. **29.** Charles's pay rate is $10.25 per hour.

Pages 94–95

1. 8, 9 **3.** 23, 25 **5.** -12, -10 **7.** 31, 33, 25 **9.** -20, -18, -16 **11.** -19, -18 **13.** 30, 31 **15.** 48 in., 49 in., 50 in. **17.** 38 in., 40 in., 42 in. **19.** 21 in., 23 in., 25 in. **21.** 46 in., 48 in., 50 in. **23.** 6, 8, 10 **25.** $8, $9, $10 **27.** 13 in., 15 in., 17 in. **29.** no solution

UNIT 4 Solving Equations and Inequalities

Page 103

1. $y = 50$ **3.** $x = 9$ **5.** $z = -2$ **7.** $p = 29$ **9.** $s = 3$ or $s = -3$ **11.** $-25 = y$ **13.** $22 = x$ **15.** $-100 = k$ **17.** $x = \frac{8}{7}$ **19.** $s = 26$ **21.** $d = 88$ **23.** $f = 8$ or $f = -8$ **25. A.** Answers will vary. Sample answer: Let p represent the original price in dollars. **B.** $p - 5.85 = 17.55$ **C.** The original price of the shirt was $23.40. **27. A.** Answers will vary. Sample answer: Let f represent the number of fans at Saturday's baseball game. **B.** $f - 129 = 2373$ **C.** 2502 fans attended Saturday's baseball game. **29. A.** Answers will vary. Sample answer: Let m represent the amount of time, in minutes, it takes Lourdes to walk a mile. **B.** $m + 3 = 20$

C. Lourdes can walk a mile in 17 minutes. **31. A.** Answers will vary. Sample answer: Let x represent the additional amount of money, in dollars, Kelly needs to save. **B.** $x + 48 = 131$ **C.** Kelly needs to save an additional \$83. **33. A.** Answers will vary. Sample answer: Let h represent the amount of time, in minutes, spent on history homework. **B.** $90 + h = 120$ **C.** Cindy spent 30 minutes on history homework. **35. A.** Answers will vary. Sample answer: Let x represent the number of additional miles driven on the second day than on the first day. Then $473 + x$ represents the distance driven on the second day. **B.** $473 + (473 + x) = 1029$ **C.** John drove 83 more miles on the second day than on the first day.

Page 107

1. $x = 36$ **3.** $-3 = z$ **5.** $n = 18$ **7.** $x = 9$ or $x = -9$ **9.** $y = -12$ **11.** $m = \frac{17}{5}$ or $m = -\frac{17}{5}$ **13.** no solution **15.** $y = 17.4$ **17.** $63 = a$ **19.** $x = 4$ **21.** $t = -32$ **23.** $x = -54$ **25. A.** Answers will vary. Sample answer: Let s represent the unit price per sheet in dollars. **B.** $250s = 15$ **C.** $s = 0.06$ **D.** The unit price was \$0.06. **27. A.** Answers will vary. Sample answer: Let f represent the cost per friend in dollars, and round to the nearest cent. **B.** $6f = 5$ **C.** $f \approx 0.83$ **D.** Each friend spent \$0.83. **29. A.** Answers will vary. Sample answer: Let n represent one night. **B.** $3n = 254.91$ **C.** $n = 84.97$ **D.** Alejandra spent \$84.97 per night.

Pages 111–112

1. $x = 54$ **3.** $y = 6$ **5.** $y = 3$ **7.** $s = -4$ **9.** $y = -12$ **11.** $2 = z$ **13.** $x = 4$ **15.** $15 = t$ **17.** $x = 88$ **19.** $m = -1$ **21.** $s = 8$ **23.** $x = 6$ **25. A.** $P = 2l + 2w$; $54 = 2(3w + 3) + 2w$; $54 = 6w + 6 + 2w$; $54 = (6w + 2w) + 6$; $54 = 8w + 6$ **B.** $6 = w$; $l = 21$ **C.** The length is 21 feet and the width is 6 feet. **27. A.** $P = 2l + 2w$; $150 = 2(w - 7) + 2w$; $36 = 2w - 14 + 2w$; $150 = 2w + 2w - 14$; $150 = 4w - 14$ **B.** $41 = w$; $l = 34$ **C.** The length is 34 feet and the width is 41 feet. **29. A.** $x + y + z = 16$; $2y + y + z = 16$; $2(z - 4) + (z - 4) + z = 16$; $2z - 8 + z - 4 + z = 16$; $2z + z + z - 8 - 4 = 16$; $4z - 12 = 16$ **B.** $z = 7$; $y = 3$; $x = 6$ **C.** Side x is 6 units long, side y is 3 units long, and side z is 7 units long.

Pages 116–117

1. zero solutions **3.** zero solutions **5.** one solution **7.** $x = 2$ **9.** $m = -1$ **11.** $p = 1$ **13.** $4 = x$ **15.** $-15 = a$ **17.** $\frac{4}{5} = y$ **19.** $y = -3$ **21.** $x = -2$ **23.** $2 = m$ **25. A.** $4n + 3 = 3n - 7$ **B.** $n = -10$ **27. A.** $2n + 5 = n - 4$ **B.** $n = -9$ **29. A.** $\frac{n}{2} - 5 = 3n - 25$ **B.** $n = 8$

Pages 121–122

1. $w = \frac{A}{l}$ **3.** $l = \frac{P - 2w}{2}$ **5.** $a = \frac{x}{b - c}$ **7.** $r = \frac{C}{2\pi}$ **9.** $c = \frac{y}{b} + d$ **11. A.** $h = \frac{2A}{b}$ **B.** $h = 18$ **C.** The height is 18 inches. **13. A.** $w = \frac{V}{lh}$ **B.** $w = 2$ **C.** The width is 2 feet. **15. A.** $h = \frac{3V}{\pi r^2}$ **B.** $h \approx 0.478$ **C.** The height of the cone is approximately 0.4777 centimeters. **17. A.** $L = S - 2\pi r^2$ **B.** $L \approx 99.52$ **C.** The lateral area of the tube is approximately 99.52 square inches. **19. A.** $m = \frac{pn}{(1 - p)}$ **B.** $m = \frac{2}{3}$ **C.** m is equal to $\frac{2}{3}$. **21. A.** $x = \frac{z}{ky}$ **B.** $x = 4$ **C.** x is equal to 4. **23. A.** $h = \frac{3V}{lw}$ **B.** $h = 30$ **C.** The height of the pyramid is 30 feet. **25. A.** $b_2 = \frac{2A}{h} - b_1$ **B.** $b_2 = 2$ **C.** The second base of the trapezoid is 2 inches. **27. A.** $b + c = 5A - a - d - c$ **B.** $b + c = 44$ **C.** The sum of b and c is 44.

Pages 127–128

1. $x \approx 9.1$ **3.** $x \approx 3.8$ **5.** $x \approx -1.2$ **7.** $x \approx -12.7$ **9.** $x \approx -4.5$ **11.** $x \approx 0.3$ **13.** $x \approx -0.2$ **15.** $x \approx 21.4$ **17.** $x = 11$ **19.** $x = -1.8$ **21.** $x \approx 3.4$ **23.** Yes. **25.** Yes. **27.** Yes. **29.** Yes.

Pages 132–133

1. A. Answers will vary. Sample answer: Let m represent buckwheat mix and $23 - m$ represent whole wheat mix. **B.** $0.45m + 42.55 = 46.60$ **C.** $m = 9$; $23 - m = 14$ **D.** The restaurant bought 9 pounds of buckwheat flour and 14 pounds of whole wheat flour. **3. A.** Answers will vary. Sample answer: Let p represent pomegranates and $15 - p$ represent oranges. **B.** $0.16p + 21 = 21.64$ **C.** $p = 4$; $15 - p = 11$ **D.** Josh bought 4 pounds of pomegranates and 11 pounds of oranges. **5. A.** Answers will vary. Sample answer: Let x represent price per foot cut. **B.** $3.5x = 42.50$ **C.** $x \approx 12.14$ **D.** Mr. Garcia paid about \$12.14 per foot. **7. A.** Answers will vary. Sample answer: Let s represent the number of servings. **B.** $8s = 144$ **C.** $s = 18$ **D.** Eighteen servings of soup can be made. **9. A.** Answers will vary. Sample answer: Let d represent drink cost and $d + 0.50$ represent dessert cost. **B.** $2d + 4.90 = 9.80$ **C.** $d = 2.45$; $d + 0.50 = 2.95$ **D.** Juan paid \$2.45 for his drink and \$2.95 for dessert. **11. A.** Answers will vary. Sample answer: Let f represent amount of fabric. **B.** $7.99f = 1$ **C.** $f \approx 0.125$ **D.** Sam purchased 0.125 yards of fabric.

13. A. Answers will vary. Sample answer: Let d represent dimes, $d + 3$ represent nickels, and $d - 5$ represent pennies. **B.** $0.16d + 0.10 = 2.02$ **C.** $d = 12$; $d + 3 = 15$; $d - 5 = 7$ **D.** Maddie had 12 dimes, 15 nickels, and 7 pennies. **15. A.** Answers will vary. Sample answer: Let p represent part-time hours. **B.** $45{,}000 + 10.50p = 48{,}570$ **C.** $p = 340$ **D.** Merv worked 340 part-time hours.
17. A. Answers will vary. Sample answer: Let s represent the price of the shorts and $s - 5$ represent the price of the shirt. **B.** $2s - 5 = 26.98$ **C.** $s = 15.99$; $s - 5 = 10.99$ **D.** The shorts cost $15.99 and the shirt cost $10.99. **19. A.** Answers will vary. Sample answer: Let c represent the CD investment and $10{,}000 - c$ represent the land venture investment. **B.** $0.01c + 800 = 850$ **C.** $c = 5000$; $10{,}000 - c = 5000$ **D.** Uniqua invested $5000 in each area. **21. A.** Answers will vary. Sample answer: Let p represent the price per vitamin. **B.** $125p = 10$ **C.** $p = 0.08$ **D.** Annika paid $0.08 per vitamin. **23. A.** Answers will vary. Sample answer: Let m represent minutes.; 1 hour $= 60$ minutes **B.** $\frac{154}{60}m = 64$ **C.** $m \approx 25$ **D.** Jana burns 64 calories in about 25 minutes. **25. A.** Answers will vary. Sample answer: Let v represent hours worked in the video store and $32 - v$ represent hours worked in the grocery store. **B.** $-1.5v + 232 = 214$ **C.** $v = 12$; $32 - v = 20$ **D.** Celia worked 12 hours at the video store and 20 hours at the grocery store. **27. A.** Answers will vary. Sample answer: Let w represent weight. **B.** $7.99w = 133$ **C.** $w \approx 0.17$ **D.** One piece is about 0.17 pounds. **29. A.** Answers will vary. Sample answer: Let v represent vegetable toppings and $12 - v$ represent meat toppings. **B.** $0.15v + 9 = 10.2$ **C.** $v = 8$; $12 - v = 4$ **D.** Gino puts 8 vegetable and 4 meat toppings on the specialty pizza.

Page 137

1. False. **3.** False. **5.** True. **7.** True. **9.** True. **11.** Yes. **13.** Yes. **15.** No. **17.** No.

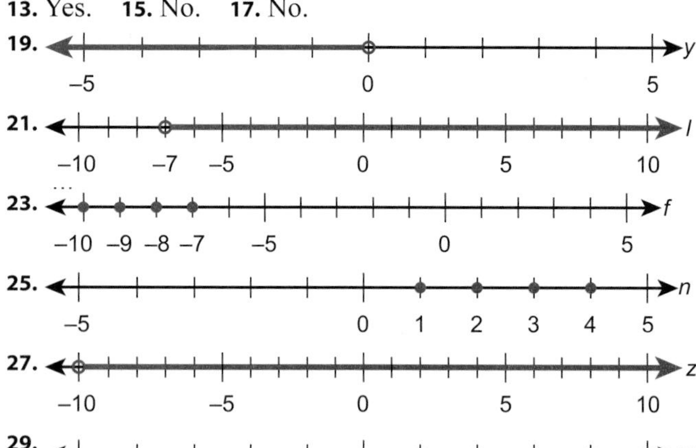

Page 142

1. $x < 21$ **3.** $n < -9$ **5.** $v \geq 1$ **7.** $x > 8$ **9.** $a > 11$ **11.** $m < 24$ **13.** $n < -17$ **15.** $k > \frac{1}{3}$ **17.** $j \leq 18$ **19.** $z > 0$ **21.** $q > 3$ **23.** 7 **25.** 11 **27.** 622, 624 **29. A.** 4 **B.** 3.6

Pages 147–148

1. $b < 2$ OR $b > 7$ **3.** $14 \leq p \leq 19$ **5.** $z < 2.75$ OR $z \geq 3.25$ **7.** $w < -7$ OR $w > 7$ **9. A.** $1 \leq t < 3$

B.

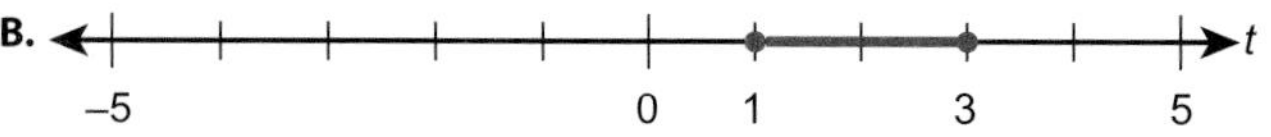

11. A. $f < \frac{-64}{6}$ OR $f > 2$

B. −12 $-\frac{64}{6}$ −8 −4 0 2 4

13. A. $48 \geq x > -60$

B.

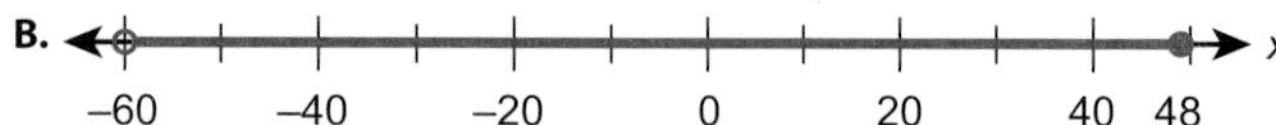

15. A. $c \geq -6$

B. −10 −6 −5 0 5 10

17. A. $m \geq -7$ AND $m \leq 2$

B.

19. A. all real numbers

B.

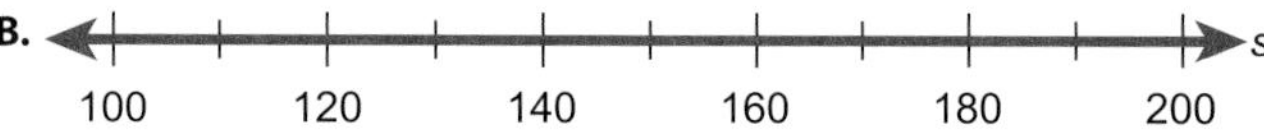

21. A. $9 > d \geq 2$

B.

23. A. $99 \leq x < 110$

B.

25. The only possible pair of consecutive odd integers is 15 and 17. **27.** The invalid pairs are 19 and 20, 20 and 21, 21 and 22, 22 and 23, 23 and 24, 24 and 25, 25 and 26.
29. A. The valid natural numbers are 5, 6, 7, …, 29, 30, 31. **B.** The valid natural numbers are 16, 17, 18, and 19.

Page 152

1. A. $x + 4 = 6$ OR $x + 4 = 26$ **B.** $x = 2$ OR $x = -10$

C.

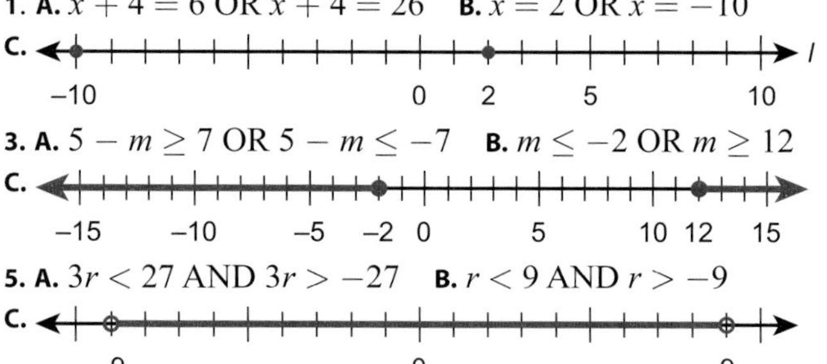

3. A. $5 - m \geq 7$ OR $5 - m \leq -7$ **B.** $m \leq -2$ OR $m \geq 12$

C.

5. A. $3r < 27$ AND $3r > -27$ **B.** $r < 9$ AND $r > -9$

C.

7. A. $2x > 18$ OR $2x < -18$ **B.** $x > 9$ OR $x < -9$

C. 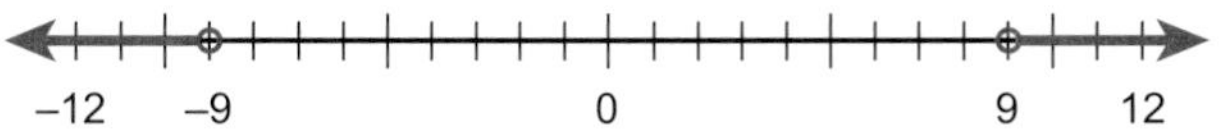

9. A. $x - 1 > -2$ OR $x - 1 < 2$ **B.** all real numbers

C. 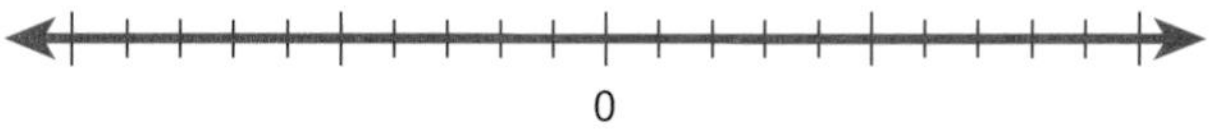

11. A. $p - 7 \leq 16$ AND $p - 7 \geq -16$ **B.** $p \leq 23$ AND $p \geq -9$

C. 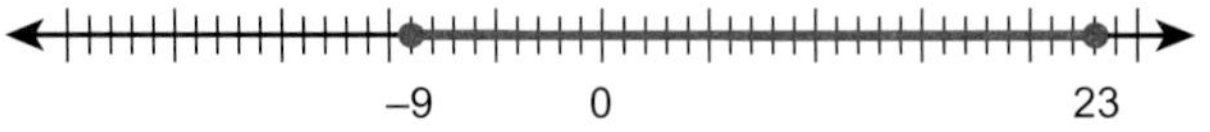

13. A. $6 - 2y > 3$ OR $6 - 2y < -3$ **B.** $y < 1.5$ OR $y > 4.5$

C. 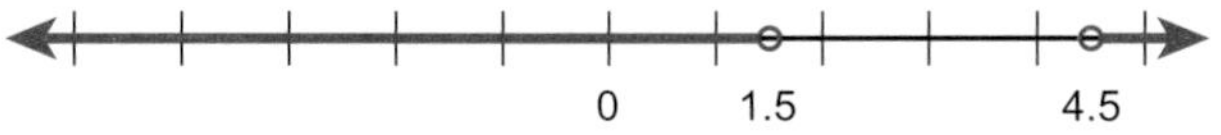

15. A. $3x + 2 \geq 11$ OR $3x + 2 \leq -11$ **B.** $x \geq 3$ OR $x \leq -4\frac{1}{3}$

17. A. $t - 2 = 2$ OR $t - 2 = -2$ **B.** $t = 4$ OR $t = 0$

19. A. $a - 4 = 1$ OR $a - 4 = -1$ **B.** $a = 5$ OR $a = 3$

21. A. $8 - b \leq 6$ AND $8 - b \geq -6$ **B.** $b \geq 2$ AND $b \leq 14$

23. A. $2 - 5y < 6$ AND $2 - 5y > -6$ **B.** $y > -0.8$ AND $y < 1.6$ **25. A.** $3b - 1 \geq -1$ OR $3b - 1 \leq 1$ **B.** all real numbers **27. A.** $|w - 40| \leq 4$ **B.** $w \leq 44$ AND $w \geq 36$ **C.** The carrots weigh between 36 and 44 ounces.

29. A. $|m - 390| \leq 75$ **B.** $m \leq 465$ AND $m \geq 315$ **C.** Li could drive between 315 and 465 miles on 15 gallons.

Pages 157–159

1. A. Answers will vary. Sample answer: Let w represent width, $2w$ represent length, and P represent perimeter. **B.** $6w \leq 120$ **C.** $w \leq 20$ **D.** The greatest possible value for the width of the rectangle is 20 units. **3. A.** Answers will vary. Sample answer: Let d represent day. **B.** $850d > 24{,}000 + 500d$ **C.** $d > 68.571...$ **D.** Ono will begin to make a profit on the 69th day. **5. A.** Answers will vary. Sample answer: Let c represent the time to make a chair and $3c$ represent the time to make a sofa. **B.** $10c \leq 20$ **C.** $c \leq 2$ **D.** It takes up to 2 hours to produce one chair. **7. A.** Answers will vary. Sample answer: Let d represent the number of deposits. **B.** $10{,}000 \leq 550d \leq 12{,}000$ **C.** $18.\overline{18} < d < 21.\overline{81}$ **D.** Suki must make between 19 and 22 deposits.

9. A. Answers will vary. Sample answer: Let r represent inches of rain. **B.** $15 \leq r + 8.2 \leq 20$ **C.** $6.8 \leq x \leq 11.8$ **D.** Between 6.8 and 11.8 inches, inclusive, is needed to meet the amount of needed rain. **11. A.** Answers will vary. Sample answer: Let t represent the time spent in the car during the first half of the trip and $\frac{1}{4}t$ represent the time spent at the rest stop. **B.** $\frac{9}{4}t \leq 6$ **C.** $t \leq 2\frac{2}{3}$; time in car: $5\frac{1}{3}$ **D.** The Davis family spent at most $5\frac{1}{3}$ hours in the car.

13. A. Answers will vary. Sample answer: Let f represent final swim time. **B.** $4.50 < \frac{f + 18.75}{5} < 5$ **C.** $3.75 < f < 6.25$ **D.** Soo-Min must swim between 3.75 and 6.25 seconds.

15. A. Answers will vary. Sample answer: Let c represent the number of quarters or dimes. **B.** $0.35c < 2$ **C.** $c < 5.7143$ **D.** Jan has at most 5 quarters and 5 dimes. **17. A.** Answers will vary. Sample answer: Let p represent points. **B.** $2699 < \frac{p + 13{,}699}{6} < 2901$ **C.** $2495 < p < 3707$ **D.** Vladimir must earn between 2495 and 3707 points.

19. A. Answers will vary. Sample answer: Let j represent a job. **B.** $100j > 60j + 1200$ **C.** $j > 30$ **D.** Eli must complete more than 30 jobs before he makes a profit. **21. A.** Answers will vary. Sample answer: Let w represent each wedding. **B.** $6000w > 5500w + 1200$ **C.** $w > 2.4$ **D.** The planner will make a profit beginning with the 3rd wedding.

23. A. Answers will vary. Sample answer: Let r represent Roberto's age and $3r - 5$ represent Gee's age. **B.** $4x - 5 > 11$ **C.** $r > 4$ **D.** Roberto is at least 5.

UNIT 5 Applying Fractions

Pages 165–166

1. $\frac{1}{4}$, 0.25 **3.** $\frac{7}{11}$, $0.\overline{63}$ **5.** 1 **7.** 3 **9.** $\frac{1}{16}$, 0.0625

11. $\frac{3}{4}$, 0.75 **13.** $\frac{1}{12}$, $0.08\overline{3}$ **15.** $\frac{9}{2}$, 4.5 **17.** $\frac{6}{7}$, $0.\overline{857142}$

19. A. Answers will vary. Sample answer: The first number can be represented by $7x$ and the second number can be represented by $4x$. **B.** $3x = 12$ **C.** $x = 4$; first number: 28, second number: 16 **D.** The two numbers are 28 and 16.

21. A. Answers will vary. Sample answer: The first number can be represented by $11x$ and the second number can be represented by $12x$. **B.** $23x = 207$ **C.** $x = 9$; first number: 99, second number: 108 **D.** The two numbers are 99 and 108. **23. A.** Answers will vary. Sample answer: The first number can be represented by $3x$ and the second number can be represented by $4x$. **B.** $-x = -1.9$ **C.** $x = 1.9$; first number 5.7, second number: 7.6 **D.** The two numbers are 5.7 and 7.6. **25. A.** Answers will vary. Sample answer: Jessica's pages can be represented by $5p$ and Jeremy's pages can be represented by $4p$. **B.** $9p = 36$ **C.** $p = 4$; Jessica's pages: 20 and Jeremy's pages: 16 **D.** Jessica read 20 pages and Jeremy read 16 pages. **27. A.** Answers will vary. Sample answer: Let aluminum be represented by $19s$ and silicon be represented by s. **B.** $20s = 40$ **C.** $s = 2$; aluminum: 38, silicon: 2 **D.** In 40 grams of the alloy, there are 38 grams of aluminum and 2 grams of silicon. **29. A.** Let r represent the radius. **B.** $\pi r^2 = 420$ **C.** $r \approx 11.57$ **D.** The radius of the smaller circle is approximately 11.57 cm. **31.** There would be no solution. **33.** She would be refunded the difference between the regular price and the discounted price, which is $\$59 - \$50.15 = \$8.85$.

Page 170

1. $x = 2$ **3.** $x = -1.\overline{54}$ **5.** $x = 5$ **7.** $x = 19$ **9.** $x = -1.5$ **11.** $x = -10.2$ **13.** $\frac{1}{35}$ **15.** $-\frac{3}{5}$ **17.** $-\frac{1}{3}$ **19. A.** Answers will vary. Sample answer: Let c represent the cost of 50 square feet of sod. **B.** $\frac{3}{11} = \frac{50}{c}$ **C.** $c = 183.\overline{3}$ **D.** Quaid will spend $183.33 for 50 square feet of sod. **21. A.** Answers will vary. Sample answer: Let b represent the cost of 15 bottles. **B.** $\frac{3}{12.05} = \frac{15}{b}$ **C.** $b = 60.25$ **D.** Abraham will spend $60.25 for 15 bottles. **23. A.** Answers will vary. Sample answer: Let p represent the perimeter of the larger triangle. **B.** $\frac{2}{7} = \frac{24}{p}$ **C.** $p = 84$ **D.** The perimeter of the larger triangle is 84 inches. **25. A.** Answers will vary. Sample answer: Let c represent the number of people who preferred comedy. **B.** $\frac{4}{5} = \frac{c}{6000}$ **C.** $c = 4800$ **D.** Four thousand eight hundred people preferred comedy shows. **27. A.** Answers will vary. Sample answer: Let a represent the area of the smaller rectangle. **B.** $\frac{2}{3} = \frac{a}{600}$ **C.** $a = 400$ **D.** The area of the smaller rectangle is 400 square feet. **29. A.** Answers will vary. Sample answer: Let c represent the cost of the 16-ounce carton. **B.** $\frac{4}{0.85} = \frac{16}{c}$ **C.** $c = 3.4$ **D.** The best buy is the 16-ounce carton. **31. A.** Answers will vary. Sample answer: Let t represent the number of people who answered the trivia question incorrectly. **B.** $\frac{1}{2} = \frac{t}{434}$ **C.** $t = 217$ **D.** Two hundred seventeen people answered the trivia question incorrectly.

Pages 173–174

1. 0.084 **3.** 1.473 **5.** 270% **7.** 80% **9.** 70% **11.** 67.5% **13.** 40% **15.** 48% **17.** 30% **19.** 40% **21.** 74% **23.** 30% **25. A.** Yoshi had $80 before paying his supermarket bill. **B.** Yoshi has $32.06 left after he bought pizza and tipped the server. **27.** Marisol answered 36 questions correctly. **29.** Tai's batting average was 32% or 0.32.

Pages 178–179

1. 62.5% decrease **3. A.** $422.50 **B.** $380.25 **5.** $23.16 **7. A.** 26% increase **B.** 47% decrease **9.** 70% increase **11.** $3.15 selling price **13.** The original price was $219. **15.** $1275 invested; $229.50 in interest **17. A.** 32% increase **B.** 317,988 tickets **19.** 25% discount **21.** 240% increase **23.** Eight thousand seven hundred seventy-five people attended the game. **25.** Chang invested $3200 at 5% and $2100 at 4%. **27.** $206.25 interest **29. A.** 4.5 years **B.** a minimum of 17 full years

Pages 182–183

1. A.

	Number of Pieces	Size per Piece	Total Size
Red	r	16	$16r$
White	$200 - r$	64	$64(200 - r)$
Total			5600

B. $r = 150$ **C.** Red: $r = 150$; White: $200 - r = 200 - 150 = 50$ **D.** She used 150 pieces of red fabric and 50 pieces of white fabric.

3. A.

	Number of Boxes	Cost per Box	Total Cost
Clipped Head	$2l$	32	$64l$
Large Round Head	l	40	$40l$
Small Round Head	$3l$	34	$102l$
Total			$824

B. $l = 4$ **C.** Clipped Head: 8; Large Round Head: 4; Small Round Head: 12 **D.** The contractor bought 8 boxes of clipped head nails, 4 boxes of large round head nails, and 12 boxes of small round head nails.

5. A.

	Number of Pounds	Cost per Pound	Total Cost
Almonds	a	14	$14a$
Cashews	$2 - a$	8	$8(2 - a)$
Total	2	10	20

B. $a = \frac{2}{3}$ **C.** Almonds: $\frac{2}{3}$; Cashews: $\frac{4}{3}$ **D.** Two-thirds pounds of organic almonds should be mixed with $\frac{4}{3}$ pounds of organic cashews.

7. A.

	Number of Movies	Cost per Rental	Total Cost
Classic	c	3.50	$3.5c$
New Releases	$20 - c$	4.50	$4.5(20 - c)$
Total			$77

B. $c = 13$ **C.** Classic: 13; New Release: 7 **D.** He rented 13 classic movies and 7 new releases.

9. A.

	Number of Songs	Time of Song	Total Time
2.5-minute Song	x	2.5	$2.5x$
3-minute Song	$22 - x$	3	$3(22 - x)$
Total			60

B. $x = 12$ **C.** 2.5-minute song: 12; 3-minute song: 10 **D.** He should use 12 2.5-minute songs and 10 3-minute songs.

11. A.

	Number of Cups	Calcium per Cup	Total Calcium
Milk	m	300	$300m$
Yogurt	$1 - 1.5m$	490	$490(1 - 1.5m)$
Banana	$0.5m$	7	$3.5m$
Total			400

B. $m \approx 0.2$ **C.** Milk: 0.2; Yogurt: 0.7; Banana: 0.1 **D.** He should mix approximately 0.2 cup milk, 0.7 cup yogurt, and 0.1 cup banana.

13. A.

	Liters of Solution	Portion Acid	Liters of Acid
50% solution	10	0.50	5
20% solution	x	0.20	$0.2x$
35% solution	$x + 10$	0.35	$0.35(x + 10)$

B. $x = 10$ **C.** 20% solution: 10; 35% solution: 20 **D.** Ten liters of 20% solution should be added to the 50% solution.

15. A.

	Number of Beads	Cost per Bead	Total Cost
22-mm	x	4.25	$4.25x$
21-mm	$30 - x$	2.75	$2.75(30 - x)$
Total			105

B. $x = 15$ **C.** 22-mm: 15; 21-mm: 15 **D.** The store owner should mix 15 22-mm beads with 15 21-mm beads.

17. A.

	Number of Coins	Value of Coin	Total Value
Quarters	q	0.25	$0.25q$
Dimes	$192 - q$	0.10	$0.1(192 - q)$
Total			\$29.55

B. $q = 69$ **C.** Quarters: 69; Dimes: 123 **D.** Sixty-nine quarters and 123 dimes were in the jar.

19. A.

	Number of Frames	Cost per Frame	Total Cost
11 × 14	x	15	$15x$
8 × 10	x	10	$10x$
5 × 7	$3x$	7	$21x$
4 × 6	$20 - 5x$	5	$5(20 - 5x)$

B. $x = 2$ **C.** 11 × 14: 2; 8 × 10: 2; 5 × 7: 6; 4 × 6: 10 **D.** She bought two 11 × 14 frames, two 8 × 10 frames, six 5 × 7 frames, and ten 4 × 6 frames.

UNIT 6 Linear Equations and Inequalities

Pages 189–191

1. Yes. **3.** No. **5.** No. **7.** No. **9.** Yes. **11.** $y = 10 - 5x$ **A.** $y = 20$ **B.** $y = -5$ **13.** $y = \frac{2}{3} + \frac{8}{3}x$ **A.** $y = 6$ **B.** $y = -2$ **C.** $y = 2$ **15.** $y = 5x - 1$ **A.** $y = -11$ **B.** $y = 14$ **17.** $y = 2 - \frac{5}{4}x$ **A.** $y = 7$ **B.** $y = 2$ **C.** $y = 5\frac{3}{4}$ **19.** $y = 2 + \frac{4}{3}x$ **A.** $y = -2$ **B.** $y = 14$ **21.** $y = 10 - 2x$ **A.** $y = 4$ **B.** $y = 12$ **C.** $y = 10\frac{2}{3}$ **23.** $y = \frac{3}{4}x - 3$ **A.** $y = -9$ **B.** $y = 1\frac{1}{2}$ **25. A.** Answers will vary. Sample answer: Let n represent the number of novels and r represent the number of reference books. **B.** $28n + 52r = 984$ **C.** $r = 6$ **D.** There are 6 reference books in the box. **27. A.** Answers will vary. Sample answer: Let m represent the price of the embroidered shirts and s represent the price of the silk-screened shirts. **B.** $68m + 97s = 2767.75$ **C.** $s = 15.95$ **D.** The silk-screened shirts cost \$15.95 each. **29. A.** Answers will vary. Sample answer: Let l represent the number of large photos and s represent the number of small photos. **B.** $3l + 1.8s = 162$ **C.** $s = 40$ **D.** Jake and Suki used 40 small photos.

Pages 194–196

1.

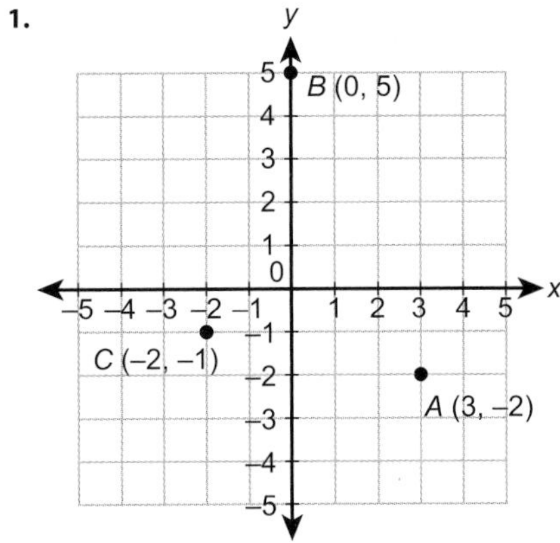

3.

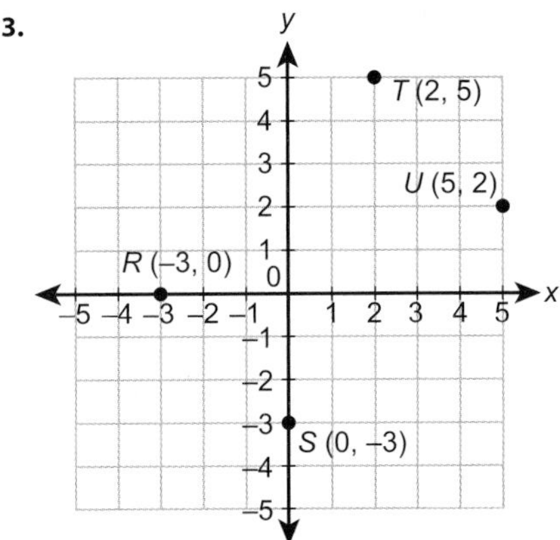

5.

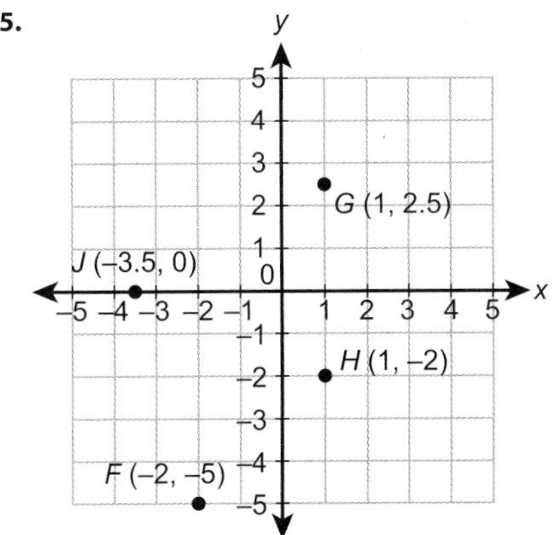

7.

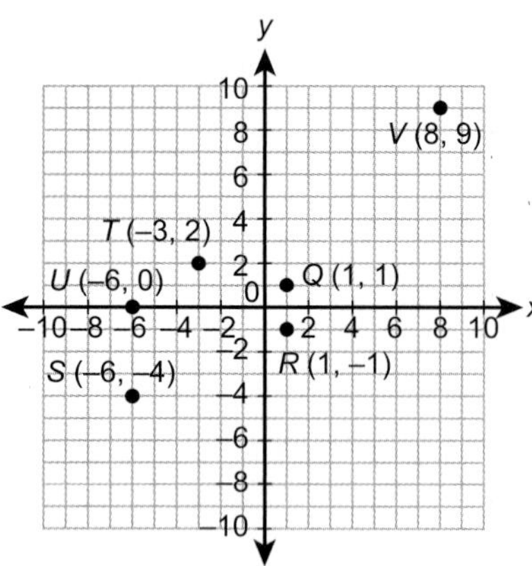

9. $A(2, 2)$, $B(3, -1)$, $C(-1, -1)$, $D(-3, 1)$ **11.** $J(4, 5)$, $K(0, -3)$, $L(-3, 0)$, $M(-1, 3)$ **13.** $A(0, 1)$, $B(5, -3)$, $C(-2.5, -1.5)$, $D(-2, 4)$ **15.** $A(-6.5, 7.5)$, $B(-3, 3)$, $C(6, 8)$, $D(4, -1.5)$, $E(0, -6)$, $F(-4, -2)$ **17.** Quadrant III **19.** Quadrant I **21.** Quadrant II **23. A.** $(-2, 3)$ Quadrant II **B.** $(0, 1)$ y-axis **25. A.** $(4, -1)$ Quadrant IV **B.** $(-1, -4)$ Quadrant III **27. A.** see part C **B.** see part C

C.

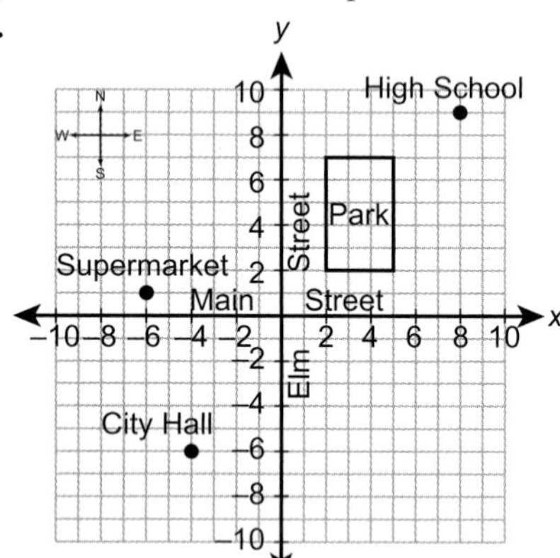

29. A. Picnic Area $(1, -4)$, Scenic Vista $(-9, 4)$, Marina $(-5, -9)$, Restroom $(-4, 9)$, Waterfall $(6.5, 5.5)$, Boulder Island $(-6, -4.5)$, Visitors' Center $(9, 4)$ **B.** $(9, -6)$ South Loop, $(-8, -7)$ Oxbow Pond, $(4, 4)$ Winding River, $(-2.5, -2.5)$ Footbridge, $(-5, 7)$ Mountain Loop

Pages 201–202

1. $x + 2y = 14$ **3.** $4x - 9y = -48$ **5.** $4x - 6y = 5$ **7.** x-intercept: -7, y-intercept: 9 **9.** x-intercept: 7.5, y-intercept: 3.5

11.

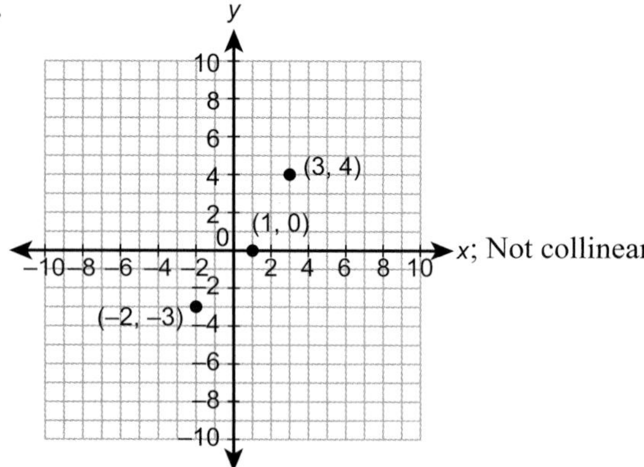

13.

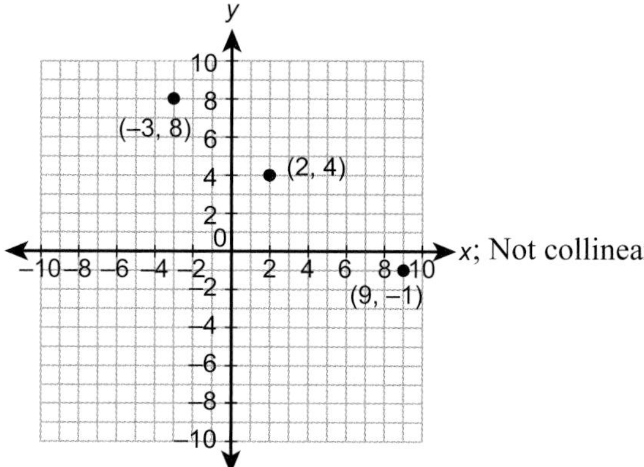

15.

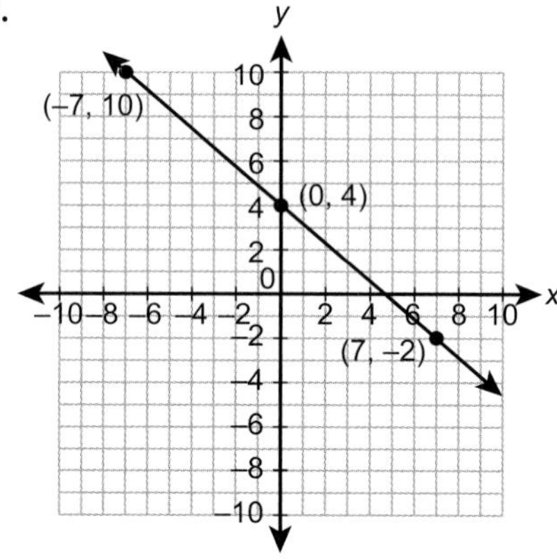

17.

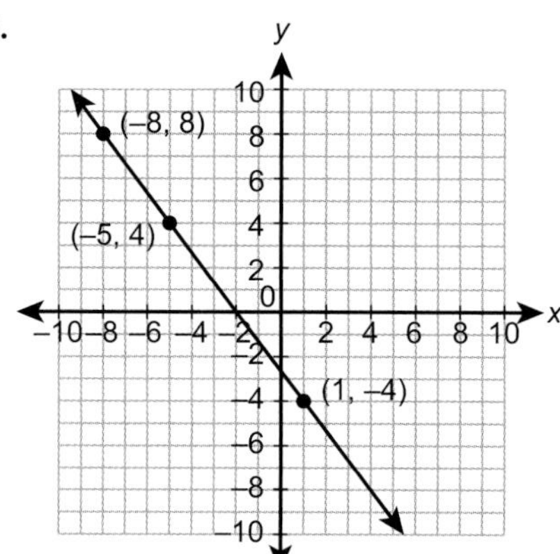

19.

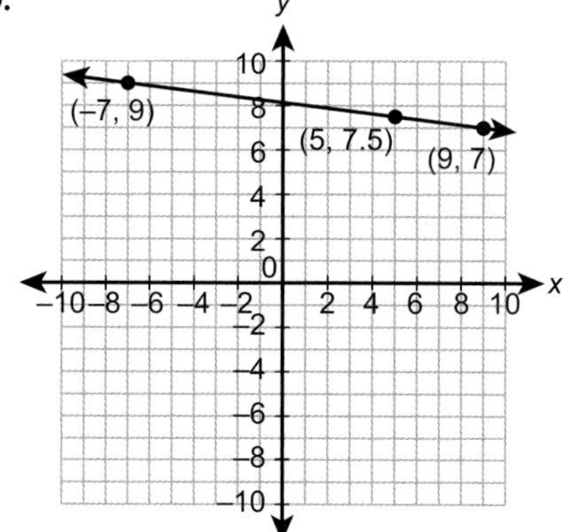

21. A. x-intercept: -9, y-intercept: 3

B.

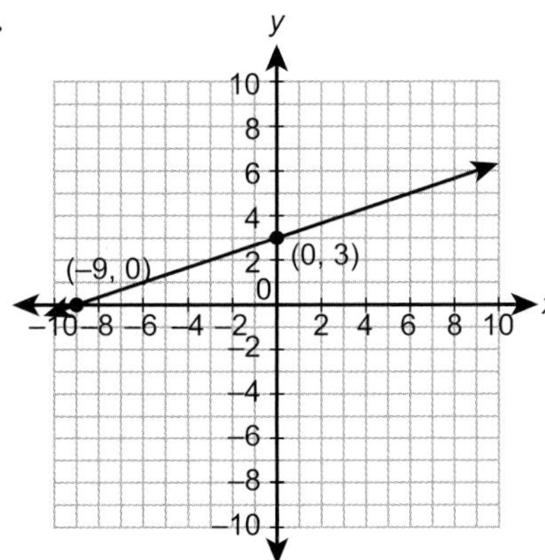

23. A. x-intercept: 4, y-intercept: -2

B.

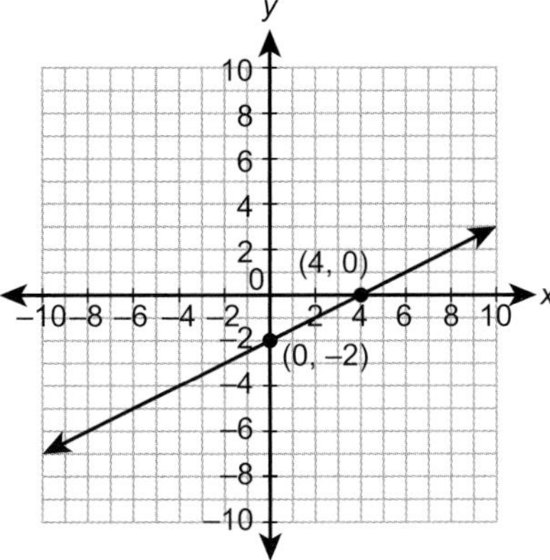

25. x-intercept: -2, y-intercept: 1.5;

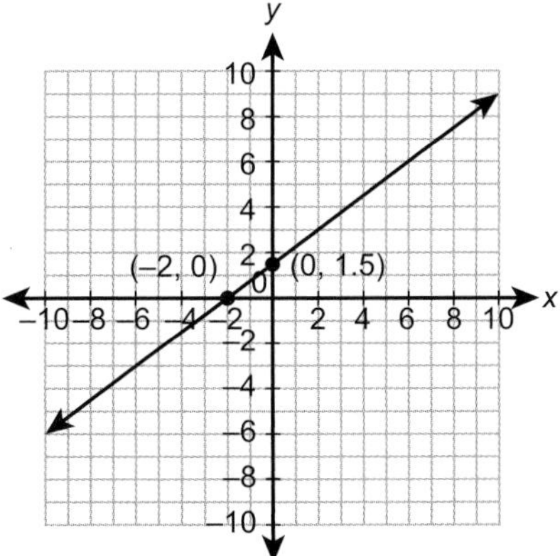

27. A. $7x + 8y = 112$ **B.** x-intercept: 16, y-intercept: 14

C.

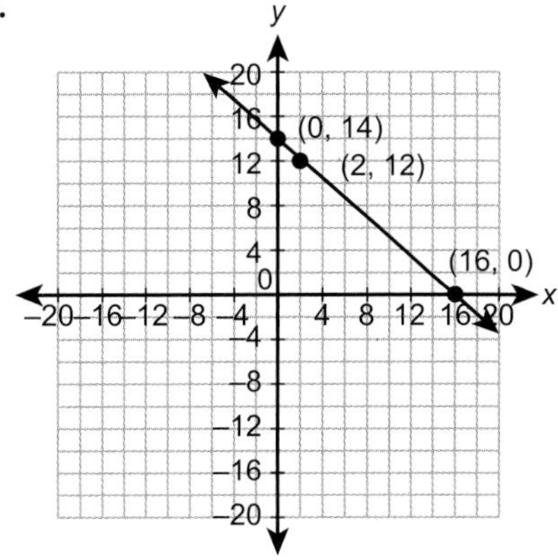

D. Answers will vary. Sample answer: Sixteen pounds of cashews and 0 pounds of pistachios; 14 pounds of pistachios and 0 pounds of cashews; 8 pounds of cashews and 7 pounds of pistachios. **29. A.** $3x + 4y = 72$ **B.** x-intercept: 24, y-intercept: 18

C.

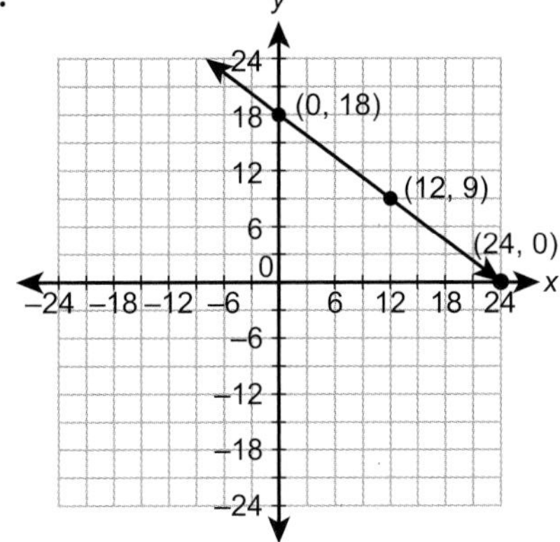

D. Answers will vary. Sample answer: Twenty-four 3-ounce glasses and zero 4-ounce glasses; eighteen 4-ounce glasses and zero 3-ounce glasses; twelve 3-ounce glasses and nine 4-ounce glasses.

Pages 207–208

1. $m = 3$ **3.** $m = \frac{2}{3}$ **5.** $m =$ undefined **7.** $m = -3$ **9.** $m = \frac{1}{4}$ **11.** zero **13.** positive **15.** zero **17. A.** $(0, 6)$, $(-10, 0)$ **B.** $m = \frac{3}{5}$ **19. A.** $(0, -24)$, $(6, 0)$ **B.** $m = 4$

21.

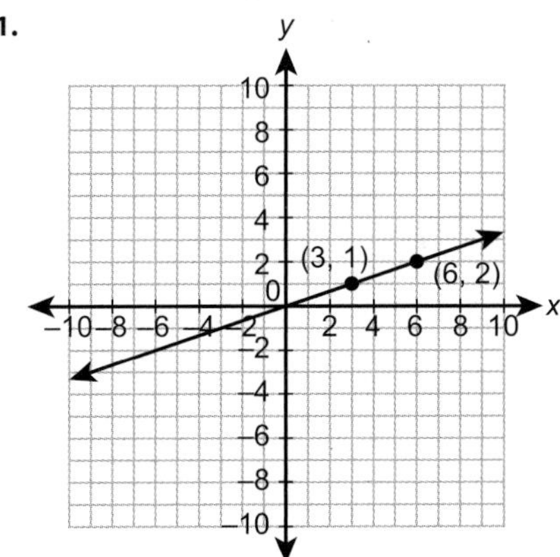

23.

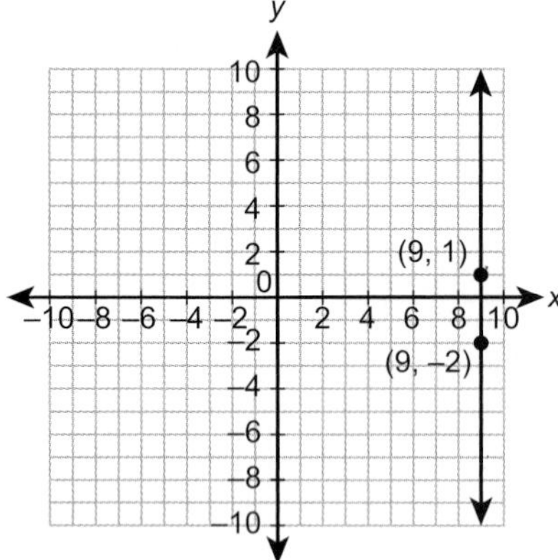

25. A. The rate of change is \$6.50 per movie ticket. **B.** The relation is linear. **C.** The rate of change is the same. **27. A.** The rate of change in profit is \$3.50 per haircut. **B.** The relation is linear. **C.** The rate of change is the same. **29. A.** The rate of change in time is 80 minutes per month. **B.** The relation is linear. **C.** The rate of change is the same.

Page 212

1. slope: 2; y-intercept: -8 **3.** slope: $\frac{1}{4}$; y-intercept: $-\frac{3}{4}$
5. slope: -7; y-intercept: $\frac{7}{2}$ **7.** $y = \frac{4}{7}x - 2$ **9.** $y = \frac{9}{2}x + 18$
11. $y = -\frac{3}{2}x - 15$

13.

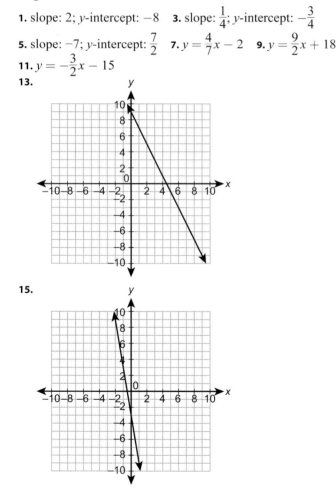

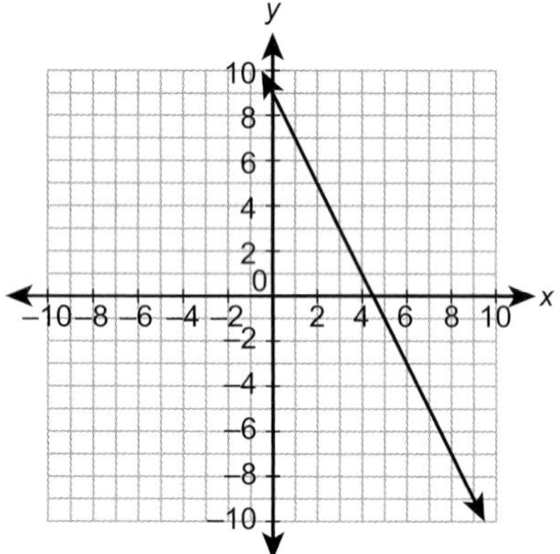

15.

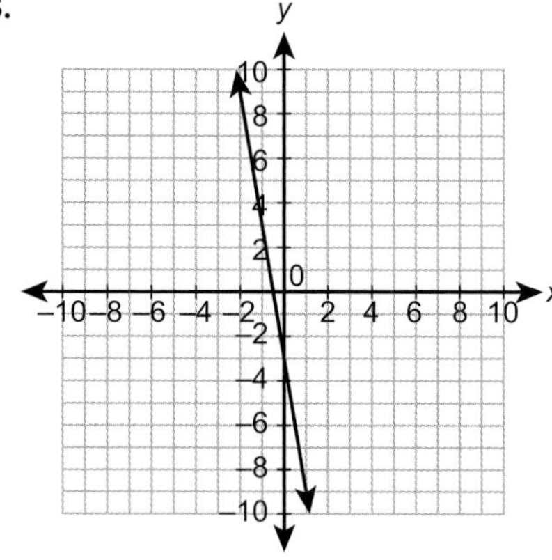

17.

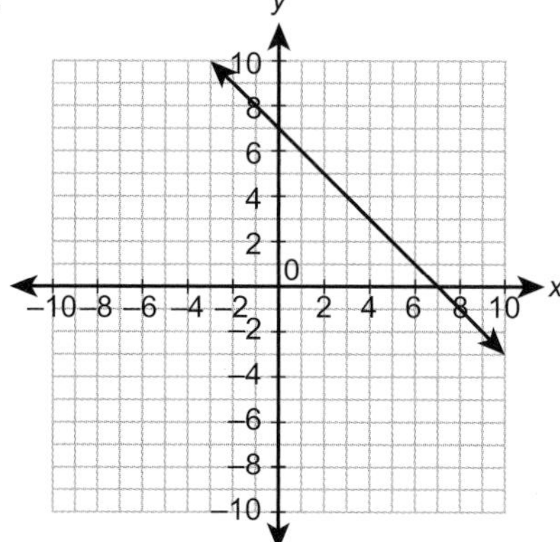

19.

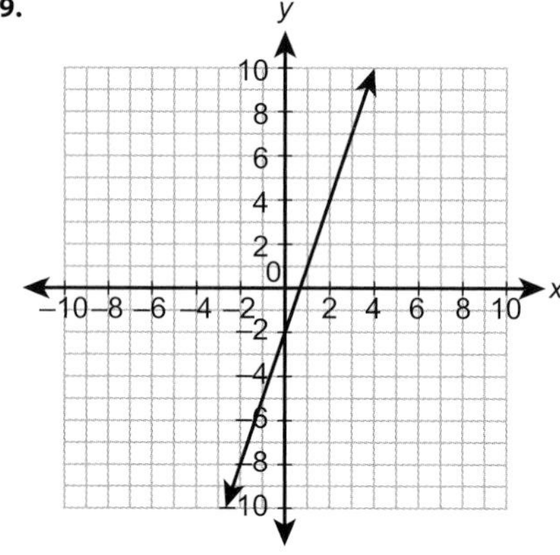

21.

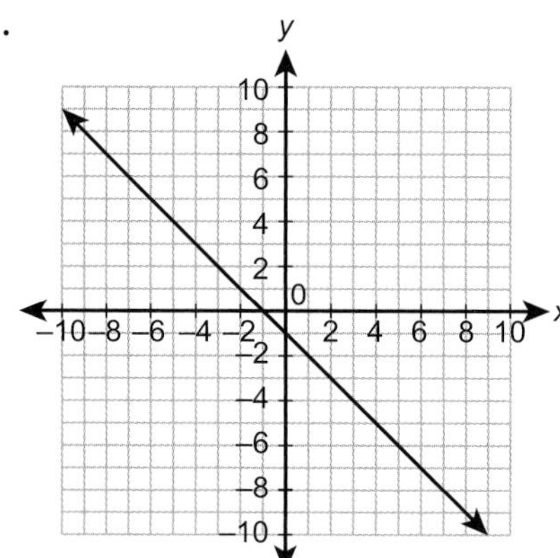

23. A. $C = 0.25x + 3$
B.

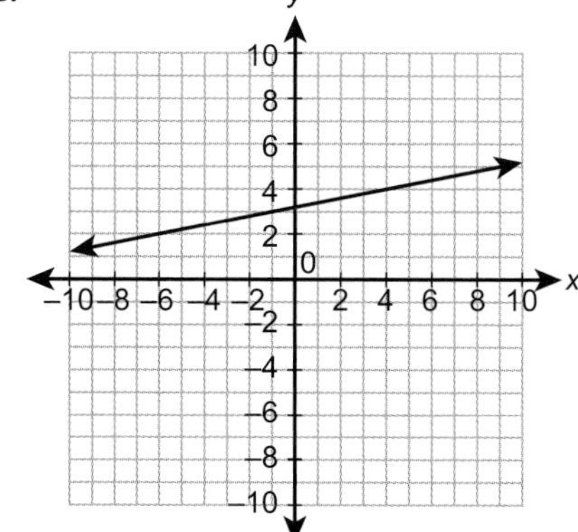

C. The y-intercept represents the cost of a bracelet with no charms. **D.** A bracelet with five charms will cost \$4.25.

25. A. $C = 0.05x + 5.50$

B.

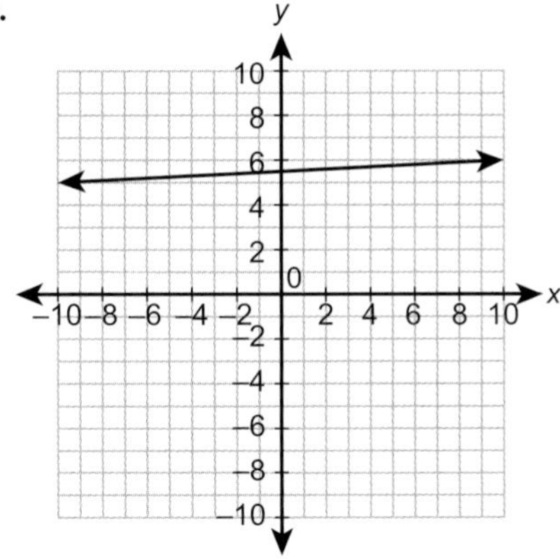

C. The y-intercept represents the initial cost to print.
D. Zain will pay \$6.75 to have 25 pictures printed.

27. A. $P = 0.50x - 12$

B.

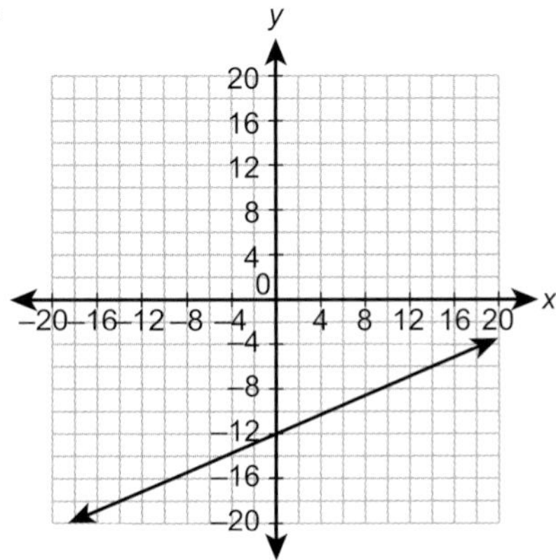

C. The y-intercept represents the cost to buy the fruit.
D. Carlos must sell 84 dried fruit bars to make a profit.

Pages 216–218

1. $m = -3$ **3.** $m = -\frac{3}{4}$ **5.** $y - 4 = 7(x + 3)$ **7.** $y = \frac{3}{4}x$
9. $y + 8 = \frac{1}{7}(x - 7)$ **11. A.** $m = -1$; **B.** Using $(-4, 6)$: $y - 6 = -1(x + 4)$; Using $(7, -5)$: $y + 5 = -1(x - 7)$
13. A. $m =$ undefined **B.** $x = 3$ **15. A.** $m = 0$ **B.** Using $(4, 8)$: $y - 8 = 0$; Using $(-1, 8)$: $y - 8 = 0$

17.

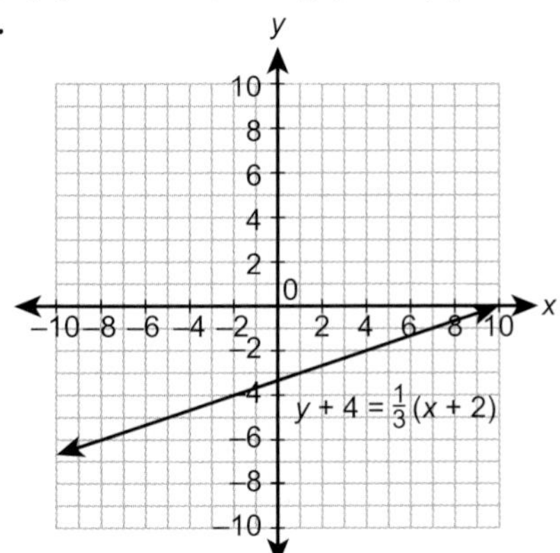

19.

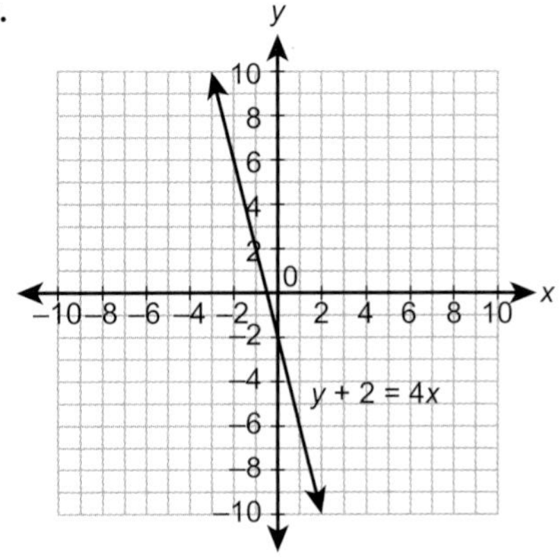

21.

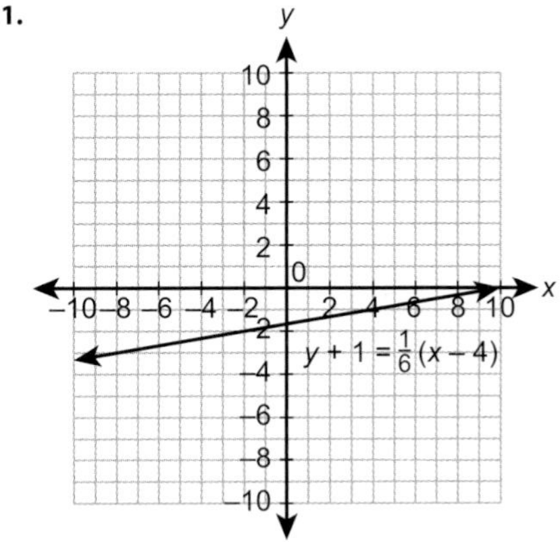

23. A. $y = x - 7$ **B.** Soo-Min will jump 10.5 inches.
25. A. $y = 50x + 25$ **B.** Alonzo will have \$1225.
27. A. $y = 15x$ **B.** It would take Lamar 150 minutes or $2\frac{1}{2}$ hours to walk 10 miles. **29. A.** $y = -0.08x + 11$
B. $(75, 5)$ indicates that when 75 sports cars were on the lot, customers bought 5. **C.** As the number of sports cars increases, the sales decrease.

Pages 222–224

1. A. $m = 2$ **B.** $m = 2$ **C.** $y = 2x - 1$ **3. A.** $m = -2$
B. $m = \frac{1}{2}$ **C.** $y = \frac{1}{2}x + 5$ **5. A.** $m = 2$ **B.** $m = 2$
C. $y = 2x + 6$ **7. A.** $m = \frac{6}{7}$ **B.** $m = -\frac{7}{6}$ **C.** $y = \frac{7}{6}x - \frac{1}{6}$
9. A. $m = -8$ **B.** $m = \frac{1}{8}$ **C.** $y = \frac{1}{8}x - \frac{35}{4}$ **11. A.** $m = -5$
B. $m = \frac{1}{5}$ **C.** $y = \frac{1}{5}x - \frac{23}{5}$ **13. A.** undefined slope **B.** $m = 0$
C. $y = 1$ **15. A.** $m = 2$ **B.** $m = -\frac{1}{2}$ **C.** $y = -\frac{1}{2}x + 15$
17. A. undefined slope **B.** undefined slope **C.** $x = 6$
19. neither **21.** parallel **23.** parallel **25.** neither
27. perpendicular **29.** $y = -\frac{1}{6}x + 5$

Pages 228–230

1. $y - 5 = \frac{9}{13}(x - 7)$ or $y + 4 = \frac{9}{13}(x + 6)$
3. $y - 7 = \frac{5}{7}(x - 9)$ or $y - 2 = \frac{5}{7}(x - 2)$
5. $y - 4 = 0(x - 5)$ or $y - 4 = 0(x + 6)$ **7.** $x = 3$
9. $3x + 5y = 17$ **11.** $-5x + 14y = 39$ **13.** $-4x + 11y = 42$

15. $y = 6$ **17.** $y = \frac{4}{11}x - \frac{52}{11}$ **19.** $y = -\frac{11}{4}x + 9$

21. $y = -\frac{3}{8}x - \frac{47}{8}$ **23.** $x = 6$

Pages 232–234

1. A.

p	5	10	15	20
t	45	60	75	90

B.

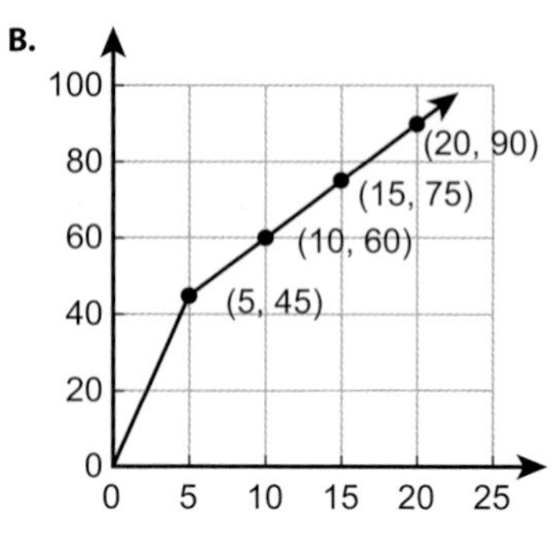

3. A.

g	0	2	4	6
s	3	9	15	21

B.

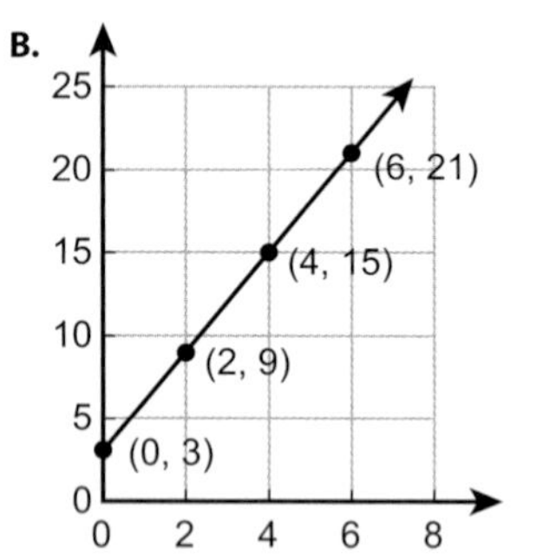

5. A.

d	0	3	6	9
s	−25	−10	5	20

B.

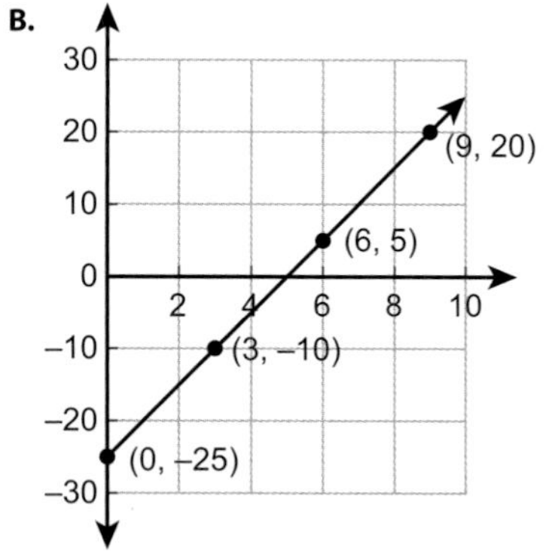

7. A.

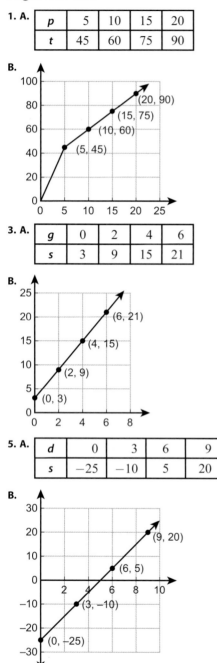

m	6	12	18	24
c	375	675	975	1275

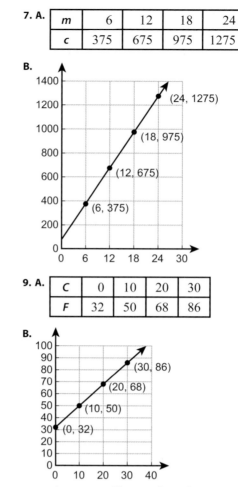

B.

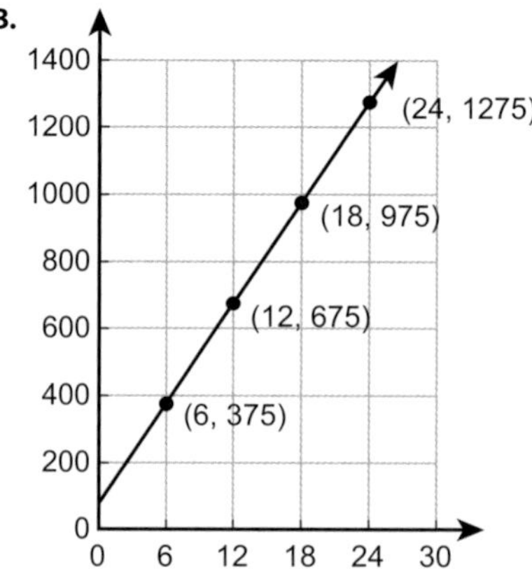

9. A.

C	0	10	20	30
F	32	50	68	86

B.

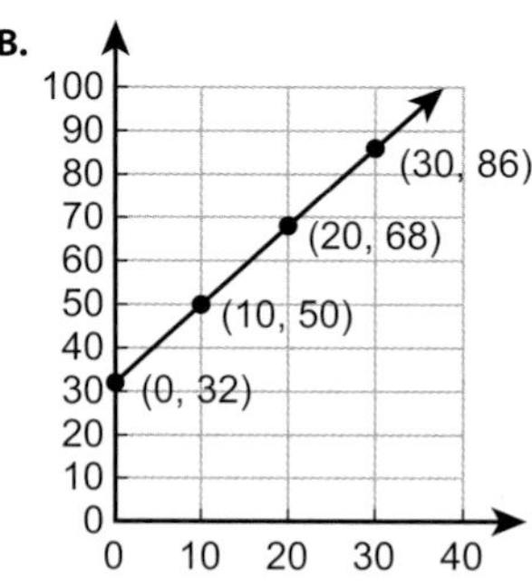

11. A. Answers will vary. Sample answer:

t	1	2	3	4
s	33	27	17	3

B. The rate of change is not constant, so the model is not linear. **13. A.** Answers will vary. Sample answer:

x	50	60	70	80
c	15	18	21	24

B. The equation is written in slope-intercept form. The slope is 0.3 and the y-intercept is 0. **15. A.** Answers will vary. Sample answer:

N	1	2	3	4
m	1	6	9	10

B. The rate of change is not constant, so the model is not linear. **17. A.** Answers will vary. Sample answer:

c	1	2	3	4
T	26.74	53.48	80.22	106.96

B. The equation can be written in slope-intercept form. The slope is 26.7393 and the y-intercept is 0. **19. A.** Answers will vary. Sample answer:

v	15,000	20,000	25,000	30,000
S	123	148	173	198

B. The equation is written in slope-intercept form. The slope is 0.005 and the y-intercept is 48.

21. A.

t	1	2	3	4
d	1850	3700	5550	7400

B. The rates of change are the same, so the model is linear.

23. A.

c	0	1	2	3
f	30	45	60	75

B. The rates of change are the same, so the model is linear.

25. A.

p	2	4	6	8
T	27	54	81	108

B. The rates of change are the same, so the model is linear.

27. A.

p	1	3	5	7
A	4.49	13.47	22.45	31.43

B. The rates of change are the same, so the model is linear.

29. A.

h	20	30	40	50	60
P	160	240	320	440	560

B. If he works 40 hours or less in a week, the linear equation in slope-intercept form that defines his pay is $P = 8h$.
If he works more than 40 hours per week, the linear equation in slope-intercept form that defines his pay is
$P = 320 + 12(h - 40) = 320 + 12h - 480 = 12h - 160$.

Pages 238–239

1. A. Yes. **B.** Yes. **3. A.** No. **B.** No. **5. A.** Yes. **B.** Yes. **7. A.** No. **B.** No. **9. A.** Yes. **B.** No.

11.

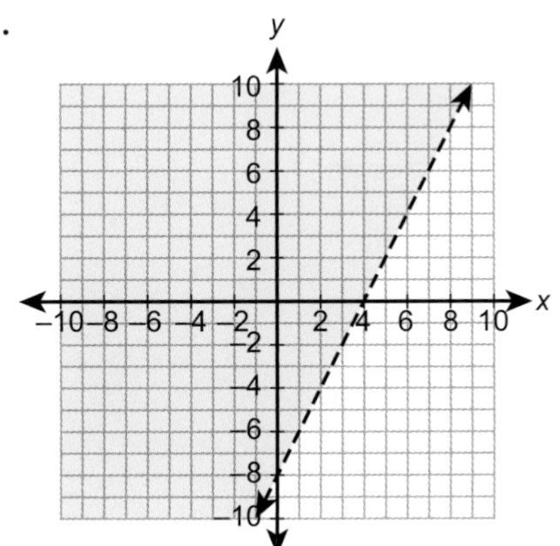

13.

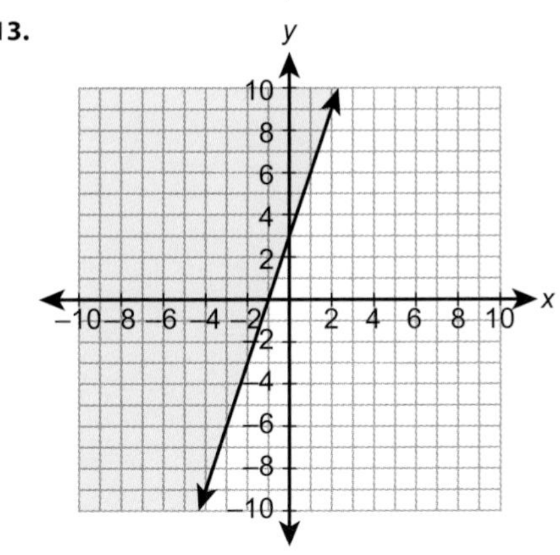

15.

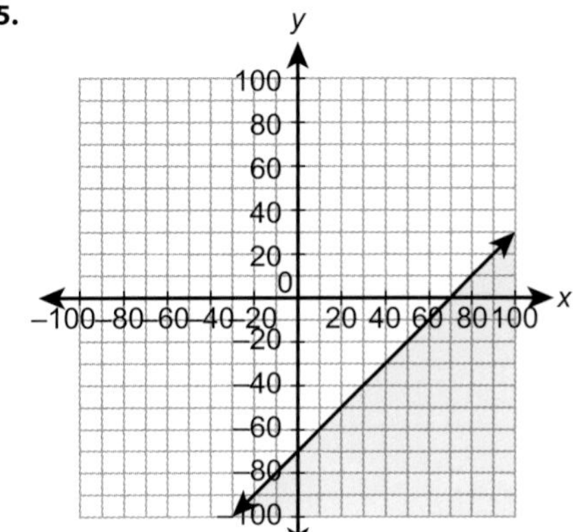

17.

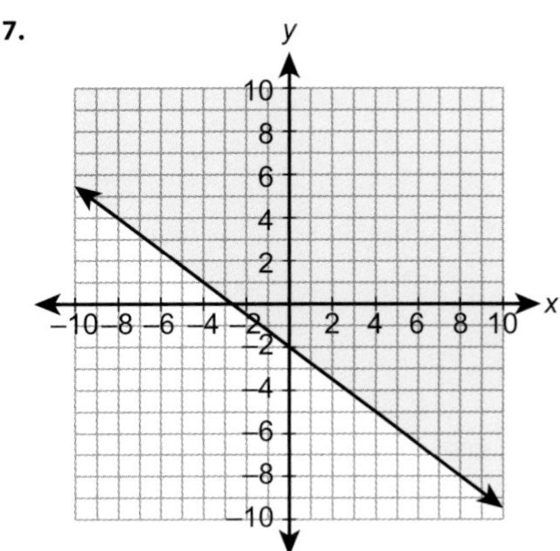

19.

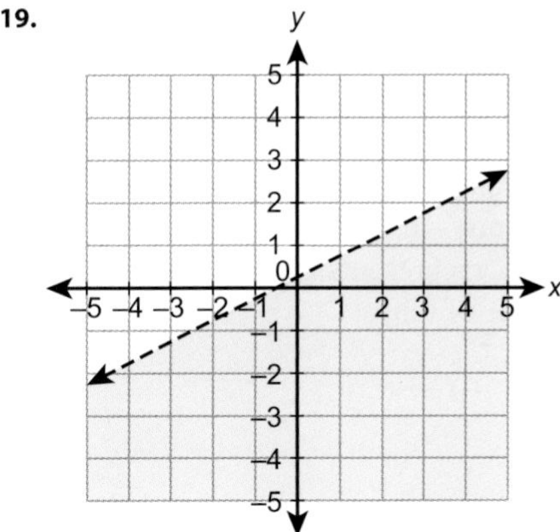

21.

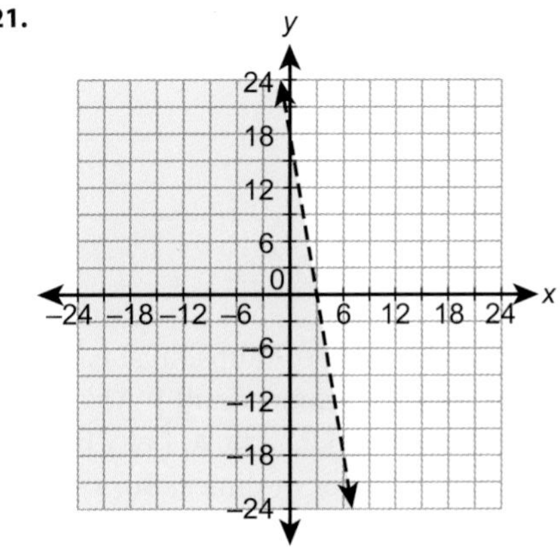

23.

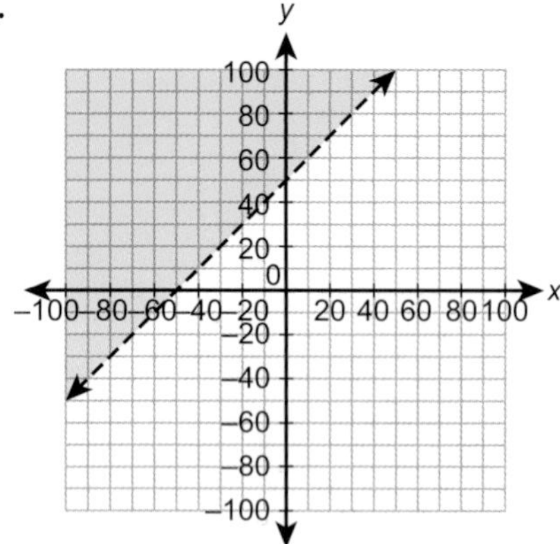

25. A. $y - 5000 \geq x$, where x represents the expenditures in dollars for a given month and y represents the income in dollars for the same month.

B.

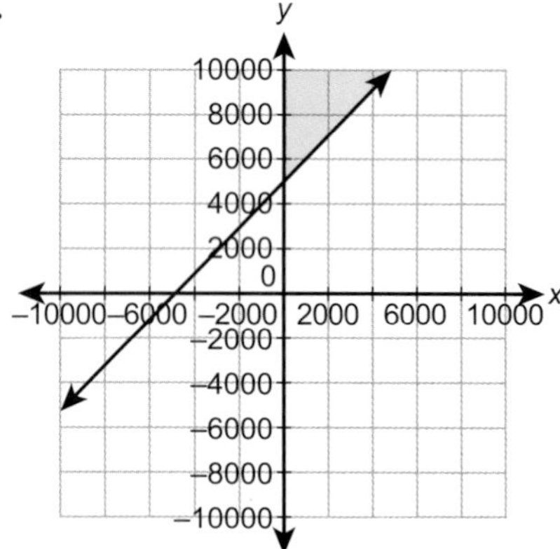

C. The income and expenditures must each be at least 0, so the graph is restricted to quadrant I. Also, the values are restricted to appropriate dollar amounts—to the hundredths place.

27. A. $5x + 4y \geq 20$, where x represents the number of roses and y represents the number of tulips.

B.

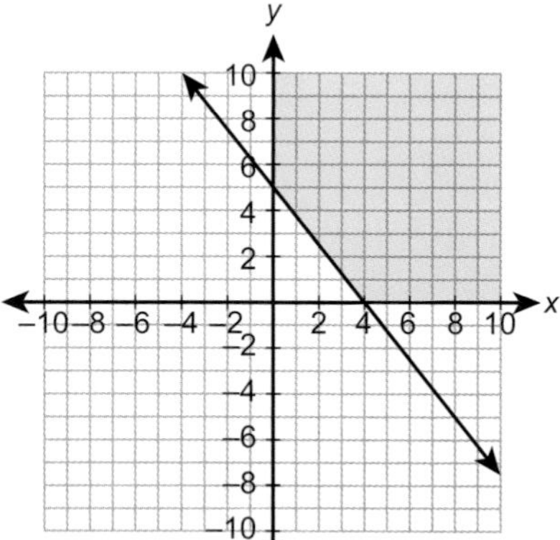

C. The number of roses and the number of tulips must each be at least 0, so the graph is restricted to quadrant I. Also, the number of each must be a whole number. **29. A.** Let x be the number of quarters and y be the number of dimes. So, $x > 50$ and $y \geq 75$. Therefore, $x + y > 125$. Also, $x + y \leq 200$.

B.

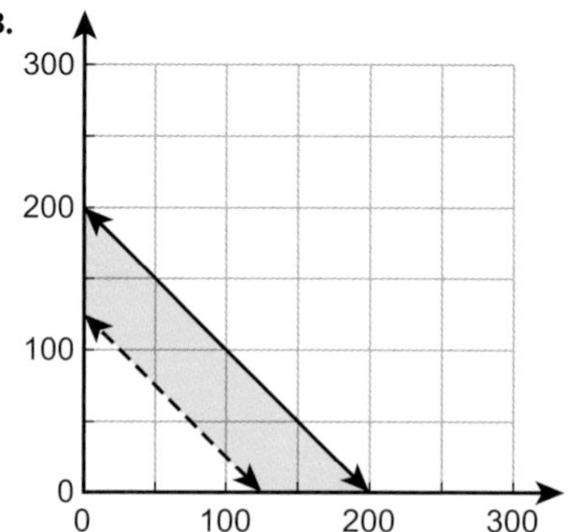

C. The sum of the quarters and dimes must be more than 125 but less than or equal to the total number of coins in the bag, which is 200, so the graph is restricted to quadrant I, between the two inequality lines. Also, the number of each must be a whole number.

Pages 242–245

1. $y \leq 2x - 4$ **3.** $y < -3x$ **5.** $y < 4x - 8$ **7.** $y \leq -5$
9. $y < -0.2x - 1$ **11.** $y > x - 50$ **13.** $x \leq 7$
15. $y < 9x - 31$ **17.** $y \geq 2x - 7$ **19.** $y > -8x + 12$
21. $y \geq -50$ **23.** The operator is $>$ because the shading is to the upper left of the boundary line and the boundary line is dashed.

UNIT 7 Systems of Equations

Pages 252–254

1.

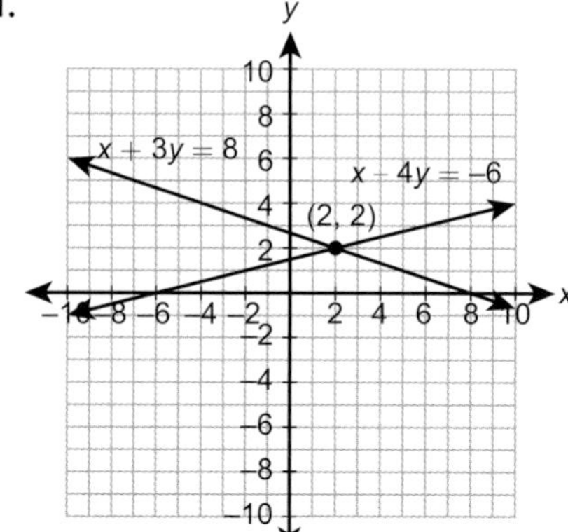

3.

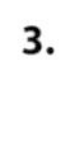

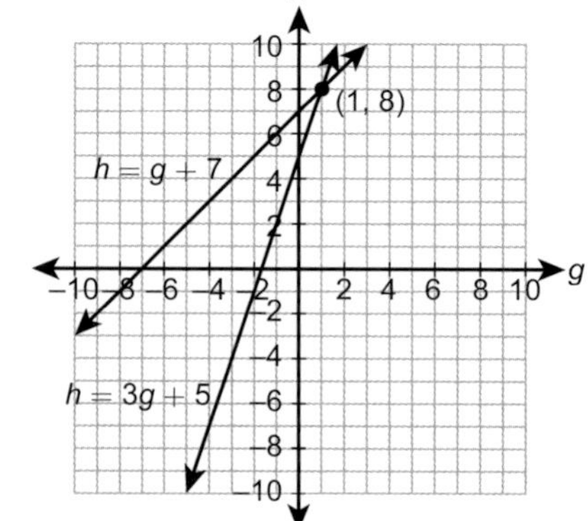

5.

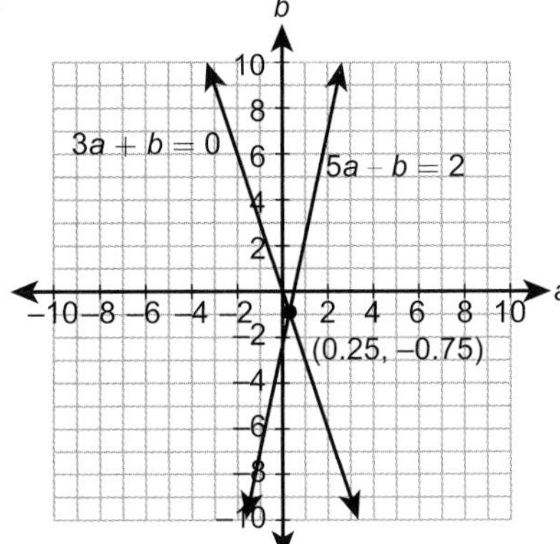

7.

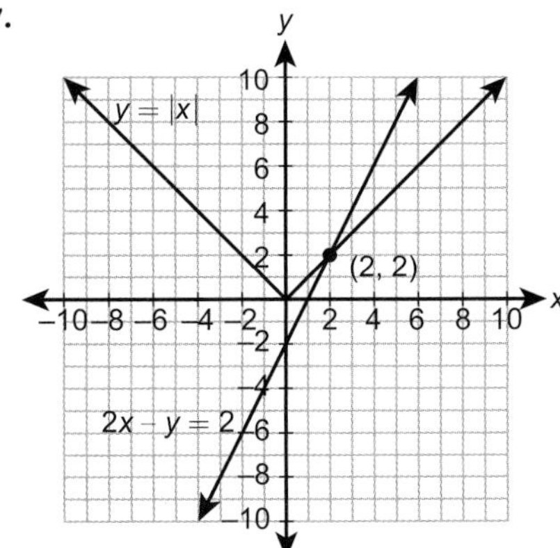

9. consistent and independent **11.** consistent and independent

13. A.

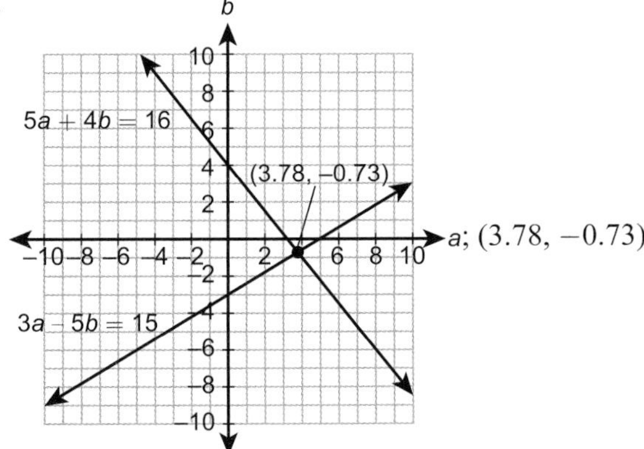

B. consistent and independent

15. A.

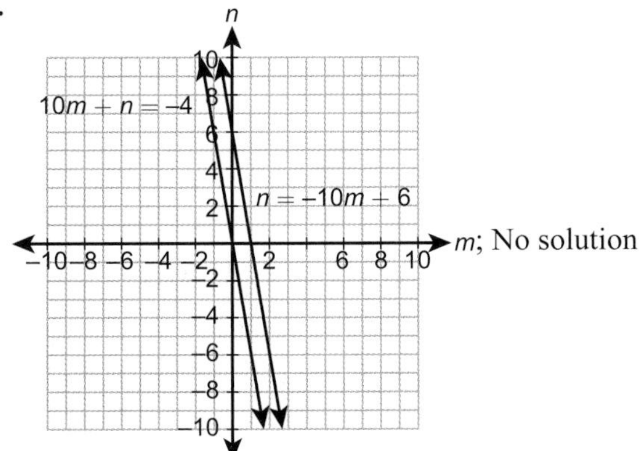

B. inconsistent

17. A.

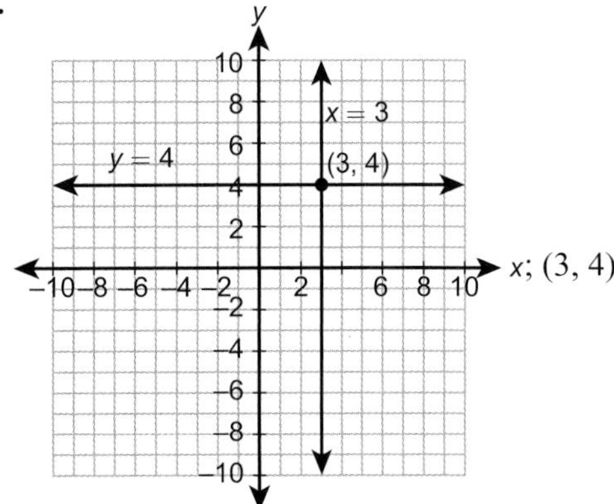

B. consistent and independent

19. A.

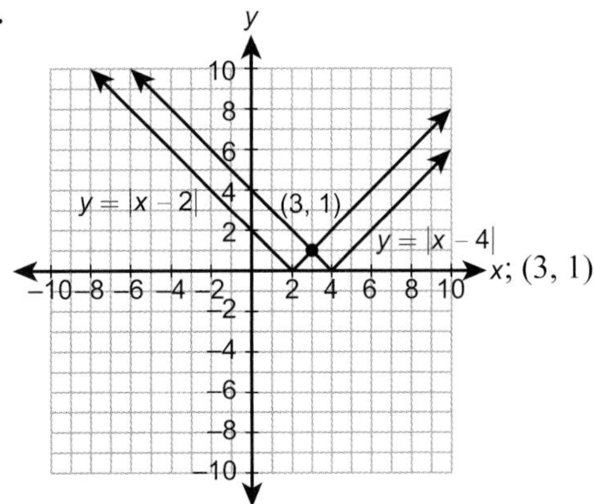

B. consistent and independent **21. A.** Answers will vary. Sample answer: Let x represent the amount in fund 1 and y represent the amount in fund 2. **B.** $0.06x + 0.07y = 340$; $x + y = 5000$

C.

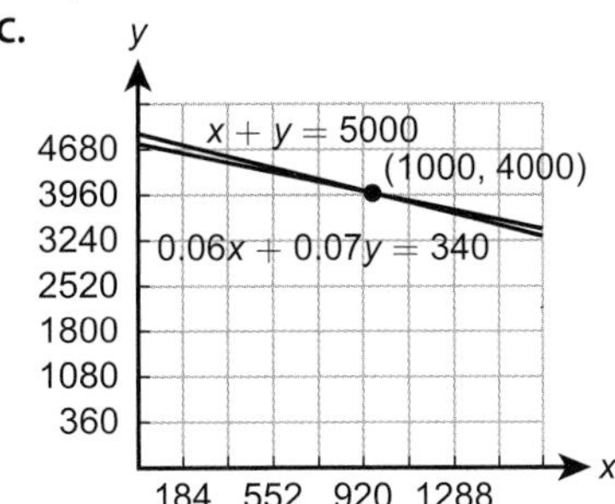

D. Sooni invested $1000 in fund 1 and $4000 in fund 2. **23. A.** Answers will vary. Sample answer: Let m represent the mechanical pencil pack and l represent the lead pencil pack. **B.** $0.40m + 0.20l = 117$; $m + l = 400$

C.

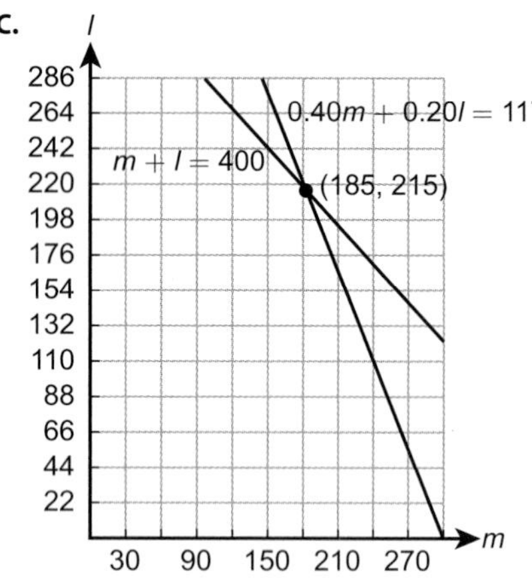

D. The Booksmart Company ordered 185 mechanical pencil packs and 215 lead pencil packs. **25. A.** Answers will vary. Sample answer: Let w represent the width of the yard, l represent the length of the yard, and f represent the amount of fencing. **B.** $wl = 3600$; $w + 2l = 205$; $2w + l = 170$

C.

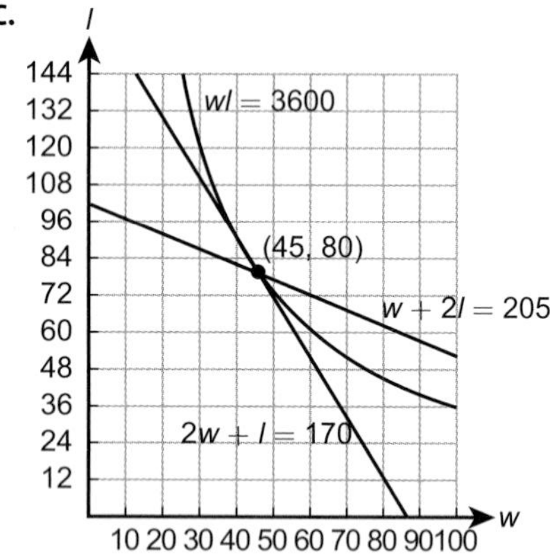

D. If the fence is around the width of the yard on both sides and the length of the yard once, Koichi needs 170 feet of fencing. If the fence is around the width of the yard once and the length of the yard on both sides, Koichi needs 205 feet of fencing.

Pages 258–259

1. $(1, 7)$ **3.** $(-1, 9)$ **5.** There are infinitely many solutions. **7.** No solution. **9.** There are infinitely many solutions. **11.** $\left(-\frac{3}{19}, -\frac{27}{19}\right)$ **13.** No solution. **15.** $\left(\frac{3}{4}, 4\right)$ **17.** $\left(5, -\frac{1}{5}\right)$ **19.** There are infinitely many solutions. **21.** No solution. **23. A.** Answers will vary. Sample answer: Let n represent the number of nickels, $2n$ represent the number of pennies, and q represent the number of quarters. **B.** Equation 1: $0.07n + 0.25q = 2.30$; Equation 2: $3n + q = 50$ **C.** $n = 15$; $q = 5$ **D.** The bank contains 30 pennies, 15 nickels, and 5 quarters. **25. A.** Answers will vary. Sample answer: Let c represent slices of cheese and s represent slices of salami. **B.** Equation 1: $0.15c + 0.25s = 1.70$; Equation 2: $c + s = 8$ **C.** $c = 3$; $s = 5$ **D.** Sumika has 3 slices of cheese and 5 slices of salami. **27. A.** Answers will vary. Sample answer: Let w represent the quarts of water and c represent the quarts of 100% cranberry juice. **B.** Equation 1: $w = 6.4$; Equation 2: $w + c = 8$ **C.** $c = 1.6$ **D.** Six and four-tenths liters of water and 1.6 liters of cranberry juice should be used. **29. A.** Answers will vary. Sample answer: Let x represent metal with 40% aluminum and y represent metal with 60% aluminum. **B.** Equation 1: $0.40x + 0.60y = 10$; Equation 2: $x + y = 20$ **C.** $x = 10$; $y = 10$ **D.** She should use 10 kilograms of each metal.

Pages 262–263

1. $(2, -3)$ **3.** $(0.5, -1)$ **5.** $(8, 12)$ **7.** $(-2, -6)$ **9.** $(-4, 3.5)$ **11.** $(-1, 6)$ **13.** $(-6.5, 3.5)$ **15.** $(1.5, -4)$ **17.** $(5, -13)$ **19.** $(-10, -18)$ **21.** $(5, -7)$ **23. A.** Answers will vary. Sample answer: Let a represent the price of adult tickets and y represent the price of youth tickets. **B.** $2a + 11y = 90.50$; $2a + 8y = 71$ **C.** $y = 6.50$; $a = 9.50$ **D.** The adult tickets cost \$9.50 and the youth tickets cost \$6.50. **25. A.** Answers will vary. Sample answer: Let x represent the first number and y represent the second number. **B.** $-2x + y = -6$; $x + y = 45$ **C.** $x = 17$; $y = 28$ **D.** The two numbers were 17 and 28. **27. A.** Answers will vary. Sample answer: Let s represent the amount of the 50% cocoa chocolate syrup and p represent the amount of 100% powdered cocoa. **B.** $0.5s + p = 16$; $s + p = 20$ **C.** $s = 8$; $p = 12$ **D.** The candy maker mixed 8 ounces of the syrup with 12 ounces of 100% powdered cocoa. **29. A.** Answers will vary. Sample answer: Let n represent the price of the notebooks and p represent the price of the pens. **B.** $3n + 10p = 24.87$; $3n + 6p = 18.51$ **C.** $p = 1.59$; $n = 2.99$ **D.** The pens cost \$1.59 and the notebooks cost \$2.99.

Pages 267–268

1. $(-2, 5)$ **3.** $\left(\frac{1}{2}, -2\right)$ **5.** $(6, -0.75)$ **7.** $(16, -1)$ **9.** $(250, 300)$ **11.** $(20, 30)$ **13.** $(15, -6)$ **15.** $(80, -75)$ **17.** $(30, -5)$ **19.** $(1, -1)$ **21.** $(-0.3, -5)$ **23.** The basic monthly rate is \$45 and the per-minute charge is \$0.02. **25.** A hot dog costs \$2.25 and a soft drink costs \$1.50. **27.** He rode on the mini-coaster 6 times and on the bumper boats 5 times. **29.** Julian invested \$1900 in stock p and \$1300 in stock q.

Pages 273–274

1. A. Answers will vary. Sample answer: Let l represent the length of the longer piece and s represent the length of the shorter piece. **B.** $l + s = 20$; $l = 2s + 2$ **C.** $s = 6$; $l = 14$ **D.** The shorter piece is 6 feet long and the longer piece is 14 feet long. **3. A.** Answers will vary. Sample answer: Let x represent the first number and y represent the second number. **B.** $x + y = 95$; $y = 2x - 16$ **C.** $x = 37$; $y = 58$ **D.** The numbers are 37 and 58. **5. A.** Answers will vary. Sample answer: Let f represent amount of the 100% fluoride and m represent the amount of the 60%/40% mixture. **B.** $f + m = 10$; $f + 0.60m = 8$ **C.** $f = 5$; $m = 5$

D. The students in Dr. Patel's class need to add 5mL of the 100% fluoride and 5mL of the 60%/40% mixture to make the desired 80%/20% mixture. **7. A.** Answers will vary. Sample answer: Let c represent the cost of a CD and b represent the cost of a book. **B.** $c = 3b$; $3b + 2c = 18$ **C.** $b = 2$; $c = 6$ **D.** The cost of a book is $2 and the cost of a CD is $6. **9. A.** Answers will vary. Sample answer: Let p represent the number of postcards and l represent the number of letters. **B.** $p + l = 30$; $0.23p + 0.37l = 9.28$ **C.** $p = 13$; $l = 17$ **D.** Jenny mailed 13 postcards and 17 letters. **11. A.** Answers will vary. Sample answer: Let s represent the cost of a senior citizen ticket and c represent the cost of a child ticket. **B.** $3s + c = 38$; $3s + 2c = 52$ **C.** $c = 14$; $s = 8$ **D.** The cost is $8 for a senior citizen and $14 for a child. **13. A.** Answers will vary. Sample answer: Let c represent the number of cows and h represent the number of horses. **B.** $c + h = 168$; $c = 5h$ **C.** $h = 28$; $c = 140$ **D.** The farmer raises 140 cows and 28 horses. **15. A.** Answers will vary. Sample answer: Let x represent the length of the first piece and y represent the length of the second piece. **B.** $x + y = 49$; $y = x + 5$ **C.** $x = 22$; $y = 29$ **D.** The pieces are 22 and 27 feet long. **17. A.** Answers will vary. Sample answer: Let j represent the amount of money Jeanie received and f represent the amount of money Ferris received. **B.** $j + f = 497{,}500$; $f = 2j + 10{,}000$ **C.** $j = 162{,}500$ **D.** Jeanie received $162,500. **19. A.** Answers will vary. Sample answer: Let x represent the assistant manager's salary and y represent the manager's salary. **B.** $x + y = 371{,}500$; $y = x + 28{,}500$ **C.** $x = 171{,}500$; $y = 200{,}000$ **D.** The manager's salary is $200,000 and the assistant manager's salary is $171,500. **21. A.** Answers will vary. Sample answer: Let c represent the total cost to operate either unit and y represent the number of years. **B.** $c = 412y + 2250$; $c = 466y + 1710$ **C.** $y = 10$; $c = 6370$ **D.** The cost will be $6730 to operate either AC unit in 10 years. **23. A.** Answers will vary. Sample answer: Let l represent the length and w represent the width. **B.** $w = l - 26$; $2w + 2l = 332$ **C.** $l = 96$; $w = 70$ **D.** The length of the screen is 96 feet and the width is 70 feet. Since the formula for area is $A = lw$, the area of the rectangle is 6720 ft^2.

Pages 279–281

1.

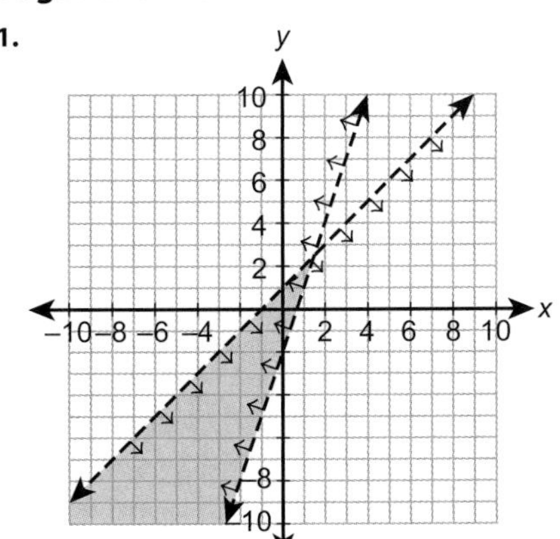

3.

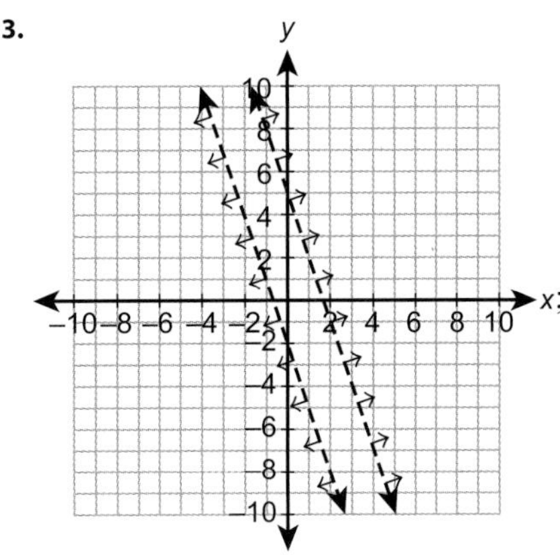

The system has no intersecting areas, therefore there is no solution.

5.

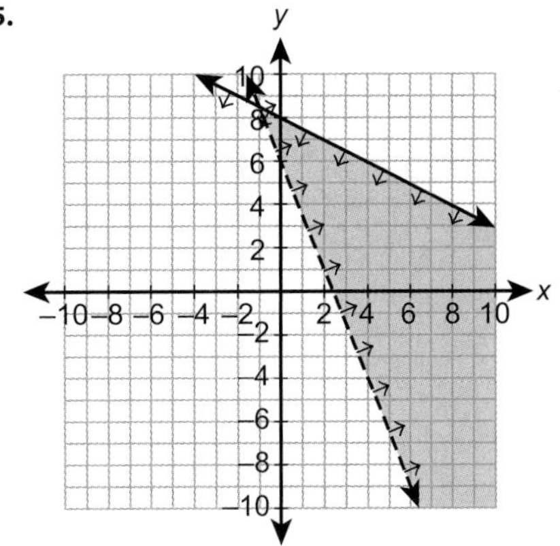

7.

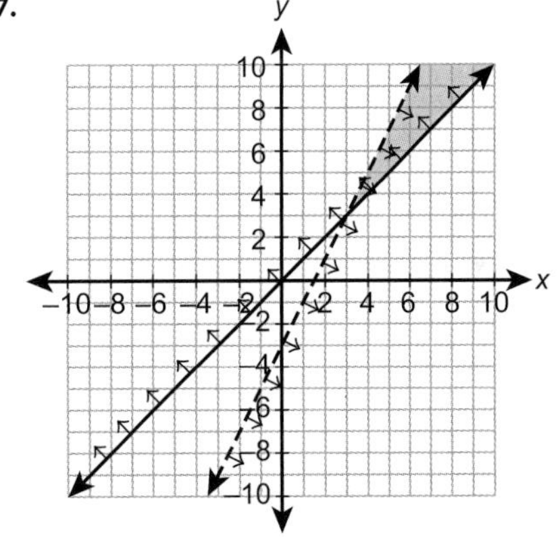

9.

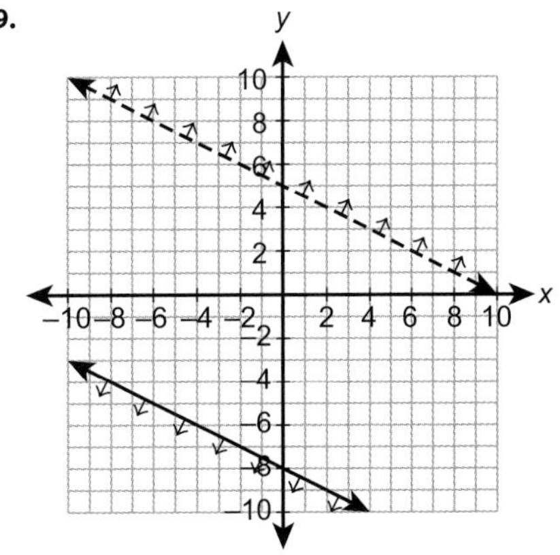

11.

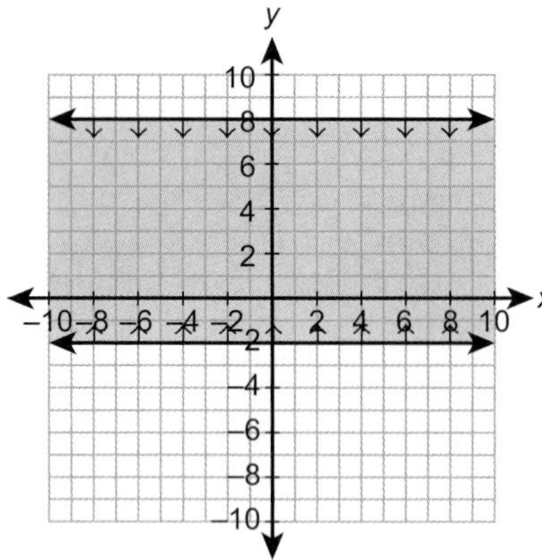

13.

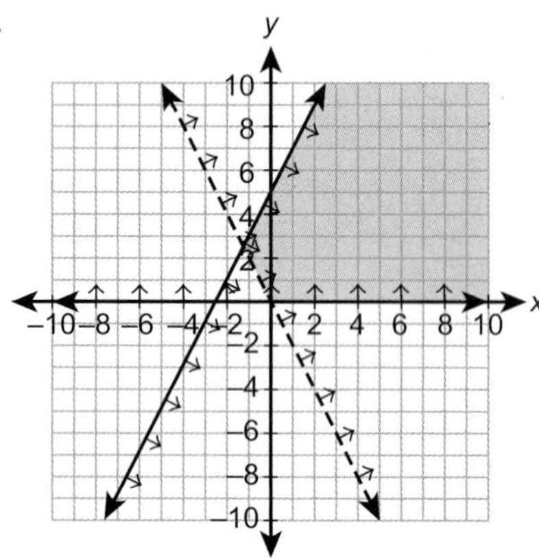

15. $y < x + 4; y \geq 4x + 1$ **17.** $y < 5; y \geq x - 4$

19. $y \leq \frac{2}{3}x + 4; y \geq -x + 1$ **21.** $y < x; y \geq -x$

23. $y \leq \frac{1}{2}x + 3; y \geq \frac{1}{2}x - 4$ **25.** $y \leq 4x - 5; y \geq -5x - 4$

27. A. $x \geq 0; y \geq 0; x + y \geq 12; 3x + 2y \leq 36;$

B.

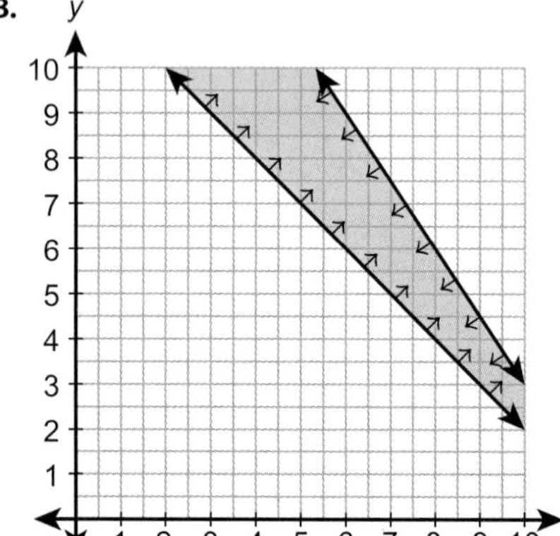

29. A. $x \geq 0; y \geq 0; x + y \geq 10; 6x + 8y \leq 96;$

B.

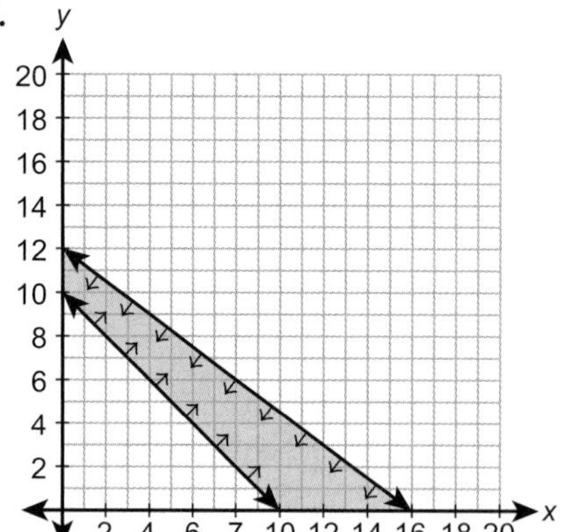

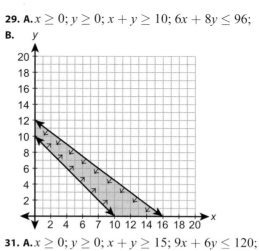

31. A. $x \geq 0; y \geq 0; x + y \geq 15; 9x + 6y \leq 120;$

B.

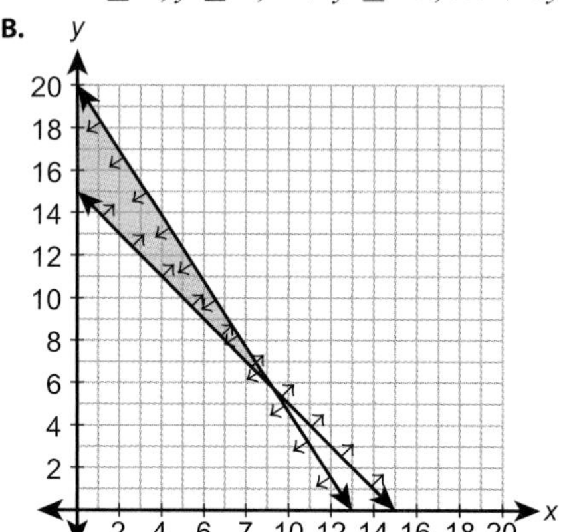

UNIT 8 Relations and Functions

Pages 286–288

1.

x	y
−4	−2
−3	1
0	4
1	−1
3	3

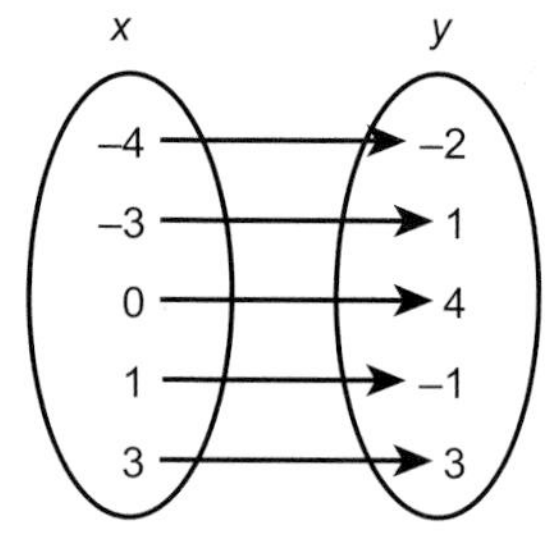

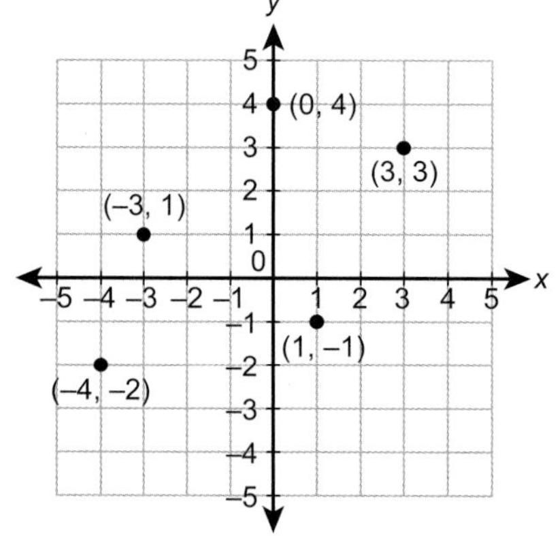

3.

x	*y*
−2	3
−1	−1
0	3
2	−2
3	−1

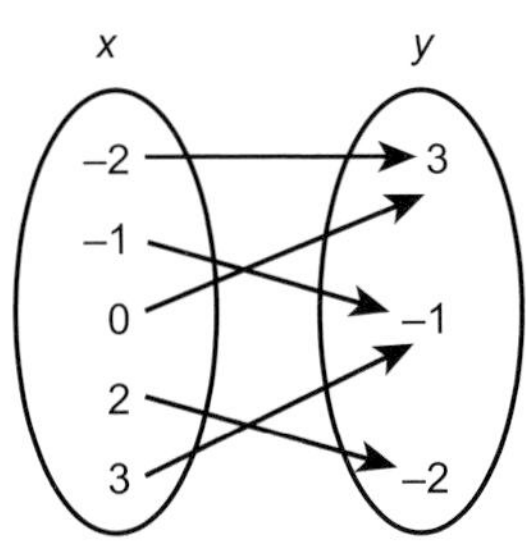

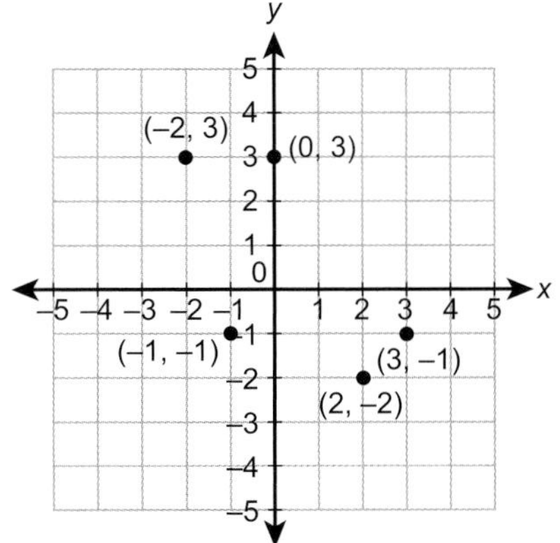

5.

x	*y*
−4	1
−2	−1
1	2
3	0
4	3

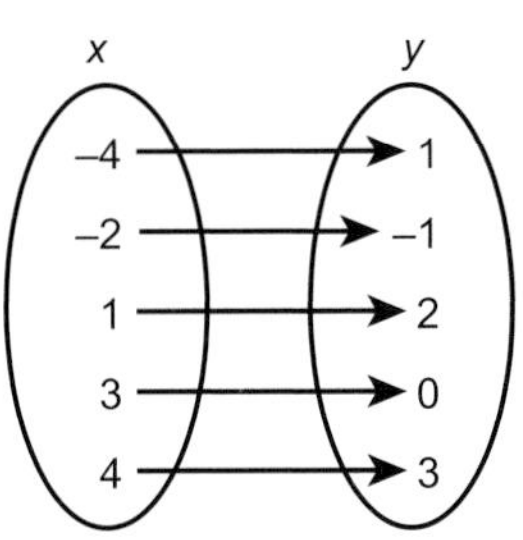

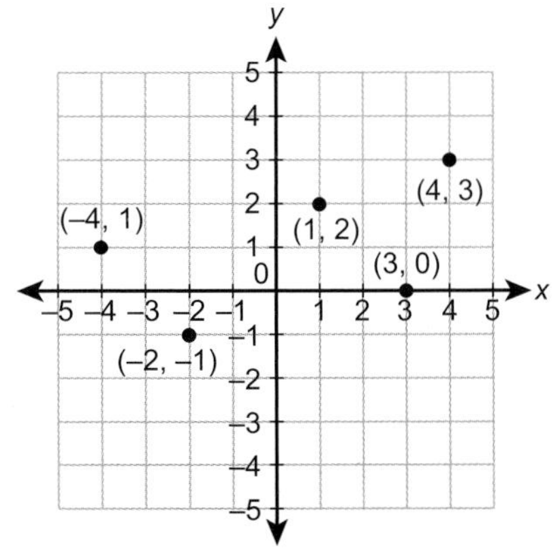

7.

x	*y*
1	1
3	2
5	3
7	5

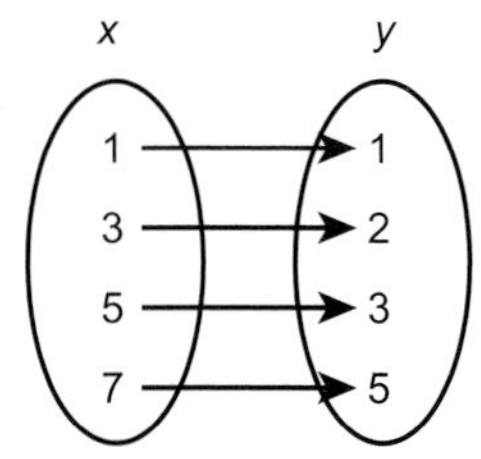

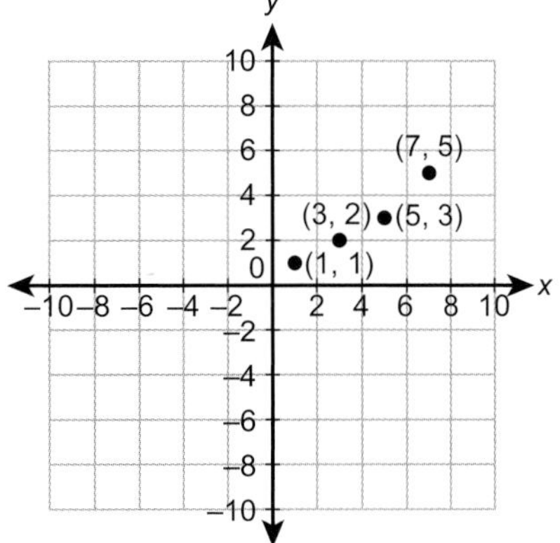

9.

x	*y*
−3	−6
−3	6
2	5
5	−6
5	5

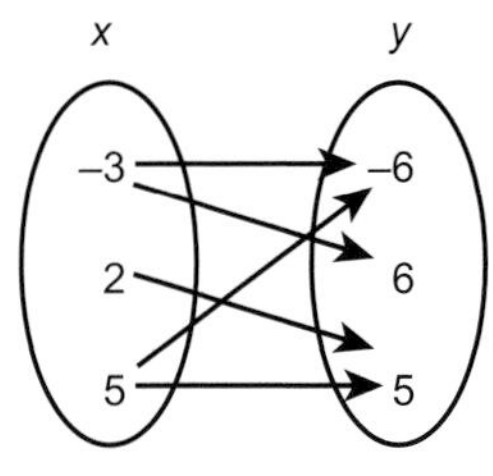

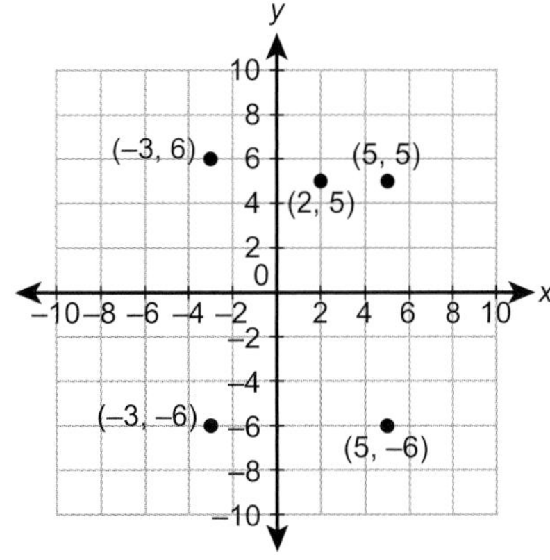

11.

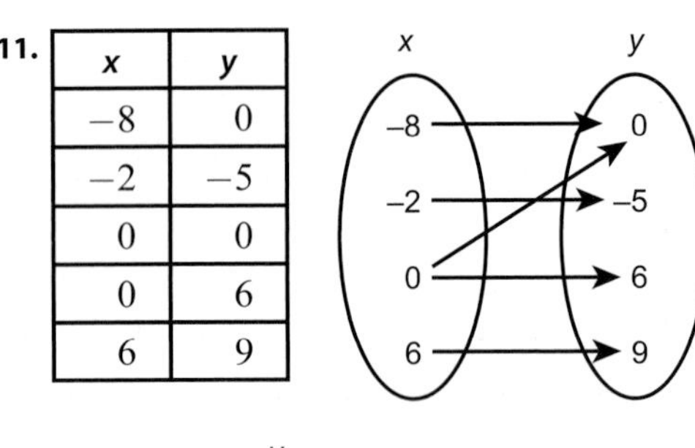

x	y
−8	0
−2	−5
0	0
0	6
6	9

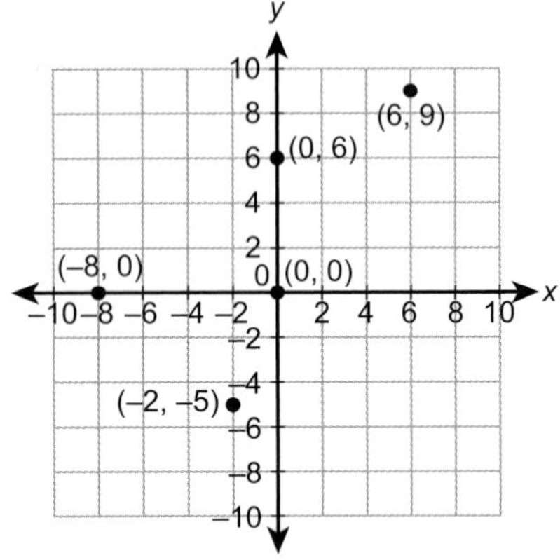

13. domain: $\{-5, 3, 4\}$; range: $\{-2, 3, 4\}$ **15.** domain: $\{2, 5, 5.8, 9, 10.5\}$; range: $\{-6, -5.8, 5, 7\}$ **17.** domain: $\{-7, -2, 0, 3\}$; range: $\{3, 5, 7\}$ **19.** domain: $\{2, 5, 8\}$; range: $\{-4, -1.5, 0, 2\}$ **21.** domain: $\{-12, -2, 2, 12\}$; range: $\{3, 4\}$ **23.** domain: $\{x|x \geq 0\}$; range: $\{y|y \leq 0\}$ **25. A.** $\{(2, 1), (3, 2), (4, 0), (5, 1), (6, 2), (7, 6), (8, 4), (9, 2), (10, 1), (11, 0), (12, 1)\}$ **B.** domain: $\{2, 3, 4, 5, 6, 7, 8, 9, 10, 11, 12\}$; range: $\{0, 1, 2, 4, 6\}$ **27. A.** $\{(1, 80), (1, 100), (1, 120), (1, 160), (2, 120), (2, 160), (2, 200), (2, 250)\}$

B.

Memory Size (GB)	Hard Drive Size (GB)
1	80
1	100
1	120
1	160
2	120
2	160
2	200
2	250

29. A. $\left\{\left(1, 2\frac{3}{4}\right), \left(2, 1\frac{3}{4}\right), \left(3, \frac{1}{2}\right), \left(4, 4\frac{1}{2}\right), \left(5, 3\frac{1}{4}\right), \left(6, 4\frac{1}{2}\right), \left(7, 2\frac{3}{4}\right), \left(8, 3\frac{1}{4}\right)\right\}$ **B.** domain: $\{1, 2, 3, 4, 5, 6, 7, 8\}$; range: $\left\{\frac{1}{2}, 1\frac{3}{4}, 2\frac{3}{4}, 3\frac{1}{4}, 4\frac{1}{2}\right\}$

Pages 293–297

1. The domain value of 3 is assigned to 2 and −2. The relation is not a function. **3.** No element from the domain is paired with more than one element from the range. The relation is a function. **5.** No element from the domain is paired with more than one element from the range. The relation is a function. **7.** The domain value of −2 is assigned to −8 and 0. The relation is not a function. **9.** No element from the domain is paired with more than one element from the range. The relation is a function. **11.** The domain value of −6 is assigned to −6 and 8. The relation is not a function. **13.** $y = -2$ **15.** $y = 3$ **17.** $y = -4$ **19.** $y = 18$ **21.** Graph A, because it shows each person's answers; graph B shows fractions of people. **23.** Graph B, because the graph shows growth, which is continuous throughout the months; graph A shows only individual years. **25.** Graph B, because it shows growth from day to day, and could show hourly reading totals as well as those at the end of each day. **27. A.** About 200 miles **B.** 45 miles per hour **29. A.** 25 inches **B.** Approximately 17 months old

Pages 300–303

1. $f(x) = -0.5x - 2$ **3.** $f(x) = 20x - 60$ **5.** $f(x) = -5x - 3$ **7.** $f(x) = -6$ **9. A.** $f(1) = 7$ **B.** $f(-5) = -11$ **11. A.** $g(-16) = -3$ **B.** $g(-4) = 0$ **13. A.** $p(2) = -3$ **B.** $p(0) = -15$ **15. A.** $v(-10) = 75$ **B.** $v(15) = -50$ **17. A.** $f(-3) = -7$ **B.** $f(2) = 3$ **19. A.** $h(-9) = (-9) + 11 = 2$ **B.** $h(-5) = (-5) + 11 = 6$ **21. A.** $z(7) = 62$ **B.** $z(5) = 36$ **23. A.** $l(1) = -\frac{1}{3}$ **B.** $l(2) = 1$ **25. A.** 3N **B.** 1N **27. A.** 5mm **B.** A period of harder rain would cause a higher rate of change in the pond depth over time, or a steeper slope. So, it rained harder during the first 20 minutes. **29. A.** At \$150, the discount is approximately \$10.50. **B.** Answers will vary. Sample answer: The tax rate, as a percentage, can be determined by the discount at \$100. $f(100) = 7$, so the tax rate is 7%. **C.** Answers will vary. Sample answer: The tax rate is the slope of the function.

Pages 306–309

1. A. $f(-4) = 3$ **B.** $f(-1) = 0$ **3. A.** $v(7) = 7$ **B.** $v(-11) = -33$ **5. A.** $m\left(-\frac{9}{4}\right) = -2.5$ **B.** $m\left(-\frac{3}{4}\right) = -1$ **7. A.** $g(6) = 2$ **B.** $g(10) = 2$ **9. A.** $x(-5) = -6$ **B.** $x(5) = -9$ **11. A.** $q(-6) = 49$ **B.** $q(14) = 169$

13.

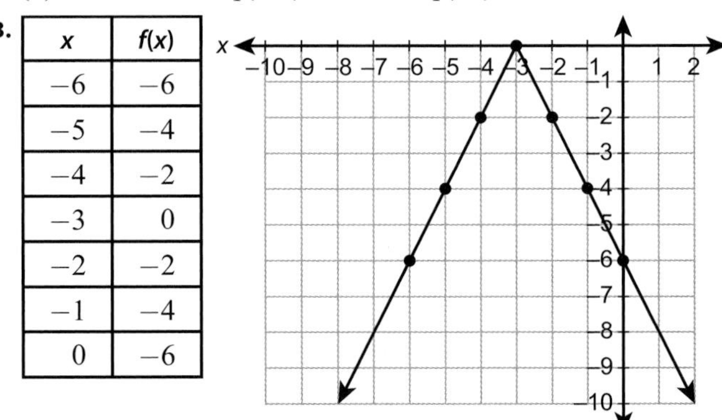

x	f(x)
−6	−6
−5	−4
−4	−2
−3	0
−2	−2
−1	−4
0	−6

15.

h	$d(h)$
−800	200
−500	100
−200	0
100	100
400	200
700	300
1000	400

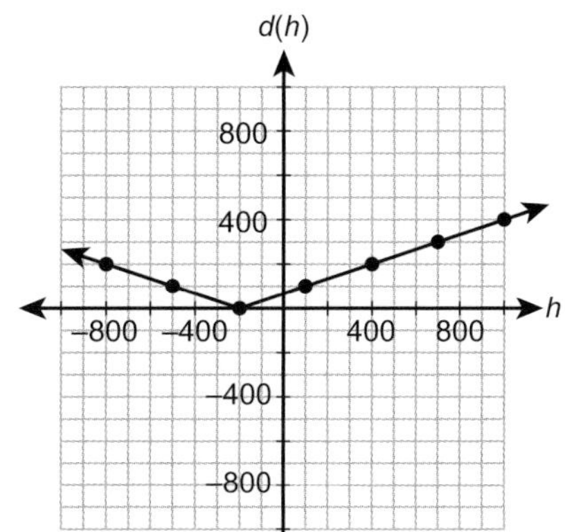

17.

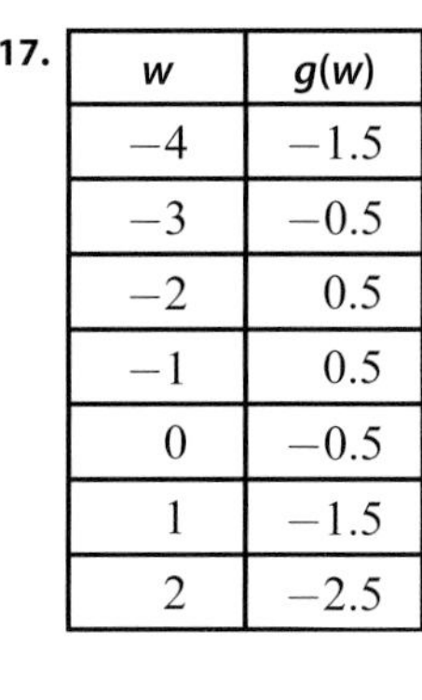

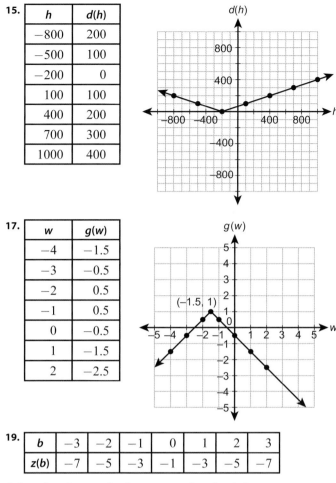

w	$g(w)$
−4	−1.5
−3	−0.5
−2	0.5
−1	0.5
0	−0.5
1	−1.5
2	−2.5

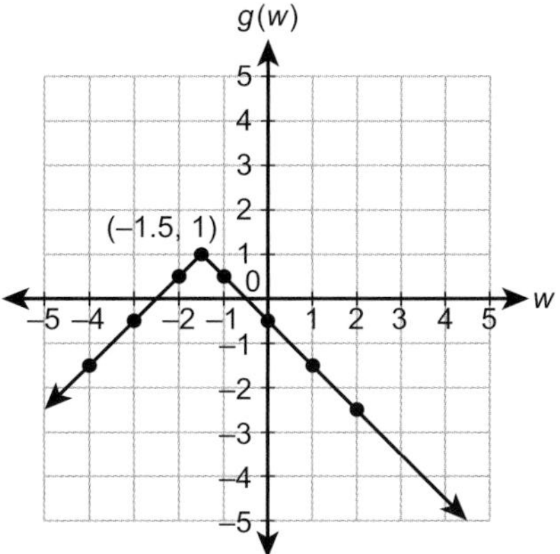

19.

b	−3	−2	−1	0	1	2	3
$z(b)$	−7	−5	−3	−1	−3	−5	−7

A function that works for every ordered pair is $z(b) = -|2b| - 1$.

21.

x	−3	−2	−1	0	1	2	3
$t(x)$	−9	−6	−3	0	−3	−6	−9

A function that works for every ordered pair is $t(x) = -3|x|$. **23. A.** $f(x) = |16 - 0.5x|$ **B.** The scale reading is off by 8 ounces. **25. A.** $f(b) = \frac{|8000 - b|}{8000}$ **B.** The actual balance deviates by 0.15% from the expected balance. **27. A.** $f(g) = \frac{|15 - g|}{15}$ **B.** The amount used deviates by 10% from his estimate. **29. A.** The mean price is \$10,350. **B.** $f(v) = |10{,}350 - v|$ **C.** The lower limit is 9650 and the upper limit is 11,050. There are two cars that are options (\$10,300 and \$9800).

Page 313

1. The relationship is a direct variation with a constant of variation of 2. **3.** The relationship is a direct variation with a constant of variation of 10. **5.** The relationship $y = \frac{9}{x}$ cannot be written in the form $y = kx$, so it does not represent a direct variation. **7.** The relationship is a direct variation with a constant of variation of 4. **9.** The direct variation equation is $f(x) = \frac{2}{3}x$. The value of x when $f(x)$ equals 7 is $\frac{21}{2}$.

11. The direct variation equation is $g(t) = \frac{1}{4}t$. The value of t when $g(t)$ equals 9 is 36. **13.** The direct variation equation is $h(d) = -3d$. The value of d when $h(d)$ equals 4 is $-\frac{4}{3}$. **15.** The direct variation equation is $f(x) = -\frac{1}{4}x$. The value of $f(x)$ when x equals 10 is $-\frac{5}{2}$. **17.** The direct variation equation is given by $y = \frac{1}{3}x$;

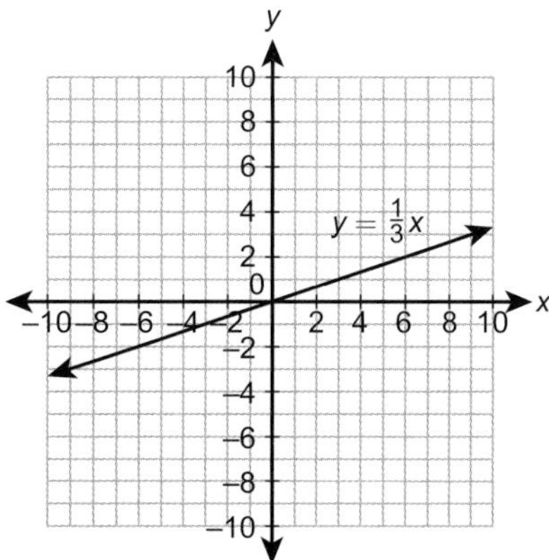

19. The direct variation equation is given by $b = -\frac{5}{2}a$;

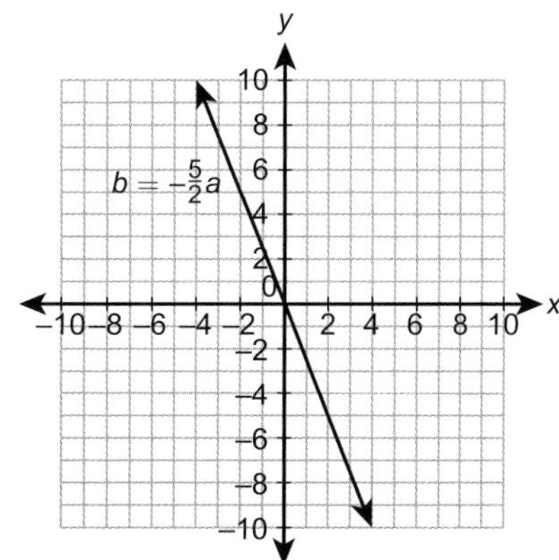

21. $k = \frac{y}{x} = \frac{2}{-8} = -\frac{1}{4}$; $y = -\frac{1}{4}x$; The direct variation equation is given by $y = -\frac{1}{4}x$;

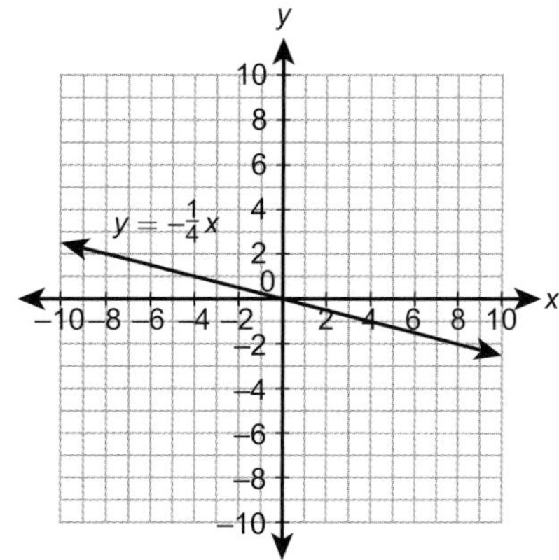

23. Let m represent the number of gallons bought and $c(m)$ represent the total cost. $c(m) = 2.67m$; There were 13 gallons of gas purchased for \$34.71. **25.** Let m represent the number of miles and $t(m)$ represent time in hours. $t(m) = 0.25m$; It will take Oni 1.425 hours to run 5.7 miles. **27.** Let l represent load and $s(l)$ represent stretch of spring. $s(l) = 0.3571l$; A load of approximately 14.001 kg would stretch the spring 5 cm. **29.** Let s represent speed and $h(s)$ represent height. $h(s) = 0.0617s^2$; The initial speed of approximately 22.050 m/s will allow the ball to travel 30 m high.

Pages 317–318

1. The relationship is a quadratic variation with a constant of variation of 8. **3.** The relationship is a quadratic variation with a constant of variation of $\frac{1}{2}$. **5.** The relationship is a quadratic variation with a constant of variation of $\frac{1}{8}$. **7.** The relationship is a quadratic variation with a constant of variation of 2. **9.** The value of $g(x)$ when x equals 1 is 2. **11.** The value of $f(x)$ when x equals 9 is 81. **13.** The value of $f(x)$ when x equals 2 is 1.2. **15.** The value of $h(w)$ when w equals 4 is 4.

17. $y = \frac{5}{2}x^2$;

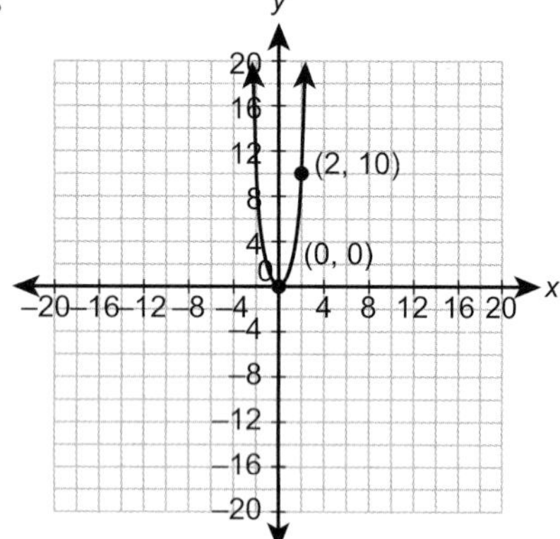

19. $k = 5g^2$;

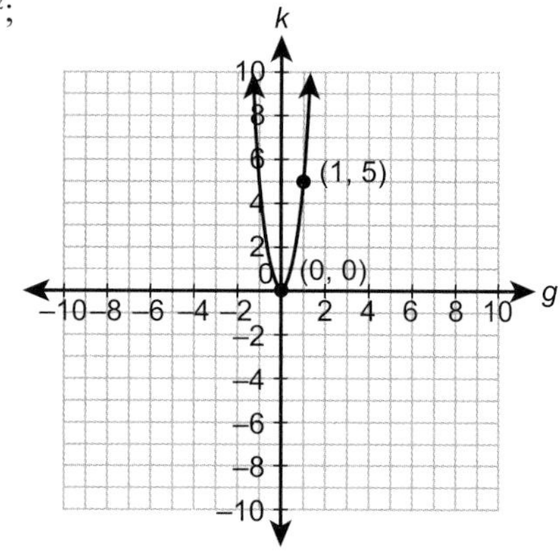

21. $y = \frac{1}{16}x^2$;

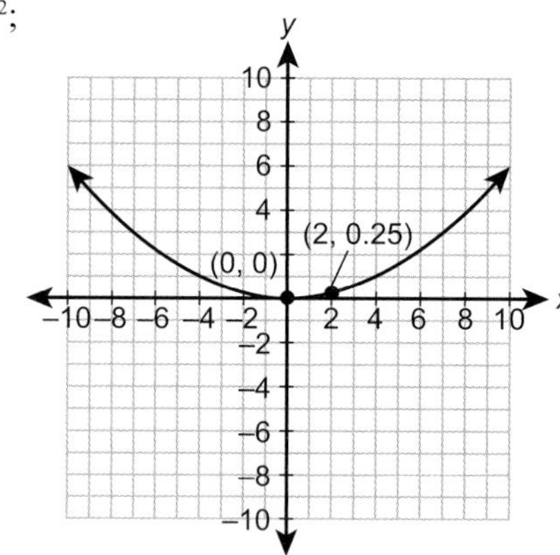

23. Let s represent the side length and $A(s)$ represent the area of the square. $A(s) = s^2$; The area of the square with side length 3 inches is 9 in^2. **25.** Let s represent the speed and $h(s)$ represent the height. $h(s) = \frac{25}{72}s^2$; The initial speed is approximately 13.15 m/s. **27.** Let s represent the speed of the wind and $w(s)$ represent the force of the wind. $w(s) = 0.1s^2$; The force is 360 N. **29.** Let r represent the radius, h represent the height, and V represent the volume. $V = 3.14hr^2$; The radius is approximately 4.9 inches.

Pages 322–323

1. The relationship is an inverse variation with a constant of variation of 36. **3.** The relationship is an inverse variation with a constant of variation of 2. **5.** The relationship cannot be written in the form $y = \frac{k}{x}$, so it does not represent an inverse variation. **7.** The relationship is an inverse variation with a constant of variation of −6. **9.** The value of y when x equals 10 is −3.2. **11.** The value of w when z equals 8 is 1.2. **13.** The value of y when x equals 9 is −96. **15.** The value of y when x equals 8 is 11.25

17. $v = \frac{-54}{t}$;

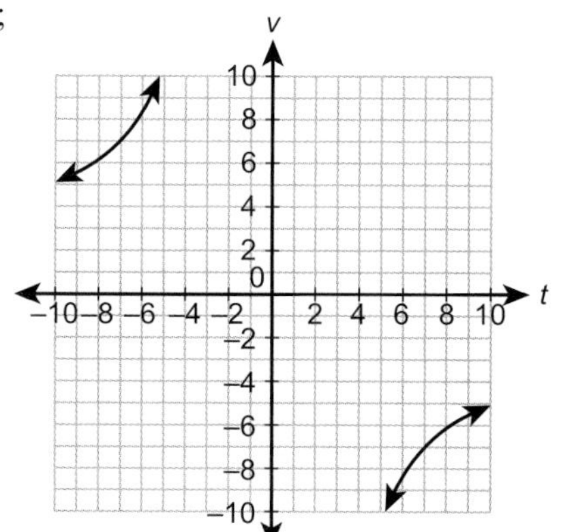

19. $y = \frac{-48}{x}$;

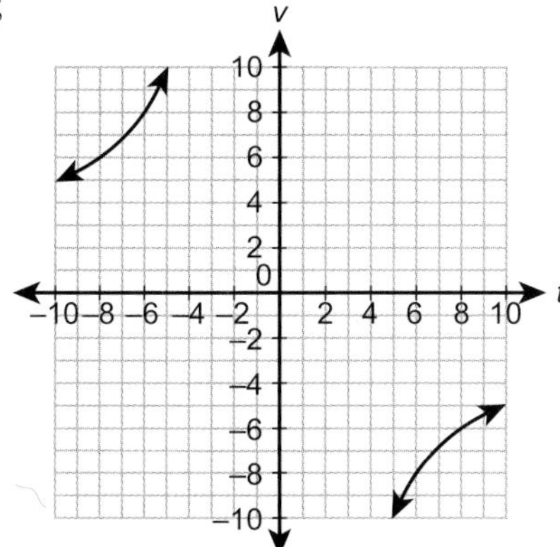

21. $s = \frac{-12}{r}$;

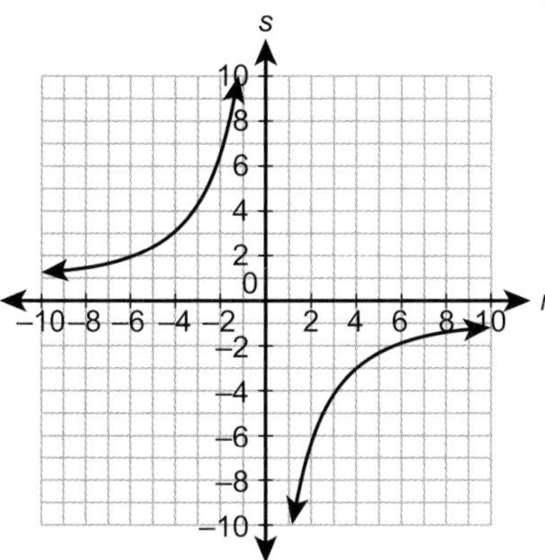

23. A. Let x represent the pressure and y represent the air inside the tire; $y = \frac{k}{x}$; The pressure is 35 psi when the volume is 120 cubic inches. **B.** Let x represent the pressure and y represent the air inside the tire; $y = \frac{k}{x}$; The pressure is 42 psi when the volume is 100 cubic inches. **25. A.** Let t represent the time and r represent the rate. $r = \frac{k}{t}$; It would take 58.5 seconds to fill the tank at the rate of 2 gallons per second. **B.** Let t represent the time and r represent the rate. $r = \frac{k}{t}$; It would take 225 minutes to fill the tank at the rate of 4 liters per minute.

Pages 327–331

1.

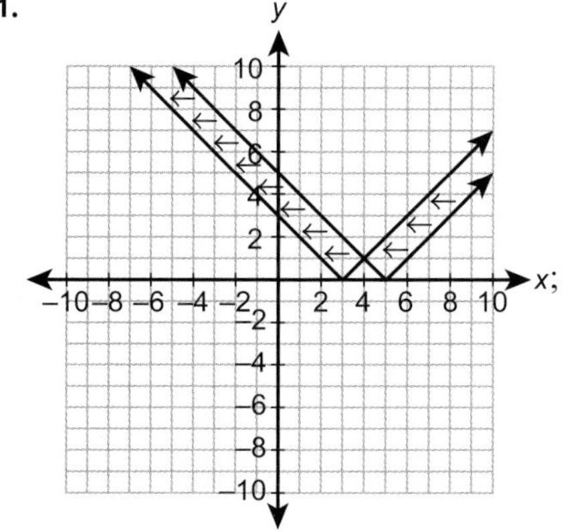

The graph is translated two units to the left.

3.

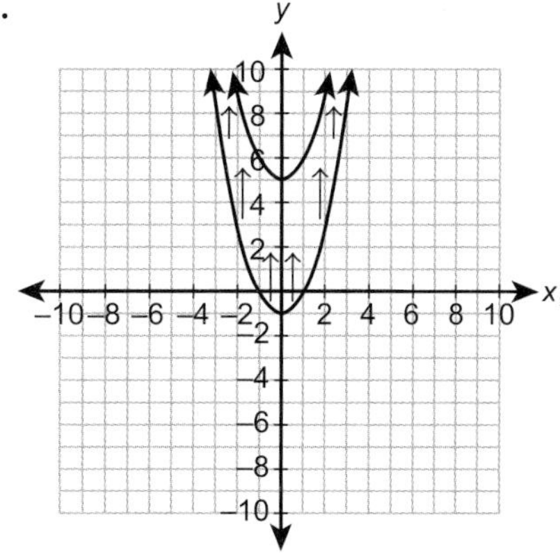

The graph is translated six units up.

5.

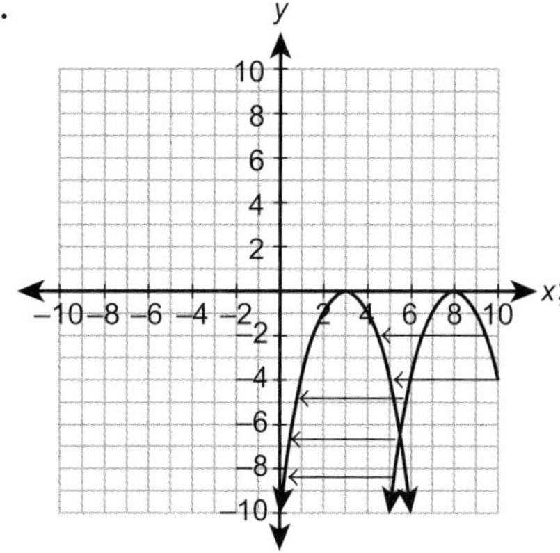

The graph is translated five units to the left.

7.

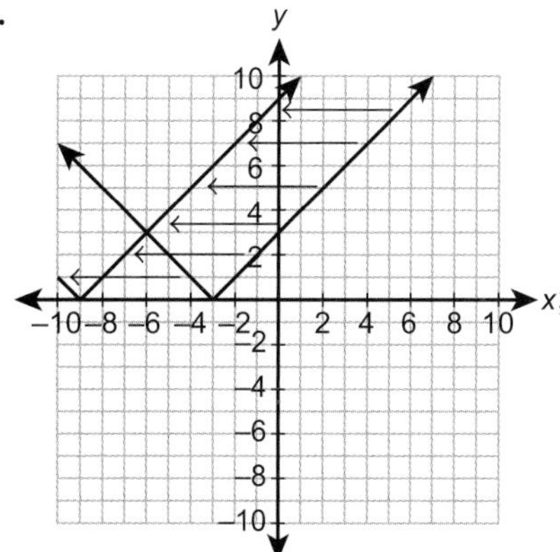

The graph is translated six units to the left.

9.

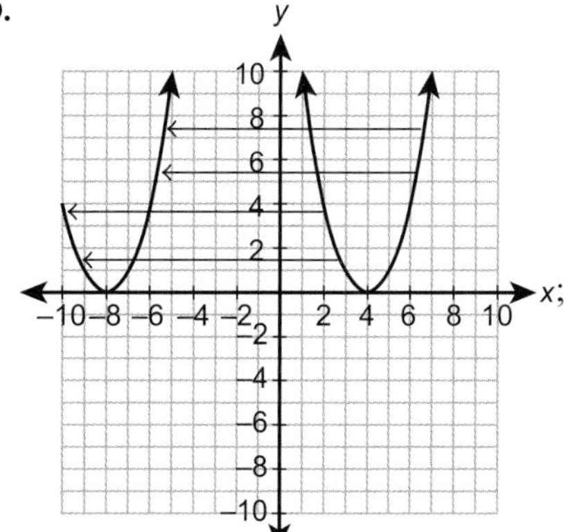

The graph is translated twelve units to the left.

11.

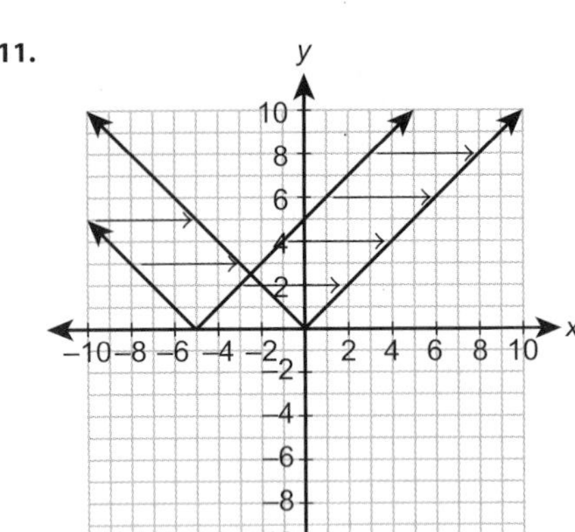

The graph is translated five units to the right. **13.** $(x, y) \rightarrow (x, y + 7)$ **15.** $(x, y) \rightarrow (x, y - 3)$ **17.** $(x, y) \rightarrow (x, y - 4)$ **19.** $(x, y) \rightarrow (x + 6, y)$ **21.** $(x, y) \rightarrow (x, y + 13)$ **23.** $(x, y) \rightarrow (x + 8, y)$ **25.** Diver A is 8 feet higher than Diver B, so the coordinate rule is $(x, y) \rightarrow (x, y - 8)$. **27.** The average score was 16 points higher after prep, so the coordinate rule is $(x, y) \rightarrow (x, y + 16)$. **29.** The cost of the trip in 2007 was \$12,000 more than in 2006, so the coordinate rule is $(x, y) \rightarrow (x, y + 12{,}000)$.

UNIT 9 Rationals, Irrationals, and Radicals

Page 338

1. cannot be written as a mixed number; proper fraction: $\frac{7}{20}$; decimal: 0.35; percent: 35% **3.** cannot be written as a mixed number; proper fraction: $\frac{5}{16}$; decimal: 0.3125; percent: 31.25% **5.** mixed number: $11\frac{1}{8}$; improper fraction: $\frac{89}{8}$; decimal: 11.125; percent: 1112.5% **7.** $>$ **9.** $=$ **11.** $<$ **13.** $<$ **15.** $\frac{8}{10}, \frac{11}{13}, \frac{7}{8}$ **17.** $\frac{1}{3}, \frac{3}{5}, \frac{5}{7}, \frac{7}{9}$ **19.** $\frac{64}{25}$, 2.58, $\frac{27}{10}$ **21.** 6.4, $\frac{69}{10}, \frac{64}{9}$ **23.** Answers will vary. Sample answer: $\frac{25}{36}$ **25.** Answers will vary. Sample answer: 7 **27.** Answers will vary. Sample answer: $\frac{5}{6}$ **29. A.** Answers will vary. Sample answer: $\frac{89}{130}$ **B.** Answers will vary. Sample answer: $\frac{191}{260}$

Page 342

1. terminates **3.** repeats **5.** repeats **7.** repeats **9.** $\frac{36}{5}$ **11.** $\frac{1}{8}$ **13.** $\frac{2}{27}$ **15.** $\frac{127}{50}$ **17.** $\frac{367}{90}$ **19.** Answers will vary. Sample answer: $\frac{61}{36}$ **21.** Answers will vary. Sample answer: $\frac{1}{4}$ **23.** Answers will vary. Sample answer: $-\frac{52}{33}$ **25.** Answers will vary. Sample answer: $\frac{103}{45}$ **27.** Answers will vary. Sample answer: $-\frac{49}{176}$ **29.** Answers will vary. Sample answer: Let $x = 19.\overline{9}$. Then $10x = 199.\overline{9}$; and $10x - x = 199.\overline{9} - 19.\overline{9}$; $9x = 180$; $x = \frac{180}{9} = 20$. Since $x = 19.\overline{9}$ from the first assumption, and $x = 20$ from the algebra, $19.\overline{9} = 20$ by the substitution property of equality. **31. A.** $\frac{13}{50} = 0.26$; $\frac{1}{4} = 0.25$ **B.** Answers will vary. Sample answer: $0.2\overline{5}$ **C.** Answers will vary. Sample answer: $\frac{23}{90}$

Page 345

1. 9 **3.** $\frac{1}{6}$ **5.** $\frac{11}{13}$ **7.** 40, −40 **9.** $8\sqrt{7}$ **11.** $\sqrt{15}$ **13.** $6\sqrt{7} + 5\sqrt{6}$ **15.** $\sqrt{10} + \sqrt{30}$ **17.** $2\sqrt{0.66}$ **19.** Does not simplify. $\sqrt{\frac{71}{91}} + \sqrt{\frac{38}{91}}$ **21.** 30 **23.** 2 **25.** $\frac{1}{210}$ **27.** $\sqrt{903}$ meters **29.** Answers will vary. Sample answer: $\sqrt{5} \cdot \sqrt{5} = \sqrt{25} = 5$ and 5 is a rational number. So, irrational numbers are not closed under multiplication.

Page 349

1. irrational **3.** irrational **5.** rational **7.** irrational **9.** $6\sqrt{2}$ **11.** 10 **13.** $-2\sqrt{3}$ **15.** 3 **17.** 14 **19.** $10\sqrt{3}$ **21.** $-12\sqrt{2}$ **23.** 13 **25.** $10\sqrt{2}$ **27. A.** $1 = 1$; $4 = 1 + 3$; $9 = 1 + 3 + 5$; $16 = 1 + 3 + 5 + 7$; $25 = 1 + 3 + 5 + 7 + 9$; $36 = 1 + 3 + 5 + 7 + 9 + 11$ **B.** 144 has 12 addends and 1024 has 32 addends

Page 352

1. 4 and 5 **3.** 3 and 4 **5.** 8 and 9 **7.** 6 and 7 **9.** 11 and 12 **11.** $\sqrt{78} \approx 8.8$ **13.** $\sqrt{85} \approx 9.2$ **15.** $\sqrt{150} \approx 12.2$ **17.** $\sqrt{55} \approx 7.4$ **19.** $\sqrt{3} \approx 1.7$ **21.** 5.5 **23.** 12.8 **25.** about 4.5 m **27.** The approximate number is 5.7.

29. $\dfrac{17 + \frac{300}{17}}{2} = \dfrac{\frac{289 + 300}{17}}{2} = \dfrac{\frac{589}{17}}{2} \approx 17.3235$; $\dfrac{17.3235 + \frac{300}{17.3235}}{2} = \dfrac{\frac{300.1036523 + 300}{17.3235}}{2} = \dfrac{\frac{600.1036523}{17.3235}}{2} \approx 17.32 \approx 17.3$

Page 356

1. x^2y^5 **3.** $9a^6b^7\sqrt{10b}$ **5.** $6x\sqrt{2x}$ **7.** $20x^7y^5z\sqrt{2y}$ **9.** 3 **11.** $\frac{\sqrt{x}}{5}$ **13.** $\frac{\sqrt{a}}{11}$ **15.** $\frac{\sqrt{11x}}{11}$ **17.** $-\frac{x\sqrt{3}}{3}$ **19.** $-\frac{2x\sqrt{3}}{9}$ **21.** $\frac{5a\sqrt{21}}{42}$ **23.** $15 + \sqrt{12} \approx 18.46$ **25.** $20 - 2\sqrt{2} \approx 17.17$ **27.** $3\sqrt{232} \approx 45.69$ **29.** Answers will vary. Sample answer: $1 + \frac{1}{2} = \frac{3}{2}$ and $\frac{1}{2} - 2 = -\frac{3}{2}$; In step 2, the square root of a negative value was taken on the right side. This is an invalid step and therefore, $1 \neq -2$.

Page 359

1. $x = \pm 8$ **3.** $n = \pm 25$ **5.** $x \approx \pm 9.8$ **7.** $x \approx \pm 2.3$ **9.** $x = \pm 3.5$ **11.** $m = \pm 6$ **13.** $z = \pm 7$ **15.** $y \approx \pm 1.9$ **17.** $x \approx \pm 4.7$ **19.** $x \approx \pm 2.7$ **21.** $x = \pm 6\sqrt{y}$ **23.** approximately 2.5 inches **25.** 58 m/s

Pages 364–365

1. $x = 5$ **3.** $x = 68$ **5.** $x = 3$ **7.** $x \approx 8.06$ **9.** Yes. **11.** No. **13.** Yes. **15.** No. **17.** 90° **19.** greater than 90° **21.** less than 90°

23. A. 41 meters; ;

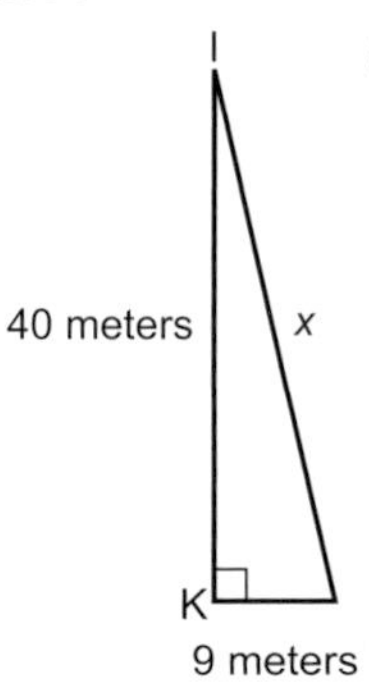

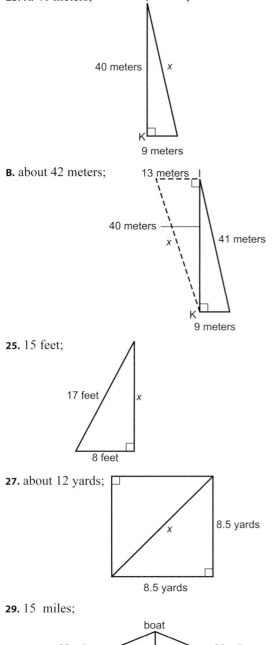

B. about 42 meters;

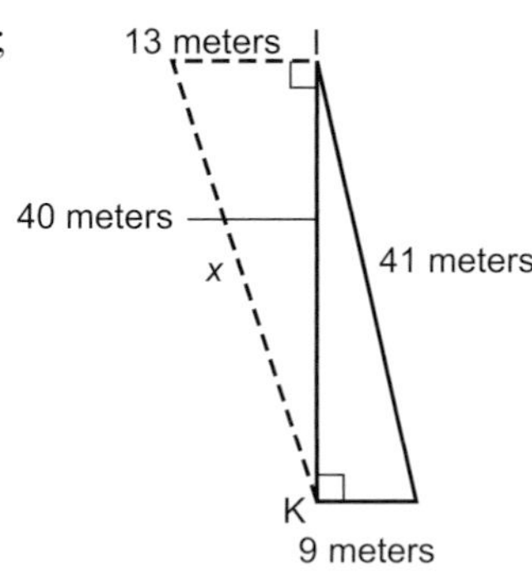

25. 15 feet;

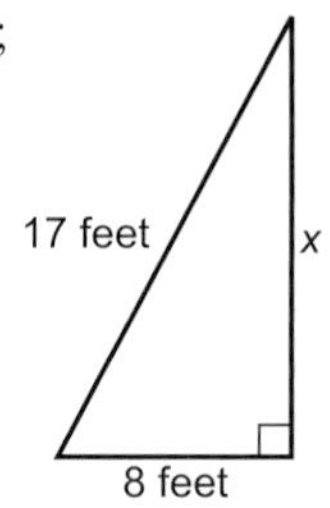

27. about 12 yards;

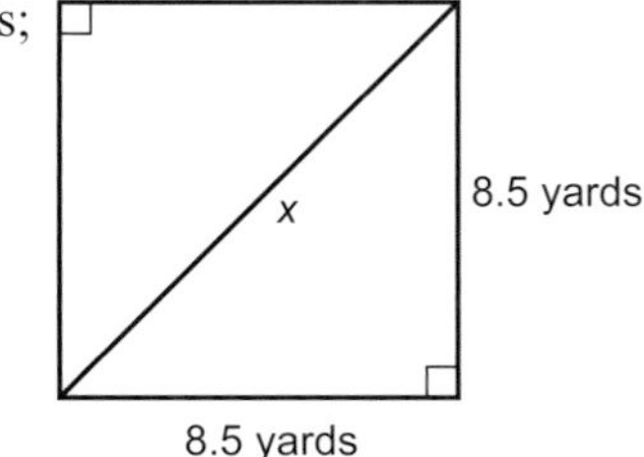

29. 15 miles;

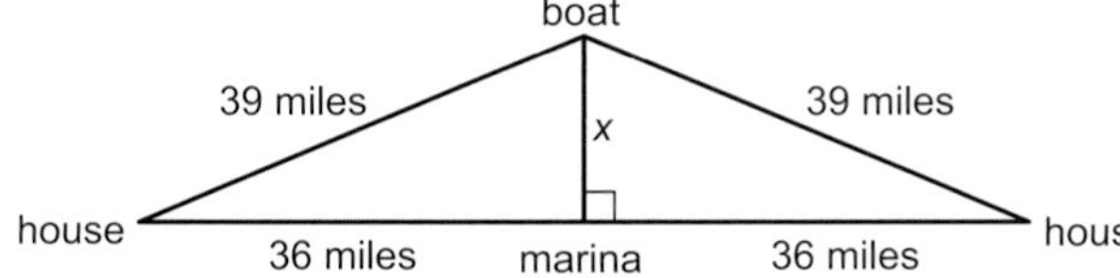

Page 369

1. 4 **3.** $2\sqrt[4]{2}$ **5.** -8 **7.** -5 **9.** Negative numbers do not have even roots. **11.** 4 **13.** Negative numbers do not have even roots. **15.** 16 **17.** 16 **19.** $\frac{7\sqrt{3}}{3}$ **21.** $\frac{9\sqrt[5]{10}}{5}$ **23.** $3\sqrt[5]{2}$ **25.** $2x^3\sqrt[3]{3x}$ **27.** $4x^3\sqrt[3]{3x^2}$ **29.** Each side of the garden is $7\sqrt[2]{2}$ feet long.

UNIT 10 Working With Polynomials

Pages 375–376

1. binomial **3.** monomial **5.** not a polynomial **7.** Degree: 3 **9.** Degree: 1 **11.** Degree: 0 **13.** Degree: 5 **15.** Degree: 7 **17.** no degree **19.** $8x^4 - 12x^2 + 11x$ **21.** $4z^4 - z^3 + 9z^2 + 2z$ **23.** $-11x^4y + 4x^3y^3 + 2x^2y^5 + 5xy^2$ **25.** $8x^6y^2z + 7x^4yz^5 - 3x^2y^2z^3 - 3xy^4z^2$ **27.** The expression is $4x^2 + 4x + 5$, so the degree is 2. **29.** The degree is 2 and the expression is a quadratic binomial.

Pages 379–380

1. $4x^2 - 6x + 11$ **3.** $3a^2 + 3a + 4$ **5.** $3x^4 + x^3 - 2x^2 + 3x + 2$ **7.** $2y - 3$ **9.** $4b + 2$ **11.** $8a^2 + 11ab - 5b^2$ **13.** $x^2 + 3xy + y^2$ **15.** $m^2 + 2m$ **17.** $3x^3 + x^2 - x - 5$ **19.** $6p^3 - 9p^2 + 19np - 13p$ **21.** $-\frac{2}{3}x^2 - 6\frac{1}{2}y^2 + 3\frac{1}{6}x + 4y$ **23.** $22x + 1$ **25.** $16x - 2$ inches **27. A.** Rectangle A: $2x + 2y + 2$; Rectangle B: $6x - 4y + 2$; Rectangle C: $10x + 6y - 6$ **B.** $18x + 4y - 2$ **29.** $11x - 8$ cm

Pages 383–384

1. 3^{11} **3.** x^8 **5.** a^{13} **7.** $3x^4y^3$ **9.** $-12b^{20}$ **11.** $3s^3t^6$ **13.** $-2z^4w^7$ **15.** $-8x^7y^8z^6$ **17.** $-2c^5d^3$ **19.** $\frac{1}{3}x^6y^8z^8$ **21.** $14a^5b^7c^3$ **23.** $36x^2$ **25. A.** $9.62y^2$ **B.** 240.5 square centimeters **27. A.** $216x^3$ **B.** 1728 cubic inches **29. A.** First floor: $93x^2$ square feet; Second floor: $84x^2$ square feet **B.** 36 square feet

Pages 387–388

1. $x^2 + 4x$ **3.** $3x^2 - 3x$ **5.** $84m - 7m^2$ **7.** $10z^4 - 50z^3$ **9.** $16n^3 - 8n^2 + 8n$ **11.** $2y^6 + 4y^4 + 5y^3$ **13.** $24x^{13} - 40x^{12} + 36x^5$ **15.** $36x^{12} - 144x^{11} - 96x^{10}$ **17.** $3x^3y^2 - 4x^2y^3 + 2x^2y^2 - 8xy$ **19.** $2m^4n^4 + 14m^3n^3 + 22m^2n^3 - 40mn^2$ **21.** $15a^{13}b^7 + 21a^{11}b^9 - 12a^4b^7 + 18ab^5$ **23.** $3a^{10}b^8c^3 - 11a^9b^7c^4 - 13a^8b^6c^5 - 14a^7b^5c^6 + a^5b^4c^2$ **25.** $2a^2b^3 + 10ab^4$ **27.** The area of the shaded region is $\frac{1}{2}s^2 + \frac{19}{2}s$. **29.** The total area is $5x + \frac{8x^2 + \pi x^2}{8}$.

Page 392

1. $x^2 + 2x - 8$ **3.** $4x^2 + 13x - 35$ **5.** $15a^2 - 19ab - 56b^2$ **7.** $9y^2 - 6y + 1$ **9.** $100a^2 - 140a + 49$ **11.** $n^3 + 3n^2 + 3n + 1$ **13.** $4x^3 - 43x^2 + 22x + 80$ **15.** $12x^3 - 52x^2y - 13xy^2 + 40y^3$ **17.** $v^4 + 2v^3 - 33v^2 + 26v - 3$ **19.** $20x^4 - 36x^3 + 47x^2 - 13x + 66$ **21.** $z^3 + 9z^2 + 23z + 15$ **23.** $2d^3 + 21d^2 - 56d - 240$ **25.** $49\pi x^2 + 14\pi x + \pi$ **27.** $13x^2 + 70x + 122$ **29.** $a^2 + b^2 + c^2 + 2ab + 2bc + 2ac$; $x^2 + 4y^2 + 9z^2 + 4xy + 12yz + 6xz$

Page 395

1. $x^2 + 6x + 8$ **3.** $d^2 - 15d + 50$ **5.** $q^2 + 6q + 5$ **7.** $x^2 - 4x - 21$ **9.** $x^2 - \frac{49}{64}$ **11.** $z + 20\sqrt{z} + 36$ **13.** $2a^2 - a - 1$ **15.** $2n^2 + 17.2n + 30.5$ **17.** $\frac{1}{10}y^2 + \frac{31}{60}y + \frac{2}{3}$ **19.** $18f^2 + 24f + 8$ **21.** $400x^2 - 21$ **23.** $b^3 + 7b^2 - 2b - 14$ **25.** $2w^3 + w^2 + 10w + 5$ **27.** $x^3 + 18x^2 + 108x + 216$ **29. A.** $3x^2 - 5x - 2$ **B.** $3x^3 + 7x^2 - 22x - 8$

UNIT 11 Factoring Polynomials

Page 402

1. $2 \cdot 2 \cdot 19 = 2^2 \cdot 19$ **3.** $2 \cdot 2 \cdot 3 \cdot 3 = 2^2 \cdot 3^2$ **5.** $2 \cdot 2 \cdot 3 \cdot 3 \cdot 5 = 2^2 \cdot 3^2 \cdot 5$ **7.** prime **9.** composite **11.** prime **13.** GCF: 18 **15.** GCF: 64 **17.** GCF: 21 **19.** GCF: 13 **21.** not relatively prime; GCF: 2 **23.** relatively prime **25.** not relatively prime; GCF: 7 **27.** relatively prime

Pages 405–406

1. Power of a Product **3.** Product of Powers **5.** Quotient of Powers **7.** a^3 **9.** $\frac{1}{y^3}$ **11.** $4a^3$ **13.** $-2xy^2$ **15.** xyz^5 **17.** $\frac{b^3}{a^6}$ **19.** $\frac{c^2}{a^2}$ **21.** $-\frac{z^5}{2x^3y}$ **23.** $\frac{3x^4}{8y^5}$ **25.** $\frac{10x}{11}$ **27. A.** $\frac{x^2}{2}$ **B.** $\frac{4}{3x}$ **29. A.** $2t^2$ months **B.** $1.5st$ months

Pages 409–410

1. $4x^3$ **3.** $25y^2$ **5.** $14x^2y$ **7.** $3x(x + 2)$ **9.** $a(2a + 1)$ **11.** $5m(m + 3)$ **13.** $6x^2y^4(3x + 4y)$ **15.** $4x^2y^4(8x - 3y)$ **17.** $2r^2s(3r^3 + 2r^2s - 4)$ **19.** $(2x - 4)(3x + 5)$ **21.** $15m^3n^5(3m - 11m^2p + 5np^4 - 7)$ **23.** $(2t^3 - 5rt^2 + 9)(3r^5s^2 - 4t + 6)$ **25.** The base is $6y + 1$ inches. **27. A.** The width of the garden is $5 - 2\frac{1}{3}x$ feet. **B.** The width of the garden is $6\frac{2}{3} + 2x$ feet.

Page 413

1. $x + 2$ **3.** $2a^2 + a$ **5.** $y + 2$ **7.** $6y^6 + 17y$ **9.** $20a^7 + 3a^2$ **11.** $3 + 4t^2$ **13.** $ab + 3a^2b^2$ **15.** $6g^5h^8 - 5gh^2$ **17.** $-8y^5z - y^5z^3$ **19.** $2u^3 + 10u^6v^2 + 4u^6$ **21.** $p^4qr^2 + 4p^2q^4r^3 + 3p^3q^6r^6$ **23.** $3f^6g^9h^5 + 5f^5g^2h^7 + 2f^3gh^5$ **25.** $3j^5k + 2h^2j^3 - h^3k^4$ **27. A.** $6a^2b$ **B.** The number of tiles needed is $2a^3b^2 + 3a^2b^4 + 6a^5b^5$.

Pages 415–416

1. The trinomial is a perfect square. $(x + 1)^2$ **3.** The trinomial is a perfect square. $(j + 20)^2$ **5.** The trinomial is a perfect square. $(y - 8)^2$ **7.** The trinomial is a perfect square. $(2a - 1)^2$ **9.** The trinomial is not a perfect square. **11.** The trinomial is a perfect square. $(f + 0.6)^2$ **13.** The trinomial is a perfect square. $(p + 1.7)^2$ **15.** The trinomial is not a perfect square. **17.** The trinomial is a perfect square. $(15v + 15)^2$ **19.** The trinomial is a perfect square. $(13q + 2)^2$ **21.** The trinomial is a perfect square. $(2f - 6)^2$ **23.** Since there is no k term, the trinomial $x^2 + 9$ is not a perfect square. **25.** The trinomial is a perfect square. $(0.8w + 0.2)^2$ **27.** The trinomial is a perfect square. $(7r + 10s)^2$ **29.** The trinomial is a perfect square. $(14k - 12l)^2$ **31.** The trinomial is a perfect square. $(2.1c - d)^2$ **33. A.** $(6j^2 + 5)^2$ **B.** $36f^2 + 60f + 25 = (6f + 5)^2$; $(6f + 5)^2 = [6 \cdot j^2 + 5]^2 = (6j^2 + 5)^2$

Page 419

1. The expression is a difference of squares; $(x + 8)(x - 8)$ **3.** The expression is a difference of squares; $(n^2 + 22)(n^2 - 22)$ **5.** The expression is a difference of squares; $(1 + d^3)(1 - d^3)$ **7.** The expression is not a difference of squares. **9.** The expression is a difference of squares. $(r + 2)(r - 2)$ **11.** The expression is a difference of squares; $\left(u + \frac{3}{13}\right)\left(u - \frac{3}{13}\right)$ **13.** The expression is a difference of squares; $(2 - x)(2 + x)$ **15.** The expression is not a difference of squares. **17.** The expression is a difference of squares; $(20g^5 + 30)(20g^5 - 30)$ **19.** The expression is not a difference of squares. **21.** The expression is a difference of squares; $(19c + 3d)(19c - 3d)$ **23.** The expression is a difference of squares; $(3j + 5k^3)(3j - 5k^3)$ **25.** The expression is a difference of squares; $(1.1y + 0.9z)(1.1y - 0.9z)$ **27.** The expression is a difference of squares; $(0.4a^3 + 0.5b^3)(0.4a^3 - 0.5b^3)$ **29. A.** $1296 - x^2$ **B.** $(36 + x)(36 - x)$ **31. A.** $0.16 - 0.25n^8$ **B.** $(0.4 + 0.5n^4)(0.4 - 0.5n^4)$ **33. A.** No, $4a^4b^6 - 144c^{11}d^8$ is not a difference of squares. **B.** Answers will vary. Sample Answer: Changing c^{11} to c^{12} would make $4a^4b^6 - 144c^{11}d^8$ a difference of squares. Then, $4a^4b^6 - 144c^{12}d^8 = (2a^2b^3)^2 - (12c^6d^4)^2 = (2a^2b^3 + 12c^6d^4)(2a^2b^3 - 12c^6d^4)$.

Page 423

1. $(x + 5)(x + 2)$ **3.** $(x + 2)(x + 3)$ **5.** prime **7.** $(x - 8)(x + 3)$ **9.** $(x + 7)(x + 8)$ **11.** $(x + 7)(x + 6)$ **13.** $(x + 15)(x - 6)$ **15.** $(x + 9)(x - 4)$ **17.** $(x + 12)(x + 11)$ **19.** $k = 10$ **21.** $k = 2$ **23.** $k = 16$ **25.** $k = 9$ or $k = 6$ **27.** The expression for the width of the garden is $x + 8$ and it is a square.

Page 426

1. $(3x + 10)(x + 2)$ **3.** prime **5.** $(2x - 9)(2x + 5)$ **7.** $(5x + 7)(x + 3)$ **9.** $(2x + 4)(3x - 2)$ **11.** $(4x + 5)(3x - 2)$ **13.** $(5x + 3)(2x - 4)$ **15.** $(4x - 5)(2x + 12)$ **17.** $(3x - 8)(5x - 9)$ **19.** $k = 10$ or $k = 22$ **21.** $k = 9$ or $k = 15$ **23.** $k = 8$ or $k = 16$ **25.** $k = 16$ or $k = 40$

Page 428

1. $(2x + 8)(x + 5)$ **3.** $2(x - 1)(x + 1)$ **5.** $(2m - 9)(2m + 9)$ **7.** $(4s^2 + 1)(2s + 1)(2s - 1)$ **9.** $(6x - 4)(4x + 7)$ **11.** $3(x - 2)(x + 2)$ **13.** $5(x - 2)(x^2 + 2x + 4)$ **15.** $-1(x - 2)(x - 1)$ **17.** $(5x + 40)(x + 8)$ **19.** $(x^2 - 3)(x^2 + 3)$ **21.** $(x + 5)^2 + y^3$ **23.** $(4x + 9)^2$ **25.** $(4y - 10)(4y + 10)(16y^2 + 100)$ **27.** $(10y + 2x)^2$

Page 431

1. $(x + 3)(y + z)$ **3.** $(x - y - 5)(x + y - 5)$ **5.** $(2z + y)(x + 5)$ **7.** $(x + 1)(3x + 4)$ **9.** $(x - 1)(4x + 3)$ **11.** $(2x + 3)(5x + 3)$ **13.** Group; $(b - 2c)(a + 2)$ **15.** Split the middle term; $(x + 2)(3x + 1)$ **17.** Group; $(x - 2y - 1)(x + 2y - 1)$ **19.** Group; $(x - 5y + 2)(x + 5y + 2)$ **21.** Group; $(x - 9y + 3)(x + 9y + 3)$ **23.** Group; $(2x - 3y + 1)(2x + 3y + 1)$ **25.** Group; $(x^2 - 11y - 2)(x^2 + 11y - 2)$ **27.** Group; $(a^2 - b - c)(a^2 - b + c)$ **29.** Split the middle term; $(4x - 7)(6x - 1)$

Pages 435–436

1. The roots are -4 and 3. **3.** The roots are -1 and 2. **5.** The roots are 7 and -5. **7.** The root is 6. **9.** The roots are $-\frac{1}{2}$ and 6. **11.** The roots are 0 and 4. **13.** The roots are 0, $\frac{1}{5}$, and $-\frac{3}{2}$. **15.** The zeros are 1 and 5. **17.** The zeros are 8 and -10. **19.** The zeros are 0 and 5. **21.** The zero is 11. **23.** The zeros are $\frac{3}{2}$ and $-\frac{3}{2}$. **25.** The zeros are 0, $-\frac{2}{5}$, and $-\frac{8}{3}$. **27.** The zeros are 0, 12, and -12. **29.** Amar has 12 nickels and 15 dimes in the collection. **31.** The hypotenuse is 5 feet and the legs measure 3 feet and 4 feet. **33.** The dimensions of the box are 10 inches by 26 inches by 30 inches.

Pages 440–441

1. The numbers are $-\frac{29}{3}$ and -24 and 8 and 29. **3.** The number is 23 or -23. **5.** The consecutive odd integers are 11 and 13 or -13 and -11. **7.** The consecutive integers are 2, 3, and 4 or -8, -7, and -6. **9.** The pocket is 9 cm by 9 cm. **11.** The width of the first strip is 12 inches, the width of the second strip is 16 inches, and the width of the third strip is 20 inches. **13.** The area of the frame is 144 square inches. **15.** Juki hit 10 homeruns, Edde hit 16, and Sami hit 15. **17.** Sienna is 10 and Kianna is 37. **19.** The oldest child is 13, the middle child is 9, and the youngest child is 5 years old. **21.** The rocket took off at time 0 seconds and hit the ground 2 seconds later.

UNIT 12 Quadratic Equations

Page 448

1. $\{-5, 5\}$ **3.** $\left\{-\frac{1}{2}, \frac{1}{2}\right\}$ **5.** $\{-3, 3\}$ **7.** $\{5, -1\}$ **9.** $\{5, 1\}$ **11.** $\{0.5, -2.55\}$ **13.** $\{-3, 3\}$ **15.** $\left\{-\frac{\sqrt{17}}{2}, \frac{\sqrt{17}}{2}\right\}$ **17.** $\left\{-\frac{2\sqrt{3}}{3}, \frac{2\sqrt{3}}{3}\right\}$ **19.** $\{3, -7\}$ **21.** $\{9, 3\}$ **23.** $\{6, 2\}$ **25.** $\left\{2, -4\frac{2}{3}\right\}$ **27.** The dimensions of the garden are 12 feet by 12 feet. **29.** The length of each side of the painting without the frame is 3.5 feet.

Pages 452–453

1. 9; $x^2 + 6x + 9$ **3.** 12.25; $x^2 - 7x + 12.25$ **5.** 1.44; $a^2 - 2.4a + 1.44$ **7.** $(x + 2)^2 = 9$; $\{-5, 1\}$ **9.** $(t - 4)^2 = 1$; $\{3, 5\}$ **11.** $(x + 7)^2 = 64$; $\{1, -15\}$ **13.** $(x - 0.25)^2 = 1.5625$; $\{1.5, -1\}$ **15.** $(p + 1.8)^2 = 0.04$; $\{-1.6, -2\}$ **17.** $(m + 2)^2 = 6.76$; $\{0.6, -4.6\}$ **19.** $(t - 3)^2 = 81$; $(12, -6\}$ **21.** $(y + 1)^2 = 5$; $\{-1 + \sqrt{5}, -1 - \sqrt{5}\}$ **23.** $\left(x - \frac{5}{4}\right)^2 = \frac{17}{16}$; $\left\{\frac{5 + \sqrt{17}}{4}, \frac{5 - \sqrt{17}}{4}\right\}$ **25.** The length of the patio is 8 feet. The width of the patio is 14 feet. **27.** The length of the corkboard is 22 inches and the width of the corkboard is 34 inches.

Pages 457–458

1. $\{0.5, -7.5\}$ **3.** $\{3, 1\}$ **5.** $\left\{1, \frac{3}{2}\right\}$ **7.** $\{-1.3, 0.3\}$ **9.** $\{0.3, -2.3\}$ **11.** $\{6.5, -0.5\}$ **13.** $\{1.4, -9.4\}$ **15.** $\{0.4, -0.9\}$ **17.** $\left\{-\frac{1}{2}, -1\right\}$ **19.** $\{0.6, -3.6\}$ **21.** no real solutions **23.** two rational solutions **25.** one rational solution **27.** two irrational solutions **29.** not factorable **31.** factorable

33. A. $ax^2 + bx + c = a\left(\frac{-b + \sqrt{b^2 - 4ac}}{2a}\right)^2 + b\left(\frac{-b + \sqrt{b^2 - 4ac}}{2a}\right) + c = \frac{a(-b + \sqrt{b^2 - 4ac})^2}{(2a)^2} + \frac{b(-b + \sqrt{b^2 - 4ac})}{2a} + c =$

$\frac{a(-b + \sqrt{b^2 - 4ac})(-b + \sqrt{b^2 - 4ac})}{(2a)^2} + \frac{b(-b + \sqrt{b^2 - 4ac})}{2a} + c =$

$\frac{a[(-b) \cdot (-b) + (-b) \cdot \sqrt{b^2 - 4ac} + \sqrt{b^2 - 4ac} \cdot (-b) + \sqrt{b^2 - 4ac} \cdot \sqrt{b^2 - 4ac}]}{2^2a^2} + \frac{b \cdot (-b) + b \cdot \sqrt{b^2 - 4ac}}{2a} + c =$

$\frac{a(b^2 - 2b \cdot \sqrt{b^2 - 4ac} + b^2 - 4ac)}{4a^2} + \frac{-b^2 + b \cdot \sqrt{b^2 - 4ac}}{2a} + c = \frac{(b^2 - 2b \cdot \sqrt{b^2 - 4ac} + b^2 - 4ac)}{4a} + \frac{-b^2 + b \cdot \sqrt{b^2 - 4ac}}{2a} + c =$

$\frac{(b^2 - 2b \cdot \sqrt{b^2 - 4ac} + b^2 - 4ac)}{4a} + \frac{-b^2 + b \cdot \sqrt{b^2 - 4ac}}{2a} \cdot \frac{2}{2} + c =$

$\frac{b^2 - 2b \cdot \sqrt{b^2 - 4ac} + b^2 - 4ac - 2b^2 + 2b \cdot \sqrt{b^2 - 4ac}}{4a} + c = \frac{-4ac}{4a} + c = -c + c = 0$

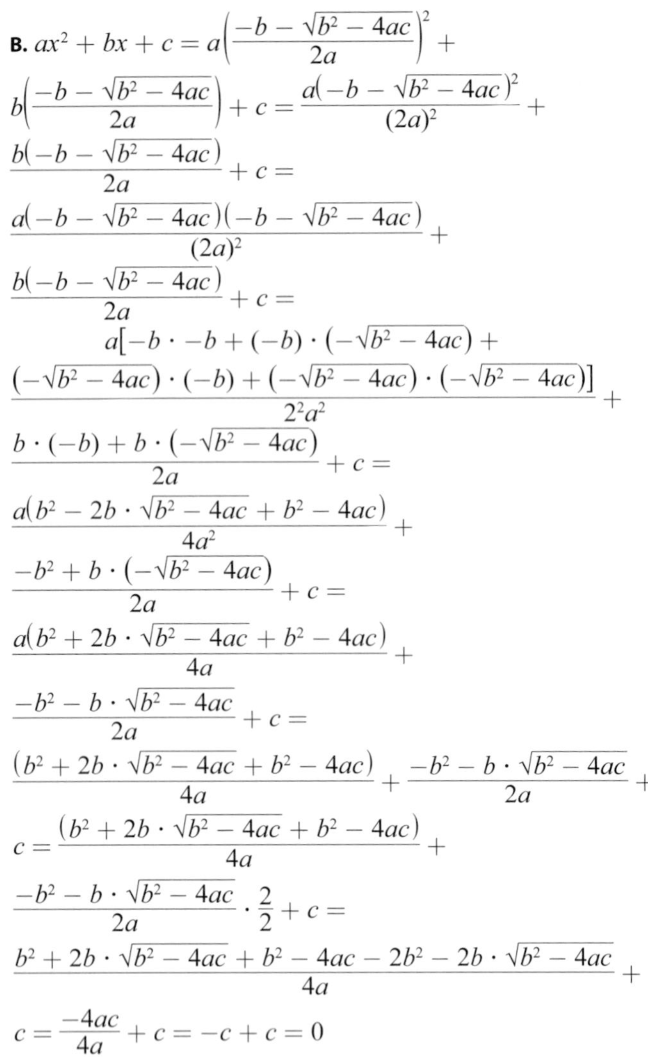

B. $ax^2 + bx + c = a\left(\frac{-b - \sqrt{b^2 - 4ac}}{2a}\right)^2 +$
$b\left(\frac{-b - \sqrt{b^2 - 4ac}}{2a}\right) + c = \frac{a(-b - \sqrt{b^2 - 4ac})^2}{(2a)^2} +$
$\frac{b(-b - \sqrt{b^2 - 4ac})}{2a} + c =$
$\frac{a(-b - \sqrt{b^2 - 4ac})(-b - \sqrt{b^2 - 4ac})}{(2a)^2} +$
$\frac{b(-b - \sqrt{b^2 - 4ac})}{2a} + c =$
$\frac{a[-b \cdot -b + (-b) \cdot (-\sqrt{b^2 - 4ac}) + (-\sqrt{b^2 - 4ac}) \cdot (-b) + (-\sqrt{b^2 - 4ac}) \cdot (-\sqrt{b^2 - 4ac})]}{2^2a^2} +$
$\frac{b \cdot (-b) + b \cdot (-\sqrt{b^2 - 4ac})}{2a} + c =$
$\frac{a(b^2 - 2b \cdot \sqrt{b^2 - 4ac} + b^2 - 4ac)}{4a^2} +$
$\frac{-b^2 + b \cdot (-\sqrt{b^2 - 4ac})}{2a} + c =$
$\frac{a(b^2 + 2b \cdot \sqrt{b^2 - 4ac} + b^2 - 4ac)}{4a} +$
$\frac{-b^2 - b \cdot \sqrt{b^2 - 4ac}}{2a} + c =$
$\frac{(b^2 + 2b \cdot \sqrt{b^2 - 4ac} + b^2 - 4ac)}{4a} + \frac{-b^2 - b \cdot \sqrt{b^2 - 4ac}}{2a} +$
$c = \frac{(b^2 + 2b \cdot \sqrt{b^2 - 4ac} + b^2 - 4ac)}{4a} +$
$\frac{-b^2 - b \cdot \sqrt{b^2 - 4ac}}{2a} \cdot \frac{2}{2} + c =$
$\frac{b^2 + 2b \cdot \sqrt{b^2 - 4ac} + b^2 - 4ac - 2b^2 - 2b \cdot \sqrt{b^2 - 4ac}}{4a} +$
$c = \frac{-4ac}{4a} + c = -c + c = 0$

Pages 461–462

1. Factor and use the zero product property. **3.** Use the quadratic formula. **5.** Take the square root of each side. **7.** $\{5 + \sqrt{45}, 5 - \sqrt{45}\}$ **9.** $\{-3, -19\}$ **11.** $\left\{\frac{9 - \sqrt{669}}{14}, \frac{9 + \sqrt{669}}{14}\right\}$ **13.** $\{-9 - \sqrt{31}, -9 + \sqrt{31}\}$ **15.** $\{11 - \sqrt{130}, 11 + \sqrt{130}\}$ **17.** The equation has no real solutions. **19.** $\{0, -17\}$ **21.** $\{8, 20\}$ **23.** $\{0.1, -0.9\}$ **25.** $l^2 - 6l - 216 = 0$; The length is 18 inches. **27.** $x^2 - 10x - 4 = 0$; The original side length is 10.4. **29. A.** $4x^2 + 12x + 9 = 100$; The original side length was 3.5. **B.** The original side length x was doubled, then increased by 3.

Page 466

1. A. no x-intercepts **B.** downward **C.** below the x-axis **3. A.** one x-intercept **B.** upward **C.** on the x-axis **5. A.** two x-intercepts **B.** upward **C.** below the x-axis **7. A.** one x-intercept **B.** upward **C.** on the x-axis **9. A.** no x-intercepts **B.** downward **C.** below the x-axis **11. A.** no x-intercepts **B.** downward **C.** below the x-axis

13.

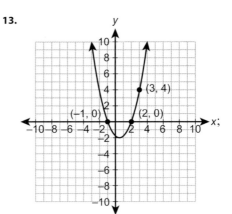

x-intercepts: (2, 0) and (−1, 0)

15.

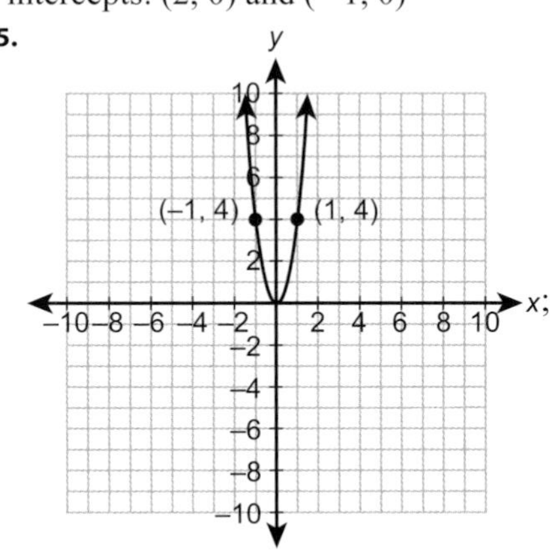

x-intercept: (0, 0)

17.

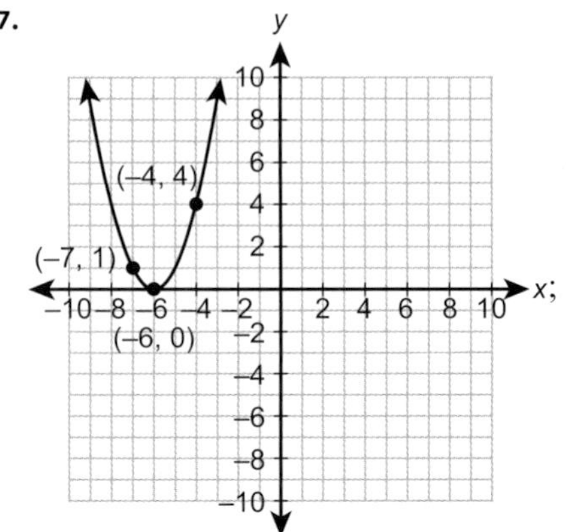

x-intercept: (−6, 0)

19.

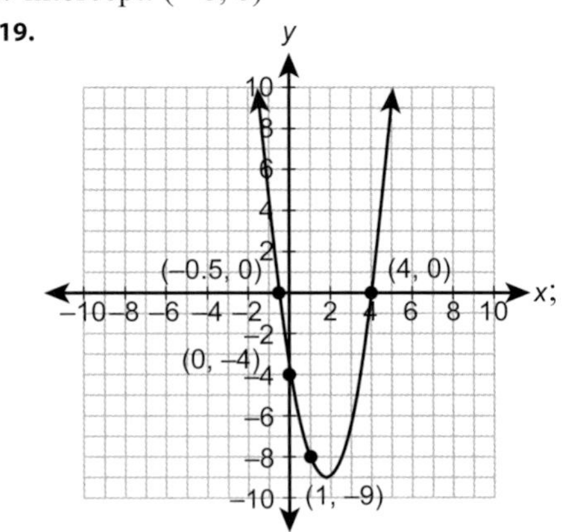

x-intercepts: $\left(-\frac{1}{2}, 0\right)$ and (4, 0)

21.

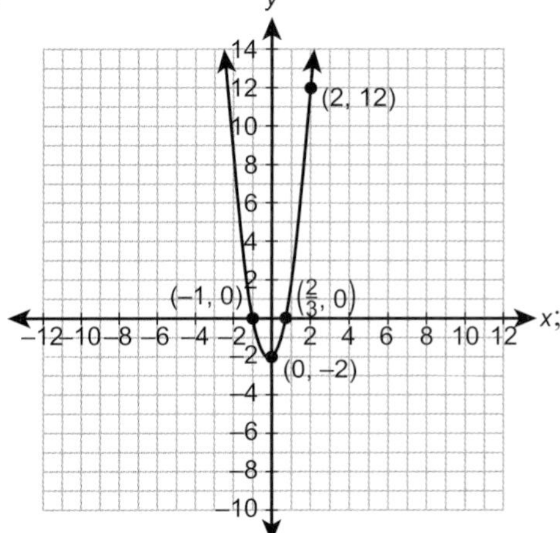

x-intercepts: $\left(\frac{2}{3}, 0\right)$ and $(-1, 0)$

23.

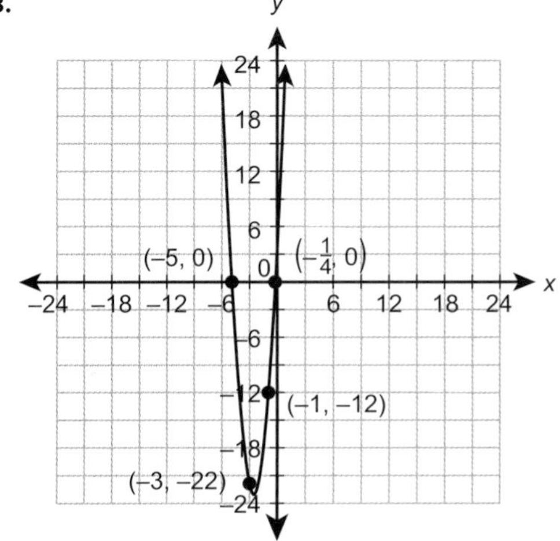

x-intercepts: $\left(-\frac{1}{4}, 0\right)$ and $(-5, 0)$

25.

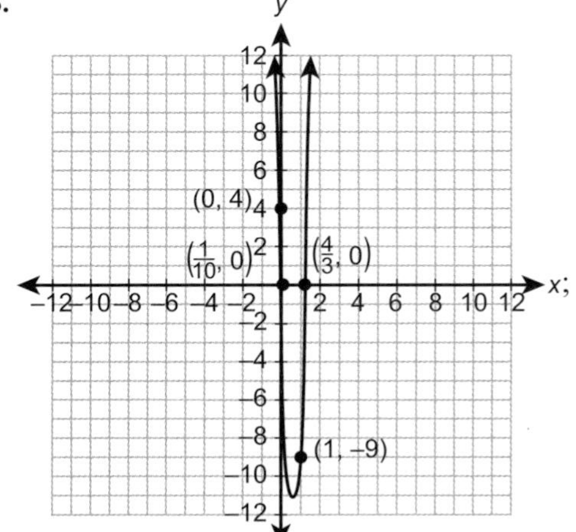

x-intercepts: $\left(\frac{1}{10}, 0\right)$ and $\left(\frac{4}{3}, 0\right)$

27.

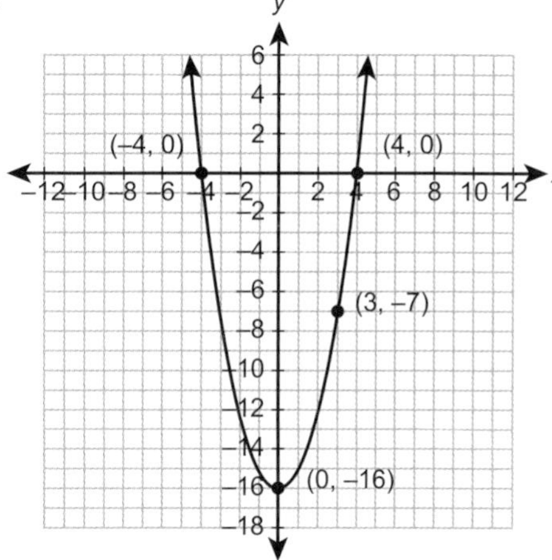

29. t-intercepts $(0, 0)$ and $(2, 0)$; The t-intercepts represent the times the firecracker is on the ground.

Pages 470–471

1. The width is 5 inches and the length is 8 inches. **3.** The height is 3 inches and the base is 7 inches. **5.** The radius is 8 meters. **7.** The height is 9 inches and the base is 36 inches. **9.** The width is about 1.39 inches and the length is about 10.78 inches. **11.** The width is 3 mm and the length is 18 mm. **13.** The width is 1.6 m and the length is 1 m. **15.** The width is 3.975 feet and the length is 25.9 feet. **17.** The height is 2.5 inches and the base is 5 inches. **19.** The radius is 19.675 or 0.3253 meters.

Page 475

1. It will take about 5.98 seconds for the object to land. **3.** It will take about 5.16 seconds for the javelin to hit the ground. **5.** It will take the ball 4.13 seconds to hit the ground. **7.** The football will be in the air for 0.75 seconds. **9.** It will take approximately 2.59 seconds for the shot put to land. **11.** The soccer ball will land after about 5.13 seconds. **13.** The ball will land at 1.75 seconds. **15.** The stone will reach the ground at about 9.14 seconds. **17. A.** The ball will be in the air for 0.90 seconds. **B.** The juggler has about 0.84 seconds to catch the ball. **19. A.** The ball will be in the air for about 5.67 seconds. **B.** The ball will travel about 510 feet.

UNIT 13 Rational Expressions

Page 481

1. The restricted value is 0. **3.** The restricted values are 2 and −2. **5.** The restricted values are 1 and −8 **7.** The restricted value is 0; $\frac{2(x+1)}{x}$ **9.** The restricted value is 0; $\frac{2x-3}{x}$ **11.** The restricted value is 0; $\frac{x^2+4}{x^2}$ **13.** The restricted values are −8 and 1; $\frac{x+2}{x-1}$ **15.** The restricted values are 5 and −3; $\frac{x+4}{x-5}$ **17.** The restricted values are 5 and −5; $\frac{x+1}{x+5}$ **19.** The restricted values are $\frac{1}{3}$ and $\frac{2}{7}$; $\frac{4x-5}{7x-2}$

21. The restricted values are 11 and −11; $\frac{2x-1}{x-11}$ **23.** The restricted value is −2; $\frac{x^2-2x+4}{2}$ **25.** The restricted values are $\frac{5}{6}$ and $-\frac{4}{3}$; $\frac{2x+1}{-(3x+4)}$ **27.** The restricted values are $-\frac{3}{4}$ and $\frac{2}{3}$; $\frac{2(x+3)}{-(3x-2)}$

Page 484

1. $\frac{2x}{y}$ **3.** 2 **5.** $\frac{n^{10}}{m^8}$ **7.** $\frac{1}{2}$ **9.** $24x^9y$ **11.** −2 **13.** The domain is all real numbers except 4 and −4; 2 **15.** The domain is all real numbers except −7, −1, and 1; $\frac{-4(r+3)}{r+1}$ **17.** The domain is all real numbers except −2 and −6; $\frac{-1}{2(s+6)}$ **19.** The domain is all real numbers except −5 and 10; $\frac{x(x-5)}{2(x-10)}$ **21.** The domain is all real numbers except 11 and −11; $\frac{1}{2(x+11)^2}$ **23.** The domain is all real numbers except −3 and −5; −21

Pages 486–487

1. $\frac{5a}{bc^2}$ **3.** $\frac{x+2}{x-5}$ **5.** $\frac{x}{x-3}$ **7.** $\frac{4n^6}{m^9}$ **9.** $\frac{10x^5}{y^3}$ **11.** The domain is all real numbers except 3, 6, and −9; $\frac{4(x-3)}{x+9}$ **13.** The domain is all real numbers except 8, −8, and −2; $\frac{2}{3(x+2)(x+8)}$ **15.** The domain is all real numbers except 3 and −3; $\frac{4}{(t+3)(t-3)}$ **17.** The domain is all real numbers except −2, and −9; $\frac{t-2}{3(t+9)}$ **19.** $\frac{3(x-1)}{x}$ **21.** $\frac{2(x+5)}{3(x+2)}$ **23.** $\frac{2(x+10)}{x(3x-1)}$

Pages 491–492

1. 175 **3.** 56 **5.** $154x^2y^3$ **7.** $4a^3b^2$ **9.** $63u^5v^4$ **11.** $2(t+2)(t-2)$ **13.** $\frac{4y}{6y^3}, \frac{7}{6y^3}$ **15.** $\frac{18z^4(z+1)}{18z^7}, \frac{7}{18z^7}$ **17.** $\frac{12j^4(5-j)}{156j^6}, \frac{572j^3}{156j^6}$, and $\frac{104}{156j^6}$ **19.** $\frac{8(x+4)}{(x+3)(x-1)(x+4)}$ and $\frac{2(x+3)}{(x-1)(x+4)(x+3)}$ **21.** $\frac{(a+15)(1-a^3)(a^2+2)}{a^9(1-a^2)(1-a^3)(a^2+2)}$, $\frac{a^{10}(1-a^2)(a^2+2)}{a^9(1-a^2)(1-a^3)(a^2+2)}$, and $\frac{4a^9(1-a^2)(1-a^3)}{a^9(1-a^2)(1-a^3)(a^2+2)}$ **23.** $\frac{cd(c+d)}{d^2(c+d)^2}, \frac{(c+d)^2}{d^2(c+d)}$, and $\frac{cd^3}{d^2(c+d)^2}$ **25. A.** With current: $\frac{7(12-c)}{(12+c)(12-c)}$; Against current: $\frac{9(12+c)}{(12+c)(12-c)}$ **B.** The total travel time is 1.4 hours. **27. A.** With wind: $\frac{2000(320-w)}{(320+w)(320-w)}$; Against wind: $\frac{2000(320+w)}{(320+w)(320-w)}$ **B.** The total travel time was about 12.5 hours. **29. A.** Mario: $\frac{125(m+7)}{m(m+7)}$; Felipa: $\frac{125m}{m(m+7)}$ **B.** It took Mario approximately an additional 15 minutes to drive.

Pages 496–497

1. $\frac{48p+15}{40p^4}$ **3.** $\frac{36x^4+1}{15x^6}$ **5.** $\frac{11-20f}{8f^4}$ **7.** $\frac{(z-2)(z+2)}{2z}$ **9.** $\frac{c^2+1-3c^5}{3c^4(c^2+1)}$ **11.** $\frac{37m-29}{8(4m+1)(m-4)}$ **13.** $\frac{5s^4-5s^3+12s+36}{3s^3(s-1)(s+3)}$ **15.** $\frac{(4j^2+j+10)}{(4j-1)(5+j)}$ **17.** $\frac{3}{x+5}$ **19.** $\frac{-g^2+5g+5}{(g-5)^2}$ **21.** $\frac{-10a^{12}+11a^{11}+a+13}{a^{11}(1+a)(1-a)}$ **23.** $\frac{1}{(q+1)(q-1)}$ **25.** The expression $\frac{480{,}000}{(300+w)(300-w)}$ represents the total time of the trip. **27.** The expression $\frac{96}{s(s-8)}$ represents how much longer her trip home was. **29.** The expression $\frac{3}{f(f-3)}$ represents how much longer it took Marion to run her second lap.

UNIT 14 Logic and Reasoning

Pages 503–505

1. Therefore, if x is an even number, then $x + 2$ is an even number. **3.** Therefore, all students that cheat are students that fail. **5.** Therefore, if corresponding angles are congruent, then alternate interior angles are congruent. **7.** If a measurement is 3 feet, then it is 1 yard. **9.** If I turn on the air conditioning, then the electric bill will be high. **11.** Therefore, if the discriminant of a quadratic function is positive, then it will cross the x-axis twice.

13. Invalid **15.** Valid **17.** Invalid **19.** Invalid **21.** Just because Jason is not wearing his jersey does not mean that the game is canceled. **23.** The new car on the street is not necessarily for Keri. It could belong to anybody who lives on the street. **25.** Stewart's book could be a rectangle. **27.** The triangle could be a right triangle with angle measures of 30°, 60°, and 90°.

Page 508

1. Hypothesis: it is Saturday; Conclusion: I have a soccer game **3.** Hypothesis: $a \cdot b = a \cdot c$; Conclusion: $b = c$ **5.** Hypothesis: you were born in 2000; Conclusion: you turned 5 in 2005 **7.** Hypothesis: a word is a proper noun; Conclusion: it starts with a capital letter **9.** Conditional: If a person is a photographer, then they will take pictures.; Hypothesis: a person is a photographer; Conclusion: they will take pictures **11.** Conditional: If a function is quadratic, then its shape is a parabola.; Hypothesis: a function is quadratic; Conclusion: its shape is a parabola **13.** Conditional: If you multiply two negative numbers, then the product is a positive number.; Hypothesis: you multiply two negative numbers; Conclusion: the product is a positive number **15.** Yes.

17. Yes. **19.** Yes. **21.** Yes. **23.** If a figure is a triangle, then the sum of the measures of the angles is 180°. **25.** If a student is chronically late to school, then the student will be suspended.

Pages 512–513

1. If a number can be written as a fraction, then it is a rational number. True. **3.** If a triangle is isosceles, then it is equilateral. False. **5.** If an integer is less than 0, then the integer is negative. True. **7.** If a polygon is a triangle, then it has three sides. True. **9.** Hypothesis: it is Tuesday; Conclusion: I have swimming lessons; Converse: If I have swimming lessons, then it is Tuesday.; Inverse: If it is not Tuesday, then I do not have swimming lessons.; Contrapositive: If I do not have swimming lessons, then it is not Tuesday. **11.** Hypothesis: I learn to cook; Conclusion: I will stop eating at restaurants; Converse: If I stop eating at restaurants, then I have learned to cook.; Inverse: If I do not learn to cook, then I will not stop eating at restaurants.; Contrapositive: If I do not stop eating at restaurants, then I did not learn to cook. **13.** Hypothesis: the football team wins the game this week; Conclusion: they will be in the championship game; Converse: If the football team is in the championship game, then they won the game this week.; Inverse: If the football team does not win the game this week, then they will not be in the championship game.; Contrapositive: If the football team is not in the championship game, then they did not win the game this week.
15. Hypothesis: the dog gets sick; Conclusion: I have to take him to the vet; Converse: If I take the dog to the vet, then he got sick.; Inverse: If the dog does not get sick, then I will not have to take him to the vet.; Contrapositive: If I do not have to take the dog to the vet, then he did not get sick. **17.** Hypothesis: a number is an integer; Conclusion: it can be positive, negative, or 0; Converse: If a number is positive, negative, or 0, then it is an integer. False.; Inverse: If a number is not an integer, then it cannot be positive, negative or 0. False.; Contrapositive: If a number is not positive, negative, or 0, then it is not an integer. True. **19.** Conditional: If a line is vertical, then it has undefined slope.; Hypothesis: a line is vertical; Conclusion: it has undefined slope; Converse: If a line has undefined slope, then it is vertical. True.; Inverse: If a line is not vertical, then it does not have undefined slope. True.; Contrapositive: If a line does not have undefined slope, then it is not vertical. True. **21.** Hypothesis: the order of operations is followed; Conclusion: an expression is simplified correctly; Converse: If an expression is simplified correctly, then the order of operations is followed. True.; Inverse: If the order of operations is not followed, then an expression is not simplified correctly. True.; Contrapositive: If an expression is not simplified correctly, then the order of operations is not followed. True. **23.** Hypothesis: $5x \neq 10$; Conclusion: $x \neq 2$.; Contrapositive: If $x = 2$, then $5x = 10$. The contrapositive is true since $5 \cdot 2 = 10$. The conditional statement is true.
25. Hypothesis: the discriminant is 0; Conclusion: the graph of the quadratic function has 1 x-intercept; Contrapositive: If the graph of the quadratic function does not have 1 x-intercept, then the discriminant is not 0. The contrapositive is true. The conditional statement is true. **27.** Hypothesis: an equation is a quadratic variation; Conclusion: it has a constant of variation; Contrapositive: If an equation does not have a constant of variation, then it is not a quadratic variation. The contrapositive is true and therefore the conditional statement is true.

Pages 516–518

1. Each term is 2 more than the preceding term. The numbers are odd so the next term is 11. **3.** Based on past events, Mr. Juarez will give a math quiz. **5.** Each term is the result of the preceding term divided by 5. The next term is $\frac{2}{25}$. **7.** Based on past events, the cafeteria will close the snack line.
9. Each term is the double of the preceding term. The next term is 64. **11.** To complete the syllogism, write the conclusion: If $3x - 2 = 6$, then $x = \frac{8}{3}$. **13.** To complete the syllogism, write the conclusion: If the slope of a line equals 4, then the graph of the line rises from left to right. **15.** To complete the syllogism, write the conclusion: If the study session began at 4 p.m., then I will miss the discussion. **17.** Form the contrapositive of the first statement: If the team does not practice indoors, then it is not snowing. Since the team is not practicing indoors, conclude that it is not snowing.
19. inductive reasoning **21.** inductive reasoning **23.** deductive reasoning **25.** inductive reasoning **27.** inductive reasoning **29.** Ed's method is an accepted mathematical proof using deductive reasoning.

Pages 521–523

1. A. Given **B.** Distributive Property of Multiplication **C.** Subtraction Property of Equality **D.** Division Property of Equality **3. A.** Given **B.** Factoring Rules **C.** Zero Product Property **D.** Subtraction Property of Equality
5. A. Given **B.** Distributive Property of Multiplication **C.** Subtraction Property of Equality **D.** Division Property of Equality **E.** Square Root Property **F.** Product Rule for Radicals; **G.** Definition of square roots **7.** $x^2 = 4$ **9.** the contrapositive is true **11.** an equation is a cubic function **13.** For any integer n, $2n$ and $2n + 2$ are even numbers. The product is $2n(2n + 2)$.

$2n(2n + 2)$	Given
$4n^2 + 4n$	Distributive Property of Multiplication
$4n(n + 1)$	Distributive Property of Multiplication

By the closure property of multiplication of integers, $n(n + 1)$ is an integer. An integer multiplied by 4 is an even number. Therefore, the product of two even numbers is an even number. **15.** For any integer a, b, c, d, where $b, d \neq 0$, $\frac{a}{b}$ and $\frac{c}{d}$ are rational numbers.

$\frac{a}{b} = \frac{c}{d}$	Given
$\frac{a}{b} + 1 = \frac{c}{d} + 1$	Addition Property of Equality
$\frac{a}{b} + \frac{b}{b} = \frac{c}{d} + \frac{d}{d}$	Renaming one
$\frac{a + b}{b} = \frac{c + d}{d}$	Simplify.

Therefore, if $\frac{a}{b} = \frac{c}{d}$, then $\frac{a+b}{b} = \frac{c+d}{d}$. **17.** For any integer a, b, c, d, where $b, d \neq 0$, $\frac{a}{b}$ and $\frac{c}{d}$ are rational numbers.

$\frac{a}{b} = \frac{c}{d}$	Given
$bd \cdot \frac{a}{b} = bd \cdot \frac{c}{d}$	Multiplication Property of Equality
$da = bc$	Definition of multiplication
$ad = bc$	Commutative Property of Multiplication

Therefore, if $\frac{a}{b} = \frac{c}{d}$, then $ad = bc$. **19.** $-2^2 = -4$ by the order of operations. Therefore, $-4 + 5 = 1$. **21.** The error is in the third line. $x(1 - x^2) = 0$ should be replaced with $x^2(1 - x) = 0$. Therefore, $x^2 = x^3$ when $x = 0, 1$. **23.** $24 \cdot 51 \neq 12.75$. There are 25 pairs of numbers, so $25 \cdot 51 = 1275$.

Pages 526–527

1. Answers will vary. Sample answer: -1. **3.** 3 is the counterexample because $3 \cdot 3^2 = 27$ and $3 \neq -3$. **5.** Answers will vary. Sample answer: 25 is a counterexample because 25 is divisible by 5 but 25 is not divisible by 10. **7.** Answers will vary. Sample answer: $x = \frac{1}{4} \cdot \frac{1}{\frac{1}{4}} = 1 \div \frac{1}{4} = 1 \cdot \frac{4}{1} = 4$. So, $4 > \frac{1}{4}$. **9.** Answers will vary. Sample answer: the quadratic function $x = y^2$ shown.

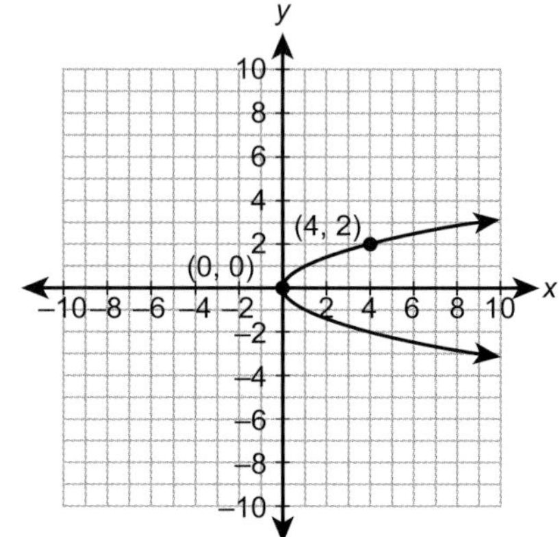

11. Answers will vary. Sample answer: $\sqrt{16} = 4$ because 4 is not an irrational number. **13.** Answers will vary. Sample answer: 9. **15.** Answers will vary. Sample answer: $x = 0$. $0^2 = 0$ so $x^2 = x$ in this example. **17.** Yes. **19.** Yes. **21.** Yes. **23.** No. A counterexample must be a slope that cannot be substituted into point-slope form. Answers will vary. Sample answer: $m =$ undefined, $(-1, 5)$ **25.** Yes.

Illustrations Credits

Key: t = top; b = bottom; c = center; l = left; r = right

Front cover photographs and montage by Bruce Avera Hunter.

Back cover: (t) © Grafissimo/iStockphoto.com; (c) © Kristin Smith/iStockphoto.com; (b) © Thinkstock/Corbis.

Unit 1: © Thinkstock/Corbis.

Unit 2: © Michelle Malven/iStockphoto.com.

Unit 3: © Grazyna Niedzieska/iStockphoto.com.

Unit 4: © Sean Jolly/iStockphoto.com.

Unit 5: © Pixtal/Punchstock.

Unit 6: © Kristin Smith/iStockphoto.com.

Unit 7: © Ron Chapple/Corbis.

Unit 8: © Grafissimo/iStockphoto.com.

Unit 9: © AbleStock.com/Jupiterimages.

Unit 10: © Edmond Van Hoorick/Punchstock.

Unit 11: © Photos.com/Index Stock.

Unit 12: © Andrea Leone/iStockphoto.com.

Unit 13: © Ethan Meleg/Getty Images.

Unit 14: © Larry Fisher/Masterfile.

Index

B

C

D

E

F

G

H

I

J

L

M

N

Q

R

S

T

U

V

W

X

Y

Z

6.1 - 6.4 Homework due

(6.5 - 9.3 - 9.5)

9.4
Mon. 9.5

(review Wed.
test mon 21st
Final 30th)

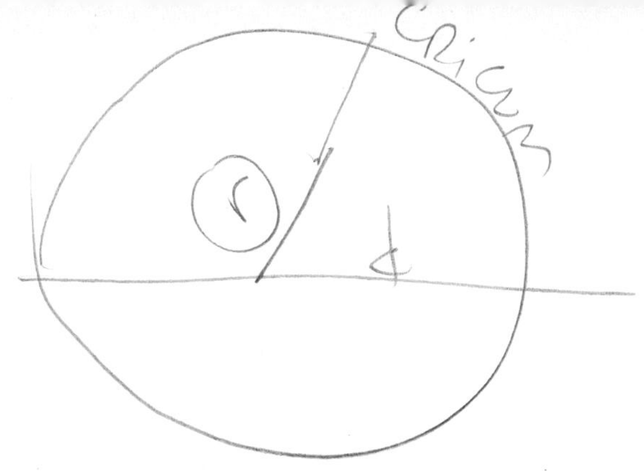

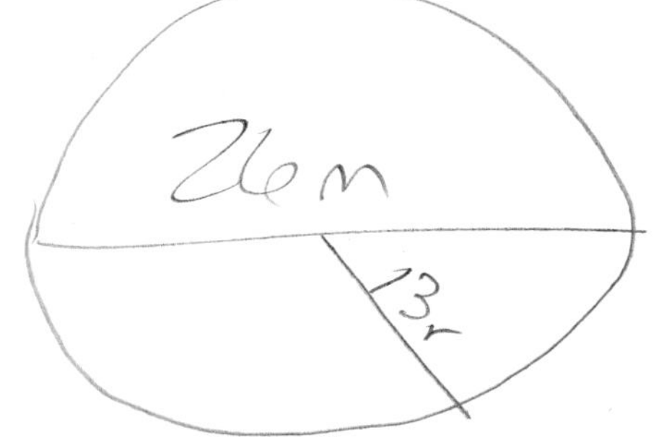

$C = d(\pi)$

$C = 2\pi(r)$

26π cm

$26(3.14)$

$(= 81.64$ cm$)$

Tipping $98/9$ $\frac{89}{9}$ 9.889 %

$\frac{\frac{89}{9}}{100/1}$

25.30 (.15) $\frac{89}{9} \cdot \frac{1}{100}$ $\left(\frac{89}{900}\right)$

9.3

1.2% = fraction or mixed #

(.012 %) $\frac{12}{1000} \div \frac{3}{250}$ 3/250

A) All Perimeter + Circumference

P = add sides

13

3 17 6

7

13

30

13 − 6

30 − 13 = 17

137
26
23
(86) IN

25.30
× .15
12650
25300
379.50

B) Circumference (1 Dimensional)

d = 14

r = 7

d (π)

C = 2 (πr)

2.5 IN

C (5 (π)

5(3.14) = 15.7

D) discounted rates
purchase (rate) = disc. price $

purchase
− discount
= total (sale)

$ 89.00 (~~.010~~)(.10)
= 8.90

  8
 89.00
− 8 90
80.10

$ 110.60 (.40)

  2
 110.60 (long multp.)
× 40
00000
44240
4424.00

$ ~~70.36~~

$ 66.36

5)

TOTAL SALES TAX is

$ 4790 TV

$4790(x) = \frac{335.30}{4790}$

= .7%

4790) 335.30

=

Sales Commission 1380.40

Find percent

$ 9860.00

$\frac{1380.40}{9860.~~00~~}$

x = 14%

Commission

$ 325,900 recieves (1.5)

325,900 (.015) = 4,888.50

$(150)(.05) = 7.50$

$799(.075) =$

+ 59.92

858.93

Total price

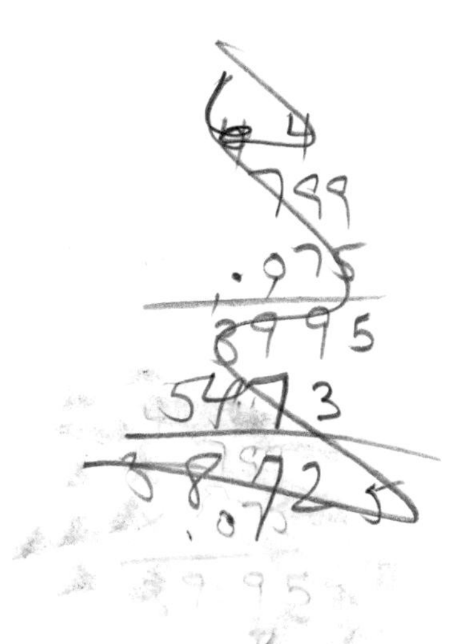

C) Commission Rates

Sale * Rate of C = total check

$250,000 6% 3% each

.06

(250,000)(.06)

(Seller Broker 70, 30)

S = 7500(.70) = 5250

B = 7500(.30) = 5250

MATH 082 Notes

$\frac{26,250}{.15} = 175,000$

4/9/14

25. Fam paid 26,250 downpymnt on home = 15% of price of home find price of home

6.4

A) Percent

Base (%) Total

Bigger # (↓ 100%) = Sm. #

9) $\frac{945,000(x)}{945,000}$ $\frac{160,650}{945,000}$

$(x = .17(\%))$

6.4

B) (% of increase or decrease)

$\frac{\text{Difference}}{\text{original \$}} = \rightarrow$ (first #)